Engineering 145
Chemistry of Materials

Supplemental Reading
Second Edition

DR. DAVID MATTHIESEN
Case Western Reserve University

WILEY
CUSTOM SERVICES

Contents

FOURTH EDITION

Materials Science and Engineering

An Introduction

William D. Callister, Jr.

Department of Metallurgical Engineering
The University of Utah

John Wiley & Sons, Inc.

New York   Chichester   Brisbane   Toronto   Singapore   Weinheim

Section One

Library of Congress Cataloging-in-Publication Data

Callister, William D., 1940–
    Materials science and engineering : an introduction / William D. Callister, Jr.—4th ed.
       p. cm.
    Includes bibliographical references and index.
    ISBN 0-471-13459-7 (cloth : alk. paper)
    1. Materials. I. Title.
TA403.C23 1996
620.1′1—dc20

96-1878
CIP

Printed in the United States of America

10 9 8 7 6 5 4 3

Contents

List of Symbols

The number of the section in which a symbol is introduced or explained is given in parentheses.

A = area

Å = angstrom unit

A_i = atomic weight of element i (2.2)

APF = atomic packing factor (3.4)

%AR = ductility, in percent area reduction (6.6)

a = lattice parameter: unit cell x-axial length (3.4)

a = crack length of a surface crack (8.5)

at% = atom percent (4.3)

B = magnetic flux density (induction) (21.2)

B_r = magnetic remanence (21.7)

BCC = body-centered cubic crystal structure (3.4)

b = lattice parameter: unit cell y-axial length (3.7)

b = Burgers vector (4.4)

C = capacitance (19.17)

C_i = concentration (composition) of component i in wt% (4.3)

C_i' = concentration (composition) of component i in at% (4.3)

C_v, C_p = heat capacity at constant volume, pressure (20.2)

CPR = corrosion penetration rate (18.3)

CVN = Charpy V-notch (8.6)

%CW = percent cold work (7.10)

c = lattice parameter: unit cell z-axial length (3.7)

c = velocity of electromagnetic radiation in a vacuum (22.2)

D = diffusion coefficient (5.3)

D = dielectric displacement (19.18)

d = diameter

d = average grain diameter (7.8)

d_{hkl} = interplanar spacing for planes of Miller indices h, k, and l (3.15)

E = energy (2.5)

E = modulus of elasticity or Young's modulus (6.3)

$\mathscr{E}$ = electric field intensity (19.3)

E_f = Fermi energy (19.5)

E_g = band gap energy (19.6)

$E_r(t)$ = relaxation modulus (16.6)

%EL = ductility, in percent elongation (6.6)

e = electric charge per electron (19.7)

e^- = electron (18.2)

erf = Gaussian error function (5.4)

exp = e, the base for natural logarithms

F = force, interatomic or mechanical (2.5, 6.2)

$\mathscr{F}$ = Faraday constant (18.2)

FCC = face-centered cubic crystal structure (3.4)

G = shear modulus (6.3)

H = magnetic field strength (21.2)

H_c = magnetic coercivity (21.7)

HB = Brinell hardness (6.10)

HCP = hexagonal close-packed crystal structure (3.4)

HK = Knoop hardness (6.10)

HRB, HRF = Rockwell hardness: B and F scales (6.10)

HR15N, HR45W = superficial Rockwell hardness: 15N and 45W scales (6.10)

HV = Vickers hardness (6.10)

h = Planck's constant (22.2)

(hkl) = Miller indices for a crystallographic plane (3.9)

I = electric current (19.2)

I = intensity of electromagnetic radiation (22.3)

i = current density (18.3)

i_C = corrosion current density (18.4)

J = diffusion flux (5.3)

J = electric current density (19.3)

K = stress intensity factor (8.5)

K_c = fracture toughness (8.5)

K_{Ic} = plane strain fracture toughness for mode I crack surface displacement (8.5)

k = Boltzmann's constant (4.2)

k = thermal conductivity (20.4)

l = length

l_c = critical fiber length (17.4)

ln = natural logarithm

log = logarithm taken to base 10

M = magnetization (21.2)

$\overline{M}_n$ = polymer number-average molecular weight (15.5)

$\overline{M}_w$ = polymer weight-average molecular weight (15.5)

mol% = mole percent

N = number of fatigue cycles (8.8)

N_A = Avogadro's number (3.5)

N_f = fatigue life (8.8)

n = principal quantum number (2.3)

n = number of atoms per unit cell (3.5)

n = strain-hardening exponent (6.7)

n = number of electrons in an electrochemical reaction (18.2)

n = number of conducting electrons per cubic meter (19.7)

n = index of refraction (22.5)

n' = for ceramics, the number of formula units per unit cell (13.2)

n_n = number-average degree of polymerization (15.5)

n_w = weight-average degree of polymerization (15.5)

P = dielectric polarization (19.18)

P–B ratio = Pilling–Bedworth ratio (18.10)

p = number of holes per cubic meter (19.10)

Q = activation energy

Q = magnitude of charge stored (19.17)

R = atomic radius (3.4)

R = gas constant

r = interatomic distance (2.5)

r = reaction rate (10.3, 18.3)

r_A, r_C = anion and cation ionic radii (13.2)

S = fatigue stress amplitude (8.8)

SEM = scanning electron microscopy or microscope

T = temperature

T_c = Curie temperature (21.6)

T_C = superconducting critical temperature (21.11)

T_g = glass transition temperature (14.2)

T_m = melting temperature

TEM = transmission electron microscopy or microscope

TS = tensile strength (6.6)

t = time

t_r = rupture lifetime (8.13)

U_r = modulus of resilience (6.6)

$[uvw]$ = indices for a crystallographic direction (3.8)

V = electrical potential difference (voltage) (18.2)

V_C = unit cell volume (3.4)

V_C = corrosion potential (18.4)

V_H = Hall voltage (19.13)

V_i = volume fraction of phase i (9.6)

v = velocity

- **List of Symbols**

vol% = volume percent

W_i = mass fraction of phase i (9.6)

wt% = weight percent (4.3)

x = length

x = space coordinate

Y = dimensionless parameter or function in fracture toughness expression (8.5)

y = space coordinate

z = space coordinate

α = lattice parameter: unit cell y–z interaxial angle (3.7)

α, β, γ = phase designations

α_l = linear coefficient of thermal expansion (20.3)

β = lattice parameter: unit cell x–z interaxial angle (3.7)

γ = lattice parameter: unit cell x–y interaxial angle (3.7)

γ = shear strain (6.2)

Δ = finite change in a parameter the symbol of which it precedes

ϵ = engineering strain (6.2)

ϵ = dielectric permittivity (19.17)

ϵ_r = dielectric constant or relative permittivity (19.17)

$\dot{\epsilon}_s$ = steady-state creep rate (8.13)

ϵ_T = true strain (6.7)

η = viscosity (13.9)

η = overvoltage (18.4)

θ = Bragg diffraction angle (3.15)

θ_D = Debye temperature (20.2)

λ = wavelength of electromagnetic radiation (3.15)

μ = magnetic permeability (21.2)

μ_B = Bohr magneton (21.2)

μ_r = relative magnetic permeability (21.2)

μ_e = electron mobility (19.7)

μ_h = hole mobility (19.10)

ν = Poisson's ratio (6.5)

ν = frequency of electromagnetic radiation (22.2)

ρ = density (3.5)

ρ = electrical resistivity (19.2)

ρ_t = radius of curvature at the tip of a crack (8.5)

σ = engineering stress, tensile or compressive (6.2)

σ = electrical conductivity (19.3)

σ_c = critical stress for crack propagation (8.5)

σ_{fs} = flexural strength (13.8)

σ_m = maximum stress (8.5)

σ_m = mean stress (8.7)

σ_T = true stress (6.7)

σ_w = safe or working stress (6.12)

σ_y = yield strength (6.6)

τ = shear stress (6.2)

τ_c = fiber–matrix bond strength (17.4)

τ_{crss} = critical resolved shear stress (7.5)

χ_m = magnetic susceptibility (21.2)

Subscripts

c = composite

cd = discontinuous fibrous composite

cl = longitudinal direction (aligned fibrous composite)

ct = transverse direction (aligned fibrous composite)

f = final

f = at fracture

f = fiber

i = instantaneous

m = matrix

m, max = maximum

min = minimum

0 = original

0 = at equilibrium

0 = in a vacuum

1

Introduction

A familiar item that is fabricated from three different material types is the beverage container. Beverages are marketed in aluminum (metal) cans (top), glass (ceramic) bottles (center), and plastic (polymer) bottles (bottom). (Permission to use these photographs was granted by the Coca-Cola Company.)

1.1 HISTORICAL PERSPECTIVE

Materials are probably more deep-seated in our culture than most of us realize. Transportation, housing, clothing, communication, recreation, and food production—virtually every segment of our everyday lives is influenced to one degree or another by materials. Historically, the development and advancement of societies have been intimately tied to the members' ability to produce and manipulate materials to fill their needs. In fact, early civilizations have been designated by the level of their materials development (i.e., Stone Age, Bronze Age).

The earliest humans had access to only a very limited number of materials, those that occur naturally: stone, wood, clay, skins, and so on. With time they discovered techniques for producing materials that had properties superior to those of the natural ones; these new materials included pottery and various metals. Furthermore, it was discovered that the properties of a material could be altered by heat treatments and by the addition of other substances. At this point, materials utilization was totally a selection process, that is, deciding from a given, rather limited set of materials the one that was best suited for an application by virtue of its characteristics. It was not until relatively recent times that scientists came to understand the relationships between the structural elements of materials and their properties. This knowledge, acquired in the past 60 years or so, has empowered them to fashion, to a large degree, the characteristics of materials. Thus, tens of thousands of different materials have evolved with rather specialized characteristics which meet the needs of our modern and complex society; these include metals, plastics, glasses, and fibers.

The development of many technologies that make our existence so comfortable has been intimately associated with the accessibility of suitable materials. An advancement in the understanding of a material type is often the forerunner to the stepwise progression of a technology. For example, automobiles would not have been possible without the availability of inexpensive steel or some other comparable substitute. In our contemporary era, sophisticated electronic devices rely on components that are made from what are called semiconducting materials.

1.2 MATERIALS SCIENCE AND ENGINEERING

The discipline of *materials science* involves investigating the relationships that exist between the structures and properties of materials. In contrast, *materials engineering* is, on the basis of these structure–property correlations, designing or engineering the structure of a material to produce a predetermined set of properties. Throughout this text we draw attention to the relationships between material properties and structural elements.

"Structure" is at this point a nebulous term that deserves some explanation. In brief, the structure of a material usually relates to the arrangement of its internal components. Subatomic structure involves electrons within the individual atoms and interactions with their nuclei. On an atomic level, structure encompasses the organization of atoms or molecules relative to one another. The next larger structural realm, which contains large groups of atoms that are normally agglomerated together, is termed "microscopic," meaning that which is subject to direct observation using some type of microscope. Finally, structural elements that may be viewed with the naked eye are termed "macroscopic."

The notion of "property" deserves elaboration. While in service use, all materials are exposed to external stimuli that evoke some type of response. For example, a specimen subjected to forces will experience deformation; or a polished metal surface will reflect light. Property is a material trait in terms of the kind and magnitude of response to a specific imposed stimulus. Generally, definitions of properties are made independent of material shape and size.

Virtually all important properties of solid materials may be grouped into six different categories: mechanical, electrical, thermal, magnetic, optical, and deteriorative. For each there is a characteristic type of stimulus capable of provoking different responses. Mechanical properties relate deformation to an applied load or force; examples include elastic modulus and strength. For electrical properties, such as electrical conductivity and dielectric constant, the stimulus is an electric field. The thermal behavior of solids can be represented in terms of heat capacity and thermal conductivity. Magnetic properties demonstrate the response of a material to the application of a magnetic field. For optical properties, the stimulus is electromagnetic or light radiation; index of refraction and reflectivity are representative optical properties. Finally, deteriorative characteristics indicate the chemical reactivity of materials. The chapters that follow discuss properties that fall within each of these six classifications.

In addition to structure and properties, two other important components are involved in the science and engineering of materials, viz. "processing" and "performance." With regard to the relationships of these four components, the structure of a material will depend on how it is processed. Furthermore, a material's performance will be a function of its properties. Thus, the interrelationship between processing, structure, properties, and performance is linear as depicted in the schematic illustration shown in Figure 1.1. Throughout this text we draw attention to the relationships between these four components in terms of the design, production, and utilization of materials.

We now present an example of these processing-structure-properties-performance principles with Figure 1.2, which is a photograph showing three thin disk specimens placed over some printed matter. It is obvious that the optical properties (i.e., the light transmittance) of each of the three materials are different; the one on the left is transparent (i.e., virtually all of the reflected light passes through it), whereas the disks in the center and on the right are, respectively, translucent and opaque. All of these specimens are of the same material, aluminum oxide, but the left-most one is what we call a single crystal—that is, it is highly perfect—which gives rise to its transparency. The center one is composed of numerous and very small single crystals that are all connected; the boundaries between these small crystals scatter a portion of the light reflected from the printed page, which makes this material optically translucent. And finally, the specimen on the right not only is composed of many small, interconnected crystals, but also a large number of very small pores or void spaces. These pores also effectively scatter the reflected light and render this material opaque.

Thus, the structures of these three specimens are different in terms of crystal boundaries and pores, which affect the optical transmittance properties. Furthermore, each material was produced using a different processing technique. And, of course, if optical transmittance is an important parameter relative to the ultimate in-service application, the performance of each material will be different.

Processing ⟶ Structure ⟶ Properties ⟶ Performance

FIGURE 1.1 The four components of the discipline of materials science and engineering and their linear interrelationship.

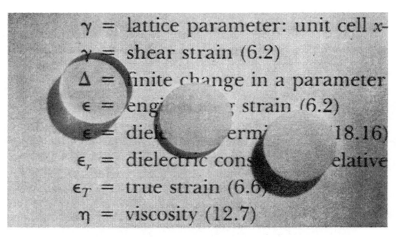

FIGURE 1.2   Photograph showing the light transmittance of three aluminum oxide specimens. From left to right: single-crystal material (sapphire), which is transparent; a polycrystalline and fully dense (nonporous) material, which is translucent; and a polycrystalline material that contains approximately 5% porosity, which is opaque. (Specimen preparation, P. A. Lessing; photography by J. Telford.)

Why do we study materials? Many an applied scientist or engineer, whether mechanical, civil, chemical, or electrical, will at one time or another be exposed to a design problem involving materials. Examples might include a transmission gear, the superstructure for a building, an oil refinery component, or an integrated circuit "chip." Of course, materials scientists and engineers are specialists who are totally involved in the investigation and design of materials.

Many times, a materials problem is one of selecting the right material from the many thousands that are available. There are several criteria on which the final decision is normally based. First of all, the in-service conditions must be characterized, for these will dictate the properties required of the material. On only rare occasions does a material possess the maximum or ideal combination of properties. Thus, it may be necessary to trade off one characteristic for another. The classic example involves strength and ductility; normally, a material having a high strength will have only a limited ductility. In such cases a reasonable compromise between two or more properties may be necessary.

A second selection consideration is any deterioration of material properties that may occur during service operation. For example, significant reductions in mechanical strength may result from exposure to elevated temperatures or corrosive environments.

Finally, probably the overriding consideration is that of economics: What will the finished product cost? A material may be found that has the ideal set of properties but is prohibitively expensive. Here again, some compromise is inevitable. The cost of a finished piece also includes any expense incurred during fabrication to produce the desired shape.

The more familiar an engineer or scientist is with the various characteristics and structure–property relationships, as well as processing techniques of materials, the more proficient and confident he or she will be to make judicious materials choices based on these criteria.

1.3 CLASSIFICATION OF MATERIALS

Solid materials have been conveniently grouped into three basic classifications: metals, ceramics, and polymers. This scheme is based primarily on chemical makeup and atomic structure, and most materials fall into one distinct grouping or another, although there are some intermediates. In addition, there are three other groups of important engineering materials—composites, semiconductors, and biomaterials. Composites consist of combinations of two or more different materials, whereas semiconductors are utilized because of their unusual electrical characteristics; biomaterials are implanted into the human body. A brief explanation of the material types and representative characteristics is offered next.

METALS

Metallic materials are normally combinations of metallic elements. They have large numbers of nonlocalized electrons; that is, these electrons are not bound to particular atoms. Many properties of metals are directly attributable to these electrons. Metals are extremely good conductors of electricity and heat and are not transparent to visible light; a polished metal surface has a lustrous appearance. Furthermore, metals are quite strong, yet deformable, which accounts for their extensive use in structural applications.

CERAMICS

Ceramics are compounds between metallic and nonmetallic elements; they are most frequently oxides, nitrides, and carbides. The wide range of materials that falls within this classification includes ceramics that are composed of clay minerals, cement, and glass. These materials are typically insulative to the passage of electricity and heat, and are more resistant to high temperatures and harsh environments than metals and polymers. With regards to mechanical behavior, ceramics are hard but very brittle.

POLYMERS

Polymers include the familiar plastic and rubber materials. Many of them are organic compounds that are chemically based on carbon, hydrogen, and other nonmetallic elements; furthermore, they have very large molecular structures. These materials typically have low densities and may be extremely flexible.

COMPOSITES

A number of composite materials have been engineered that consist of more than one material type. Fiberglass is a familiar example, in which glass fibers are embedded within a polymeric material. A composite is designed to display a combination of the best characteristics of each of the component materials. Fiberglass acquires strength from the glass and flexibility from the polymer. Many of the recent material developments have involved composite materials.

SEMICONDUCTORS

Semiconductors have electrical properties that are intermediate between the electrical conductors and insulators. Furthermore, the electrical characteristics of these materials are extremely sensitive to the presence of minute concentrations of impurity atoms, which concentrations may be controlled over very small spatial regions. The semiconductors have made possible the advent of integrated circuitry that has totally revolutionized the electronics and computer industries (not to mention our lives) over the past two decades.

BIOMATERIALS

Biomaterials are employed in components implanted into the human body for replacement of diseased or damaged body parts. These materials must not produce toxic substances and must be compatible with body tissues (i.e., must not cause adverse biological reactions). All of the above materials—metals, ceramics, polymers, composites, and semiconductors—may be used as biomaterials. For example, in Section 23.8 are discussed some of the biomaterials that are utilized in the artificial hip replacement.

1.4 ADVANCED MATERIALS

Materials that are utilized in high-technology (or high-tech) applications are sometimes termed *advanced materials*. By high technology we mean a device or product that operates or functions using relatively intricate and sophisticated principles; examples include electronic equipment (VCRs, CD players, etc.), computers, fiber-optic systems, spacecraft, aircraft, and military rocketry. These advanced materials are typically either traditional materials whose properties have been enhanced or they are newly developed, high-performance materials. Furthermore, they may be of all material types (e.g., metals, ceramics, polymers), and are normally relatively expensive. In subsequent chapters are discussed the properties and applications of a number of advanced materials—for example, materials that are used for lasers, integrated circuits, magnetic information storage, liquid crystals displays (LCDs), fiber optics, and the thermal protection system for the Space Shuttle Orbiter.

1.5 MODERN MATERIALS NEEDS

In spite of the tremendous progress that has been made in the discipline of materials science and engineering within the past few years, there still remain technological challenges, including the development of even more sophisticated and specialized materials, as well as consideration of the environmental impact of materials production. Some comment is appropriate relative to these issues so as to round out this perspective.

Nuclear energy holds some promise, but the solutions to the many problems that remain will necessarily involve materials, from fuels to containment structures to facilities for the disposal of radioactive waste.

Significant quantities of energy are involved in transportation. Reducing the weight of transportation vehicles (automobiles, aircraft, trains, etc.), as well as increasing engine operating temperatures, will enhance fuel efficiency. New high-strength, low-density structural materials remain to be developed, as well as materials that have higher-temperature capabilities, for use in engine components.

Furthermore, there is a recognized need to find new, economical sources of energy, and to use the present resources more efficiently. Materials will undoubtedly play a significant role in these developments. For example, the direct conversion of solar into electrical energy has been demonstrated. Solar cells employ some rather complex and expensive materials. To ensure a viable technology, materials that are highly efficient in this conversion process yet less costly must be developed.

Furthermore, environmental quality depends on our ability to control air and water pollution. Pollution control techniques employ various materials. In addition, materials processing and refinement methods need to be improved so that they produce less environmental degradation, that is, less pollution and less despoilage of the landscape from the mining of raw materials. Also, in some materials manufacturing processes, toxic substances are produced, and the ecological impact of their disposal must be considered.

Many materials that we use are derived from resources that are nonrenewable, that is, not capable of being regenerated. These include polymers, for which the prime raw material is oil, and some metals. These nonrenewable resources are gradually becoming depleted, which necessitates: 1) the discovery of additional reserves, 2) the development of new materials having comparable properties with less adverse environmental impact, and/or 3) increased recycling efforts and the development of new recycling technologies. As a consequence of the economics of not only production but also of environmental impact and ecological factors, it is becoming increasingly important to consider the "cradle-to-grave" life cycle of materials relative to the overall manufacturing process.

The roles that materials scientists and engineers play relative to these, as well as other environmental and societal issues, are discussed in more detail in Chapter 24.

REFERENCES

The October 1986 issue of *Scientific American,* Vol. 255, No. 4, is devoted entirely to various advanced materials and their uses. Other references for Chapter 1 are textbooks that cover the basic fundamentals of the field of materials science and engineering.

Ashby, M. F. and D. R. H. Jones, *Engineering Materials 1, An Introduction to Their Properties and Applications,* Pergamon Press, Oxford, 1980.

Ashby, M. F. and D. R. H. Jones, *Engineering Materials 2, An Introduction to Microstructures, Processing and Design,* Pergamon Press, Oxford, 1986.

Askeland, D. R., *The Science and Engineering of Materials,* 3rd edition, PWS-Kent Publishing Co., Boston, 1994.

Barrett, C. R., W. D. Nix, and A. S. Tetelman, *The Principles of Engineering Materials,* Prentice Hall, Inc., Englewood Cliffs, NJ, 1973.

Flinn, R. A. and P. K. Trojan, *Engineering Materials and Their Applications,* 4th edition, Houghton Mifflin Co., Boston, 1990.

Jacobs, J. A. and T. F. Kilduff, *Engineering Materials Technology,* 2nd edition, Prentice Hall, Englewood Cliffs, NJ, 1994.

Keyser, C. A., *Materials Science in Engineering,* 4th edition, Macmillan Publishing Company, New York, 1986.

McMahon, C. J., Jr. and C. D. Graham, Jr., *Introduction to Engineering Materials: The Bicycle and the Walkman,* Merion Books, Philadelphia, 1992.

Murray, G. T., *Introduction to Engineering Materials—Behavior, Properties, and Selection,* Marcel Dekker, Inc., New York, 1993.

Ralls, K. M., T. H. Courtney, and J. Wulff, *Introduction to Materials Science and Engineering,* John Wiley & Sons, New York, 1976.

Schaffer, J. P., A. Saxena, S. D. Antolovich, T. H. Sanders, Jr., and S. B. Warner, *The Science and Design of Engineering Materials,* Richard D. Irwin, Inc., Chicago, 1995.

Shackelford, J. F., *Introduction to Materials Science for Engineers,* 4th edition, Prentice-Hall, Inc., Upper Saddle River, NJ, 1996.

Smith, W. F., *Foundations of Materials Science and Engineering,* 2nd edition, McGraw-Hill Book Co., New York, 1993.

Smith, W. F., *Principles of Materials Science and Engineering,* 3rd edition, McGraw-Hill Book Company, New York, 1995.

Van Vlack, L. H., *Elements of Materials Science and Engineering,* 6th edition, Addison-Wesley Publishing Co., Reading, MA, 1989.

2

Atomic Structure and Interatomic Bonding

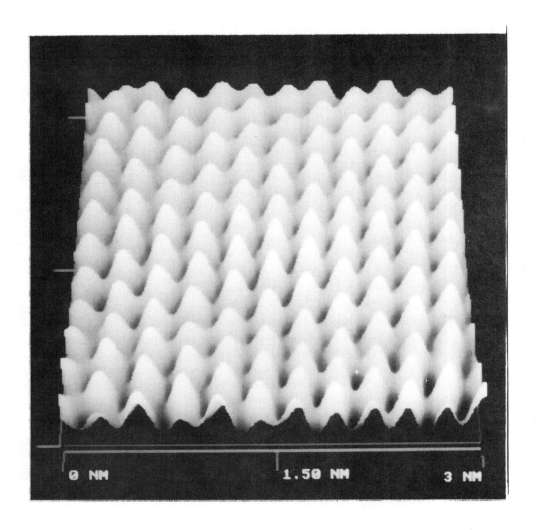

0 NM   1.50 NM   3 NM

T his micrograph which represents the surface of a gold specimen was taken with a sophisticated atomic force microscope (AFM). Individual atoms for this (111) crystallographic surface plane are resolved. Also note the dimensional scale (in the nanometer range) below the micrograph. (Image courtesy of Dr. Michael Green, TopoMetrix Corporation.)

2.1 Introduction

Some of the important properties of solid materials depend on geometrical atomic arrangements, and also the interactions that exist among constituent atoms or molecules. This chapter, by way of preparation for subsequent discussions, considers several fundamental and important concepts, namely: atomic structure, electron configurations in atoms and the periodic table, and the various types of primary and secondary interatomic bonds that hold together the atoms comprising a solid. These topics are reviewed briefly, under the assumption that some of the material is familiar to the reader.

ATOMIC STRUCTURE

2.2 Fundamental Concepts

Each atom consists of a very small nucleus composed of protons and neutrons, which is encircled by moving electrons. Both electrons and protons are electrically charged, the charge magnitude being 1.60×10^{-19} C, which is negative in sign for electrons and positive for protons; neutrons are electrically neutral. Masses for these subatomic particles are infinitesimally small; protons and neutrons have approximately the same mass, 1.67×10^{-27} kg, which is significantly larger than that for an electron, 9.11×10^{-31} kg.

Each chemical element is characterized by the number of protons in the nucleus, or the **atomic number** (Z).[1] For an electrically neutral or complete atom, the atomic number also equals the number of electrons. This atomic number ranges in integral units from 1 for hydrogen to 94 for plutonium, the highest of the naturally occurring elements.

The *atomic mass* (A) of a specific atom may be expressed as the sum of the masses of protons and neutrons within the nucleus. Although the number of protons is the same for all atoms of a given element, the number of neutrons (N) may be variable. Thus atoms of some elements have two or more different atomic masses, which are called **isotopes.** The **atomic weight** corresponds to the weighted average of the atomic masses of the atom's naturally occurring isotopes. The **atomic mass unit (amu)** may be used for computations of atomic weight. A scale has been established whereby 1 amu is defined as $\frac{1}{12}$ of the atomic mass of the most common isotope of carbon, carbon 12 (^{12}C) ($A = 12.00000$). Within this scheme, the masses of protons and neutrons are slightly greater than unity, and

$$A \cong Z + N \tag{2.1}$$

The atomic weight of an element or the molecular weight of a compound may be specified on the basis of amu's per atom (molecule) or mass per mole of material. In one **mole** of a substance there are 6.023×10^{23} (Avogadro's number) atoms or molecules. These two atomic weight schemes are related through the following equation:

$$1 \text{ amu/atom (or molecule)} = 1 \text{ g/mol}$$

---

[1] Terms appearing in boldface type are defined in the Glossary, which follows Appendix E.

For example, the atomic weight of iron is 55.85 amu/atom, or 55.85 g/mol. Sometimes use of amu per atom or molecule is convenient; on other occasions g (or kg)/mol is preferred; the latter is used in this book.

2.3 ELECTRONS IN ATOMS

ATOMIC MODELS

During the latter part of the nineteenth century it was realized that many phenomena involving electrons in solids could not be explained in terms of classical mechanics. What followed was the establishment of a set of principles and laws that govern systems of atomic and subatomic entities, which came to be known as **quantum mechanics.** An understanding of the behavior of electrons in atoms and crystalline solids necessarily involves the discussion of quantum-mechanical concepts. However, a detailed exploration of these principles is beyond the scope of this book, and only a very superficial and simplified treatment is given.

One early outgrowth of quantum mechanics was the simplified **Bohr atomic model,** in which electrons are assumed to revolve around the atomic nucleus in discrete orbitals, and the position of any particular electron is more or less well defined in terms of its orbital. This model of the atom is represented in Figure 2.1.

Another important quantum-mechanical principle stipulates that the energies of electrons are quantized; that is, electrons are permitted to have only specific values of energy. An electron may change energy, but in doing so it must make a quantum jump either to an allowed higher energy (with absorption of energy) or to a lower energy (with the emission of energy). Often, it is convenient to think of these allowed electron energies as being associated with *energy levels* or *states*. These states do not vary continuously with energy, that is, adjacent states are separated by finite energies. For example, allowed states for the Bohr hydrogen atom are represented in Figure 2.2a. These energies are taken to be negative, whereas the zero reference is the unbound or free electron. Of course, the single electron associated with the hydrogen atom will fill only one of these states.

Thus, the Bohr model represents an early attempt to describe electrons in atoms, in terms of both position (electron orbitals) and energy (quantized energy levels).

This Bohr model was eventually found to have some significant limitations because of its inability to explain several phenomena involving electrons. A resolution was reached with a **wave-mechanical model,** in which the electron is considered to exhibit both wave-like and particle-like characteristics. With this model, an

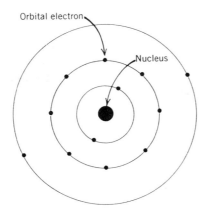

FIGURE 2.1 Schematic representation of the Bohr atom.

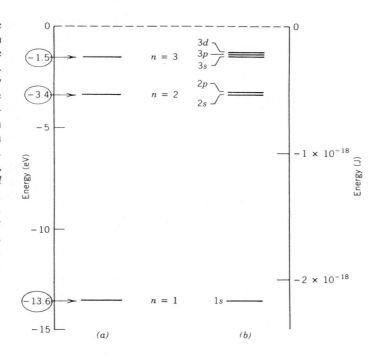

FIGURE 2.2 (a) The first three electron energy states for the Bohr hydrogen atom. (b) Electron energy states for the first three shells of the wave-mechanical hydrogen atom. (Adapted from W. G. Moffatt, G. W. Pearsall, and J. Wulff, *The Structure and Properties of Materials,* Vol. I, *Structure,* p. 10. Copyright © 1964 by John Wiley & Sons, New York. Reprinted by permission of John Wiley & Sons, Inc.)

electron is no longer treated as a particle moving in a discrete orbital; but rather, position is considered to be the probability of an electron's being at various locations around the nucleus. In other words, position is described by a probability distribution or electron cloud. Figure 2.3 compares Bohr and wave-mechanical models for the hydrogen atom. Both these models are used throughout the course of this book; the choice depends on which model allows the more simple explanation.

QUANTUM NUMBERS

Using wave mechanics, every electron in an atom is characterized by four parameters called **quantum numbers.** The size, shape, and spatial orientation of an electron's probability density are specified by three of these quantum numbers. Furthermore, Bohr energy levels separate into electron subshells, and quantum numbers dictate the number of states within each subshell. Shells are specified by a *principal quantum number n*, which may take on integral values beginning with unity; sometimes these shells are designated by the letters K, L, M, N, O, and so on, which correspond, respectively, to $n = 1, 2, 3, 4, 5, \ldots$, as indicated in Table 2.1. It should also be noted that this quantum number, and it only, is also associated with the Bohr model. This quantum number is related to the distance of an electron from the nucleus, or its position.

The second quantum number, l, signifies the subshell, which is denoted by a lowercase letter—an s, p, d, or f; it is related to the shape of the electron subshell. In addition, the number of these subshells is restricted by the magnitude of n. Allowable subshells for the several n values are also presented in Table 2.1. The number of energy states for each subshell is determined by the third quantum number, m_l. For an s subshell, there is a single energy state, whereas for p, d, and f subshells, three, five, and seven states exist, respectively (Table 2.1). In the absence of an external magnetic field, the states within each subshell are identical. However,

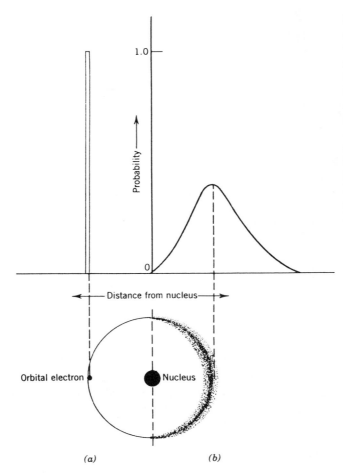

FIGURE 2.3 Comparison of the (a) Bohr and (b) wave-mechanical atom models in terms of electron distribution. (Adapted from Z. D. Jastrzebski, *The Nature and Properties of Engineering Materials,* 3rd edition, p. 4. Copyright © 1987 by John Wiley & Sons, New York. Reprinted by permission of John Wiley & Sons, Inc.)

Table 2.1   The Number of Available Electron States in Some of the Electron Shells and Subshells

Principal Quantum Number n	Shell Designation	Subshells	Number of States	Number of Electrons	
				Per Subshell	*Per Shell*
1	K	s	1	2	2
2	L	s	1	2	8
		p	3	6	
3	M	s	1	2	18
		p	3	6	
		d	5	10	
4	N	s	1	2	32
		p	3	6	
		d	5	10	
		f	7	14	

when a magnetic field is applied these subshell states split, each state assuming a slightly different energy.

Associated with each electron is a *spin moment,* which must be oriented either up or down. Related to this spin moment is the fourth quantum number, m_s, for which two values are possible ($+\frac{1}{2}$ and $-\frac{1}{2}$), one for each of the spin orientations.

Thus, the Bohr model was further refined by wave mechanics, in which the introduction of three new quantum numbers gives rise to electron subshells within each shell. A comparison of these two models on this basis is illustrated, for the hydrogen atom, in Figures 2.2a and 2.2b.

A complete energy level diagram for the various shells and subshells using the wave-mechanical model is shown in Figure 2.4. Several features of the diagram are worth noting. First, the smaller the principal quantum number, the lower the energy level; for example, the energy of a 1s state is less than that of a 2s state, which in turn is lower than the 3s. Second, within each shell, the energy of a subshell level increases with the value of the *l* quantum number. For example, the energy of a 3d state is greater than a 3p, which is larger than 3s. Finally, there may be overlap in energy of a state in one shell with states in an adjacent shell, which is especially true of *d* and *f* states; for example, the energy of a 3d state is greater than that for a 4s.

ELECTRON CONFIGURATIONS

The preceding discussion has dealt primarily with **electron states**—values of energy that are permitted for electrons. To determine the manner in which these states are filled with electrons, we use the **Pauli exclusion principle,** another quantum-mechanical concept. This principle stipulates that each electron state can hold no more than two electrons, which must have opposite spins. Thus, *s*, *p*, *d*, and *f* subshells may each accommodate, respectively, a total of 2, 6, 10, and 14 electrons; Table 2.1 summarizes the maximum number of electrons that may occupy each of the first four shells.

Of course, not all possible states in an atom are filled with electrons. For most atoms, the electrons fill up the lowest possible energy states in the electron shells

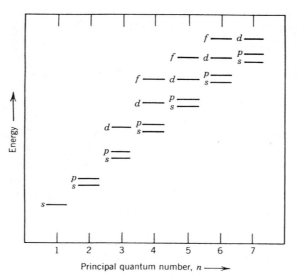

FIGURE 2.4 Schematic representation of the relative energies of the electrons for the various shells and subshells. (From K. M. Ralls, T. H. Courtney, and J. Wulff, *Introduction to Materials Science and Engineering,* p. 22. Copyright © 1976 by John Wiley & Sons, New York. Reprinted by permission of John Wiley & Sons, Inc.)

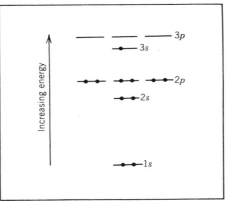

FIGURE 2.5 Schematic representation of the filled energy states for a sodium atom.

and subshells, two electrons (having opposite spins) per state. The energy structure for a sodium atom is represented schematically in Figure 2.5. When all the electrons occupy the lowest possible energies in accord with the foregoing restrictions, an atom is said to be in its **ground state.** However, electron transitions to higher energy states are possible, as discussed in Chapters 19 and 22. The **electron configuration** or structure of an atom represents the manner in which these states are occupied. In the conventional notation the number of electrons in each subshell is indicated by a superscript after the shell–subshell designation. For example, the electron configurations for hydrogen, helium, and sodium are, respectively, $1s^1$, $1s^2$, and $1s^2 2s^2 2p^6 3s^1$. Electron configurations for some of the more common elements are listed in Table 2.2; a tabulation for all the elements is contained in Appendix B.

At this point, comments regarding these electron configurations are necessary. First, the **valence electrons** are those that occupy the outermost filled shell. These electrons are extremely important; as will be seen, they participate in the bonding between atoms to form atomic and molecular aggregates. Furthermore, many of the physical and chemical properties of solids are based on these valence electrons.

In addition, some atoms have what are termed "stable electron configurations"; that is, the states within the outermost or valence electron shell are completely filled. Normally this corresponds to the occupation of just the s and p states for the outermost shell by a total of eight electrons, as in neon, argon, and krypton; one exception is helium, which contains only two $1s$ electrons. These elements (Ne, Ar, Kr, and He) are the inert, or noble, gases, which are virtually unreactive chemically. Some atoms of the elements that have unfilled valence shells assume stable electron configurations by gaining or losing electrons to form charged ions, or by sharing electrons with other atoms. This is the basis for some chemical reactions, and also for atomic bonding in solids, as explained in Section 2.6.

Under special circumstances, the s and p orbitals combine to form hybrid sp^n orbitals, where n indicates the number of p orbitals involved, which may have a value of 1, 2, or 3. The 3A, 4A, and 5A group elements of the periodic table (Figure 2.6) are those which most often form these hybrids. The driving force for the formation of hybrid orbitals is a lower energy state for the valence electrons. For carbon the sp^3 hybrid is of primary importance in organic and polymer chemistries. The shape of the sp^3 hybrid is what determines the 109° (or tetrahedral) angle found in polymer chains (Chapter 15).

Table 2.2 A Listing of the Expected Electron Configurations for Some of the Common Elements[a]

Element	Symbol	Atomic Number	Electron Configuration
Hydrogen	H	1	$1s^1$
Helium	He	2	$1s^2$
Lithium	Li	3	$1s^2 2s^1$
Beryllium	Be	4	$1s^2 2s^2$
Boron	B	5	$1s^2 2s^2 2p^1$
Carbon	C	6	$1s^2 2s^2 2p^2$
Nitrogen	N	7	$1s^2 2s^2 2p^3$
Oxygen	O	8	$1s^2 2s^2 2p^4$
Fluorine	F	9	$1s^2 2s^2 2p^5$
Neon	Ne	10	$1s^2 2s^2 2p^6$
Sodium	Na	11	$1s^2 2s^2 2p^6 3s^1$
Magnesium	Mg	12	$1s^2 2s^2 2p^6 3s^2$
Aluminum	Al	13	$1s^2 2s^2 2p^6 3s^2 3p^1$
Silicon	Si	14	$1s^2 2s^2 2p^6 3s^2 3p^2$
Phosphorus	P	15	$1s^2 2s^2 2p^6 3s^2 3p^3$
Sulfur	S	16	$1s^2 2s^2 2p^6 3s^2 3p^4$
Chlorine	Cl	17	$1s^2 2s^2 2p^6 3s^2 3p^5$
Argon	Ar	18	$1s^2 2s^2 2p^6 3s^2 3p^6$
Potassium	K	19	$1s^2 2s^2 2p^6 3s^2 3p^6 4s^1$
Calcium	Ca	20	$1s^2 2s^2 2p^6 3s^2 3p^6 4s^2$
Scandium	Sc	21	$1s^2 2s^2 2p^6 3s^2 3p^6 3d^1 4s^2$
Titanium	Ti	22	$1s^2 2s^2 2p^6 3s^2 3p^6 3d^2 4s^2$
Vanadium	V	23	$1s^2 2s^2 2p^6 3s^2 3p^6 3d^3 4s^2$
Chromium	Cr	24	$1s^2 2s^2 2p^6 3s^2 3p^6 3d^5 4s^1$
Manganese	Mn	25	$1s^2 2s^2 2p^6 3s^2 3p^6 3d^5 4s^2$
Iron	Fe	26	$1s^2 2s^2 2p^6 3s^2 3p^6 3d^6 4s^2$
Cobalt	Co	27	$1s^2 2s^2 2p^6 3s^2 3p^6 3d^7 4s^2$
Nickel	Ni	28	$1s^2 2s^2 2p^6 3s^2 3p^6 3d^8 4s^2$
Copper	Cu	29	$1s^2 2s^2 2p^6 3s^2 3p^6 3d^{10} 4s^1$
Zinc	Zn	30	$1s^2 2s^2 2p^6 3s^2 3p^6 3d^{10} 4s^2$
Gallium	Ga	31	$1s^2 2s^2 2p^6 3s^2 3p^6 3d^{10} 4s^2 4p^1$
Germanium	Ge	32	$1s^2 2s^2 2p^6 3s^2 3p^6 3d^{10} 4s^2 4p^2$
Arsenic	As	33	$1s^2 2s^2 2p^6 3s^2 3p^6 3d^{10} 4s^2 4p^3$
Selenium	Se	34	$1s^2 2s^2 2p^6 3s^2 3p^6 3d^{10} 4s^2 4p^4$
Bromine	Br	35	$1s^2 2s^2 2p^6 3s^2 3p^6 3d^{10} 4s^2 4p^5$
Krypton	Kr	36	$1s^2 2s^2 2p^6 3s^2 3p^6 3d^{10} 4s^2 4p^6$

[a] When some elements covalently bond, they form sp hybrid bonds. This is especially true for C, Si, and Ge.

2.4 THE PERIODIC TABLE

All the elements have been classified according to electron configuration in the **periodic table** (Figure 2.6). Here, the elements are situated, with increasing atomic number, in seven horizontal rows called periods. The arrangement is such that all elements that are arrayed in a given column or group have similar valence electron structures, as well as chemical and physical properties. These properties change gradually and systematically, moving horizontally across each period.

Key:
29 — Atomic number
Cu — Symbol
63.54 — Atomic weight

Metal / Nonmetal / Intermediate

IA	IIA	IIIB	IVB	VB	VIB	VIIB	VIII	VIII	VIII	IB	IIB	IIIA	IVA	VA	VIA	VIIA	0
1 H 1.0080																	2 He 4.0026
3 Li 6.939	4 Be 9.0122											5 B 10.811	6 C 12.011	7 N 14.007	8 O 15.999	9 F 18.998	10 Ne 20.183
11 Na 22.990	12 Mg 24.312											13 Al 26.982	14 Si 28.086	15 P 30.974	16 S 32.064	17 Cl 35.453	18 Ar 39.948
19 K 39.102	20 Ca 40.08	21 Sc 44.956	22 Ti 47.90	23 V 50.942	24 Cr 51.996	25 Mn 54.938	26 Fe 55.847	27 Co 58.933	28 Ni 58.71	29 Cu 63.54	30 Zn 65.37	31 Ga 69.72	32 Ge 72.59	33 As 74.922	34 Se 78.96	35 Br 79.91	36 Kr 83.80
37 Rb 85.47	38 Sr 87.62	39 Y 88.91	40 Zr 91.22	41 Nb 92.91	42 Mo 95.94	43 Tc (99)	44 Ru 101.07	45 Rh 102.91	46 Pd 106.4	47 Ag 107.87	48 Cd 112.40	49 In 114.82	50 Sn 118.69	51 Sb 121.75	52 Te 127.60	53 I 126.90	54 Xe 131.30
55 Cs 132.91	56 Ba 137.34	Rare earth series	72 Hf 178.49	73 Ta 180.95	74 W 183.85	75 Re 186.2	76 Os 190.2	77 Ir 192.2	78 Pt 195.09	79 Au 196.97	80 Hg 200.59	81 Tl 204.37	82 Pb 207.19	83 Bi 208.98	84 Po (210)	85 At (210)	86 Rn (222)
87 Fr (223)	88 Ra (226)	Actinide series															

Rare earth series:

57 La 138.91	58 Ce 140.12	59 Pr 140.91	60 Nd 144.24	61 Pm (145)	62 Sm 150.35	63 Eu 151.96	64 Gd 157.25	65 Tb 158.92	66 Dy 162.50	67 Ho 164.93	68 Er 167.26	69 Tm 168.93	70 Yb 173.04	71 Lu 174.97

Actinide series:

89 Ac (227)	90 Th 232.04	91 Pa (231)	92 U 238.03	93 Np (237)	94 Pu (242)	95 Am (243)	96 Cm (247)	97 Bk (247)	98 Cf (249)	99 Es (254)	100 Fm (253)	101 Md (256)	102 No (254)	103 Lw (257)

FIGURE 2.6 The periodic table of the elements. The numbers in parentheses are the atomic weights of the most stable or common isotopes.

The elements positioned in Group 0, the right-most group, are the inert gases, which have filled electron shells and stable electron configurations. Group VIIA and VIA elements are one and two electrons deficient, respectively, from having stable structures. The Group VIIA elements (F, Cl, Br, I, and At) are sometimes termed the halogens. The alkali and the alkaline earth metals (Li, Na, K, Be, Mg, Ca, etc.) are labeled as Groups IA and IIA, having, respectively, one and two electrons in excess of stable structures. The elements in the three long periods, Groups IIIB through IIB, are termed the transition metals, which have partially filled d electron states and in some cases one or two electrons in the next higher energy shell. Groups IIIA, IVA, and VA (B, Si, Ge, As, etc.) display characteristics that are intermediate between the metals and nonmetals by virtue of their valence electron structures.

As may be noted from the periodic table, most of the elements really come under the metal classification. These are sometimes termed **electropositive** elements, indicating that they are capable of giving up their few valence electrons to become positively charged ions. Furthermore, the elements situated on the right-hand side of the table are **electronegative;** that is, they readily accept electrons to form negatively charged ions, or sometimes they share electrons with other atoms. Figure 2.7 displays electronegativity values that have been assigned to the various elements arranged in the periodic table. As a general rule, electronegativity increases in moving from left to right and from bottom to top. Atoms are more likely to accept electrons if their outer shells are almost full, and if they are less "shielded" from (i.e., closer to) the nucleus.

IA	IIA	IIIB	IVB	VB	VIB	VIIB	VIII			IB	IIB	IIIA	IVA	VA	VIA	VIIA	0
1 H 2.1																	2 He –
3 Li 1.0	4 Be 1.5											5 B 2.0	6 C 2.5	7 N 3.0	8 O 3.5	9 F 4.0	10 Ne –
11 Na 0.9	12 Mg 1.2											13 Al 1.5	14 Si 1.8	15 P 2.1	16 S 2.5	17 Cl 3.0	18 Ar –
19 K 0.8	20 Ca 1.0	21 Sc 1.3	22 Ti 1.5	23 V 1.6	24 Cr 1.6	25 Mn 1.5	26 Fe 1.8	27 Co 1.8	28 Ni 1.8	29 Cu 1.9	30 Zn 1.6	31 Ga 1.6	32 Ge 1.8	33 As 2.0	34 Se 2.4	35 Br 2.8	36 Kr –
37 Rb 0.8	38 Sr 1.0	39 Y 1.2	40 Zr 1.4	41 Nb 1.6	42 Mo 1.8	43 Tc 1.9	44 Ru 2.2	45 Rh 2.2	46 Pd 2.2	47 Ag 1.9	48 Cd 1.7	49 In 1.7	50 Sn 1.8	51 Sb 1.9	52 Te 2.1	53 I 2.5	54 Xe –
55 Cs 0.7	56 Ba 0.9	57–71 La–Lu 1.1–1.2	72 Hf 1.3	73 Ta 1.5	74 W 1.7	75 Re 1.9	76 Os 2.2	77 Ir 2.2	78 Pt 2.2	79 Au 2.4	80 Hg 1.9	81 Tl 1.8	82 Pb 1.8	83 Bi 1.9	84 Po 2.0	85 At 2.2	86 Rn –
87 Fr 0.7	88 Ra 0.9	89–102 Ac–No 1.1–1.7															

FIGURE 2.7 The electronegativity values for the elements. (Adapted from Linus Pauling, *The Nature of the Chemical Bond,* 3rd edition. Copyright 1939 and 1940, 3rd edition copyright © 1960, by Cornell University. Used by permission of the publisher, Cornell University Press.)

ATOMIC BONDING IN SOLIDS

2.5 BONDING FORCES AND ENERGIES

An understanding of many of the physical properties of materials is predicated on a knowledge of the interatomic forces that bind the atoms together. Perhaps the principles of atomic bonding are best illustrated by considering the interaction between two isolated atoms as they are brought into close proximity from an infinite separation. At large distances, the interactions are negligible; but as the atoms approach, each exerts forces on the other. These forces are of two types, attractive and repulsive, and the magnitude of each is a function of the separation or interatomic distance. The origin of an attractive force F_A depends on the particular type of bonding that exists between the two atoms. Its magnitude varies with the distance, as represented schematically in Figure 2.8a. Ultimately, the outer electron shells of the two atoms begin to overlap, and a strong repulsive force F_R comes into play. The net force F_N between the two atoms is just the sum of both attractive and repulsive components; that is,

$$F_N = F_A + F_R \qquad (2.2)$$

which is also a function of the interatomic separation as also plotted in Figure 2.8a. When F_A and F_R balance, or become equal, there is no net force; that is,

$$F_A + F_R = 0 \qquad (2.3)$$

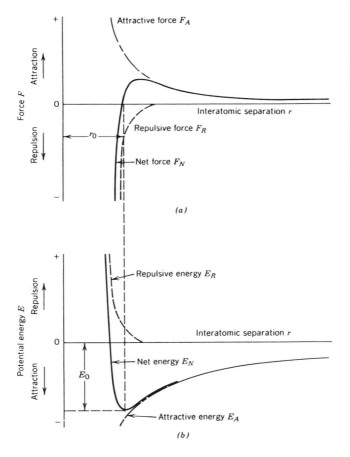

FIGURE 2.8 (a) The dependence of repulsive, attractive, and net forces as a function of interatomic separation for two isolated atoms. (b) The dependence of repulsive, attractive, and net potential energies as a function of interatomic separation for two isolated atoms.

Then a state of equilibrium exists. The centers of the two atoms will remain separated by the equilibrium spacing r_0, as indicated in Figure 2.8a. For many atoms, r_0 is approximately 0.3 nm (3 Å). Once in this position, the two atoms will counteract any attempt to separate them by an attractive force, or to push them together by a repulsive action.

Sometimes it is more convenient to work with the potential energies between two atoms instead of forces. Mathematically, energy (E) and force (F) are related as

$$E = \int F \, dr \tag{2.4}$$

Or, for atomic systems,

$$E_N = \int_{\infty}^{r} F_N \, dr \tag{2.5}$$

$$= \int_{\infty}^{r} F_A \, dr + \int_{\infty}^{r} F_R \, dr \tag{2.6}$$

$$= E_A + E_R \tag{2.7}$$

in which E_N, E_A, and E_R are respectively the net, attractive, and repulsive energies for two isolated and adjacent atoms.

Figure 2.8b plots attractive, repulsive, and net potential energies as a function of interatomic separation for two atoms. The net curve, which is again the sum of the other two, has a potential energy trough or well around its minimum. Here, the same equilibrium spacing, r_0, corresponds to the separation distance at the minimum of the potential energy curve. The **bonding energy** for these two atoms, E_0, corresponds to the energy at this minimum point (also shown in Figure 2.8b); it represents the energy that would be required to separate these two atoms to an infinite separation.

Although the preceding treatment has dealt with an ideal situation involving only two atoms, a similar yet more complex condition exists for solid materials because force and energy interactions among many atoms must be considered. Nevertheless, a bonding energy, analogous to E_0 above, may be associated with each atom. The magnitude of this bonding energy and the shape of the energy-versus-interatomic separation curve vary from material to material, both variables depending on the type of atomic bonding. Solid substances are formed for large bonding energies, whereas for small energies the gaseous state is favored; liquids prevail when the energies are of intermediate magnitude. In general, for solid materials, melting temperature as well as cohesive properties reflect the magnitude of the bonding energy.

Three different types of primary or chemical bond are found in solids—ionic, covalent, and metallic. For each type, the bonding necessarily involves the valence electrons; furthermore, the nature of the bond depends on the electron structures of the constituent atoms. In general, each of these three types of bonding arises from the tendency of the atoms to assume stable electron structures, like those of the inert gases, by completely filling the outermost electron shell.

Secondary or physical forces and energies are also found in many solid materials; they are weaker than the primary ones, but nonetheless influence the physical properties of some materials. The sections that follow explain the several kinds of primary and secondary interatomic bonds.

2.6 PRIMARY INTERATOMIC BONDS

IONIC BONDING

Perhaps **ionic bonding** is the easiest to describe and visualize. It is always found in compounds that are composed of both metallic and nonmetallic elements, elements that are situated at the horizontal extremities of the periodic table. Atoms of a

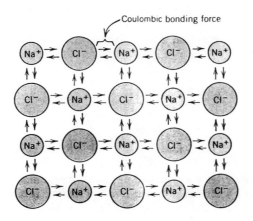

FIGURE 2.9 Schematic representation of ionic bonding in sodium chloride (NaCl).

metallic element easily give up their valence electrons to the nonmetallic atoms. In the process all the atoms acquire stable or inert gas configurations and, in addition, an electrical charge; that is, they become ions. Sodium chloride (NaCl) is the classical ionic material. A sodium atom can assume the electron structure of neon (and a net single positive charge) by a transfer of its one valence $3s$ electron to a chlorine atom. After such a transfer, the chlorine ion has a net negative charge and an electron configuration identical to that of argon. In sodium chloride, all the sodium and chlorine exist as ions. This type of bonding is illustrated schematically in Figure 2.9.

The attractive bonding forces are **coulombic;** that is, positive and negative ions, by virtue of their net electrical charge, attract one another. For two isolated ions, the attractive energy E_A is a function of the interatomic distance according to[2]

$$E_A = -\frac{A}{r} \tag{2.8}$$

An analogous equation for the repulsive energy is

$$E_R = \frac{B}{r^n} \tag{2.9}$$

In these expressions, A, B, and n are constants whose values depend on the particular ionic system. The value of n is approximately 8.

Ionic bonding is termed nondirectional, that is, the magnitude of the bond is equal in all directions around an ion. It follows that for ionic materials to be stable, all positive ions must have as nearest neighbors negatively charged ions in a three-dimensional scheme, and vice versa. The predominant bonding in ceramic materials is ionic. Some of the ion arrangements for these materials are discussed in Chapter 13.

Bonding energies, which generally range between 600 and 1500 kJ/mol (3 and 8 eV/atom), are relatively large, as reflected in high melting temperatures.[3] Table 2.3 contains bonding energies and melting temperatures for several ionic materials. Ionic materials are characteristically hard and brittle and, furthermore, electrically and thermally insulative. As discussed in subsequent chapters, these properties are a direct consequence of electron configurations and/or the nature of the ionic bond.

COVALENT BONDING

In **covalent bonding** stable electron configurations are assumed by the sharing of electrons between adjacent atoms. Two atoms that are covalently bonded will each contribute at least one electron to the bond, and the shared electrons may be

---

[2] The constant A in Equation 2.8 is equal to

$$\frac{1}{4\pi\epsilon_0}(Z_1 e)(Z_2 e)$$

where ϵ_0 is the permittivity of a vacuum (8.85×10^{-12} F/m), Z_1 and Z_2 are the valences of the two ion types, and e is the electronic charge (1.602×10^{-19} C).

[3] Sometimes bonding energies are expressed per atom or per ion. Under these circumstances the electron volt (eV) is a conveniently small unit of energy. It is, by definition, the energy imparted to an electron as it falls through an electric potential of one volt. The joule equivalent of the electron volt is as follows: 1.602×10^{-19} J = 1 eV.

Table 2.3 Bonding Energies and Melting Temperatures for Various Substances

Bonding Type	Substance	Bonding Energy		Melting Temperature (°C)
		kJ/mol (kcal/mol)	eV/Atom, Ion, Molecule	
Ionic	NaCl	640 (153)	3.3	801
	MgO	1000 (239)	5.2	2800
Covalent	Si	450 (108)	4.7	1410
	C (diamond)	713 (170)	7.4	>3550
Metallic	Hg	68 (16)	0.7	−39
	Al	324 (77)	3.4	660
	Fe	406 (97)	4.2	1538
	W	849 (203)	8.8	3410
van der Waals	Ar	7.7 (1.8)	0.08	−189
	Cl₂	31 (7.4)	0.32	−101
Hydrogen	NH₃	35 (8.4)	0.36	−78
	H₂O	51 (12.2)	0.52	0

considered to belong to both atoms. Covalent bonding is schematically illustrated in Figure 2.10 for a molecule of methane (CH_4). The carbon atom has four valence electrons, whereas each of the four hydrogen atoms has a single valence electron. Each hydrogen atom can acquire a helium electron configuration (two $1s$ valence electrons) when the carbon atom shares with it one electron. The carbon now has four additional shared electrons, one from each hydrogen, for a total of eight valence electrons, and the electron structure of neon. The covalent bond is directional; that is, it is between specific atoms and may exist only in the direction between one atom and another that participates in the electron sharing.

Many nonmetallic elemental molecules (H_2, Cl_2, F_2, etc.) as well as molecules containing dissimilar atoms, such as CH_4, H_2O, HNO_3, and HF, are covalently bonded. Furthermore, this type of bonding is found in elemental solids such as diamond (carbon), silicon, and germanium and other solid compounds composed of elements that are located on the right-hand side of the periodic table, such as gallium arsenide (GaAs), indium antimonide (InSb), and silicon carbide (SiC).

The number of covalent bonds that are possible for a particular atom is determined by the number of valence electrons. For N' valence electrons, an atom can

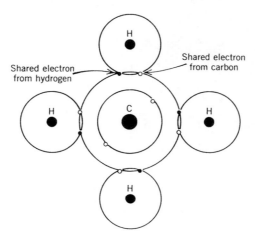

FIGURE 2.10 Schematic representation of covalent bonding in a molecule of methane (CH_4).

covalently bond with at most $8 - N'$ other atoms. For example, $N' = 7$ for chlorine, and $8 - N' = 1$, which means that one Cl atom can bond to only one other atom, as in Cl_2. Similarly, for carbon, $N' = 4$, and each carbon atom has $8 - 4$, or four, electrons to share. Diamond is simply the three-dimensional interconnecting structure wherein each carbon atom covalently bonds with four other carbon atoms. This arrangement is represented in Figure 13.15.

Covalent bonds may be very strong, as in diamond, which is very hard and has a very high melting temperature, >3550°C (6400°F), or they may be very weak, as with bismuth, which melts at about 270°C (518°F). Bonding energies and melting temperatures for a few covalently bonded materials are presented in Table 2.3. Polymeric materials typify this bond, the basic molecular structure being a long chain of carbon atoms that are covalently bonded together with two of their available four bonds per atom. The remaining two bonds normally are shared with other atoms, which also covalently bond. Polymeric molecular structures are discussed in detail in Chapter 15.

It is possible to have interatomic bonds that are partially ionic and partially covalent, and, in fact, very few compounds exhibit pure ionic or covalent bonding. For a compound, the degree of either bond type depends on the relative positions of the constituent atoms in the periodic table (Figure 2.6) or the difference in their electronegativities (Figure 2.7). The wider the separation (both horizontally—relative to Group IVA—and vertically) from the lower left to the upper-right-hand corner (i.e., the greater the difference in electronegativity), the more ionic the bond. Conversely, the closer the atoms are together (i.e., the smaller the difference in electronegativity), the greater the degree of covalency.

METALLIC BONDING

Metallic bonding, the final primary bonding type, is found in metals and their alloys. A relatively simple model has been proposed that very nearly approximates the bonding scheme. Metallic materials have one, two, or at most, three valence electrons. With this model, these valence electrons are not bound to any particular atom in the solid and are more or less free to drift throughout the entire metal. They may be thought of as belonging to the metal as a whole, or forming a "sea of electrons" or an "electron cloud." The remaining nonvalence electrons and atomic nuclei form what are called *ion cores,* which possess a net positive charge,

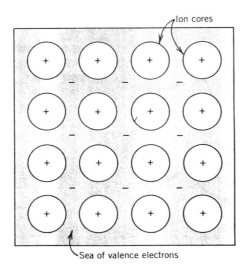

FIGURE 2.11 Schematic illustration of metallic bonding.

equal in magnitude to the total valence electron charge per atom. Figure 2.11 is a schematic illustration of metallic bonding. The free electrons shield the positively charged ion cores from mutually repulsive electrostatic forces, which they would otherwise exert upon one another; consequently the metallic bond is nondirectional in character. In addition, these free electrons act as a "glue" to hold the ion cores together. Bonding energies and melting temperatures for several metals are listed in Table 2.3. Bonding may be weak or strong; energies range from 68 kJ/mol (0.7 eV/atom) for mercury to 850 kJ/mol (8.8 eV/atom) for tungsten. Their respective melting temperatures are −39 and 3410°C (−38 and 6170°F).

This type of bonding is found for Group IA and IIA elements in the periodic table and, in fact, for all elemental metals. These materials are good conductors of both electricity and heat, as a consequence of the free valence electrons.

2.7 SECONDARY BONDING OR VAN DER WAALS BONDING

Secondary, van der Waals, or physical bonds are weak in comparison to the primary or chemical ones; bonding energies are typically on the order of only 10 kJ/mol (0.1 eV/atom). Secondary bonding exists between virtually all atoms or molecules, but its presence may be obscured if any of the three primary bonding types is present. Secondary bonding is evidenced for the inert gases, which have stable electron structures, and, in addition, between molecules in molecular structures that are covalently bonded.

Secondary bonding forces arise from atomic or molecular **dipoles.** In essence, an electric dipole exists whenever there is some separation of positive and negative portions of an atom or molecule. The bonding results from the coulombic attraction between the positive end of one dipole and the negative region of an adjacent one, as indicated in Figure 2.12. Dipole interactions occur between induced dipoles, between induced dipoles and polar molecules (which have permanent dipoles), and between polar molecules. **Hydrogen bonding,** a special type of secondary bonding, is found to exist between some molecules that have hydrogen as one of the constituents. These bonding mechanisms are now discussed briefly.

FLUCTUATING INDUCED DIPOLE BONDS

A dipole may be created or induced in an atom or molecule that is normally electrically symmetric; that is, the overall spatial distribution of the electrons is symmetric with respect to the positively charged nucleus, as shown in Figure 2.13a. All atoms are experiencing constant vibrational motion, which can cause instantaneous and short-lived distortions of this electrical symmetry for some of the atoms or molecules, and the creation of small electric dipoles, as represented in Figure 2.13b. One of these dipoles can in turn produce a displacement of the electron distribution of an adjacent molecule or atom, which induces the second one also to become a dipole that is then weakly attracted or bonded to the first; this is one type of van der Waals bonding. These attractive forces may exist between large numbers of atoms or molecules, which forces are temporary and fluctuate with time.

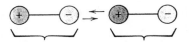

Atomic or molecular dipoles

FIGURE 2.12 Schematic illustration of van der Waals bonding between two dipoles.

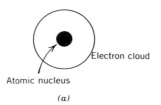

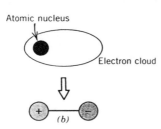

FIGURE 2.13 Schematic representations of (a) an electrically symmetric atom and (b) an induced atomic dipole.

The liquefaction and, in some cases, the solidification of the inert gases and other electrically neutral and symmetric molecules such as H_2 and Cl_2 are realized because of this type of bonding. Melting and boiling temperatures are extremely low in materials for which induced dipole bonding predominates; of all possible intermolecular bonds, these are the weakest. Bonding energies and melting temperatures for argon and chlorine are also tabulated in Table 2.3.

POLAR MOLECULE-INDUCED DIPOLE BONDS

Permanent dipole moments exist in some molecules by virtue of an asymmetrical arrangement of positively and negatively charged regions; such molecules are termed **polar molecules.** Figure 2.14 is a schematic representation of a hydrogen chloride molecule; a permanent dipole moment arises from net positive and negative charges that are respectively associated with the hydrogen and chlorine ends of the HCl molecule.

Polar molecules can also induce dipoles in adjacent nonpolar molecules, and a bond will form as a result of attractive forces between the two molecules. Furthermore, the magnitude of this bond will be greater than for fluctuating induced dipoles.

PERMANENT DIPOLE BONDS

Van der Waals forces will also exist between adjacent polar molecules. The associated bonding energies are significantly greater than for bonds involving induced dipoles.

The strongest secondary bonding type, the hydrogen bond, is a special case of polar molecule bonding. It occurs between molecules in which hydrogen is covalently bonded to fluorine (as in HF), oxygen (as in H_2O), and nitrogen (as in NH_3).

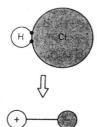

FIGURE 2.14 Schematic representation of a polar hydrogen chloride (HCl) molecule.

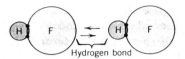

FIGURE 2.15   Schematic representation of hydrogen bonding in hydrogen fluoride (HF).

For each H—F, H—O, or H—N bond, the single hydrogen electron is shared with the other atom. Thus, the hydrogen end of the bond is essentially a positively charged bare proton, which is unscreened by any electrons. This highly positively charged end of the molecule is capable of a strong attractive force with the negative end of an adjacent molecule, as demonstrated in Figure 2.15 for HF. In essence, this single proton forms a bridge between two negatively charged atoms. The magnitude of the hydrogen bond is generally greater than that for the other types of secondary bonds, and may be as high as 51 kJ/mol (0.52 eV/molecule) as shown in Table 2.3. Melting and boiling temperatures for hydrogen fluoride and water are abnormally high in light of their low molecular weights, as a consequence of hydrogen bonding.

2.8 MOLECULES

At the conclusion of this chapter, let us take a moment to discuss the concept of a **molecule** in terms of solid materials. A molecule may be defined as a group of atoms that are bonded together by strong primary bonds. Within this context, the entirety of ionic and metallically bonded solid specimens may be considered as a single molecule. However, this is not the case for many substances in which covalent bonding predominates; these include elemental diatomic molecules (F_2, O_2, H_2, etc.) as well as a host of compounds (H_2O, CO_2, HNO_3, C_6H_6, CH_4, etc.). In the condensed liquid and solid states, bonds between molecules are weak secondary ones. Consequently, molecular materials have relatively low melting and boiling temperatures. Most of those that have small molecules composed of a few atoms are gases at ordinary, or ambient, temperatures and pressures. On the other hand, many of the modern polymers, being molecular materials composed of extremely large molecules, exist as solids; some of their properties are strongly dependent on the presence of van der Waals and hydrogen secondary bonds.

SUMMARY

This chapter began with a survey of the fundamentals of atomic structure, presenting the Bohr and wave-mechanical models of electrons in atoms. Whereas the Bohr model assumes electrons to be particles orbiting the nucleus in discrete paths, in wave mechanics we consider them to be wavelike and treat electron position in terms of a probability distribution.

Electron energy states are specified in terms of quantum numbers that give rise to electron shells and subshells. The electron configuration of an atom corresponds to the manner in which these shells and subshells are filled with electrons in compliance with the Pauli exclusion principle. The periodic table of the elements is generated by arrangement of the various elements according to valence electron configuration.

Atomic bonding in solids may be considered in terms of attractive and repulsive forces and energies. The three types of primary bond in solids are ionic, covalent, and metallic. For ionic bonds, electrically charged ions are formed by the transference of valence electrons from one atom type to another; forces are coulombic. There is a sharing of valence electrons between adjacent atoms when bonding is covalent.

With metallic bonding, the valence electrons form a "sea of electrons" that is uniformly dispersed around the metal ion cores and acts as a form of glue for them.

Both van der Waals and hydrogen bonds are termed secondary, being weak in comparison to the primary ones. They result from attractive forces between electric dipoles, of which there are two types—induced and permanent. For the hydrogen bond, highly polar molecules form when hydrogen covalently bonds to a nonmetallic element such as fluorine.

IMPLICATIONS

Several important properties of materials are dependent on the type and characteristics of their interatomic/interionic/intermolecular bonds; some of these are listed as follows:

1. Melting temperature is a function of the interatomic bonding energy; the higher this energy, the greater the melting temperature (Section 2.6).

2. Modulus of elasticity (i.e., stiffness) of a material (Section 6.3) is related to the shape of a material's force versus atomic separation curve, Figure 2.8a.

3. The strengths of some polymeric materials are functions of the degree of secondary bonding between adjacent molecules (Section 16.3).

4. Electrical conductivity is dependent on the type of interatomic bond (Section 19.6). Metallic bonded materials are typically electrical conductors, while those that are ionically and covalently bonded tend to be insulators and semiconductors.

5. The magnitude of the coefficient of thermal expansion (Section 20.3) is dependent on the shape of a material's potential energy-atomic separation curve, Figure 2.8b.

IMPORTANT TERMS AND CONCEPTS

Atomic mass unit (amu)	Electronegative	Periodic table
Atomic number	Electropositive	Polar molecule
Atomic weight	Ground state	Primary bonding
Bohr atomic model	Hydrogen bond	Quantum mechanics
Bonding energy	Ionic bond	Quantum number
Coulombic force	Isotope	Secondary bonding
Covalent bond	Metallic bond	Valence electron
Dipole (electric)	Mole	van der Waals bond
Electron configuration	Molecule	Wave-mechanical model
Electron state	Pauli exclusion principle	

REFERENCES

Most of the material in this chapter is covered in college-level chemistry textbooks. Below, two are listed as references.

Kotz, J. C. and K. F. Purcell, *Chemistry and Chemical Reactivity,* 2nd edition, Saunders College Publishing, Philadelphia, 1991.

Masterton, W. L. and C. N. Hurley, *Chemistry, Principles and Reactions,* Saunders College Publishing, Philadelphia, 1989.

Note: In each chapter, most of the terms listed in the "Important Terms and Concepts" section are defined in the Glossary, which follows Appendix E. The others are important enough to warrant treatment in a full section of the text and can be referenced from the table of contents or the index.

QUESTIONS AND PROBLEMS

2.1 (a) What is an isotope?

(b) Why are the atomic weights of the elements not integers? Cite two reasons.

2.2 Cite the difference between atomic mass and atomic weight.

2.3 (a) How many grams are there in 1 amu of a material?

(b) Mole, in the context of this book, is taken in units of gram-mole. On this basis, how many atoms are there in a pound-mole of a substance?

2.4 (a) Cite two important quantum-mechanical concepts associated with the Bohr model of the atom.

(b) Cite two important additional refinements that resulted from the wave-mechanical atomic model.

2.5 Relative to electrons and electron states, what does each of the four quantum numbers specify?

2.6 Allowed values for the quantum numbers of electrons are as follows:

$$n = 1, 2, 3, \ldots$$
$$l = 0, 1, 2, 3, \ldots, n - 1$$
$$m_l = 0, \pm 1, \pm 2, \pm 3, \ldots, \pm l$$
$$m_s = \pm \tfrac{1}{2}$$

The relationships between n and the shell designations are noted in Table 2.1. Relative to the subshells,

$l = 0$ corresponds to an s subshell

$l = 1$ corresponds to a p subshell

$l = 2$ corresponds to a d subshell

$l = 3$ corresponds to an f subshell

For the K shell, the four quantum numbers for each of the two electrons in the $1s$ state, in the order of nlm_lm_s, are $100(\tfrac{1}{2})$ and $100(-\tfrac{1}{2})$.
Write the four quantum numbers for all of the electrons in the L and M shells, and note which correspond to the s, p, and d subshells.

2.7 Give the electron configurations for the following ions: P^{5+}, P^{3-}, Sn^{4+}, Se^{2-}, I^-, and Ni^{2+}.

2.8 Cesium bromide (CsBr) exhibits predominantly ionic bonding. The Cs^+ and Br^- ions have electron structures that are identical to which two inert gases?

2.9 With regard to electron configuration, what do all the elements in Group VIIA of the periodic table have in common?

2.10 Without consulting Figure 2.6 or Table 2.2, determine whether each of the electron configurations given below is an inert gas, a halogen, an alkali metal, an alkaline earth metal, or a transition metal. Justify your choices.

(a) $1s^2 2s^2 2p^6 3s^2 3p^5$.

(b) $1s^2 2s^2 2p^6 3s^2 3p^6 3d^7 4s^2$.

(c) $1s^2 2s^2 2p^6 3s^2 3p^6 3d^{10} 4s^2 4p^6$.

(d) $1s^2 2s^2 2p^6 3s^2 3p^6 4s^1$.

(e) $1s^2 2s^2 2p^6 3s^2 3p^6 3d^{10} 4s^2 4p^6 4d^5 5s^2$.

(f) $1s^2 2s^2 2p^6 3s^2$.

2.11 (a) What electron subshell is being filled for the rare earth series of elements on the periodic table?

(b) What electron subshell is being filled for the actinide series?

2.12 Calculate the force of attraction between a K^+ and an O^{2-} ion the centers of which are separated by a distance of 1.5 nm.

2.13 The net potential energy between two adjacent ions, E_N, may be represented by the sum of Equations 2.8 and 2.9, that is,

$$E_N = -\frac{A}{r} + \frac{B}{r^n} \qquad (2.10)$$

Calculate the bonding energy E_0 in terms of the parameters A, B, and n using the following procedure:

1. Differentiate E_N with respect to r, and then set the resulting expression equal to zero, since the curve of E_N versus r is a minimum at E_0.

2. Solve for r in terms of A, B, and n, which yields r_0, the equilibrium interionic spacing.

3. Determine the expression for E_0 by substitution of r_0 into Equation 2.10.

2.14 For a K^+–Cl^- ion pair, attractive and repulsive energies E_A and E_R, respectively, depend on the distance between the ions r, according to

$$E_A = -\frac{1.436}{r}$$

$$E_R = \frac{5.86 \times 10^{-6}}{r^9}$$

For these expressions, energies are expressed in electron volts per K^+–Cl^- pair, and r is the distance in nanometers. The net energy E_N is just the sum of the two expressions above.

(a) Superimpose on a single plot E_N, E_R, and E_A versus r up to 1.0 nm.

(b) On the basis of this plot, determine (i) the equilibrium spacing r_0 between the K^+ and Cl^- ions, and (ii) the magnitude of the bonding energy E_0 between the two ions.

(c) Mathematically determine the r_0 and E_0 values using the solutions to Problem 2.13 and compare these with the graphical results from part b.

2.15 The net potential energy E_N between two adjacent ions is sometimes represented by the expression

$$E_N = -\frac{C}{r} + D \exp\left(-\frac{r}{\rho}\right) \quad (2.11)$$

in which r is the interionic separation and C, D, and ρ are constants whose values depend on the specific material.

(a) Derive an expression for the bonding energy E_0 in terms of the equilibrium interionic separation r_0 and the constants D and ρ using the following procedure:
  1. Differentiate E_N with respect to r and set the resulting expression equal to zero.
  2. Solve for C in terms of D, ρ, and r_0.
  3. Determine the expression for E_0 by substitution for C in Equation 2.11.

(b) Derive another expression for E_0 in terms of r_0, C, and ρ using a procedure analogous to the one outlined in part a.

2.16 (a) Briefly cite the main differences between ionic, covalent, and metallic bonding.

(b) State the Pauli exclusion principle.

2.17 Offer an explanation as to why covalently bonded materials are generally less dense than ionically or metallically bonded ones.

2.18 The percent ionic character of a bond between elements A and B (A being the most electronegative) may be approximated by the expression

$$\% \text{ ionic character} = [1 - e^{-(0.25)(X_A - X_B)^2}] \times 100$$

$$(2.12)$$

where X_A and X_B are the electronegativities for the respective elements. Compute the percents ionic character of the interatomic bonds for the following compounds: TiO_2, $ZnTe$, $CsCl$, $InSb$, and $MgCl_2$.

2.19 Make a plot of bonding energy versus melting temperature for the metals listed in Table 2.3. Using this plot, approximate the bonding energy for molybdenum, which has a melting temperature of 2617°C.

2.20 Using Table 2.2 determine the number of covalent bonds that are possible for atoms of the following elements: germanium, phosphorous, selenium, and chlorine.

2.21 What type(s) of bonding would be expected for each of the following materials: solid xenon, calcium fluoride (CaF_2), bronze, cadmium telluride ($CdTe$), rubber, and tungsten?

2.22 Explain why hydrogen fluoride (HF) has a higher boiling temperature than hydrogen chloride (HCl) (19.4 vs. −85°C), even though HF has a lower molecular weight.

2.23 On the basis of the hydrogen bond, explain the anomalous behavior of water when it freezes. That is, why is there volume expansion upon solidification?

The Structure of Crystalline Solids

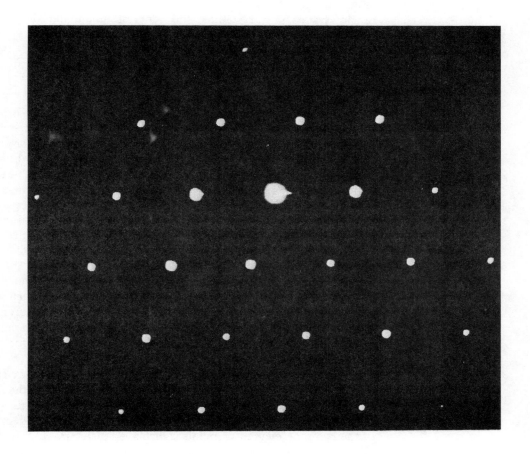

_H_igh velocity electron beams that are produced when electrons are accelerated across large voltages become wavelike in character. Their wavelengths are shorter than interatomic spacings, and, thus, these beams may be diffracted by atomic planes in crystalline materials, in the same manner as x-rays experience diffraction.

This photograph shows a diffraction pattern produced for a single crystal of gallium arsenide using a transmission electron microscope. The brightest spot near the center is produced by the incident electron beam which is parallel to a ⟨110⟩ crystallographic direction. Each of the other white spots results from an electron beam that is diffracted by a specific set of crystallographic planes. (Photograph courtesy of Dr. Raghaw S. Rai, Motorola, Inc., Austin, Texas.)

3.1 INTRODUCTION

Chapter 2 was concerned primarily with the various types of atomic bonding, which are determined by the electron structure of the individual atoms. The present discussion is devoted to the next level of the structure of materials, specifically, to some of the arrangements that may be assumed by atoms in the solid state. Within this framework, concepts of crystallinity and noncrystallinity are introduced. For crystalline solids the notion of crystal structure is presented, specified in terms of a unit cell. The three common crystal structures found in metals are then detailed, along with the scheme by which crystallographic directions and planes are expressed. Single crystals, polycrystalline, and noncrystalline materials are considered.

CRYSTAL STRUCTURES

3.2 FUNDAMENTAL CONCEPTS

Solid materials may be classified according to the regularity with which atoms or ions are arranged with respect to one another. A **crystalline** material is one in which the atoms are situated in a repeating or periodic array over large atomic distances; that is, long-range order exists, such that upon solidification, the atoms will position themselves in a repetitive three-dimensional pattern, in which each atom is bonded to its nearest-neighbor atoms. All metals, many ceramic materials, and certain polymers form crystalline structures under normal solidification conditions. For those that do not crystallize, this long-range atomic order is absent; these *noncrystalline* or *amorphous* materials are discussed briefly at the end of this chapter.

Some of the properties of crystalline solids depend on the **crystal structure** of the material, the manner in which atoms, ions, or molecules are spatially arranged. There is an extremely large number of different crystal structures all having long-range atomic order; these vary from relatively simple structures for metals, to exceedingly complex ones, as displayed by some of the ceramic and polymeric materials. The present discussion deals with several common metallic crystal structures. Chapters 13 and 15 are devoted to crystal structures for ceramics and polymers, respectively.

When describing crystalline structures, atoms (or ions) are thought of as being solid spheres having well-defined diameters. This is termed the *atomic hard sphere model* in which spheres representing nearest-neighbor atoms touch one another. An example of the hard sphere model for the atomic arrangement found in some of the common elemental metals is displayed in Figure 3.1c. In this particular case all the atoms are identical. Sometimes the term **lattice** is used in the context of crystal structures; in this sense "lattice" means a three-dimensional array of points coinciding with atom positions (or sphere centers).

3.3 UNIT CELLS

The atomic order in crystalline solids indicates that small groups of atoms form a repetitive pattern. Thus, in describing crystal structures, it is often convenient to subdivide the structure into small repeat entities called **unit cells.** Unit cells for most crystal structures are parallelepipeds or prisms having three sets of parallel faces; one is drawn within the aggregate of spheres (Figure 3.1c), which in this case happens to be a cube. A unit cell is chosen to represent the symmetry of the

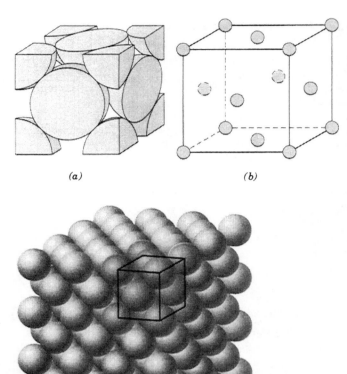

(a)   (b)

(c)

FIGURE 3.1 For the face-centered cubic crystal structure: (*a*) a hard sphere unit cell representation, (*b*) a reduced-sphere unit cell, and (*c*) an aggregate of many atoms. (Figure *c* adapted from W. G. Moffatt, G. W. Pearsall, and J. Wulff, *The Structure and Properties of Materials,* Vol. I, *Structure,* p. 51. Copyright © 1964 by John Wiley & Sons, New York. Reprinted by permission of John Wiley & Sons, Inc.)

crystal structure, wherein all the atom positions in the crystal may be generated by translations of the unit cell integral distances along each of its edges. Thus, the unit cell is the basic structural unit or building block of the crystal structure and defines the crystal structure by virtue of its geometry and the atom positions within. Convenience usually dictates that parallelepiped corners coincide with centers of the hard sphere atoms. Furthermore, more than a single unit cell may be chosen for a particular crystal structure; however, we generally use the unit cell having the highest level of geometrical symmetry.

3.4 METALLIC CRYSTAL STRUCTURES

The atomic bonding in this group of materials is metallic, and thus nondirectional in nature. Consequently, there are no restrictions as to the number and position of nearest-neighbor atoms; this leads to relatively large numbers of nearest neighbors and dense atomic packings for most metallic crystal structures. Also, for metals, using the hard sphere model for the crystal structure, each sphere represents an ion core. Table 3.1 presents the atomic radii for a number of metals. Three relatively simple crystal structures are found for most of the common metals: face-centered cubic, body-centered cubic, and hexagonal close-packed.

Table 3.1 **Atomic Radii and Crystal Structures for 16 Metals**

Metal	Crystal Structure[a]	Atomic Radius[b] (nm)	Metal	Crystal Structure	Atomic Radius (nm)
Aluminum	FCC	0.1431	Molybdenum	BCC	0.1363
Cadmium	HCP	0.1490	Nickel	FCC	0.1246
Chromium	BCC	0.1249	Platinum	FCC	0.1387
Cobalt	HCP	0.1253	Silver	FCC	0.1445
Copper	FCC	0.1278	Tantalum	BCC	0.1430
Gold	FCC	0.1442	Titanium (α)	HCP	0.1445
Iron (α)	BCC	0.1241	Tungsten	BCC	0.1371
Lead	FCC	0.1750	Zinc	HCP	0.1332

[a] FCC = face-centered cubic; HCP = hexagonal close-packed; BCC = body-centered cubic.

[b] A nanometer (nm) equals 10^{-9} m; to convert from nanometers to angstrom units (Å), multiply the nanometer value by 10.

THE FACE-CENTERED CUBIC CRYSTAL STRUCTURE

The crystal structure found for many metals has a unit cell of cubic geometry, with atoms located at each of the corners and the centers of all the cube faces. It is aptly called the **face-centered cubic (FCC)** crystal structure. Some of the familiar metals having this crystal structure are copper, aluminum, silver, and gold (see also Table 3.1). Figure 3.1a shows a hard sphere model for the FCC unit cell, whereas in Figure 3.1b the atom centers are represented by small circles to provide a better perspective of atom positions. The aggregate of atoms in Figure 3.1c represents a section of crystal consisting of many FCC unit cells. These spheres or ion cores touch one another across a face diagonal; the cube edge length a and the atomic radius R are related through

$$a = 2R\sqrt{2}$$

(3.1)

This result is obtained as an example problem.

For the FCC crystal structure, each corner atom is shared among eight unit cells, whereas a face-centered atom belongs to only two. Therefore, one eighth of each of the eight corner atoms and one half of each of the six face atoms, or a total of four whole atoms, may be assigned to a given unit cell. This is depicted in Figure 3.1a, where only sphere portions are represented within the confines of the cube. The cell comprises the volume of the cube, which is generated from the centers of the corner atoms as shown in the figure.

Corner and face positions are really equivalent; that is, translation of the cube corner from an original corner atom to the center of a face atom will not alter the cell structure.

Two other important characteristics of a crystal structure are the **coordination number** and the **atomic packing factor (APF).** For metals, each atom has the same number of nearest-neighbor or touching atoms, which is the coordination number. For face-centered cubics, the coordination number is 12. This may be confirmed by examination of Figure 3.1a; the front face atom has four corner nearest-neighbor atoms surrounding it, four face atoms that are in contact from behind, and four other equivalent face atoms residing in the next unit cell to the front, which is not shown.

The APF is the fraction of solid sphere volume in a unit cell, assuming the atomic hard sphere model, or

$$APF = \frac{\text{volume of atoms in a unit cell}}{\text{total unit cell volume}} \tag{3.2}$$

For the FCC structure, the atomic packing factor is 0.74, which is the maximum packing possible for spheres all having the same diameter. Computation of this APF is also included as an example problem. Metals typically have relatively large atomic packing factors to maximize the shielding provided by the free electron cloud.

THE BODY-CENTERED CUBIC CRYSTAL STRUCTURE

Another common metallic crystal structure also has a cubic unit cell with atoms located at all eight corners and a single atom at the cube center. This is called a **body-centered cubic (BCC)** crystal structure. A collection of spheres depicting this crystal structure is shown in Figure 3.2c, whereas Figures 3.2a and 3.2b are diagrams of BCC unit cells with the atoms represented by hard sphere and reduced-sphere models, respectively. Center and corner atoms touch one another along cube diagonals, and unit cell length a and atomic radius R are related through

$$a = \frac{4R}{\sqrt{3}} \tag{3.3}$$

Chromium, iron, tungsten, as well as several other metals listed in Table 3.1 exhibit a BCC structure.

Two atoms are associated with each BCC unit cell: the equivalence of one atom from the eight corners, each of which is shared among eight unit cells, and the single center atom, which is wholly contained within its cell. In addition, corner and center atom positions are equivalent. The coordination number for the BCC crystal structure is 8; each center atom has as nearest neighbors its eight corner atoms. Since the coordination number is less for BCC than FCC, so also is the atomic packing factor for BCC lower—0.68 versus 0.74.

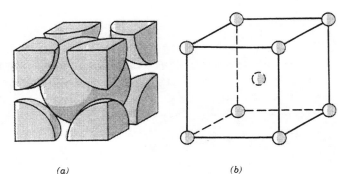
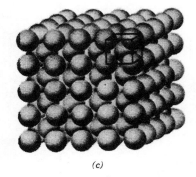

(a)   (b)   (c)

FIGURE 3.2   For the body-centered cubic crystal structure, (a) a hard sphere unit cell representation, (b) a reduced-sphere unit cell, and (c) an aggregate of many atoms. (Figure (c) from W. G. Moffatt, G. W. Pearsall, and J. Wulff, *The Structure and Properties of Materials,* Vol. I, *Structure,* p. 51. Copyright © 1964 by John Wiley & Sons, New York. Reprinted by permission of John Wiley & Sons, Inc.)

THE HEXAGONAL CLOSE-PACKED CRYSTAL STRUCTURE

Not all metals have unit cells with cubic symmetry; the final common metallic crystal structure to be discussed has a unit cell that is hexagonal. Figure 3.3a shows a reduced-sphere unit cell for this structure, which is termed **hexagonal close-packed (HCP);** an assemblage of several HCP unit cells is presented in Figure 3.3b. The top and bottom faces of the unit cell consist of six atoms that form regular hexagons and surround a single atom in the center. Another plane that provides three additional atoms to the unit cell is situated between the top and bottom planes. The atoms in this midplane have as nearest neighbors atoms in both of the adjacent two planes. The equivalence of six atoms is contained in each unit cell; one-sixth of each of the 12 top and bottom face corner atoms, one-half of each of the 2 center face atoms, and all the 3 midplane interior atoms. If a and c represent, respectively, the short and long unit cell dimensions of Figure 3.3a, the c/a ratio should be 1.633; however, for some HCP metals this ratio deviates from the ideal value.

The coordination number and the atomic packing factor for the HCP crystal structure are the same as for FCC: 12 and 0.74, respectively. The HCP metals include cadmium, magnesium, titanium, and zinc; some of these are listed in Table 3.1.

EXAMPLE PROBLEM 3.1

Calculate the volume of an FCC unit cell in terms of the atomic radius R.

SOLUTION

In the FCC unit cell illustrated,

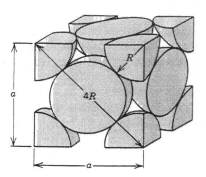

the atoms touch one another across a face-diagonal the length of which is $4R$. Since the unit cell is a cube, its volume is a^3, where a is the cell edge length. From the right triangle on the face,

$$a^2 + a^2 = (4R)^2$$

or, solving for a,

$$a = 2R\sqrt{2} \tag{3.1}$$

The FCC unit cell volume V_C may be computed from

$$V_C = a^3 = (2R\sqrt{2})^3 = 16R^3\sqrt{2} \tag{3.4}$$

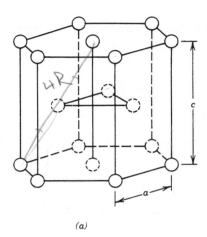
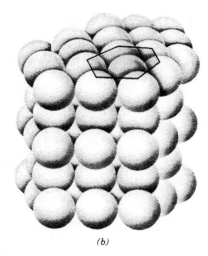

(a)

(b)

FIGURE 3.3   For the hexagonal close-packed crystal structure, (a) a reduced-sphere unit cell (a and c represent the short and long edge lengths, respectively), and (b) an aggregate of many atoms. (Figure (b) from W. G. Moffatt, G. W. Pearsall, and J. Wulff, *The Structure and Properties of Materials*, Vol. I, *Structure*, p. 51. Copyright © 1964 by John Wiley & Sons, New York. Reprinted by permission of John Wiley & Sons, Inc.)

EXAMPLE PROBLEM 3.2

Show that the atomic packing factor for the FCC crystal structure is 0.74.

SOLUTION

The APF is defined as the fraction of solid sphere volume in a unit cell, or

$$\text{APF} = \frac{\text{total sphere volume}}{\text{total unit cell volume}} = \frac{V_S}{V_C}$$

Both the total sphere and unit cell volumes may be calculated in terms of the atomic radius R. The volume for a sphere is $\frac{4}{3}\pi R^3$, and since there are four atoms per FCC unit cell, the total FCC sphere volume is

$$V_S = (4)\frac{4}{3}\pi R^3 = \frac{16}{3}\pi R^3$$

From Example Problem 3.1, the total unit cell volume is

$$V_C = 16R^3 \sqrt{2}$$

Therefore, the atomic packing factor is

$$\text{APF} = \frac{V_S}{V_C} = \frac{\left(\frac{16}{3}\right)\pi R^3}{16R^3 \sqrt{2}} = 0.74$$

3.5 DENSITY COMPUTATIONS

A knowledge of the crystal structure of a metallic solid permits computation of its true density ρ through the relationship

$$\rho = \frac{nA}{V_C N_A} \tag{3.5}$$

where

n = number of atoms associated with each unit cell

A = atomic weight

V_C = volume of the unit cell

N_A = Avogadro's number (6.023×10^{23} atoms/mol)

EXAMPLE PROBLEM 3.3

Copper has an atomic radius of 0.128 nm (1.28 Å), an FCC crystal structure, and an atomic weight of 63.5 g/mol. Compute its density and compare the answer with its measured density.

SOLUTION

Equation 3.5 is employed in the solution of this problem. Since the crystal structure is FCC, n, the number of atoms per unit cell, is 4. Furthermore, the atomic weight A_{Cu} is given as 63.5 g/mol. The unit cell volume V_C for FCC was determined in Example Problem 3.1 as $16R^3\sqrt{2}$, where R, the atomic radius, is 0.128 nm.

Substitution for the various parameters into Equation 3.5 yields

$$\rho = \frac{nA_{Cu}}{V_C N_A} = \frac{nA_{Cu}}{(16R^3\sqrt{2})N_A}$$

$$= \frac{(4 \text{ atoms/unit cell})(63.5 \text{ g/mol})}{[16\sqrt{2}(1.28 \times 10^{-8} \text{ cm})^3/\text{unit cell}](6.023 \times 10^{23} \text{ atoms/mol})}$$

$$= 8.89 \text{ g/cm}^3$$

The literature value for the density of copper is 8.94 g/cm³, which is in very close agreement with the foregoing result.

3.6 POLYMORPHISM AND ALLOTROPY

Some metals, as well as nonmetals, may have more than one crystal structure, a phenomenon known as **polymorphism.** When found in elemental solids, the condition is often termed **allotropy.** The prevailing crystal structure depends on both the temperature and the external pressure. One familiar example is found in carbon: graphite is the stable polymorph at ambient conditions, whereas diamond is formed at extremely high pressures. Also, pure iron has a BCC crystal structure at room temperature, which changes to FCC iron at 912°C (1674°F). Most often a modifica-

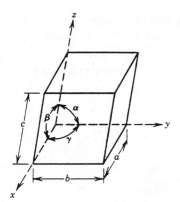

FIGURE 3.4 A unit cell with x, y, and z coordinate axes, showing axial lengths (a, b, and c) and interaxial angles (α, β, and γ).

tion of the density and other physical properties accompanies a polymorphic transformation.

3.7 CRYSTAL SYSTEMS

Since there are many different possible crystal structures, it is sometimes convenient to divide them into groups according to unit cell configurations and/or atomic arrangements. One such scheme is based on the unit cell geometry, that is, the shape of the appropriate unit cell parallelepiped without regard to the atomic positions in the cell. Within this framework, an x, y, z coordinate system is established with its origin at one of the unit cell corners; each of the x, y, and z axes coincides with one of the three parallelepiped edges that extend from this corner, as illustrated in Figure 3.4. The unit cell geometry is completely defined in terms of six parameters: the three edge lengths a, b, and c, and the three interaxial angles α, β, and γ. These are indicated in Figure 3.4, and are sometimes termed the **lattice parameters** of a crystal structure.

On this basis there are found crystals having seven different possible combinations of a, b, and c, and α, β, and γ, each of which represents a distinct **crystal system.** These seven crystal systems are cubic, tetragonal, hexagonal, orthorhombic, rhombohedral, monoclinic, and triclinic. The lattice parameter relationships and unit cell sketches for each are represented in Table 3.2. The cubic system, for which $a = b = c$ and $\alpha = \beta = \gamma = 90°$, has the greatest degree of symmetry. Least symmetry is displayed by the triclinic system, since $a \neq b \neq c$ and $\alpha \neq \beta \neq \gamma$.

From the discussion of metallic crystal structures, it should be apparent that both FCC and BCC structures belong to the cubic crystal system, whereas HCP falls within hexagonal. The conventional hexagonal unit cell really consists of three parallelepipeds situated as shown in Table 3.2.

CRYSTALLOGRAPHIC DIRECTIONS AND PLANES

When dealing with crystalline materials, it often becomes necessary to specify some particular crystallographic plane of atoms or a crystallographic direction. Labeling conventions have been established in which three integers or indices are used to designate directions and planes. The basis for determining index values is the unit

Table 3.2 Lattice Parameter Relationships and Figures Showing Unit Cell Geometries for the Seven Crystal Systems

Crystal System	Axial Relationships	Interaxial Angles	Unit Cell Geometry
Cubic	$a = b = c$	$\alpha = \beta = \gamma = 90°$	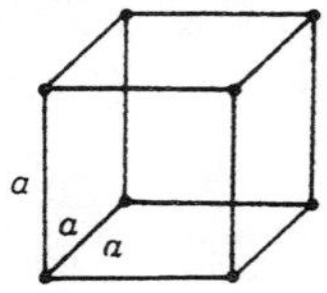
Hexagonal	$a = b \neq c$	$\alpha = \beta = 90°, \gamma = 120°$	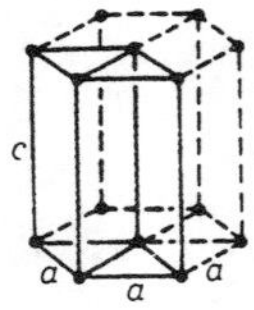
Tetragonal	$a = b \neq c$	$\alpha = \beta = \gamma = 90°$	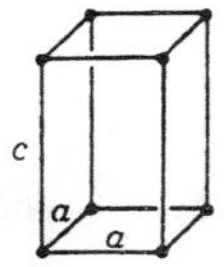
Rhombohedral	$a = b = c$	$\alpha = \beta = \gamma \neq 90°$	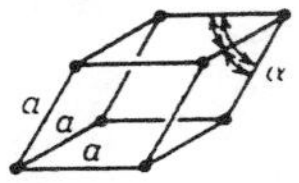
Orthorhombic	$a \neq b \neq c$	$\alpha = \beta = \gamma = 90°$	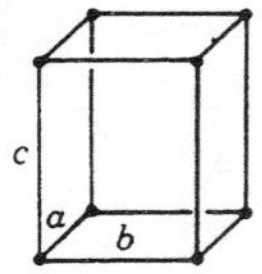
Monoclinic	$a \neq b \neq c$	$\alpha = \gamma = 90° \neq \beta$	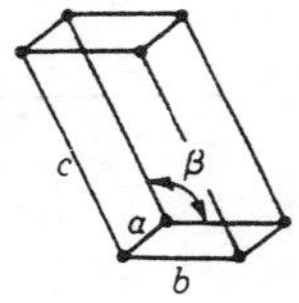
Triclinic	$a \neq b \neq c$	$\alpha \neq \beta \neq \gamma \neq 90°$	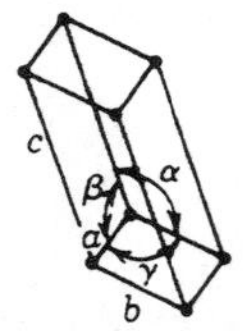

cell, with a coordinate system consisting of three (x, y, and z) axes situated at one of the corners and coinciding with the unit cell edges, as shown in Figure 3.4. For some crystal systems—namely, hexagonal, rhombohedral, monoclinic, and triclinic—the three axes are *not* mutually perpendicular, as in the familiar Cartesian coordinate scheme.

3.8 CRYSTALLOGRAPHIC DIRECTIONS

A crystallographic direction is defined as a line between two points, or a vector. The following steps are utilized in the determination of the three directional indices:

1. A vector of convenient length is positioned such that it passes through the origin of the coordinate system. Any vector may be translated throughout the crystal lattice without alteration, if parallelism is maintained.
2. The length of the vector projection on each of the three axes is determined; *these are measured in terms of the unit cell dimensions a, b, and c.*
3. These three numbers are multiplied or divided by a common factor to reduce them to the smallest integer values.
4. The three indices, not separated by commas, are enclosed in square brackets, thus: [uvw]. The u, v, and w integers correspond to the reduced projections along the x, y, and z axes, respectively.

For each of the three axes, there will exist both positive and negative coordinates. Thus negative indices are also possible, which are represented by a bar over the appropriate index. For example, the [$1\bar{1}1$] direction would have a component in the $-y$ direction. Also, changing the signs of all indices produces an antiparallel direction; that is, [$\bar{1}1\bar{1}$] is directly opposite to [$1\bar{1}1$]. If more than one direction or plane is to be specified for a particular crystal structure, it is imperative for the maintaining of consistency that a positive–negative convention, once established, not be changed.

The [100], [110], and [111] directions are common ones; they are drawn in the unit cell shown in Figure 3.5.

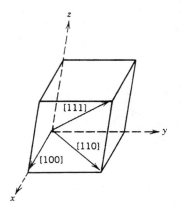

FIGURE 3.5 The [100], [110], and [111] directions within a unit cell.

EXAMPLE PROBLEM 3.4

Determine the indices for the direction shown in the accompanying figure.

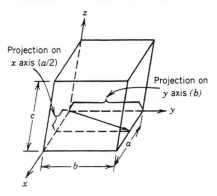

SOLUTION

The vector, as drawn, passes through the origin of the coordinate system, and therefore no translation is necessary. Projections of this vector onto the x, y, and z axes are, respectively, $a/2$, b, and $0c$, which become $\frac{1}{2}$, 1, and 0 in terms of the unit cell parameters (i.e., when the a, b, and c are dropped). Reduction of these numbers to the lowest set of integers is accompanied by multiplication of each by the factor 2. This yields the integers 1, 2, and 0, which are then enclosed in brackets as [120].

This procedure may be summarized as follows:

	x	y	z
Projections	$a/2$	b	$0c$
Projections (in terms of a, b, and c)	$\frac{1}{2}$	1	0
Reduction	1	2	0
Enclosure		[120]	

EXAMPLE PROBLEM 3.5

Draw a $[1\bar{1}0]$ direction within a cubic unit cell.

SOLUTION

First construct an appropriate unit cell and coordinate axes system. In the accompanying figure the unit cell is cubic, and the origin of the coordinate system, point O, is located at one of the cube corners.

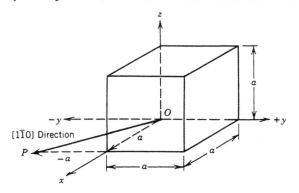

This problem is solved by reversing the procedure of the preceding example. For this [1$\bar{1}$0] direction, the projections along x, y, z axes are a, $-a$, and $0a$, respectively. This direction is defined by a vector passing from the origin to point P, which is located by first moving along the x axis a units, and from this position, parallel to the y axis $-a$ units, as indicated in the figure. There is no z component to the vector, since the z projection is zero.

For some crystal structures, several nonparallel directions with different indices are actually equivalent; this means that the spacing of atoms along each direction is the same. For example, in cubic crystals, all the directions represented by the following indices are equivalent: [100], [$\bar{1}$00], [010], [0$\bar{1}$0], [001], and [00$\bar{1}$]. As a convenience, equivalent directions are grouped together into a *family*, which are enclosed in angle brackets, thus: ⟨100⟩. Furthermore, directions in cubic crystals having the same indices without regard to order or sign, for example, [123] and [$\bar{2}$1$\bar{3}$], are equivalent. This is, in general, not true for other crystal systems. For example, for crystals of tetragonal symmetry, [100] and [010] directions are equivalent, whereas [100] and [001] are not.

HEXAGONAL CRYSTALS

A problem arises for crystals having hexagonal symmetry in that some crystallographic equivalent directions will not have the same set of indices. This is circumvented by utilizing a four-axis, or *Miller-Bravais*, coordinate system as shown in Figure 3.6. The three a_1, a_2, and a_3 axes are all contained within a single plane (called the basal plane), and at 120° angles to one another. The z axis is perpendicular to this basal plane. Directional indices, which are obtained as described above, will be denoted by four indices, as [$uvtw$]; by convention, the first three indices pertain to projections along the respective a_1, a_2, and a_3 axes in the basal plane.

Conversion from the three-index system to the four-index system,

$$[u'v'w'] \longrightarrow [uvtw]$$

is accomplished by the following formulas:

$$u = \frac{n}{3}(2u' - v') \tag{3.6a}$$

$$v = \frac{n}{3}(2v' - u') \tag{3.6b}$$

$$t = -(u + v) \tag{3.6c}$$

$$w = nw' \tag{3.6d}$$

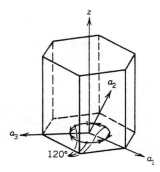

FIGURE 3.6 Coordinate axis system for a hexagonal unit cell (Miller–Bravais scheme).

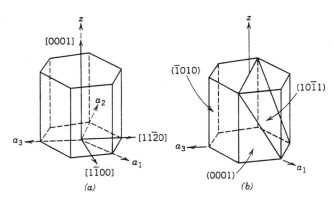

FIGURE 3.7 For the hexagonal crystal system, (a) [0001], [1$\bar{1}$00], and [11$\bar{2}$0] directions, and (b) the (0001), (10$\bar{1}$1), and ($\bar{1}$010) planes.

where primed indices are associated with the three-index scheme and unprimed, with the new Miller–Bravais four-index system; n is a factor that may be required to reduce u, v, t, and w to the smallest integers. For example, using this conversion the [010] direction becomes [$\bar{1}$2$\bar{1}$0]. Several different directions are indicated in the hexagonal unit cell (Figure 3.7a).

3.9 CRYSTALLOGRAPHIC PLANES

The orientations of planes for a crystal structure are represented in a similar manner. Again, the unit cell is the basis, with the three-axis coordinate system as represented in Figure 3.4. In all but the hexagonal crystal system, crystallographic planes are specified by three **Miller indices** as (hkl). Any two planes parallel to each other are equivalent and have identical indices. The procedure employed in determination of the h, k, and l index numbers is as follows:

1. If the plane passes through the selected origin, either another parallel plane must be constructed within the unit cell by an appropriate translation, or a new origin must be established at the corner of another unit cell.

2. At this point the crystallographic plane either intersects or parallels each of the three axes; the length of the planar intercept for each axis is determined in terms of the lattice parameters a, b, and c.

3. The reciprocals of these numbers are taken. A plane that parallels an axis may be considered to have an infinite intercept, and, therefore, a zero index.

4. If necessary, these three numbers are changed to the set of smallest integers by multiplication or division by a common factor.[1]

5. Finally, the integer indices, not separated by commas, are enclosed within parentheses, thus: (hkl).

An intercept on the negative side of the origin is indicated by a bar or minus sign positioned over the appropriate index. Furthermore, reversing the directions

---

[1] On occasion, index reduction is not carried out (e.g., for x-ray diffraction studies that are described in Section 3.15); for example, (002) is not reduced to (001). In addition, for ceramic materials, the ionic arrangement for a reduced-index plane may be different than that for a nonreduced one [see Problems 13.25(a) and (b)].

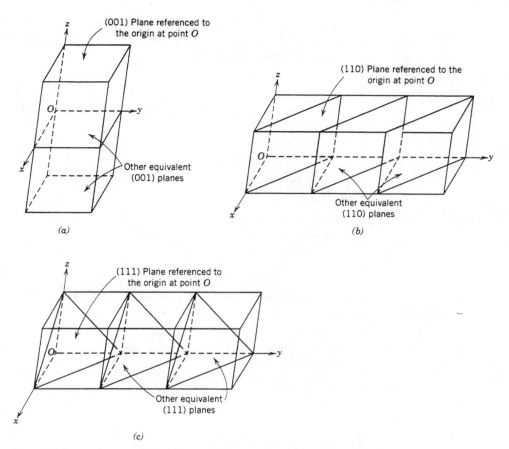

FIGURE 3.8 Representations of a series each of (*a*) (001), (*b*) (110), and (*c*) (111) crystallographic planes.

of all indices specifies another plane parallel to, on the opposite side of and equidistant from, the origin. Several low-index planes are represented in Figure 3.8.

One interesting and unique characteristic of cubic crystals is that planes and directions having the same indices are perpendicular to one another; however, for other crystal systems there are no simple geometrical relationships between planes and directions having the same indices.

EXAMPLE PROBLEM 3.6

Determine the Miller indices for the plane shown in the accompanying sketch (*a*).

SOLUTION

Since the plane passes through the selected origin O, a new origin must be chosen at the corner of an adjacent unit cell, taken as O', and shown in sketch (*b*). This plane is parallel to the x axis, and the intercept may be taken as ∞a. The y and z axes intersections, referenced to the new origin O', are $-b$, and $c/2$, respectively. Thus, in terms of the lattice parameters a, b, and c, these intersections are ∞, −1, and ½. The reciprocals of these numbers are 0, −1, and 2; and since all are integers, no further reduction is necessary. Finally, enclosure in parentheses yields ($0\bar{1}2$).

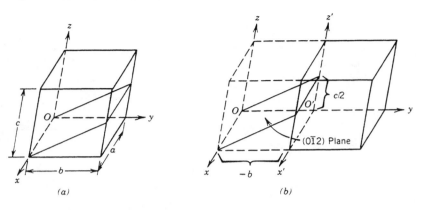

(a)   (b)

These steps are briefly summarized below:

	x	y	z
Intercepts	∞ a	−b	$c/2$
Intercepts (in terms of lattice parameters)	∞	−1	½
Reciprocals	0	−1	2
Reductions (unnecessary)			
Enclosure		($0\bar{1}2$)	

EXAMPLE PROBLEM 3.7

Construct a ($0\bar{1}1$) plane within a cubic unit cell.

SOLUTION

To solve this problem, carry out the procedure used in the preceding example in reverse order. To begin, the indices are removed from the parentheses, and reciprocals are taken, which yields ∞, −1, and 1. This means that the particular plane parallels the x axis while intersecting the y and z axes at −b and c, respectively, as indicated in the accompanying sketch (a). This plane has been drawn in sketch (b). A plane is indicated by lines representing its intersections

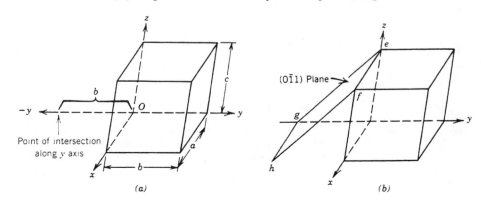

(a)   (b)

with the planes that constitute the faces of the unit cell or their extensions. For example, in this figure, line *ef* is the intersection between the $(0\bar{1}1)$ plane and the top face of the unit cell; also, line *gh* represents the intersection between this same $(0\bar{1}1)$ plane and the plane of the bottom unit cell face extended. Similarly, lines *eg* and *fh* are the intersections between $(0\bar{1}1)$ and back and front cell faces, respectively.

ATOMIC ARRANGEMENTS

The atomic arrangement for a crystallographic plane, which is often of interest, depends on the crystal structure. The (110) atomic planes for FCC and BCC crystal structures are represented in Figures 3.9 and 3.10; reduced-sphere unit cells are also included. Note that the atomic packing is different for each case. The circles represent atoms lying in the crystallographic planes as would be obtained from a slice taken through the centers of the full-sized hard spheres.

A "family" of planes contains all those planes that are crystallographically equivalent—that is, having the same atomic packing; and a family is designated by indices that are enclosed in braces—e.g., {100}. For example, in cubic crystals the (111), $(\bar{1}\bar{1}1)$, $(\bar{1}11)$, $(1\bar{1}\bar{1})$, $(11\bar{1})$, $(\bar{1}11)$, $(\bar{1}1\bar{1})$, and $(1\bar{1}1)$ planes all belong to the {111} family. On the other hand, for tetragonal crystal structures, the {100} family would contain only the (100), $(\bar{1}00)$, (010), and $(0\bar{1}0)$ since the (001) and $(00\bar{1})$ planes are not crystallographically equivalent. Also, in the cubic system only, planes having the same indices, irrespective of order and sign, are equivalent. For example, both $(1\bar{2}3)$ and $(3\bar{1}2)$ belong to the {123} family.

HEXAGONAL CRYSTALS

For crystals having hexagonal symmetry, it is desirable that equivalent planes have the same indices; as with directions, this is accomplished by the Miller-Bravais

FIGURE 3.9 (a) Reduced-sphere FCC unit cell with (110) plane. (b) Atomic packing of an FCC (110) plane. Corresponding atom positions from (a) are indicated.

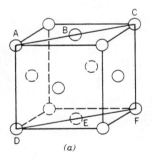

(a)

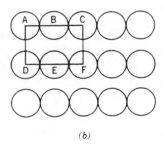

(b)

FIGURE 3.10 (a) Reduced-sphere BCC unit cell with (110) plane. (b) Atomic packing of a BCC (110) plane. Corresponding atom positions from (a) are indicated.

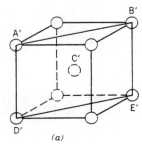

(a)

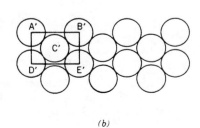

(b)

system shown in Figure 3.6. This convention leads to the four-index (*hkil*) scheme, which is favored in most instances, since it more clearly identifies the orientation of a plane in a hexagonal crystal. There is some redundancy in that *i* is determined by the sum of *h* and *k* through

$$i = -(h + k) \tag{3.7}$$

Otherwise the three *h*, *k*, and *l* indices are identical for both indexing systems. Figure 3.7*b* presents several of the common planes that are found for crystals having hexagonal symmetry.

3.10 LINEAR AND PLANAR ATOMIC DENSITIES

The two previous sections discussed the equivalency of nonparallel directions and planes, where equivalency is related to the degree of atomic spacing or atomic packing. It is felt appropriate at this time to introduce the concepts of atomic linear and planar densities. *Linear density* corresponds to the fraction of line length in a particular crystallographic direction that passes through atom centers. Similarly, *planar density* is simply the fraction of total crystallographic plane area that is occupied by atoms (represented as circles); the plane must pass through an atom's center for the particular atom to be included. These concepts, the one- and two-dimensional analogs of the atomic packing factor, are illustrated in the following example problems.

EXAMPLE PROBLEM 3.8

Calculate the linear density of the [100] direction for BCC.

SOLUTION

A BCC unit cell (reduced sphere) and the [100] direction therein are shown in Figure 3.11*a*; represented in Figure 3.11*b* is the linear packing in this direction. As a basis for our computation let us use the line length within the unit cell,

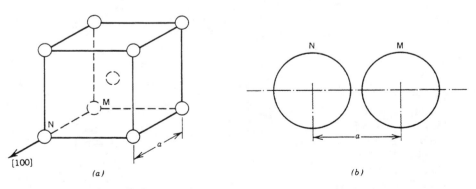

(a)   *(b)*

FIGURE 3.11   (*a*) Reduced-sphere BCC unit cell with the [100] direction indicated. (*b*) Atomic spacing in the [100] direction for the BCC crystal structure—between atoms M and N in (*a*).

L_l, which in this case is the lattice parameter a—the distance between the centers of atoms M and N. In terms of the atomic radius R,

$$L_l = a = \frac{4R}{\sqrt{3}} \qquad \text{(see Equation 3.3)}$$

Now, the total line length intersecting circles (atoms M and N), L_c, is equal to $2R$. And, the linear density LD is just the following ratio:

$$\text{LD} = \frac{L_c}{L_l} = \frac{2R}{4R/\sqrt{3}} = 0.866$$

EXAMPLE PROBLEM 3.9

Calculate the planar density of the (110) plane for FCC.

SOLUTION

The atomic packing of this plane is represented in Figure 3.9b. Consider that portion of the plane that intersects a unit cell (Figure 3.9b), and then compute both this planar area and total circle area in terms of the atomic radius R. Planar density, then, is just the ratio of these two areas.

The unit cell plane area, A_p, is simply that of the rectangle circumscribed by the centers of the atoms A, C, D, and F (Figure 3.9b). The rectangle length ($\overline{AC}$) and width ($\overline{AD}$) are, respectively,

$$\overline{AC} = 4R$$
$$\overline{AD} = 2R\sqrt{2} \qquad \text{(see Equation 3.1)}$$

Therefore,

$$A_p = (\overline{AC})(\overline{AD})$$
$$= (4R)(2R\sqrt{2}) = 8R^2\sqrt{2}$$

Now, for the total circle area, one fourth of each of atoms A, C, D, and F and one half of atoms B and E reside within this rectangle, which gives a total of 2 equivalent circles. Thus the total circle area A_c is just

$$A_c = (2)\pi R^2$$

Finally, the planar density PD is just

$$\text{PD} = \frac{A_c}{A_p} = \frac{2\pi R^2}{8R^2\sqrt{2}} = 0.555$$

Linear and planar densities are important considerations relative to the process of slip—that is, the mechanism by which metals plastically deform (Section 7.4). Slip occurs on the most densely packed crystallographic planes and, in those planes, along directions having the greatest atomic packing.

3.11 CLOSE-PACKED CRYSTAL STRUCTURES

It may be remembered from the discussion on metallic crystal structures that both face-centered cubic and hexagonal close-packed crystal structures have atomic packing factors of 0.74, which is the most efficient packing of equal-sized spheres or atoms. In addition to unit cell representations, these two crystal structures may be described in terms of close-packed planes of atoms (i.e., planes having a maximum atom or sphere-packing density); a portion of one such plane is illustrated in Figure 3.12a. Both crystal structures may be generated by the stacking of these close-packed planes on top of one another; the difference between the two structures lies in the stacking sequence.

Let the centers of all the atoms in one close-packed plane be labeled A. Associated with this plane are two sets of equivalent triangular depressions formed by three adjacent atoms, into which the next close-packed plane of atoms may rest. Those having the triangle vertex pointing up are arbitrarily designated as B positions, while the remaining depressions are those with the down vertices, which are marked C in Figure 3.12a.

A second close-packed plane may be positioned with the centers of its atoms over either B or C sites; at this point both are equivalent. Suppose that the B positions are arbitrarily chosen; the stacking sequence is termed AB, which is illustrated in Figure 3.12b. The real distinction between FCC and HCP lies in where the third close-packed layer is positioned. For HCP, the centers of this layer are aligned directly above the original A positions. This stacking sequence, ABABAB . . . , is repeated over and over. Of course, the ACACAC . . . arrangement would be equivalent. These close-packed planes for HCP are (0001)-type planes, and the correspondence between this and the unit cell representation is shown in Figure 3.13.

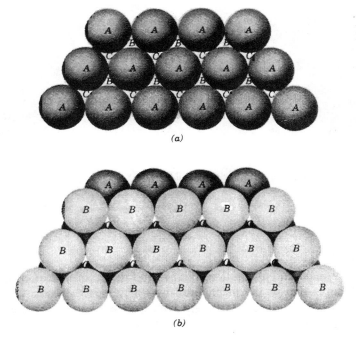

(a)

(b)

FIGURE 3.12 (a) A portion of a close-packed plane of atoms; A, B, and C positions are indicated. (b) The AB stacking sequence for close-packed atomic planes. (Adapted from W. G. Moffatt, G. W. Pearsall, and J. Wulff, *The Structure and Properties of Materials*, Vol. I, *Structure*, p. 50. Copyright © 1964 by John Wiley & Sons, New York. Reprinted by permission of John Wiley & Sons, Inc.)

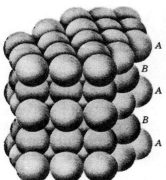

FIGURE 3.13 Close-packed plane stacking sequence for hexagonal close-packed. (Adapted from W. G. Moffatt, G. W. Pearsall, and J. Wulff, *The Structure and Properties of Materials,* Vol. I, *Structure,* p. 51. Copyright © 1964 by John Wiley & Sons, New York. Reprinted by permission of John Wiley & Sons, Inc.)

For the face-centered crystal structure, the centers of the third plane are situated over the *C* sites of the first plane (Figure 3.14*a*). This yields an *ABCABCABC* . . . stacking sequence; that is, the atomic alignment repeats every third plane. It is more difficult to correlate the stacking of close-packed planes to the FCC unit cell. However, this relationship is demonstrated in Figure 3.14*b*; these planes are of the (111) type. The significance of these FCC and HCP close-packed planes will become apparent in Chapter 7.

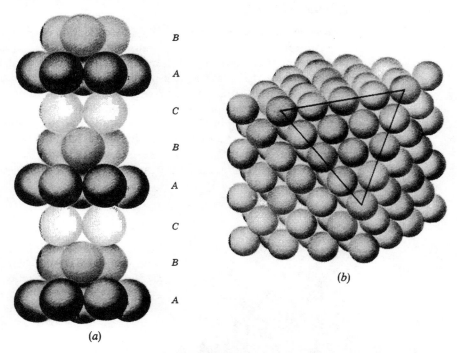

FIGURE 3.14 (*a*) Close-packed stacking sequence for face-centered cubic. (*b*) A corner has been removed to show the relation between the stacking of close-packed planes of atoms and the FCC crystal structure; the heavy triangle outlines a (111) plane. (Figure (*b*) from W. G. Moffatt, G. W. Pearsall, and J. Wulff, *The Structure and Properties of Materials,* Vol. I, *Structure,* p. 51. Copyright © 1964 by John Wiley & Sons, New York. Reprinted by permission of John Wiley & Sons, Inc.)

CRYSTALLINE AND NONCRYSTALLINE MATERIALS

3.12 SINGLE CRYSTALS

For a crystalline solid, when the periodic and repeated arrangement of atoms is perfect or extends throughout the entirety of the specimen without interruption, the result is a **single crystal.** All unit cells interlock in the same way and have the same orientation. Single crystals exist in nature, but they may also be produced artificially. They are ordinarily difficult to grow, because the environment must be carefully controlled.

If the extremities of a single crystal are permitted to grow without any external constraint, the crystal will assume a regular geometric shape having flat faces, as with some of the gem stones; the shape is indicative of the crystal structure. A photograph of several single crystals is shown in Figure 3.15. Within the past few years, single crystals have become extremely important in many of our modern technologies, in particular electronic microcircuits, which employ single crystals of silicon and other semiconductors.

3.13 POLYCRYSTALLINE MATERIALS

Most crystalline solids are composed of a collection of many small crystals or **grains;** such materials are termed **polycrystalline.** Various stages in the solidification of a polycrystalline specimen are represented schematically in Figure 3.16. Initially, small crystals or nuclei form at various positions. These have random crystallographic orientations, as indicated by the square grids. The small grains grow by the successive addition from the surrounding liquid of atoms to the structure of each. The extremities of adjacent grains impinge on one another as the solidification process approaches completion. As indicated in Figure 3.16, the crystallographic orientation varies from grain to grain. Also, there exists some atomic mismatch within the region where two grains meet; this area, called a **grain boundary,** is discussed in more detail in Section 4.5.

FIGURE 3.15 Photograph showing several single crystals of fluorite, CaF_2. (Smithsonian Institution photograph number 38181P.)

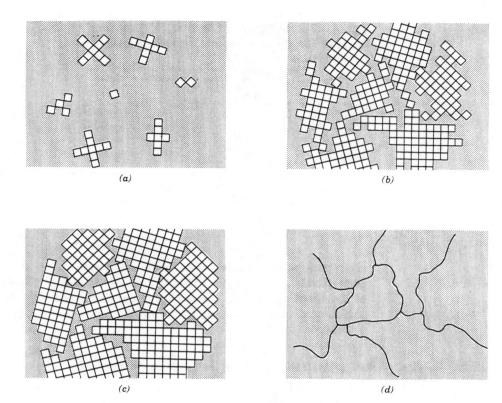

FIGURE 3.16 Schematic diagrams of the various stages in the solidification of a polycrystalline material; the square grids depict unit cells. (*a*) Small crystallite nuclei. (*b*) Growth of the crystallites; the obstruction of some grains that are adjacent to one another is also shown. (*c*) Upon completion of solidification, grains having irregular shapes have formed. (*d*) The grain structure as it would appear under the microscope; dark lines are the grain boundaries. (Adapted from W. Rosenhain, *An Introduction to the Study of Physical Metallurgy*, 2nd edition, Constable & Company Ltd., London, 1915.)

3.14 ANISOTROPY

The physical properties of single crystals of some substances depend on the crystallographic direction in which measurements are taken. For example, the elastic modulus, the electrical conductivity, and the index of refraction may have different values in the [100] and [111] directions. This directionality of properties is termed **anisotropy,** and it is associated with the variance of atomic or ionic spacing with crystallographic direction. Substances in which measured properties are independent of the direction of measurement are **isotropic.** The extent and magnitude of anisotropic effects in crystalline materials are functions of the symmetry of the crystal structure; the degree of anisotropy increases with decreasing structural symmetry—triclinic structures normally are highly anisotropic. The modulus of elasticity values at [100], [110], and [111] orientations for several materials are presented in Table 3.3.

For many polycrystalline materials, the crystallographic orientations of the individual grains are totally random. Under these circumstances, even though each

Table 3.3 Modulus of Elasticity Values for Several Metals at Various Crystallographic Orientations

	Modulus of Elasticity (GPa)		
Metal	[100]	[110]	[111]
Aluminum	63.7	72.6	76.1
Copper	66.7	130.3	191.1
Iron	125.0	210.5	272.7
Tungsten	384.6	384.6	384.6

Source: R. W. Hertzberg, *Deformation and Fracture Mechanics of Engineering Materials,* 3rd edition. Copyright © 1989 by John Wiley & Sons, New York. Reprinted by permission of John Wiley & Sons, Inc.

grain may be anisotropic, a specimen composed of the grain aggregate behaves isotropically. Also, the magnitude of a measured property represents some average of the directional values. Sometimes the grains in polycrystalline materials have a preferential crystallographic orientation, in which case the material is said to have a "texture."

3.15 X-RAY DIFFRACTION: DETERMINATION OF CRYSTAL STRUCTURES

Historically much of our understanding regarding the atomic and molecular arrangements in solids has resulted from x-ray diffraction investigations; furthermore, x-rays are still very important in developing new materials. A brief overview of the diffraction phenomenon and how, using x-rays, atomic interplanar distances and crystal structures are deduced will now be given.

THE DIFFRACTION PHENOMENON

Diffraction occurs when a wave encounters a series of regularly spaced obstacles, that (1) are capable of scattering the wave, and (2) have spacings that are comparable in magnitude to the wavelength. Furthermore, diffraction is a consequence of specific phase relationships that are established between two or more waves that have been scattered by the obstacles.

Consider waves 1 and 2 in Figure 3.17a, which have the same wavelength (λ) and are in phase at point $O-O'$. Now let us suppose that both waves are scattered in such a way that they traverse different paths. The phase relationship between the scattered waves, which will depend upon the difference in path length, is important. One possibility results when this path length difference is an integral number of wavelengths. As noted in Figure 3.17a, these scattered waves (now labeled 1' and 2') are still in phase. They are said to mutually reinforce (or constructively interfere with) one another; and, when amplitudes are added, the wave shown on the right side of the figure results. This is a manifestation of **diffraction,** and we refer to a diffracted beam as one composed of a large number of scattered waves that mutually reinforce one another.

Other phase relationships are possible between scattered waves that will not lead to this mutual reinforcement. The other extreme is that demonstrated in Figure

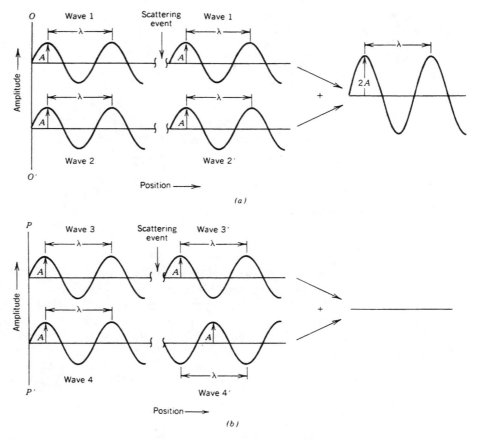

FIGURE 3.17 (a) Demonstration of how two waves (labeled 1 and 2) that have the same wavelength λ and remain in phase after a scattering event (waves 1' and 2') constructively interfere with one another. The amplitudes of the scattered waves add together in the resultant wave. (b) Demonstration of how two waves (labeled 3 and 4) that have the same wavelength and become out of phase after a scattering event (waves 3' and 4') destructively interfere with one another. The amplitudes of the two scattered waves cancel one another.

3.17b, wherein the path length difference after scattering is some integral number of *half* wavelengths. The scattered waves are out of phase—that is, corresponding amplitudes cancel or annul one another, or destructively interfere (i.e., the resultant wave has zero amplitude), as indicated on the extreme right side of the figure. Of course, phase relationships intermediate between these two extremes exist, resulting in only partial reinforcement.

X-RAY DIFFRACTION AND BRAGG'S LAW

X-Rays are a form of electromagnetic radiation that have high energies and short wavelengths—wavelengths on the order of the atomic spacings for solids. When a beam of x-rays impinges on a solid material, a portion of this beam will be scattered in all directions by the electrons associated with each atom or ion that lies within the beam's path. Let us now examine the necessary conditions for diffraction of x-rays by a periodic arrangement of atoms.

FIGURE 3.18
Diffraction of x-rays by
planes of atoms (A–A′
and B–B′).

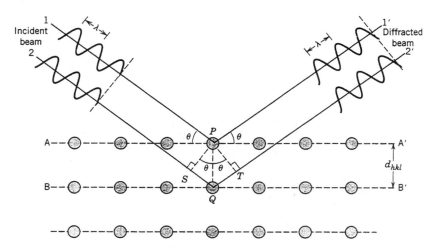

Consider the two parallel planes of atoms A–A′ and B–B′ in Figure 3.18, which have the same h, k, and l Miller indices and are separated by the interplanar spacing d_{hkl}. Now assume that a parallel, monochromatic, and coherent (in-phase) beam of x-rays of wavelength λ is incident on these two planes at an angle θ. Two rays in this beam, labeled 1 and 2, are scattered by atoms P and Q. Constructive interference of the scattered rays 1′ and 2′ occurs also at an angle θ to the planes, if the path length difference between 1–P–1′ and 2–Q–2′ (i.e., $\overline{SQ} + \overline{QT}$) is equal to a whole number, n, of wavelengths. That is, the condition for diffraction is

$$n\lambda = \overline{SQ} + \overline{QT} \tag{3.8}$$

or

$$n\lambda = d_{hkl}\sin\theta + d_{hkl}\sin\theta = 2d_{hkl}\sin\theta \tag{3.9}$$

Equation 3.9 is known as **Bragg's law;** also, n is the order of reflection, which may be any integer (1, 2, 3, . . .) consistent with $\sin\theta$ not exceeding unity. Thus, we have a simple expression relating the x-ray wavelength and interatomic spacing to the angle of the diffracted beam. If Bragg's law is not satisfied, then the interference will be nonconstructive in nature so as to yield a very low-intensity diffracted beam.

The magnitude of the distance between two adjacent and parallel planes of atoms (i.e., the interplanar spacing d_{hkl}) is a function of the Miller indices (h, k, and l) as well as the lattice parameter(s). For example, for crystal structures having cubic symmetry,

$$d_{hkl} = \frac{a}{\sqrt{h^2 + k^2 + l^2}} \tag{3.10}$$

in which a is the lattice parameter (unit cell edge length). Relationships similar to Equation 3.10, but which are more complex, exist for the other six crystal systems noted in Table 3.2.

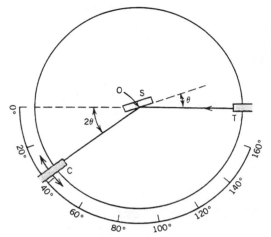

FIGURE 3.19 Schematic diagram of an x-ray diffractometer; T = x-ray source, S = specimen, C = detector, and O = the axis around which the specimen and detector rotate.

Bragg's law, Equation 3.9, is a necessary but not sufficient condition for diffraction by real crystals. It specifies when diffraction will occur for unit cells having atoms positioned only at cell corners. However, atoms situated at other sites (e.g., face and interior unit cell positions as with FCC and BCC) act as extra scattering centers, which can produce out-of-phase scattering at certain Bragg angles. The net result is the absence of some diffracted beams which, according to Equation 3.9, should be present. For example, for the BCC crystal structure, $h + k + l$ must be even if diffraction is to occur, whereas for FCC, h, k, and l must all be either odd or even.

DIFFRACTION TECHNIQUES

One common diffraction technique employs a powdered or polycrystalline specimen consisting of many fine and randomly oriented particles that are exposed to monochromatic x-radiation. Each powder particle (or grain) is a crystal, and having a large number of them with random orientations ensures that some particles are properly oriented such that every possible set of crystallographic planes will be available for diffraction.

The *diffractometer* is an apparatus used to determine the angles at which diffraction occurs for powdered specimens; its features are represented schematically in Figure 3.19. A specimen S in the form of a flat plate is supported so that rotations about the axis labeled O are possible; this axis is perpendicular to the plane of the page. The monochromatic x-ray beam is generated at point T, and the intensities of diffracted beams are detected with a counter labeled C in the figure. The specimen, x-ray source, and counter are all coplanar.

The counter is mounted on a movable carriage which may also be rotated about the O axis; its angular position in terms of 2θ is marked on a graduated scale.[2] Carriage and specimen are mechanically coupled such that a rotation of the specimen

---

[2] It should be pointed out that the symbol θ has been used in two different contexts for this discussion. Here, θ represents the angular locations of both x-ray source and counter relative to the specimen surface. Previously (e.g., Equation 3.9), it denoted the angle at which the Bragg criterion for diffraction is satisfied.

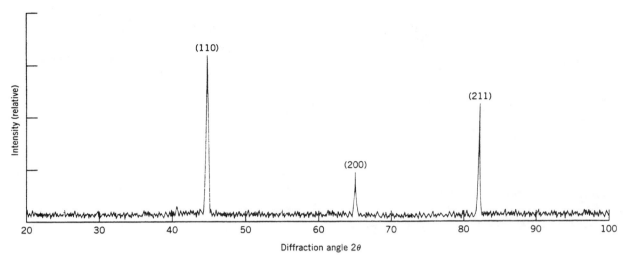

Figure 3.20 Diffraction pattern for polycrystalline α-iron.

through θ is accompanied by a 2θ rotation of the counter; this assures that the incident and reflection angles are maintained equal to one another (Figure 3.19). Collimators are incorporated within the beam path to produce a well-defined and focused beam. Utilization of a filter provides a near-monochromatic beam.

As the counter moves at constant angular velocity, a recorder automatically plots the diffracted beam intensity (monitored by the counter) as a function of 2θ; 2θ is termed the *diffraction angle*, which is measured experimentally. Figure 3.20 shows a diffraction pattern for a polycrystalline specimen of iron. The high-intensity peaks result when the Bragg diffraction condition is satisfied by some set of crystallographic planes. These peaks are plane-indexed in the figure.

Other powder techniques have been devised wherein diffracted beam intensity and position are recorded on a photographic film instead of being measured by a counter.

One of the primary uses of x-ray diffractometry is for the determination of crystal structure. The unit cell size and geometry may be resolved from the angular positions of the diffraction peaks, whereas arrangement of atoms within the unit cell is associated with the relative intensities of these peaks.

X-Rays, as well as electron and neutron beams, are also used in other types of material investigations. For example, crystallographic orientations of single crystals are possible using x-ray diffraction (or Laue) photographs. On page 29 is shown a photograph that was generated using an incident electron beam that was directed on a gallium arsenide crystal; each spot (with the exception of the brightest one near the center) resulted from an electron beam that was diffracted by a specific set of crystallographic planes. Other uses of x-rays include qualitative and quantitative chemical identifications, and the determination of residual stresses and crystal size.

EXAMPLE PROBLEM 3.10

For BCC iron, compute (a) the interplanar spacing, and (b) the diffraction angle for the (220) set of planes. The lattice parameter for Fe is 0.2866 nm

(2.886 Å). Also, assume that monochromatic radiation having a wavelength of 0.1790 nm (1.790 Å) is used, and the order of reflection is 1.

SOLUTION

(a) The value of the interplanar spacing d_{hkl} is determined using Equation 3.10, with $a = 0.2866$ nm, and $h = 2$, $k = 2$, and $l = 0$, since we are considering the (220) planes. Therefore,

$$d_{hkl} = \frac{a}{\sqrt{h^2 + k^2 + l^2}}$$

$$= \frac{0.2866 \text{ nm}}{\sqrt{(2)^2 + (2)^2 + (0)^2}} = 0.1013 \text{ nm } (1.013 \text{ Å})$$

(b) The value of θ may now be computed using Equation 3.9, with $n = 1$, since this is a first-order reflection:

$$\sin \theta = \frac{n\lambda}{2d_{hkl}} = \frac{(1)(0.1790 \text{ nm})}{(2)(0.1013 \text{ nm})} = 0.884$$

$$\theta = \sin^{-1}(0.884) = 62.13°$$

The diffraction angle is 2θ, or

$$2\theta = (2)(62.13°) = 124.26°$$

3.16 NONCRYSTALLINE SOLIDS

It has been mentioned that **noncrystalline** solids lack a systematic and regular arrangement of atoms over relatively large atomic distances. Sometimes such materials are also called **amorphous** (meaning literally without form), or supercooled liquids inasmuch as their atomic structure resembles that of a liquid.

An amorphous condition may be illustrated by comparison of the crystalline and noncrystalline structures of the ceramic compound silicon dioxide (SiO_2), which may exist in both states. Figures 3.21*a* and 3.21*b* present two-dimensional schematic

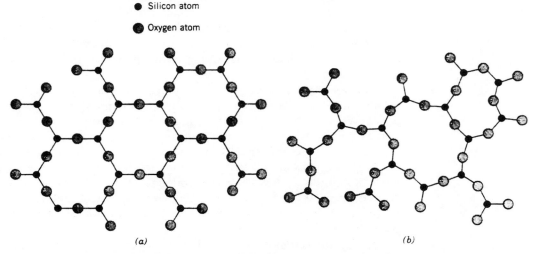

● Silicon atom

● Oxygen atom

(a)   (b)

FIGURE 3.21 Two-dimensional schemes of the structure of (*a*) crystalline silicon dioxide and (*b*) noncrystalline silicon dioxide.

diagrams for both structures of SiO_2. Even though each silicon ion bonds to three oxygen ions for both states, beyond this, the structure is much more disordered and irregular for the noncrystalline structure.

Whether a crystalline or amorphous solid forms depends on the ease with which a random atomic structure in the liquid can transform to an ordered state during solidification. Amorphous materials, therefore, are characterized by atomic or molecular structures that are relatively complex and become ordered only with some difficulty. Furthermore, rapidly cooling through the freezing temperature favors the formation of a noncrystalline solid, since little time is allowed for the ordering process.

Metals normally form crystalline solids; but some ceramic materials are crystalline, whereas others, the inorganic glasses, are amorphous. Polymers may be completely crystalline, entirely noncrystalline, or a mixture of the two. More about the structure and properties of amorphous ceramics and polymers is contained in Chapters 13 and 15.

SUMMARY

Atoms in crystalline solids are positioned in an orderly and repeated pattern, which is in contrast to the random and disordered atomic distribution found in noncrystalline or amorphous materials. Atoms may be represented as solid spheres, and, for crystalline solids, crystal structure is just the spatial arrangement of these spheres. The various crystal structures are specified in terms of parallelepiped unit cells, which are characterized by geometry and atom positions within.

Most common metals exist in at least one of three relatively simple crystal structures: face-centered cubic (FCC), body-centered cubic (BCC), and hexagonal close-packed (HCP). Two features of a crystal structure are coordination number (or number of nearest-neighbor atoms) and atomic packing factor (the fraction of solid sphere volume in the unit cell). Coordination number and atomic packing factor are the same for both FCC and HCP crystal structures, each of which may be generated by the stacking of close-packed planes of atoms.

Crystallographic planes and directions are specified in terms of an indexing scheme. The basis for the determination of each index is a coordinate axis system defined by the unit cell for the particular crystal structure. Directional indices are computed in terms of vector projections on each of the coordinate axes, whereas planar indices are determined from the reciprocals of axial intercepts. For hexagonal unit cells, a four-index scheme for both directions and planes is found to be more convenient.

Crystallographic directional and planar equivalencies are related to atomic linear and planar densities, respectively. The atomic packing (i.e., planar density) of spheres in a crystallographic plane depends on both the indices of the plane as well as the crystal structure. For a given crystal structure, planes having identical atomic packing yet different Miller indices belong to the same family.

Single crystals are materials in which the atomic order extends uninterrupted over the entirety of the specimen; under some circumstances, they may have flat faces and regular geometric shapes. The vast majority of crystalline solids, however, are polycrystalline, being composed of many small crystals or grains having different crystallographic orientations.

X-Ray diffractometry is used for crystal structure and interplanar spacing determinations. A beam of x-rays directed on a crystalline material may experience diffraction (constructive interference) as a result of its interaction with a series of parallel atomic planes according to Bragg's law. Interplanar spacing is a function of the Miller indices and lattice parameter(s) as well as the crystal structure.

IMPLICATIONS

A knowledge and understanding of the concepts discussed in this chapter are important for a number of reasons; some of these are as follows:

1. Some of the properties of materials (e.g., ductility [Section 6.6]) may be dependent on their crystal structure.

2. Being able to specify crystallographic planes and directions allows us to understand and explain the mechanism of plastic deformation for most crystalline metals and ceramics (Section 7.4).

3. Anisotropic properties in single crystals must necessarily be specified in terms of crystallographic directions.

4. Anisotropic effects often need to be considered in the applications and processing of materials.

5. Thermodynamic principles relating to solid materials involve understanding allotropic and polymorphic transformations.

6. The properties and the applications of materials may depend on whether they are single crystals or polycrystalline.

7. X-ray analytical techniques are often used to characterize materials.

8. The crystal structures of materials and other important crystallographic information may be deduced through x-ray diffraction analyses.

IMPORTANT TERMS AND CONCEPTS

Allotropy	Crystal system	Lattice
Amorphous	Crystalline	Lattice parameters
Anisotropy	Diffraction	Miller indices
Atomic packing factor (APF)	Face-centered cubic (FCC)	Noncrystalline
Body-centered cubic (BCC)	Grain	Polycrystalline
Bragg's law	Grain boundary	Polymorphism
Coordination number	Hexagonal close-packed (HCP)	Single crystal
Crystal structure	Isotropic	Unit cell

REFERENCES

Azaroff, L. F., *Elements of X-Ray Crystallography,* McGraw-Hill Book Company, New York, 1968. Reprinted by TechBooks, Fairfax, VA.

Barrett, C. S. and T. B. Massalski, *Structure of Metals,* 3rd edition, Pergamon Press, Oxford, 1980.

Buerger, M. J., *Elementary Crystallography,* John Wiley & Sons, New York, 1956.

Cohen, J. B., *Diffraction Methods in Materials Science,* The Macmillan Co., New York, 1966.

Cullity, B. D., *Elements of X-Ray Diffraction,* 2nd edition, Addison-Wesley Publishing Co., Reading, MA, 1978.

Schwartz, L. H. and J. B. Cohen, *Diffraction from Materials,* 2nd edition, Springer-Verlag, New York, 1987.

Wyckoff, R. W. G., *Crystal Structures,* 2nd edition, Interscience Publishers, 1963. Reprinted by Krieger Publishing Company, Melbourne, FL, 1986.

QUESTIONS AND PROBLEMS

3.1 What is the difference between atomic structure and crystal structure?

3.2 What is the difference between a crystal structure and a crystal system?

3.3 If the atomic radius of lead is 0.175 nm, calculate the volume of its unit cell in cubic meters.

3.4 Show for the body-centered cubic crystal structure that the unit cell edge length a and the atomic radius R are related through $a = 4R/\sqrt{3}$.

3.5 For the HCP crystal structure, show that the ideal c/a ratio is 1.633.

3.6 Show that the atomic packing factor for BCC is 0.68.

3.7 Show that the atomic packing factor for HCP is 0.74.

3.8 Molybdenum has a BCC crystal structure, an atomic radius of 0.1363 nm, and an atomic weight of 95.94 g/mol. Compute and compare its density with the experimental value found in Table C.1, Appendix C.

3.9 Calculate the radius of a palladium atom, given that Pd has an FCC crystal structure, a density of 12.0 g/cm³, and an atomic weight of 106.4 g/mol. *(FCC, D=33.4%/cm³, W=1977g/mol)*

3.10 Calculate the radius of a tantalum atom, given that Ta has a BCC crystal structure, a density of 16.6 g/cm³, and an atomic weight of 180.9 g/mol. *(BCC, D=5.96   W=50.9)*

3.11 Some hypothetical metal has the simple cubic crystal structure shown in Figure 3.22. If its atomic weight is 70.4 g/mol and the atomic radius is 0.126 nm, compute its density.

3.12 Zirconium has an HCP crystal structure and a density of 6.51 g/cm³.

(a) What is the volume of its unit cell in cubic meters?

(b) If the c/a ratio is 1.593, compute the values of c and a.

3.13 Using atomic weight, crystal structure, and atomic radius data tabulated inside the front cover, compute the theoretical densities of lead, chromium, copper, and cobalt, and then compare these values with the measured densities listed in this same table. The c/a ratio for cobalt is 1.623.

3.14 Rhodium has an atomic radius of 0.1345 nm (1.345 Å) and a density of 12.41 g/cm³. Determine whether it has an FCC or BCC crystal structure.

3.15 Below are listed the atomic weight, density, and atomic radius for three hypothetical alloys. For each determine whether its crystal structure is FCC, BCC, or simple cubic and then justify your determination. A simple cubic unit cell is shown in Figure 3.22.

Alloy	Atomic Weight (g/mol)	Density (g/cm³)	Atomic Radius (nm)
A	77.4	8.22	0.125
B	107.6	13.42	0.133
C	127.3	9.23	0.142

3.16 The unit cell for tin has tetragonal symmetry, with a and b lattice parameters of 0.583 and 0.318 nm, respectively. If its density, atomic weight, and atomic radius are 7.30 g/cm³, 118.69 g/mol, and 0.151 nm, respectively, compute the atomic packing factor.

3.17 Iodine has an orthorhombic unit cell for which the a, b, and c lattice parameters are 0.479, 0.725, and 0.978 nm, respectively.

(a) If the atomic packing factor and atomic radius are 0.547 and 0.177 nm, respectively, determine the number of atoms in each unit cell.

(b) The atomic weight of iodine is 126.91 g/mol; compute its density.

3.18 Titanium has an HCP unit cell for which the ratio of the lattice parameters c/a is 1.58. If the radius of the Ti atom is 0.1445 nm, **(a)** determine the unit cell volume, and **(b)** calculate the density of Ti and compare it with the literature value.

3.19 Zinc has an HCP crystal structure, a c/a ratio of 1.856, and a density of 7.13 g/cm³. Calculate the atomic radius for Zn.

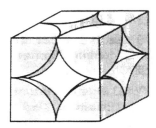

FIGURE 3.22 Hard-sphere unit cell representation of the simple cubic crystal structure.

3.20 Rhenium has an HCP crystal structure, an atomic radius of 0.137 nm, and a *c/a* ratio of 1.615. Compute the volume of the unit cell for Re.

3.21 This is a unit cell for a hypothetical metal:

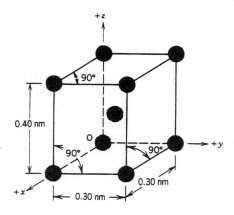

(a) To which crystal system does this unit cell belong?

(b) What would this crystal structure be called?

(c) Calculate the density of the material, given that its atomic weight is 114 g/mol.

3.22 Sketch a unit cell for the body-centered ortho-rhombic crystal structure.

3.23 Draw an orthorhombic unit cell, and within that cell a [2$\bar{1}$1] direction and a (02$\bar{1}$) plane.

3.24 Sketch a monoclinic unit cell, and within that cell a [$\bar{1}$01] direction and a (200) plane.

3.25 Here are unit cells for two hypothetical metals:

(a) What are the indices for the directions indicated by the two vectors in sketch (*a*)?

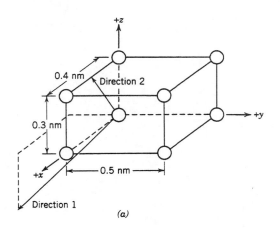

(a)

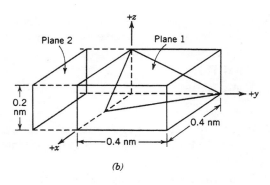

(b)

(b) What are the indices for the two planes drawn in sketch (*b*)?

3.26 Within a cubic unit cell, sketch the following directions:

(a) [$\bar{1}$10];   **(d)** [1$\bar{3}$3];   **(g)** [1$\bar{2}\bar{3}$];

(b) [$\bar{1}$2$\bar{1}$];   **(e)** [$\bar{1}\bar{1}$1];   **(h)** [$\bar{1}$03].

(c) [0$\bar{1}$2];   **(f)** [$\bar{1}$22];

3.27 Determine the indices for the directions shown in the following cubic unit cell:

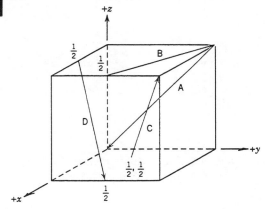

3.28 Determine the indices for the directions shown in the following cubic unit cell:

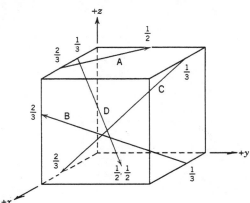

3.29 For tetragonal crystals, cite the indices of directions that are equivalent to each of the following directions:

  (a) [101];

  (b) [110];

  (c) [010].

3.30 (a) Convert the [110] and [00$\bar{1}$] directions into the four-index Miller–Bravais scheme for hexagonal unit cells.

  (b) Make the same conversion for the (111) and (0$\bar{1}$2) planes.

3.31 Determine the Miller indices for the planes shown in the following unit cell:

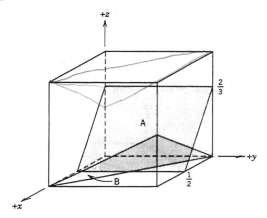

3.32 Determine the Miller indices for the planes shown in the following unit cell:

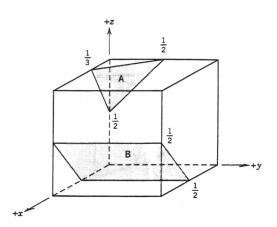

3.33 Determine the Miller indices for the planes shown in the following unit cell:

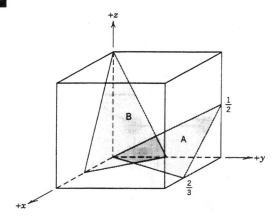

3.34 Sketch the (1$\bar{1}$01) and (11$\bar{2}$0) planes in a hexagonal unit cell.

3.35 Determine the indices for the planes shown in the hexagonal unit cells shown below.

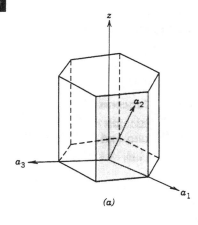

(a)

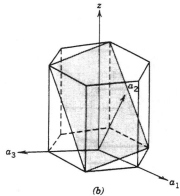

(b)

3.36 Sketch within a cubic unit cell the following planes:

(a) $(0\bar{1}\bar{1})$;

(b) $(11\bar{2})$;

(c) $(10\bar{2})$;

(d) $(1\bar{3}1)$;

(e) $(\bar{1}1\bar{1})$;

(f) $(1\bar{2}\bar{2})$;

(g) $(\bar{1}2\bar{3})$;

(h) $(0\bar{1}3)$.

3.37 Sketch the atomic packing of **(a)** the (100) plane for the FCC crystal structure, and **(b)** the (111) plane for the BCC crystal structure (similar to Figures 3.9*b* and 3.10*b*).

3.38 Consider the reduced-sphere unit cell shown in Problem 3.21, having an origin of the coordinate system positioned at the atom labeled with an O. For the following sets of planes, determine which are equivalent:

(a) (100), $(0\bar{1}0)$, and (001).

(b) (110), (101), (011), and $(\bar{1}10)$.

(c) (111), $(1\bar{1}1)$, $(11\bar{1})$, and $(\bar{1}1\bar{1})$.

3.39 Cite the indices of the direction that results from the intersection of each of the following pair of planes within a cubic crystal: **(a)** (110) and (111) planes; **(b)** (110) and $(1\bar{1}0)$ planes; and **(c)** $(10\bar{1})$ and (001) planes.

3.40 Compute and compare the linear densities of the [100], [110], and [111] directions for FCC.

3.41 Compute and compare the linear densities of the [110] and [111] directions for BCC.

3.42 Calculate and compare the planar densities of the (100) and (111) planes for FCC.

3.43 Calculate and compare the planar densities of the (100) and (110) planes for BCC.

3.44 Calculate the planar density of the (0001) plane for HCP.

3.45 Here are shown the atomic packing schemes for several different crystallographic directions for some hypothetical metal. For each direction the circles represent only those atoms contained within a unit cell, which circles are reduced from their actual size.

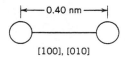

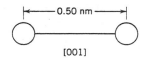

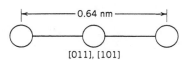

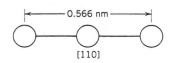

(a) To what crystal system does the unit cell belong?

(b) What would this crystal structure be called?

3.46 Below are shown three different crystallographic planes for a unit cell of some hypothetical metal; the circles represent atoms:

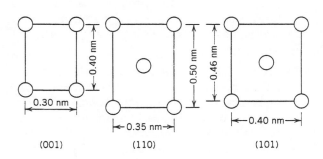

(a) To what crystal system does the unit cell belong?

(b) What would this crystal structure be called?

(c) If the density of this metal is 8.95 g/cm³, determine its atomic weight.

3.47 Explain why the properties of polycrystalline materials are most often isotropic.

3.48 Using the data for molybdenum in Table 3.1, compute the interplanar spacing for the (111) set of planes.

3.49 Determine the expected diffraction angle for the first-order reflection from the (113) set of planes for FCC platinum when monochromatic radiation of wavelength 0.1542 nm is used.

3.50 Using the data for aluminum in Table 3.1, compute the interplanar spacings for the (110) and (221) sets of planes.

3.51 The metal iridium has an FCC crystal structure. If the angle of diffraction for the (220) set of planes occurs at 69.22° (first-order reflection) when monochromatic x-radiation having a wavelength of 0.1542 nm is used, compute **(a)** the interplanar spacing for this set of planes, and **(b)** the atomic radius for an iridium atom.

3.52 The metal rubidium has a BCC crystal structure. If the angle of diffraction for the (321) set of planes occurs at 27.00° (first-order reflection) when monochromatic x-radiation having a wavelength of 0.0711 nm is used, compute **(a)** the interplanar spacing for this set of planes, and **(b)** the atomic radius for the rubidium atom.

3.53 For which set of crystallographic planes will a first-order diffraction peak occur at a diffraction angle of 46.21° for BCC iron when monochromatic radiation having a wavelength of 0.0711 nm is used?

3.54 Figure 3.20 shows an x-ray diffraction pattern for α-iron taken using a diffractometer and monochromatic x-radiation having a wavelength of 0.1542 nm; each diffraction peak on the pattern has been indexed. Compute the interplanar spacing for each set of planes in-dexed; also determine the lattice parameter of Fe for each of the peaks.

3.55 The diffraction peaks shown in Figure 3.20 are indexed according to the reflection rules for BCC (i.e., the sum $h + k + l$ must be even). Cite the h, k, and l indices for the first four diffraction peaks for FCC crystals consistent with h, k, and l all being either odd or even.

3.56 Figure 3.23 shows the first four peaks of the x-ray diffraction pattern for copper which has an FCC crystal structure; monochromatic x-radiation having a wavelength of 0.1542 nm was used.

(a) Index (i.e., give h, k, and l indices) for each of these peaks.

(b) Determine the interplanar spacing for each of the peaks.

(c) For each peak, determine the atomic radius for Cu and compare these with the value presented in Table 3.1.

3.57 Would you expect a material in which the atomic bonding is predominantly ionic in nature to be more or less likely to form a non-crystalline solid upon solidification than a co-valent material? Why? (See Section 2.6.)

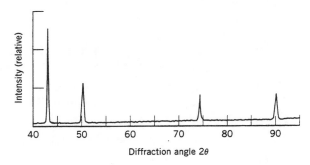

FIGURE 3.23 Diffraction pattern for polycrystalline copper.

Imperfections in Solids

A field ion micrograph taken at the tip of a pointed tungsten specimen. Field ion microscopy is a sophisticated and fascinating technique that permits observation of individual atoms in a solid, which are represented by white spots. The symmetry and regularity of the atom arrangements are evident from the positions of the spots in this micrograph. A disruption of this symmetry occurs along a grain boundary which is traced by the arrows. Approximately 3,460,000×. (Photomicrograph courtesy of J. J. Hren and R. W. Newman.)

4.1 INTRODUCTION

Thus far it has been tacitly assumed that perfect order exists throughout crystalline materials on an atomic scale. However, such an idealized solid does not exist; all contain large numbers of various defects or imperfections. As a matter of fact, many of the properties of materials are profoundly sensitive to deviations from crystalline perfection; the influence is not always adverse, and often specific characteristics are deliberately fashioned by the introduction of controlled amounts or numbers of particular defects, as detailed in succeeding chapters.

By "crystalline defect" is meant a lattice irregularity having one or more of its dimensions on the order of an atomic diameter. Classification of crystalline imperfections is frequently made according to geometry or dimensionality of the defect. Several different imperfections are discussed in this chapter, including point defects (those associated with one or two atomic positions), linear (or one-dimensional) defects, as well as interfacial defects, or boundaries, which are two-dimensional. Impurities in solids are also discussed, since impurity atoms may exist as point defects. Finally, techniques for the microscopic examination of defects and the structure of materials are briefly described.

POINT DEFECTS

4.2 VACANCIES AND SELF-INTERSTITIALS

The simplest of the point defects is a **vacancy,** or vacant lattice site, one normally occupied from which an atom is missing (Figure 4.1). Vacancies are formed during solidification, and also as a result of atomic vibrations, which can cause the displacement of atoms from their normal lattice sites.

The equilibrium number of vacancies N_v for a given quantity of material depends on and increases with temperature according to

$$N_v = N \exp\left(-\frac{Q_v}{kT}\right) \tag{4.1}$$

In this expression, N is the total number of atomic sites, Q_v is the energy required for the formation of a vacancy, T is the absolute temperature,[1] in kelvins, and k is the gas or **Boltzmann's constant.** The value of k is 1.38×10^{-23} J/atom-K, or 8.62×10^{-5} eV/atom-K, depending on the units of Q_v.[2] Thus, the number of vacancies increases exponentially with temperature; that is, as T in Equation 4.1 increases, so does also the expression $\exp -(Q_v/kT)$. For most metals, the fraction of vacancies N_v/N just below the melting temperature is on the order of 10^{-4}; that is, one lattice site out of 10,000 will be empty. As ensuing discussions indicate, a number of other material parameters have an exponential dependence on temperature similar to that of Equation 4.1.

A **self-interstitial** is an atom from the crystal that is crowded into an interstitial site, a small void space that under ordinary circumstances is not occupied. This kind of defect is also represented in Figure 4.1. In metals, a self-interstitial introduces

---

[1] Absolute temperature in kelvins (K) is equal to °C + 273.
[2] Boltzmann's constant per mole of atoms becomes the gas constant R; in such a case $R = 8.31$ J/mol-K, or 1.987 cal/mol-K.

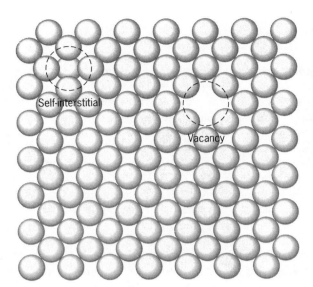

FIGURE 4.1 Two-dimensional representations of a vacancy and a self-interstitial. (Adapted from W. G. Moffatt, G. W. Pearsall and J. Wulff, *The Structure and Properties of Materials,* Vol. I, *Structure,* p. 77. Copyright © 1964 by John Wiley & Sons, New York. Reprinted by permission of John Wiley & Sons, Inc.)

relatively large distortions in the surrounding lattice because the atom is substantially larger than the interstitial position in which it is situated. Consequently, the formation of this defect is not highly probable, and it exists in very small concentrations, which are significantly lower than for vacancies.

EXAMPLE PROBLEM 4.1

Calculate the equilibrium number of vacancies per cubic meter for copper at 1000°C. The energy for vacancy formation is 0.9 eV/atom; the atomic weight and density (at 1000°C) for copper are 63.5 g/mol and 8.4 g/cm³, respectively.

SOLUTION

This problem may be solved by using Equation 4.1; it is first necessary, however, to determine the value of N, the number of atomic sites per cubic meter for copper from its atomic weight A_{Cu}, its density ρ, and Avogadro's number N_A, according to

$$N = \frac{N_A \rho}{A_{Cu}} \tag{4.2}$$

$$= \frac{(6.023 \times 10^{23} \text{ atoms/mol})(8.4 \text{ g/cm}^3)(10^6 \text{ cm}^3/\text{m}^3)}{63.5 \text{ g/mol}}$$

$$= 8.0 \times 10^{28} \text{ atoms/m}^3$$

Thus, the number of vacancies at 1000°C (1273 K) is equal to

$$N_v = N \exp\left(-\frac{Q_v}{kT}\right)$$

$$= (8.0 \times 10^{28} \text{ atoms/m}^3) \exp\left[-\frac{(0.9 \text{ eV})}{(8.62 \times 10^{-5} \text{ eV/K})(1273 \text{ K})}\right]$$

$$= 2.2 \times 10^{25} \text{ vacancies/m}^3$$

4.3 IMPURITIES IN SOLIDS

A pure metal consisting of only one type of atom just isn't possible; impurity or foreign atoms will always be present, and some will exist as crystalline point defects. In fact, even with relatively sophisticated techniques, it is difficult to refine metals to a purity in excess of 99.9999%. At this level, on the order of 10^{22} to 10^{23} impurity atoms will be present in one cubic meter of material. Most familiar metals are not highly pure; rather, they are **alloys,** in which impurity atoms have been added intentionally to impart specific characteristics to the material. Ordinarily alloying is used in metals to improve mechanical strength and corrosion resistance. For example, sterling silver is a 92.5% silver–7.5% copper alloy. In normal ambient environments, pure silver is highly corrosion resistant, but also very soft. Alloying with copper enhances the mechanical strength significantly, without depreciating the corrosion resistance appreciably.

The addition of impurity atoms to a metal will result in the formation of a **solid solution** and/or a new *second phase,* depending on the kinds of impurity, their concentrations, and the temperature of the alloy. The present discussion is concerned with the notion of a solid solution; treatment of the formation of a new phase is deferred to Chapter 9.

Several terms relating to impurities and solid solutions deserve mention. With regard to alloys, **solute** and **solvent** are terms that are commonly employed. "Solvent" represents the element or compound that is present in the greatest amount; on occasion, solvent atoms are also called *host atoms.* "Solute" is used to denote an element or compound present in a minor concentration.

SOLID SOLUTIONS

A solid solution forms when, as the solute atoms are added to the host material, the crystal structure is maintained, and no new structures are formed. Perhaps it is useful to draw an analogy with a liquid solution. If two liquids, soluble in each other (such as water and alcohol) are combined, a liquid solution is produced as the molecules intermix, and its composition is homogeneous throughout. A solid solution is also compositionally homogeneous; the impurity atoms are randomly and uniformly dispersed within the solid.

Impurity point defects are found in solid solutions, of which there are two types: **substitutional** and **interstitial.** For substitutional, solute or impurity atoms replace or substitute for the host atoms (Figure 4.2). There are several features of the solute and solvent atoms that determine the degree to which the former dissolves in the latter; these are as follows:

1. *Atomic size factor.* Appreciable quantities of a solute may be accommodated in this type of solid solution only when the difference in atomic radii between the two atom types is less than about ±15%. Otherwise the solute atoms will create substantial lattice distortions and a new phase will form.

2. *Crystal structure.* For appreciable solid solubility the crystal structures for metals of both atom types must be the same.

3. *Electronegativity.* The more electropositive one element and the more electronegative the other, the greater is the likelihood that they will form an intermetallic compound instead of a substitutional solid solution.

4. *Valences.* Other factors being equal, a metal will have more of a tendency to dissolve another metal of higher valency than one of a lower valency.

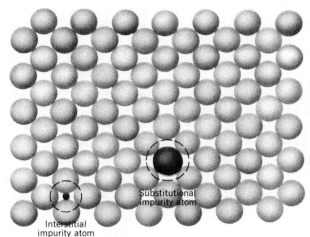

FIGURE 4.2 Two-dimensional schematic representations of substitutional and interstitial impurity atoms. (Adapted from W. G. Moffatt, G. W. Pearsall, and J. Wulff, *The Structure and Properties of Materials,* Vol. I, *Structure,* p. 77. Copyright © 1964 by John Wiley & Sons, New York. Reprinted by permission of John Wiley & Sons, Inc.)

An example of a substitutional solid solution is found for copper and nickel. These two elements are completely soluble in one another at all proportions. With regard to the aforementioned rules that govern degree of solubility, the atomic radii for copper and nickel are 0.128 and 0.125 nm (1.28 and 1.25 Å), respectively, both have the FCC crystal structure, and their electronegativities are 1.9 and 1.8 (Figure 2.7); finally, the most common valences are +1 for copper (although it sometimes can be +2) and +2 for nickel.

For interstitial solid solutions, impurity atoms fill the voids or interstices among the host atoms (see Figure 4.2). For metallic materials that have relatively high atomic packing factors, these interstitial positions are relatively small. Consequently, the atomic diameter of an interstitial impurity must be substantially smaller than that of the host atoms. Normally, the maximum allowable concentration of interstitial impurity atoms is low (less than 10%). Even very small impurity atoms are ordinarily larger than the interstitial sites, and as a consequence they introduce some lattice strains on the adjacent host atoms. Problem 4.5 calls for determination of the radii of impurity atoms (in terms of R, the host atom radius) that will just fit into interstitial positions without introducing any lattice strains for both FCC and BCC crystal structures.

Carbon forms an interstitial solid solution when added to iron; the maximum concentration of carbon is about 2%. The atomic radius of the carbon atom is much less than that for iron: 0.071 nm (0.71 Å) versus 0.124 nm (1.24 Å). Solid solutions are also possible for ceramic materials, as discussed in Section 13.5.

SPECIFICATION OF COMPOSITION

It is often necessary to express the **composition** (or *concentration*)[3] of an alloy in terms of its constituent elements. The two most common ways to specify composition are weight (or mass) percent and atom percent. The basis for **weight percent** (wt%) is the weight of a particular element relative to the total alloy weight. For an alloy that contains two hypothetical atoms denoted by 1 and 2, the concentration of 1

---

[3] The terms *composition* and *concentration* will be assumed to have the same meaning in this book (i.e., the relative content of a specific element or constituent in an alloy) and will be used interchangeably.

in wt%, C_1, is defined as

$$C_1 = \frac{m_1}{m_1 + m_2} \times 100 \tag{4.3}$$

where m_1 and m_2 represent the weight (or mass) of elements 1 and 2, respectively. The concentration of 2 would be computed in an analogous manner.

The basis for **atom percent** (at%) calculations is the number of moles of an element in relation to the total moles of the elements in the alloy. The number of moles in some specified mass of a hypothetical element 1, n_{m1}, may be computed as follows:

$$n_{m1} = \frac{m_1'}{A_1} \tag{4.4}$$

Here, m_1' and A_1 denote the mass (in grams) and atomic weight, respectively, for element 1.

Concentration in terms of atom percent of element 1 in an alloy containing 1 and 2 atoms, C_1', is defined by[4]

$$C_1' = \frac{n_{m1}}{n_{m1} + n_{m2}} \times 100 \tag{4.5}$$

In like manner, the atom percent of 2 may be determined.

Atom percent computations also can be carried out on the basis of the number of atoms instead of moles, since one mole of all substances contains the same number of atoms.

COMPOSITION CONVERSIONS

Sometimes it is necessary to convert from one composition scheme to another—e.g., from weight percent to atom percent. We will now present equations for making these conversions in terms of the two hypothetical elements 1 and 2. Using the convention of the previous section (i.e., weight percents denoted by C_1 and C_2, atom percents by C_1' and C_2', and atomic weights as A_1 and A_2), these conversion expressions are as follows:

$$C_1' = \frac{C_1 A_2}{C_1 A_2 + C_2 A_1} \times 100 \tag{4.6a}$$

$$C_2' = \frac{C_2 A_1}{C_1 A_2 + C_2 A_1} \times 100 \tag{4.6b}$$

$$C_1 = \frac{C_1' A_1}{C_1' A_1 + C_2' A_2} \times 100 \tag{4.7a}$$

$$C_2 = \frac{C_2' A_2}{C_1' A_1 + C_2' A_2} \times 100 \tag{4.7b}$$

---

[4] In order to avoid confusion in notations and symbols that are being used in this section, it should be pointed out that the prime (as in C_1' and m_1') is used to designate both composition, in atom percent, as well as mass of material in units of grams.

Since we are considering only two elements, computations involving the preceding equations are simplified when it is realized that

$$C_1 + C_2 = 100 \qquad (4.8a)$$

$$C_1' + C_2' = 100 \qquad (4.8b)$$

In addition, it sometimes becomes necessary to convert concentration from weight percent to mass of one component per unit volume of material (i.e., from units of wt% to kg/m^3); this latter composition scheme is often used in diffusion computations (Section 5.3). Concentrations in terms of this basis will be denoted using a double prime (i.e., C_1'' and C_2''), and the relevant equations are as follows:

$$C_1'' = \left(\frac{C_1}{\dfrac{C_1}{\rho_1} + \dfrac{C_2}{\rho_2}} \right) \times 10^3 \qquad (4.9a)$$

$$C_2'' = \left(\frac{C_2}{\dfrac{C_1}{\rho_1} + \dfrac{C_2}{\rho_2}} \right) \times 10^3 \qquad (4.9b)$$

For density ρ in units of g/cm^3, these expressions yield C_1'' and C_2'' in kg/m^3.

Furthermore, on occasion we desire to determine the density and atomic weight of a binary alloy given the composition in terms of either weight percent or atom percent. If we represent alloy density and atomic weight by ρ_{ave} and A_{ave}, respectively, then

$$\rho_{ave} = \frac{100}{\dfrac{C_1}{\rho_1} + \dfrac{C_2}{\rho_2}} \qquad (4.10a)$$

$$\rho_{ave} = \frac{C_1'A_1 + C_2'A_2}{\dfrac{C_1'A_1}{\rho_1} + \dfrac{C_2'A_2}{\rho_2}} \qquad (4.10b)$$

$$A_{ave} = \frac{100}{\dfrac{C_1}{A_1} + \dfrac{C_2}{A_2}} \qquad (4.11a)$$

$$A_{ave} = \frac{C_1'A_1 + C_2'A_2}{100} \qquad (4.11b)$$

It should be noted that Equations 4.9 and 4.11 are not always exact. In their derivations, it is assumed that total alloy volume is exactly equal to the sum of the volumes of the individual elements. This normally is not the case for most alloys; however, it is a reasonably valid assumption and does not lead to significant errors for dilute solutions and over composition ranges where solid solutions exist.

EXAMPLE PROBLEM 4.2

Derive Equation 4.6a.

SOLUTION

To simplify this derivation, it will be assumed that masses are expressed in units of grams, and denoted with a prime (e.g., m_1'). Furthermore, the total alloy mass (in grams) M' is

$$M' = m_1' + m_2' \tag{4.12}$$

Using the definition of C_1' (Equation 4.5) and incorporation of the expression for n_{m1}, Equation 4.4, and the analogous expression for n_{m2} yields

$$C_1' = \frac{n_{m1}}{n_{m1} + n_{m2}} \times 100$$

$$= \frac{\dfrac{m_1'}{A_1}}{\dfrac{m_1'}{A_1} + \dfrac{m_2'}{A_2}} \times 100 \tag{4.13}$$

Rearrangement of the mass-in-grams equivalent of Equation 4.3 leads to

$$m_1' = \frac{C_1 M'}{100} \tag{4.14}$$

Substitution of this expression and its m_2' equivalent into Equation 4.13 gives

$$C_1' = \frac{\dfrac{C_1 M'}{100 A_1}}{\dfrac{C_1 M'}{100 A_1} + \dfrac{C_2 M'}{100 A_2}} \times 100 \tag{4.15}$$

And upon simplification we have

$$C_1' = \frac{C_1 A_2}{C_1 A_2 + C_2 A_1} \times 100$$

which is identical to Equation 4.6a.

EXAMPLE PROBLEM 4.3

Determine the composition, in atom percent, of an alloy that consists of 97 wt% aluminum and 3 wt% copper.

SOLUTION

If we denote the respective weight percent compositions as $C_{Al} = 97$ and $C_{Cu} = 3$, substitution into Equations 4.6a and 4.6b yields

$$C_{Al}' = \frac{C_{Al} A_{Cu}}{C_{Al} A_{Cu} + C_{Cu} A_{Al}} \times 100$$

$$= \frac{(97)(63.55 \text{ g/mol})}{(97)(63.55 \text{ g/mol}) + (3)(26.98 \text{ g/mol})} \times 100$$

$$= 98.7 \text{ at}\%$$

And

$$C'_{Cu} = \frac{C_{Cu}A_{Al}}{C_{Cu}A_{Al} + C_{Al}A_{Cu}} \times 100$$

$$= \frac{(3)(26.98 \text{ g/mol})}{(3)(26.98 \text{ g/mol}) + (97)(63.55 \text{ g/mol})} \times 100$$

$$= 1.30 \text{ at}\%$$

MISCELLANEOUS IMPERFECTIONS

4.4 DISLOCATIONS — LINEAR DEFECTS

 A *dislocation* is a linear or one-dimensional defect around which some of the atoms are misaligned. One type of dislocation is represented in Figure 4.3: an extra portion of a plane of atoms, or half-plane, the edge of which terminates within the crystal. This is termed an **edge dislocation;** it is a linear defect that centers around the line that is defined along the end of the extra half-plane of atoms. This is sometimes termed the **dislocation line,** which, for the edge dislocation in Figure 4.3, is perpendicular to the plane of the page. Within the region around the dislocation line there is some localized lattice distortion. The atoms above the dislocation line in Figure 4.3 are squeezed together, and those below are pulled apart; this is reflected in the slight curvature for the vertical planes of atoms as they bend around this extra half-plane. The magnitude of this distortion decreases with distance away from the dislocation line; at positions far removed, the crystal lattice is virtually perfect. Sometimes the edge dislocation in Figure 4.3 is represented by the symbol ⊥, which also indicates the position of the dislocation line. An edge dislocation may also be formed by an extra half-plane of atoms that is included in the bottom portion of the crystal; its designation is a ⊤.

Another type of dislocation, called a **screw dislocation,** exists, which may be thought of as being formed by a shear stress that is applied to produce the distortion

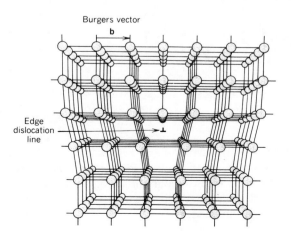

Burgers vector
b

Edge
dislocation
line

➤ ⊥

FIGURE 4.3 The atom positions around an edge dislocation; extra half-plane of atoms shown in perspective. (Adapted from A. G. Guy, *Essentials of Materials Science,* McGraw-Hill Book Company, New York, 1976, p. 153.)

FIGURE 4.4 (*a*) A screw dislocation within a crystal. (*b*) The screw dislocation in (*a*) as viewed from above. The dislocation line extends along line *AB*. Atom positions above the slip plane are designated by open circles, those below by solid circles. (Figure (*b*) from W. T. Read, Jr., *Dislocations in Crystals*, McGraw-Hill Book Company, New York, 1953.)

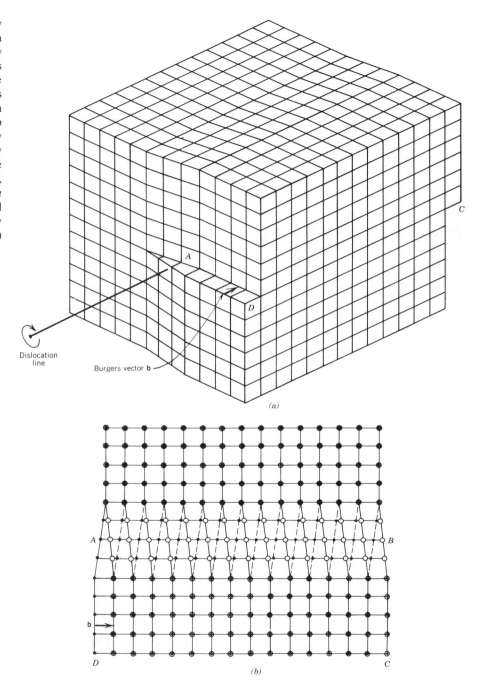

Dislocation line

Burgers vector **b**

(*a*)

(*b*)

shown in Figure 4.4*a*: the upper front region of the crystal is shifted one atomic distance to the right relative to the bottom portion. The atomic distortion associated with a screw dislocation is also linear and along a dislocation line, line *AB* in Figure 4.4*b*. The screw dislocation derives its name from the spiral or helical path or ramp that is traced around the dislocation line by the atomic planes of atoms. Sometimes the symbol ↻ is used to designate a screw dislocation.

Most dislocations found in crystalline materials are probably neither pure edge nor pure screw, but exhibit components of both types; these are termed **mixed dislocations.** All three dislocation types are represented schematically in Figure 4.5; the lattice distortion that is produced away from the two faces is mixed, having varying degrees of screw and edge character.

FIGURE 4.5 (*a*) Schematic representation of a dislocation that has edge, screw, and mixed character. (*b*) Top view, where open circles denote atom positions above the slip plane. Solid circles, atom positions below. At point *A*, the dislocation is pure screw, while at point *B*, it is pure edge. For regions in between where there is curvature in the dislocation line, the character is mixed edge and screw. (Figure (*b*) from W. T. Read, Jr., *Dislocations in Crystals,* McGraw-Hill Book Company, New York, 1953.)

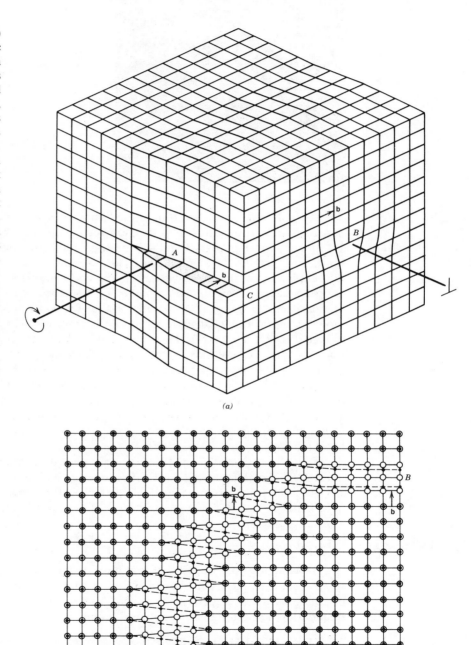

(a)

(b)

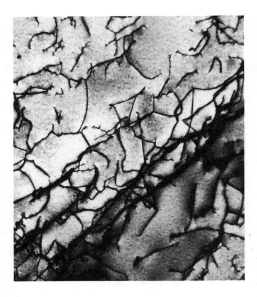

FIGURE 4.6 A transmission electron micrograph of a titanium alloy in which the dark lines are dislocations. 51,450×. (Courtesy of M. R. Plichta, Michigan Technological University.)

The magnitude and direction of the lattice distortion associated with a dislocation is expressed in terms of a **Burgers vector,** denoted by a **b**. Burgers vectors are indicated in Figures 4.3 and 4.4 for edge and screw dislocations, respectively. Furthermore, the nature of a dislocation (i.e., edge, screw, or mixed) is defined by the relative orientations of dislocation line and Burgers vector. For an edge, they are perpendicular (Figure 4.3), whereas for a screw, both are parallel (Figure 4.4); they are neither perpendicular nor parallel for a mixed dislocation. Also, even though a dislocation changes direction and nature within a crystal (e.g., from edge to mixed to screw), the Burgers vector will be the same at all points along its line. For example, all positions of the curved dislocation in Figure 4.5 will have the Burgers vector shown. For metallic materials, the Burgers vector for a dislocation will point in a close-packed crystallographic direction and will be of magnitude equal to the interatomic spacing.

Dislocations can be observed in crystalline materials using electron-microscopic techniques. In Figure 4.6, a high-magnification transmission electron micrograph, the dark lines are the dislocations.

Virtually all crystalline materials contain some dislocations that were introduced during solidification, during plastic deformation, and as a consequence of thermal stresses that result from rapid cooling. Dislocations are involved in the plastic deformation of crystalline materials, as discussed in Chapter 7.

4.5 INTERFACIAL DEFECTS

Interfacial defects are boundaries that have two dimensions and normally separate regions of the materials that have different crystal structures and/or crystallographic orientations. These imperfections include external surfaces, grain boundaries, twin boundaries, stacking faults, and phase boundaries.

EXTERNAL SURFACES

One of the most obvious boundaries is the external surface, along which the crystal structure terminates. Surface atoms are not bonded to the maximum number of nearest neighbors, and are therefore in a higher energy state than the atoms at interior positions. The bonds of these surface atoms that are not satisfied give rise to a surface energy, expressed in units of energy per unit area (J/m^2 or erg/cm^2). To reduce this energy, materials tend to minimize, if at all possible, the total surface area. For example, liquids assume a shape having a minimum area—the droplets become spherical. Of course, this is not possible with solids, which are mechanically rigid.

GRAIN BOUNDARIES

Another interfacial defect, the grain boundary, was introduced in Section 3.13 as the boundary separating two small grains or crystals having different crystallographic orientations in polycrystalline materials. A grain boundary is represented schematically from an atomic perspective in Figure 4.7. Within the boundary region, which is probably just several atom distances wide, there is some atomic mismatch in a transition from the crystalline orientation of one grain to that of an adjacent one.

Various degrees of crystallographic misalignment between adjacent grains are possible (Figure 4.7). When this orientation mismatch is slight, on the order of a few degrees, then the term *small-angle grain boundary* is used. These boundaries can be described in terms of dislocation arrays. One simple small-angle grain boundary is formed when edge dislocations are aligned in the manner of Figure 4.8. This type is called a *tilt boundary;* the angle of misorientation, θ, is also indicated in the figure. When the angle of misorientation is parallel to the boundary, a *twist boundary* results, which can be described by an array of screw dislocations.

The atoms are bonded less regularly along a grain boundary (e.g., bond angles are longer), and consequently, there is an interfacial or grain boundary energy similar to the surface energy described above. The magnitude of this energy is a function of the degree of misorientation, being larger for high-angle boundaries. Grain boundaries are more chemically reactive than the grains themselves as a consequence of this boundary energy. Furthermore, impurity atoms often preferentially segregate along these boundaries because of their higher energy state. The total interfacial energy is lower in large or coarse-grained materials than in fine-grained ones, since there is less total boundary area in the former. Grains grow at

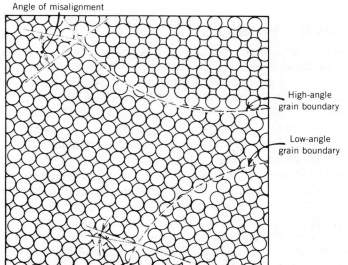

Angle of misalignment

High-angle grain boundary

Low-angle grain boundary

Angle of misalignment

FIGURE 4.7 Schematic diagram showing low- and high-angle grain boundaries and the adjacent atom positions.

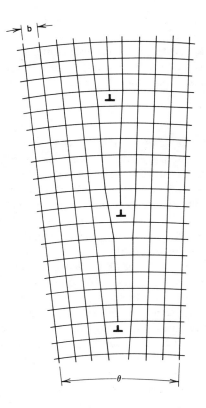

FIGURE 4.8 Demonstration of how a tilt boundary having an angle of misorientation θ results from an alignment of edge dislocations.

elevated temperatures to reduce the total boundary energy, a phenomenon explained in Section 7.13.

In spite of this disordered arrangement of atoms and lack of regular bonding along grain boundaries, a polycrystalline material is still very strong; cohesive forces within and across the boundary are present. Furthermore, the density of a polycrystalline specimen is virtually identical to that of a single crystal of the same material.

TWIN BOUNDARIES

A *twin boundary* is a special type of grain boundary across which there is a specific mirror lattice symmetry; that is, atoms on one side of the boundary are located in mirror image positions of the atoms on the other side (Figure 4.9). The region of material between these boundaries is appropriately termed a *twin*. Twins result from atomic displacements that are produced from applied mechanical shear forces (mechanical twins), and also during annealing heat treatments following deformation (annealing twins). Twinning occurs on a definite crystallographic plane and in a specific direction, both of which depend on the crystal structure. Annealing twins are typically found in metals that have the FCC crystal structure, while mechanical twins are observed in BCC and HCP metals. The role of mechanical twins in the deformation process is discussed in Section 7.7. Annealing twins may be observed in the photomicrograph of the polycrystalline brass specimen shown in Figure 4.11c. The twins correspond to those regions having relatively straight and parallel sides and a different visual contrast than the untwinned regions of the grains within which they reside. An explanation for the variety of textural contrasts in this photomicrograph is provided in Section 4.9.

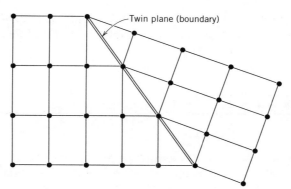

FIGURE 4.9 Schematic diagram showing a twin plane or boundary and the adjacent atom positions (dark circles).

Twin plane (boundary)

MISCELLANEOUS INTERFACIAL DEFECTS

Other possible interfacial defects include stacking faults, phase boundaries, and ferromagnetic domain walls. Stacking faults are found in FCC metals when there is an interruption in the *ABCABCABC* . . . stacking sequence of close-packed planes (Section 3.11). Phase boundaries exist in multiphase materials (Section 9.3) across which there is a sudden change in physical and/or chemical characteristics. For ferromagnetic and ferrimagnetic materials, the boundary that separates regions having different directions of magnetization is termed a domain wall, which is discussed in Section 21.7.

Associated with each of the defects discussed in this section is an interfacial energy, the magnitude of which depends on boundary type, and which will vary from material to material. Normally, the interfacial energy will be greatest for external surfaces and least for domain walls.

4.6 BULK OR VOLUME DEFECTS

Other defects exist in all solid materials that are much larger than those heretofore discussed. These include pores, cracks, foreign inclusions, and other phases. They are normally introduced during processing and fabrication steps. Some of these defects and their effects on the properties of materials are discussed in subsequent chapters.

4.7 ATOMIC VIBRATIONS

Every atom in a solid material is vibrating very rapidly about its lattice position within the crystal. In a sense, these vibrations may be thought of as imperfections or defects. At any instant of time not all atoms vibrate at the same frequency and amplitude, nor with the same energy. At a given temperature there will exist a distribution of energies for the constituent atoms about an average energy. Over time the vibrational energy of any specific atom will also vary in a random manner. With rising temperature, this average energy increases, and, in fact, the temperature of a solid is really just a measure of the average vibrational activity of atoms and molecules. At room temperature, a typical vibrational frequency is on the order of 10^{13} vibrations per second, whereas the amplitude is a few thousandths of a nanometer.

Many properties and processes in solids are manifestations of this vibrational atomic motion. For example, melting occurs when the vibrations are vigorous enough to rupture large numbers of atomic bonds. A more detailed discussion of atomic vibrations and their influence on the properties of materials is presented in Chapter 20.

MICROSCOPIC EXAMINATION

4.8 GENERAL

On occasion it is necessary or desirable to examine the structural elements and defects that influence the properties of materials. The capacity to perform such examinations is important, first to ensure that the associations between the properties and structure (and defects) are properly understood, and second to predict the properties of materials once these relationships have been established. Several of the techniques that are commonly used in such investigations are discussed next.

Some structural elements are of *macroscopic* dimensions, that is, are large enough to be observed with the unaided eye. For example, the shape and average size or diameter of the grains for a polycrystalline specimen are important structural elements. Macroscopic grains are often evident on aluminum street light posts and also on garbage cans. Relatively large grains having different textures are clearly visible on the surface of the sectioned lead ingot shown in Figure 4.10. However, in most materials the constituent grains are of *microscopic* dimensions, having diameters that may be on the order of microns,[5] and their details must be investigated using some type of microscope. Grain size and shape are only two features of what is termed the **microstructure;** these and other microstructural characteristics are discussed in subsequent chapters.

4.9 MICROSCOPY

Both optical and electron microscopes are commonly used in **microscopy.** These instruments aid in investigations of the microstructural features of all material types.

FIGURE 4.10 High-purity polycrystalline lead ingot in which the individual grains may be discerned. 0.7×. (Reproduced with permission from *Metals Handbook,* Vol. 9, 9th edition, *Metallography and Microstructures,* American Society for Metals, Metals Park, OH, 1985.)

---

[5] A micron (μm), sometimes called a micrometer, is 10^{-6} m.

FIGURE 4.11 (*a*) Polished and etched grains as they might appear when viewed with an optical microscope. (*b*) Section taken through these grains showing how the etching characteristics and resulting surface texture vary from grain to grain because of differences in crystallographic orientation. (*c*) Photomicrograph of a polycrystalline brass specimen. 60×. (Photomicrograph courtesy of J. E. Burke, General Electric Co.)

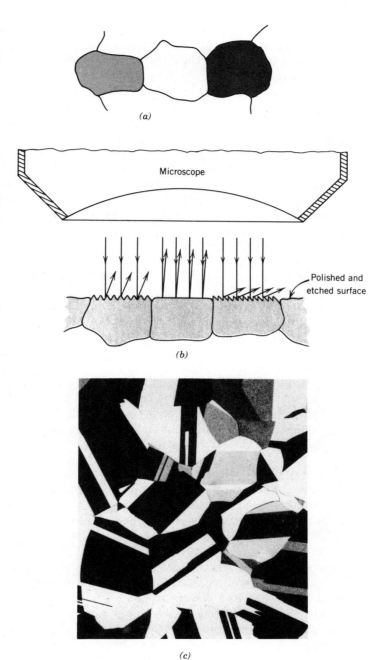

Most of these techniques employ photographic equipment in conjunction with the microscope; the photograph on which the image is recorded is called a **photomicrograph.**

OPTICAL MICROSCOPY

With optical microscopy, the light microscope is used to study the microstructure; optical and illumination systems are its basic elements. For materials that are opaque to visible light (all metals and many ceramics and polymers), only the surface is subject to observation, and the light microscope must be used in a reflecting mode. Contrasts in the image produced result from differences in reflectivity of the various regions of the microstructure. Investigations of this type are often termed *metallographic*, since metals were first examined using this technique.

Normally, careful and meticulous surface preparations are necessary to reveal the important details of the microstructure. The specimen surface must first be ground and polished to a smooth and mirrorlike finish. This is accomplished by using successively finer abrasive papers and powders. The microstructure is revealed by a surface treatment using an appropriate chemical reagent in a procedure termed *etching*. The chemical reactivity of the grains of some single-phase materials depends on crystallographic orientation. Consequently, in a polycrystalline specimen, etching characteristics vary from grain to grain. Figure 4.11*b* shows how normally incident light is reflected by three etched surface grains, each having a different orientation. Figure 4.11*a* depicts the surface structure as it might appear when viewed with the microscope; the luster or texture of each grain depends on its reflectance properties. A photomicrograph of a polycrystalline specimen exhibiting these characteristics is shown in Figure 4.11*c*.

Also, small grooves form along grain boundaries as a consequence of etching. Since atoms along grain boundary regions are more chemically active, they dissolve at a greater rate than those within the grains. These grooves become discernible when viewed under a microscope because they reflect light at an angle different from that of the grains themselves; this effect is displayed in Figure 4.12*a*. Figure 4.12*b* is a photomicrograph of a polycrystalline specimen in which the grain boundary grooves are clearly visible as dark lines.

When the microstructure of a two-phase alloy is to be examined, an etchant is chosen that produces a different texture for each phase so that the different phases may be distinguished from each other.

ELECTRON MICROSCOPY

The upper limit to the magnification possible with an optical microscope is approximately 2000 diameters. Consequently, some structural elements are too fine or small to permit observation using optical microscopy. Under such circumstances the electron microscope, which is capable of much higher magnifications, may be employed.

An image of the structure under investigation is formed using beams of electrons instead of light radiation. According to quantum mechanics, a high-velocity electron will become wavelike, having a wavelength that is inversely proportional to its velocity. When accelerated across large voltages, electrons can be made to have wavelengths on the order of 0.003 nm (3 pm). High magnifications and resolving powers of these microscopes are consequences of the short wavelengths of electron beams. The electron beam is focused and the image formed with magnetic lenses; otherwise the geometry of the microscope components is essentially the same as with optical systems. Both transmission and reflection beam modes of operation are possible for electron microscopes.

Transmission Electron Microscopy

The image seen with a **transmission electron microscope (TEM)** is formed by an electron beam that passes through the specimen. Details of internal microstructural features are accessible to observation; contrasts in the image are produced by differences in beam scattering or diffraction produced between various elements of

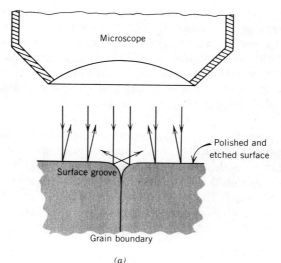

FIGURE 4.12 (a) Section of a grain boundary and its surface groove produced by etching; the light reflection characteristics in the vicinity of the groove are also shown. (b) Photomicrograph of the surface of a polished and etched polycrystalline specimen of an iron-chromium alloy in which the grain boundaries appear dark. 100×. (Photomicrograph courtesy of L. C. Smith and C. Brady, the National Bureau of Standards, Washington, DC.)

(a)

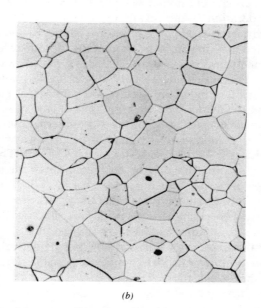

(b)

the microstructure or defect. Since solid materials are highly absorptive to electron beams, a specimen to be examined must be prepared in the form of a very thin foil; this ensures transmission through the specimen of an appreciable fraction of the incident beam. The transmitted beam is projected onto a fluorescent screen or a photographic film so that the image may be viewed. Magnifications approaching 1,000,000× are possible with transmission electron microscopy, which is frequently utilized in the study of dislocations.

Scanning Electron Microscopy

A more recent and extremely useful investigative tool, is the **scanning electron microscope (SEM).** The surface of a specimen to be examined is scanned with an electron beam, and the reflected (or back-scattered) beam of electrons is collected, then displayed at the same scanning rate on a cathode ray tube (similar to a TV screen). The image on the screen, which may be photographed, represents the surface features of the specimen. The surface may or may not be polished and etched, but it must be electrically conductive; a very thin metallic surface coating must be applied to nonconductive materials. Magnifications ranging from 10 to in excess of 50,000 diameters are possible, as are also very great depths-of-field. Accessory equipment permits qualitative and semiquantitative analysis of the elemental composition of very localized surface areas.

Microscopic examination is an extremely useful tool in the study and characterization of materials. This will become apparent in subsequent chapters that correlate the microstructure with various characteristics and properties. Examination of microstructure is also used to determine the mode of mechanical fracture, to predict the mechanical properties of alloys, to show whether an alloy has been correctly heat treated, and also to design alloys with new property combinations.

4.10 GRAIN SIZE DETERMINATION

The **grain size** is often determined when the properties of a polycrystalline material are under consideration. In this regard, there exist a number of techniques by which size is specified in terms of average grain volume, diameter, or area. Grain size may be estimated by using an intercept method, described as follows. Straight lines all the same length are drawn through several photomicrographs that show the grain structure. The grains intersected by each line segment are counted; the line length is then divided by an average of the number of grains intersected, taken over all the line segments. The average grain diameter is found by dividing this result by the linear magnification of the photomicrographs.

Probably the most common method utilized, however, is that devised by the American Society for Testing and Materials (ASTM).[6] The ASTM has prepared several standard comparison charts, all having different average grain sizes. To each is assigned a number ranging from 1 to 10, which is termed the *grain size number;* the larger this number, the smaller the grains. A specimen must be properly prepared to reveal the grain structure, which is photographed at a magnification of 100×. Grain size is expressed as the grain size number of the chart that most nearly matches the grains in the micrograph. Thus, a relatively simple and convenient visual determination of grain size number is possible. Grain size number is used extensively in the specification of steels.

The rationale behind the assignment of the grain size number to these various charts is as follows. Let n represent the grain size number, and N the average number of grains per square inch at a magnification of 100×. These two parameters are related to each other through the expression

$$N = 2^{n-1} \tag{4.16}$$

SUMMARY

All solid materials contain large numbers of imperfections or deviations from crystalline perfection. The several types of imperfection are categorized on the basis of their geometry and size. Point defects are those associated with one or two atomic

---

[6] ASTM Standard E 112, "Standard Methods for Estimating the Average Grain Size for Metals."

positions, including vacancies (or vacant lattice sites), self-interstitials (host atoms that occupy interstitial sites), and impurity atoms.

A solid solution may form when impurity atoms are added to a solid, in which case the original crystal structure is retained and no new phases are formed. For substitutional solid solutions, impurity atoms substitute for host atoms, and appreciable solubility is possible only when atomic diameters and electronegativities for both atom types are similar, and when both elements have the same crystal structure and same valence. Interstitial solid solutions form for relatively small impurity atoms that occupy interstitial sites among the host atoms.

Composition of an alloy may be specified in weight percent or atom percent. The basis for weight percent computations is the weight (or mass) of each alloy constituent relative to the total alloy weight. Atom percents are calculated in terms of the number of moles for each constituent relative to the total moles of all the elements in the alloy.

Dislocations are one-dimensional crystalline defects of which there are two pure types: edge and screw. An edge may be thought of in terms of the lattice distortion along the end of an extra half-plane of atoms; a screw, by a helical planar ramp. For mixed dislocations, components of both pure edge and screw are found. The magnitude and direction of lattice distortion associated with a dislocation is specified by its Burgers vector. The relative orientations of Burgers vector and dislocation line are (1) perpendicular for edge, (2) parallel for screw, and (3) neither perpendicular nor parallel for mixed.

Other imperfections include interfacial defects [external surfaces, grain boundaries (both low- and high-angle), twin boundaries, etc.], volume defects (cracks, pores, etc.), and atomic vibrations. Each type of imperfection has some influence on the properties of a material.

Many of the important defects and structural elements of materials are of microscopic dimensions, and observation is possible only with the aid of a microscope. Both optical and electron microscopes are employed, usually in conjunction with photographic equipment. Transmissive and reflective modes are possible for each microscope type; preference is dictated by the nature of the specimen as well as the structural element or defect to be examined.

Grain size of polycrystalline materials is frequently determined using photomicrographic techniques. Two methods are commonly employed: intercept and standard comparison charts.

IMPLICATIONS

As mentioned in the Introduction section, the properties of some materials are profoundly influenced by the presence of imperfections; therefore, it is important to have a knowledge about the types of imperfections that exist, and the roles they play in affecting the behavior of materials. Some examples are as follows:

1. Integrated circuit microelectronic devices found in our computers, calculators, and home appliances function because of highly controlled concentrations of specific impurities that are incorporated into small, localized regions of semiconducting materials (Sections 19.11 and 19.14).

2. A knowledge of the role that dislocations play in the plastic deformation process allows us to understand strengthening mechanisms for metals (Chapter 7).

3. The strengths of metals are enhanced as a result of interactions between impurity atoms (in solid solution) and dislocations (Section 7.9).

4. The presence of grain boundaries may affect material properties [e.g., the optical characteristics of normally transparent materials (Figure 1.2)].

5. Mass transport by diffusion involves the motion of vacancies and interstitial impurity atoms (Section 5.2).

IMPORTANT TERMS AND CONCEPTS

Alloy	Interstitial solid solution	Solid solution
Atom percent	Microscopy	Solute
Atomic vibration	Microstructure	Solvent
Boltzmann's constant	Mixed dislocation	Substitutional solid solution
Burgers vector	Photomicrograph	Transmission electron micro-
Composition	Point defect	scope (TEM)
Dislocation line	Scanning electron microscope	Vacancy
Edge dislocation	(SEM)	Weight percent
Grain size	Screw dislocation	
Imperfection	Self-Interstitial	

REFERENCES

ASM Handbook, Vol. 9, *Metallography and Micro-structures,* ASM International, Materials Park, OH, 1985.

Moffatt, W. G., G. W. Pearsall, and J. Wulff, *The Structure and Properties of Materials,* Vol. 1, *Structure,* John Wiley & Sons, New York, 1964.

Phillips, V. A., *Modern Metallographic Techniques and Their Applications,* Wiley-Interscience, New York, 1971.

Van Bueren, H. G., *Imperfections in Crystals,* North-Holland Publishing Co., Amsterdam (Wiley-Interscience, New York), 1960.

Vander Voort, G. F., *Metallography, Principles and Practice,* McGraw-Hill Book Co., New York, 1984.

QUESTIONS AND PROBLEMS

4.1 Calculate the fraction of atom sites that are vacant for copper at its melting temperature of 1084°C (1357 K). Assume an energy for vacancy formation of 0.90 eV/atom.

4.2 Calculate the number of vacancies per cubic meter in iron at 850°C. The energy for vacancy formation is 1.08 eV/atom. Furthermore, the density and atomic weight for Fe are 7.65 g/cm^3 and 55.85 g/mol, respectively.

4.3 Calculate the energy for vacancy formation in aluminum, given that the equilibrium number of vacancies at 500°C (773 K) is 7.57 × 10^{23} m^{-3}. The atomic weight and density (at 500°C) for aluminum are, respectively, 26.98 g/mol and 2.62 g/cm^3.

4.4 Below, atomic radius, crystal structure, electronegativity, and the most common valence are tabulated, for several elements; for those that are nonmetals, only atomic radii are indicated.

Element	Atomic Radius (nm)	Crystal Structure	Electro-nega-tivity	Valence
Ni	0.1246	FCC	1.8	2+
C	0.071			
H	0.046			
O	0.060			
Ag	0.1445	FCC	1.9	1+
Al	0.1431	FCC	1.5	3+
Co	0.1253	HCP	1.8	2+
Cr	0.1249	BCC	1.6	3+
Fe	0.1241	BCC	1.8	2+
Pt	0.1387	FCC	2.2	2+
Zn	0.1332	HCP	1.6	2+

Which of these elements would you expect to form the following with nickel:
(a) A substitutional solid solution having complete solubility?
(b) A substitutional solid solution of incomplete solubility?
(c) An interstitial solid solution?

4.5 For both FCC and BCC crystal structures, interstitial sites that may be occupied by impurity atoms are located at the centers of each of the unit cell edges. Compute the radius r of an impurity atom that will just fit into one of these sites for each of the two crystal structures in terms of the atomic radius R of the host atom. For which crystal structure is r larger? Consult Section 3.4.

4.6 Derive the following equations:
(a) Equation 4.7a.
(b) Equation 4.9a.
(c) Equation 4.10a.
(d) Equation 4.11b.

4.7 What is the composition, in atom percent, of an alloy that consists of 30 wt% Zn and 70 wt% Cu?

4.8 What is the composition, in weight percent, of an alloy that consists of 6 at% Pb and 94 at% Sn?

4.9 Calculate the composition, in weight percent, of an alloy that contains 218.0 kg titanium, 14.6 kg of aluminum, and 9.7 kg of vanadium.

4.10 What is the composition, in atom percent, of an alloy that contains 98 g tin and 65 g of lead?

4.11 What is the composition, in atom percent, of an alloy that contains 99.7 lb_m copper, 102 lb_m zinc, and 2.1 lb_m lead?

4.12 What is the composition, in atom percent, of an alloy that consists of 97 wt% Fe and 3 wt% Si?

4.13 Convert the atom percent composition in Problem 4.11 to weight percent.

4.14 Calculate the number of atoms per cubic meter in lead.

4.15 The concentration of carbon in an iron-carbon alloy is 0.15 wt%. What is the concentration in kilograms of carbon per cubic meter of alloy?

4.16 For a solid solution consisting of two elements (designated as 1 and 2), sometimes it is desirable to determine the number of atoms per cubic centimeter of one element in a solid solution, N_1, given the concentration of that element specified in weight percent, C_1. This computation is possible using the following expression:

$$N_1 = \frac{N_A C_1}{\frac{C_1 A_1}{\rho_1} + \frac{A_1}{\rho_2}(100 - C_1)} \qquad (4.17)$$

where

N_A = Avogadro's number
ρ_1 and ρ_2 = densities of the two elements
A_1 = the atomic weight of element 1

Derive Equation 4.17 using Equation 4.2 and expressions contained in Section 4.3.

4.17 Gold forms a substitutional solid solution with silver. Compute the number of gold atoms per cubic centimeter for a silver-gold alloy that contains 10 wt% Au and 90 wt% Ag. The densities of pure gold and silver are 19.32 and 10.49 g/cm^3, respectively.

4.18 Germanium forms a substitutional solid solution with silicon. Compute the number of germanium atoms per cubic centimeter for a germanium-silicon alloy that contains 15 wt% Ge and 85 wt% Si. The densities of pure germanium and silicon are 5.32 and 2.33 g/cm^3, respectively.

4.19 Sometimes it is desirable to be able to determine the weight percent of one element, C_1, that will produce a specified concentration in terms of the number of atoms per cubic centimeter, N_1, for an alloy composed of two types of atoms. This computation is possible using the following expression:

$$C_1 = \frac{100}{1 + \dfrac{N_A \rho_2}{N_1 A_1} - \dfrac{\rho_2}{\rho_1}}$$ (4.18)

where

N_A = Avogadro's number

ρ_1 and ρ_2 = densities of the two elements

A_1 and A_2 = the atomic weights of the two elements

Derive Equation 4.18 using Equation 4.2 and expressions contained in Section 4.3.

4.20 Molybdenum forms a substitutional solid solution with tungsten. Compute the weight percent of molybdenum that must be added to tungsten to yield an alloy that contains 1.0×10^{22} Mo atoms per cubic centimeter. The densities of pure Mo and W are 10.22 and 19.30 g/cm^3, respectively.

4.21 Niobium forms a substitutional solid solution with vanadium. Compute the weight percent of niobium that must be added to vanadium to yield an alloy that contains 1.55×10^{22} Nb atoms per cubic centimeter. The densities of pure Nb and V are 8.57 and 6.10 g/cm^3, respectively.

4.22 Cite the relative Burgers vector–dislocation line orientations for edge, screw, and mixed dislocations.

4.23 For both FCC and BCC crystal structures, the Burgers vector **b** may be expressed as

$$\mathbf{b} = \frac{a}{2}[hkl]$$

where a is the unit cell edge length and $[hkl]$ is the crystallographic direction having the greatest linear atomic density.
(a) What are the Burgers vector representations for FCC, BCC, and simple cubic crystal structures? See Problems 3.40 and 3.41 at the end of Chapter 3.
(b) If the magnitude of the Burgers vector $|\mathbf{b}|$ is

$$|\mathbf{b}| = \frac{a}{2}(h^2 + k^2 + l^2)^{1/2}$$

determine the values of $|\mathbf{b}|$ for aluminum and tungsten. You may want to consult Table 3.1.

4.24 **(a)** The surface energy of a single crystal depends on the crystallographic orientation with respect to the surface. Explain why this is so.
(b) For an FCC crystal, such as aluminum, would you expect the surface energy for a (100) plane to be greater or less than that for a (111) plane? Why?

4.25 **(a)** For a given material, would you expect the surface energy to be greater than, the same as, or less than the grain boundary energy? Why?
(b) The grain boundary energy of a low-angle grain boundary is less than for a high-angle one. Why is this so?

4.26 **(a)** Briefly describe a twin and a twin boundary.
(b) Cite the difference between mechanical and annealing twins.

4.27 For each of the following stacking sequences found in FCC metals, cite the type of planar defect that exists:
(a) . . . A B C A B C B A C B A . . .
(b) . . . A B C A B C B C A B C . . .
Now, copy the stacking sequences and indicate the position(s) of planar defect(s) with a vertical dashed line.

4.28 Using the intercept method, determine the average grain size, in millimeters, of the specimen whose microstructure is shown in Figure 4.12b; assume that the magnification is 100×, and use at least seven straight-line segments.

4.29 Employing the intercept technique, determine the average grain size for the steel specimen whose microstructure is shown in Figure 9.23a; use at least seven straight-line segments.

4.30 **(a)** For an ASTM grain size of 6, approximately how many grains would there be per square inch in a micrograph taken at a magnification of 100×?
(b) Estimate the grain size number for the photomicrograph in Figure 4.12b, assuming a magnification of 100×.

4.31 A photomicrograph was taken of some metal at a magnification of 100× and it was determined that the average number of grains per square inch is 10. Compute the ASTM grain size number for this alloy.

5

Diffusion

Photograph of a steel gear that has been "case hardened." The outer surface layer was selectively hardened by a high-temperature heat treatment during which carbon from the surrounding atmosphere diffused into the surface. The "case" appears as the dark outer rim of that segment of the gear that has been sectioned. Actual size. (Photograph courtesy of Surface Division Midland-Ross.)

5.1 INTRODUCTION

Many reactions and processes that are important in the treatment of materials rely on the transfer of mass either within a specific solid (ordinarily on a microscopic level) or from a liquid, a gas, or another solid phase. This is necessarily accomplished by **diffusion,** the phenomenon of material transport by atomic motion. This chapter discusses the atomic mechanisms by which diffusion occurs, the mathematics of diffusion, and the influence of temperature and diffusing species on the rate of diffusion.

The phenomenon of diffusion may be demonstrated with the use of a *diffusion couple,* which is formed by joining bars of two different metals together so that there is intimate contact between the two faces, as illustrated for copper and nickel in Figure 5.1, which includes schematic representations of atom positions and composition across the interface. This couple is heated for an extended period at an elevated temperature (but below the melting temperature of both metals), and cooled to room temperature. Chemical analysis will reveal a condition similar to that represented in Figure 5.2, namely, pure copper and nickel at the two extremities of the couple, separated by an alloyed region. Concentrations of both metals vary with position as shown in Figure 5.2c. This result indicates that copper atoms have migrated or diffused into the nickel, and that nickel has diffused into copper. This process, whereby atoms of one metal diffuse into another, is termed **interdiffusion,** or **impurity diffusion.**

Interdiffusion may be discerned from a macroscopic perspective by changes in concentration which occur over time, as in the example for the Cu–Ni diffusion couple. There is a net drift or transport of atoms from high to low concentration regions. Diffusion also occurs for pure metals, but all atoms exchanging positions are of the same type; this is termed **self-diffusion.** Of course, self-diffusion is not normally subject to observation by noting compositional changes.

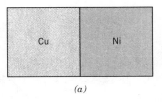

(a)

FIGURE 5.1 (a) A copper–nickel diffusion couple before a high-temperature heat treatment. (b) Schematic representations of Cu (colored circles) and Ni (black circles) atom locations within the diffusion couple. (c) Concentrations of copper and nickel as a function of position across the couple.

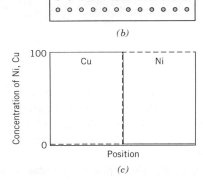

(b)

(c)

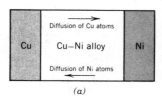

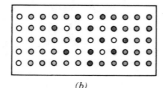

(a)

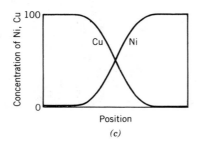

(b)

FIGURE 5.2 (a) A copper–nickel diffusion couple after a high-temperature heat treatment, showing the alloyed diffusion zone. (b) Schematic representations of Cu (colored circles) and Ni (black circles) atom locations within the couple. (c) Concentrations of copper and nickel as a function of position across the couple.

5.2 DIFFUSION MECHANISMS

From an atomic perspective, diffusion is just the stepwise migration of atoms from lattice site to lattice site. In fact, the atoms in solid materials are in constant motion, rapidly changing positions. For an atom to make such a move, two conditions must be met: (1) there must be an empty adjacent site, and (2) the atom must have sufficient energy to break bonds with its neighbor atoms and then cause some lattice distortion during the displacement. This energy is vibrational in nature (Section 4.7). At a specific temperature some small fraction of the total number of atoms are capable of diffusive motion, by virtue of the magnitudes of their vibrational energies. This fraction increases with rising temperature.

Several different models for this atomic motion have been proposed; of these possibilities, two dominate for metallic diffusion.

VACANCY DIFFUSION

One mechanism involves the interchange of an atom from a normal lattice position to an adjacent vacant lattice site or vacancy, as represented schematically in Figure 5.3a. This mechanism is aptly termed **vacancy diffusion.** Of course, this process necessitates the presence of vacancies, and the extent to which vacancy diffusion can occur is a function of the number of these defects that are present; significant concentrations of vacancies may exist in metals at elevated temperatures (Section 4.2). Since diffusing atoms and vacancies exchange positions, the diffusion of atoms in one direction corresponds to the motion of vacancies in the opposite direction. Both self-diffusion and interdiffusion occur by this mechanism; for the latter, the impurity atoms must substitute for host atoms.

FIGURE 5.3 Schematic representations of (*a*) vacancy diffusion and (*b*) interstitial diffusion.

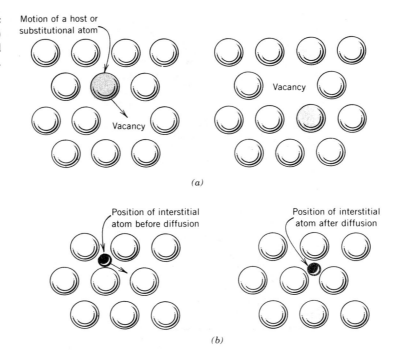

INTERSTITIAL DIFFUSION

The second type of diffusion involves atoms that migrate from an interstitial position to a neighboring one that is empty. This mechanism is found for interdiffusion of impurities such as hydrogen, carbon, nitrogen, and oxygen, which have atoms that are small enough to fit into the interstitial positions. Host or substitutional impurity atoms rarely form interstitials and do not normally diffuse via this mechanism. This phenomenon is appropriately termed **interstitial diffusion** (Figure 5.3*b*).

In most metal alloys, interstitial diffusion occurs much more rapidly than diffusion by the vacancy mode, since the interstitial atoms are smaller, and thus more mobile. Furthermore, there are more empty interstitial positions than vacancies; hence, the probability of interstitial atomic movement is greater than for vacancy diffusion.

5.3 STEADY-STATE DIFFUSION

Diffusion is a time-dependent process—that is, in a macroscopic sense, the quantity of an element that is transported within another is a function of time. Often it is necessary to know how fast diffusion occurs, or the rate of mass transfer. This rate is frequently expressed as a **diffusion flux** (J), defined as the mass (or, equivalently, the number of atoms) M diffusing through and perpendicular to a unit cross-sectional area of solid per unit of time. In mathematical form, this may be represented as

$$J = \frac{M}{At} \qquad\qquad (5.1a)$$

where A denotes the area across which diffusion is occurring and t is the elapsed diffusion time. In differential form, this expression becomes

$$J = \frac{1}{A}\frac{dM}{dt}$$ (5.1b)

The units for J are kilograms or atoms per meter squared per second (kg/m²-s or atoms/m²-s).

If the diffusion flux does not change with time, a steady-state condition exists. One common example of **steady-state diffusion** is the diffusion of atoms of a gas through a plate of metal for which the concentrations (or pressures) of the diffusing species on both surfaces of the plate are held constant. This is represented schematically in Figure 5.4a.

When concentration C is plotted versus position (or distance) within the solid x, the resulting curve is termed the **concentration profile;** the slope at a particular point on this curve is the **concentration gradient:**

$$\text{concentration gradient} = \frac{dC}{dx}$$ (5.2a)

In the present treatment, the concentration profile is assumed to be linear, as depicted in Figure 5.4b, and

$$\text{concentration gradient} = \frac{\Delta C}{\Delta x} = \frac{C_A - C_B}{x_A - x_B}$$ (5.2b)

For diffusion problems, it is sometimes convenient to express concentration in terms of mass of diffusing species per unit volume of solid (kg/m³ or g/cm³).[1]

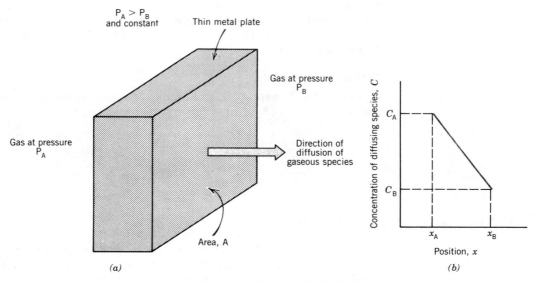

(a) *(b)*

FIGURE 5.4 *(a)* Steady-state diffusion across a thin plate. *(b)* A linear concentration profile for the diffusion situation in *(a)*.

---

[1] Conversion of concentration from weight percent to mass per unit volume (in kg/m³) is possible using Equation 4.9.

The mathematics of steady-state diffusion in a single (x) direction are relatively simple, in that the flux is proportional to the concentration gradient through the expression

$$J = -D \frac{dC}{dx} \tag{5.3}$$

The constant of proportionality D is called the **diffusion coefficient,** which is expressed in square meters per second. The negative sign in this expression indicates that the direction of diffusion is down the concentration gradient, from a high to a low concentration. Equation 5.3 is sometimes called **Fick's first law.**

Sometimes the term **driving force** is used in the context of what compels a reaction to occur. For diffusion reactions, several such forces are possible; but when diffusion is according to Equation 5.3, the concentration gradient is the driving force.

One practical example of steady-state diffusion is found in the purification of hydrogen gas. One side of a thin sheet of palladium metal is exposed to the impure gas composed of hydrogen and other gaseous species such as nitrogen, oxygen, and water vapor. The hydrogen selectively diffuses through the sheet to the opposite side, which is maintained at a constant and lower hydrogen pressure.

EXAMPLE PROBLEM 5.1

A plate of iron is exposed to a carburizing (carbon-rich) atmosphere on one side and a decarburizing (carbon-deficient) atmosphere on the other side at 700°C (1300°F). If a condition of steady state is achieved, calculate the diffusion flux of carbon through the plate if the concentrations of carbon at positions of 5 and 10 mm (5×10^{-3} and 10^{-2} m) beneath the carburizing surface are 1.2 and 0.8 kg/m^3, respectively. Assume a diffusion coefficient of 3×10^{-11} m^2/s at this temperature.

SOLUTION

Fick's first law, Equation 5.3, is utilized to determine the diffusion flux. Substitution of the values above into this expression yields

$$J = -D \frac{C_A - C_B}{x_A - x_B} = -(3 \times 10^{-11} \text{ m}^2/\text{s}) \frac{(1.2 - 0.8) \text{ kg/m}^3}{(5 \times 10^{-3} - 10^{-2}) \text{ m}}$$

$$= 2.4 \times 10^{-9} \text{ kg/m}^2\text{-s}$$

5.4 NONSTEADY-STATE DIFFUSION

Most practical diffusion situations are nonsteady-state ones. That is, the diffusion flux and the concentration gradient at some particular point in a solid vary with time, with a net accumulation or depletion of the diffusing species resulting. This is illustrated in Figure 5.5, which shows concentration profiles at three different diffusion times. Under conditions of nonsteady state, use of Equation 5.3 is no longer convenient; instead, the partial differential equation

$$\frac{\partial C}{\partial t} = \frac{\partial}{\partial x} \left(D \frac{\partial C}{\partial x} \right) \tag{5.4a}$$

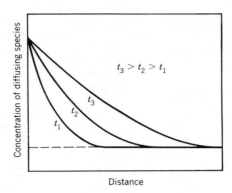

FIGURE 5.5 Concentration profiles for nonsteady-state diffusion taken at three different times, t_1, t_2, and t_3.

known as **Fick's second law,** is used. If the diffusion coefficient is independent of composition (which should be verified for each particular diffusion situation), Equation 5.4a simplifies to

$$\frac{\partial C}{\partial t} = D \frac{\partial^2 C}{\partial x^2}$$

(5.4b)

Solutions to this expression (concentration in terms of both position and time) are possible when physically meaningful boundary conditions are specified. Comprehensive collections of these are given by Crank, and Carslaw and Jaeger (see References).

One practically important solution is for a semi-infinite solid[2] in which the surface concentration is held constant. Frequently, the source of the diffusing species is a gas phase, the partial pressure of which is maintained at a constant value. Furthermore, the following assumptions are made:

1. Before diffusion, any of the diffusing solute atoms in the solid are uniformly distributed with concentration of C_0.
2. The value of x at the surface is zero and increases with distance into the solid.
3. The time is taken to be zero the instant before the diffusion process begins.

These boundary conditions are simply stated as

For $t = 0$, $C = C_0$ at $0 \leq x \leq \infty$

For $t > 0$, $C = C_s$ (the constant surface concentration) at $x = 0$

$C = C_0$ at $x = \infty$

Application of these boundary conditions to Equation 5.4b yields the solution

$$\frac{C_x - C_0}{C_s - C_0} = 1 - \mathrm{erf}\left(\frac{x}{2\sqrt{Dt}}\right)$$

(5.5)

---

[2] A bar of solid is considered to be semi-infinite if none of the diffusing atoms reaches the bar end during the time over which diffusion takes place. A bar of length l is considered to be semi-infinite when $l > 10\sqrt{Dt}$.

Table 5.1 Tabulation of Error Function Values

z	$erf(z)$	z	$erf(z)$	z	$erf(z)$
0	0	0.55	0.5633	1.3	0.9340
0.025	0.0282	0.60	0.6039	1.4	0.9523
0.05	0.0564	0.65	0.6420	1.5	0.9661
0.10	0.1125	0.70	0.6778	1.6	0.9763
0.15	0.1680	0.75	0.7112	1.7	0.9838
0.20	0.2227	0.80	0.7421	1.8	0.9891
0.25	0.2763	0.85	0.7707	1.9	0.9928
0.30	0.3286	0.90	0.7970	2.0	0.9953
0.35	0.3794	0.95	0.8209	2.2	0.9981
0.40	0.4284	1.0	0.8427	2.4	0.9993
0.45	0.4755	1.1	0.8802	2.6	0.9998
0.50	0.5205	1.2	0.9103	2.8	0.9999

where C_x represents the concentration at depth x after time t. The expression $erf(x/2\sqrt{Dt})$ is the Gaussian error function,[3] values of which are given in mathematical tables for various $x/2\sqrt{Dt}$ values; a partial listing is given in Table 5.1. The concentration parameters that appear in Equation 5.5 are noted in Figure 5.6, a concentration profile taken at a specific time. Equation 5.5 thus demonstrates the relationship between concentration, position, and time, namely, that C_x, being a function of the dimensionless parameter $x/\sqrt{Dt}$, may be determined at any time and position if the parameters C_0, C_s, and D are known.

Suppose that it is desired to achieve some specific concentration of solute, C_1, in an alloy; the left-hand side of Equation 5.5 now becomes

$$\frac{C_1 - C_0}{C_s - C_0} = \text{constant}$$

This being the case, the right-hand side of this same expression is also a constant, and subsequently

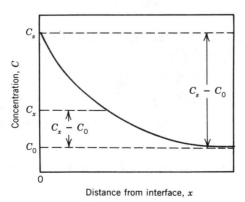

FIGURE 5.6 Concentration profile for nonsteady-state diffusion; concentration parameters relate to Equation 5.5.

---

[3] This Gaussian error function is defined by

$$\text{erf}(z) = \frac{2}{\sqrt{\pi}} \int_0^z e^{-y^2}\, dy$$

where $x/2\sqrt{Dt}$ has been replaced by the variable z.

$$\frac{x}{2\sqrt{Dt}} = \text{constant} \qquad\qquad (5.6a)$$

or

$$\frac{x^2}{Dt} = \text{constant} \qquad\qquad (5.6b)$$

Some diffusion computations are thus facilitated on the basis of this relationship, as demonstrated in Example Problem 5.3.

EXAMPLE PROBLEM 5.2

For some applications, it is necessary to harden the surface of a steel (or iron-carbon alloy) above that of its interior. One way this may be accomplished is by increasing the surface concentration of carbon in a process termed **carburizing;** the steel piece is exposed, at an elevated temperature, to an atmosphere rich in a hydrocarbon gas, such as methane (CH_4).

Consider one such alloy that initially has a uniform carbon concentration of 0.25 wt% and is to be treated at 950°C (1750°F). If the concentration of carbon at the surface is suddenly brought to and maintained at 1.20 wt%, how long will it take to achieve a carbon content of 0.80 wt% at a position 0.5 mm below the surface? The diffusion coefficient for carbon in iron at this temperature is 1.6×10^{-11} m^2/s; assume that the steel piece is semi-infinite.

SOLUTION

Since this is a nonsteady-state diffusion problem in which the surface composition is held constant, Equation 5.5 is used. Values for all the parameters in this expression except time t are specified in the problem as follows:

$$C_0 = 0.25 \text{ wt\% C}$$

$$C_s = 1.20 \text{ wt\% C}$$

$$C_x = 0.80 \text{ wt\% C}$$

$$x = 0.50 \text{ mm} = 5 \times 10^{-4} \text{ m}$$

$$D = 1.6 \times 10^{-11} \text{ m}^2/\text{s}$$

Thus,

$$\frac{C_x - C_0}{C_s - C_0} = \frac{0.80 - 0.25}{1.20 - 0.25} = 1 - \text{erf}\left[\frac{(5 \times 10^{-4} \text{ m})}{2\sqrt{(1.6 \times 10^{-11} \text{ m}^2/\text{s})(t)}}\right]$$

$$0.4210 = \text{erf}\left(\frac{62.5 \text{ s}^{1/2}}{\sqrt{t}}\right)$$

We must now determine from Table 5.1 the value of z for which the error function is 0.4210. An interpolation is necessary, as

z	erf(z)
0.35	0.3794
z	0.4210
0.40	0.4284

$$\frac{z - 0.35}{0.40 - 0.35} = \frac{0.4210 - 0.3794}{0.4284 - 0.3794}$$

or

$$z = 0.392$$

Therefore,

$$\frac{62.5 \text{ s}^{1/2}}{\sqrt{t}} = 0.392$$

and solving for t,

$$t = \left(\frac{62.5 \text{ s}^{1/2}}{0.392}\right)^2 = 25{,}400 \text{ s} = 7.1 \text{ h}$$

EXAMPLE PROBLEM 5.3

The diffusion coefficients for copper in aluminum at 500 and 600°C are 4.8×10^{-14} and 5.3×10^{-13} m^2/s, respectively. Determine the approximate time at 500°C that will produce the same diffusion result (in terms of concentration of Cu at some specific point in Al) as a 10-h heat treatment at 600°C.

SOLUTION

This is a diffusion problem in which Equation 5.6b may be employed. The composition in both diffusion situations will be equal at the same position (i.e., x is also a constant), thus

$$Dt = \text{constant} \tag{5.7}$$

at both temperatures. That is,

$$(Dt)_{500} = (Dt)_{600}$$

or

$$t_{500} = \frac{(Dt)_{600}}{D_{500}} = \frac{(5.3 \times 10^{-13} \text{ m}^2/\text{s})(10 \text{ h})}{4.8 \times 10^{-14} \text{ m}^2/\text{s}} = 110.4 \text{ h}$$

5.5 FACTORS THAT INFLUENCE DIFFUSION

DIFFUSING SPECIES

The magnitude of the diffusion coefficient D is indicative of the rate at which atoms diffuse. Coefficients, both self- and interdiffusion, for several metallic systems are listed in Table 5.2. The diffusing species as well as the host material influence the diffusion coefficient. For example, there is a significant difference in magnitude between self- and carbon interdiffusion in α iron at 500°C, the D value being greater for the carbon interdiffusion (3.0×10^{-21} vs. 2.4×10^{-12} m^2/s). This comparison also provides a contrast between rates of diffusion via vacancy and interstitial modes as discussed above. Self-diffusion occurs by a vacancy mechanism, whereas carbon diffusion in iron is interstitial.

TEMPERATURE

Temperature has a most profound influence on the coefficients and diffusion rates. For example, for the self-diffusion of Fe in α-Fe, the diffusion coefficient increases approximately six orders of magnitude (from 3.0×10^{-21} to 1.8×10^{-15} m^2/s) in rising temperature from 500 to 900°C (Table 5.2). The temperature dependence of diffusion coefficients is related to temperature according to

$$D = D_0 \exp\left(-\frac{Q_d}{RT}\right) \tag{5.8}$$

where

D_0 = a temperature-independent preexponential (m^2/s)

Q_d = the **activation energy** for diffusion (J/mol, cal/mol, or eV/atom)

R = the gas constant, 8.31 J/mol-K, 1.987 cal/mol-K, or 8.62×10^{-5} eV/atom

T = absolute temperature (K)

The activation energy may be thought of as that energy required to produce the diffusive motion of one mole of atoms. A large activation energy results in a relatively small diffusion coefficient. Table 5.2 also contains a listing of D_0 and Q_d values for several diffusion systems.

Taking natural logarithms of Equation 5.8 yields

$$\ln D = \ln D_0 - \frac{Q_d}{R}\left(\frac{1}{T}\right) \tag{5.9a}$$

Or in terms of logarithms to the base 10

$$\log D = \log D_0 - \frac{Q_d}{2.3R}\left(\frac{1}{T}\right) \tag{5.9b}$$

Table 5.2   A Tabulation of Diffusion Data

Diffusing Species	Host Metal	$D_0 (m^2/s)$	Activation Energy Q_d kJ/mol	Activation Energy Q_d eV/atom	Calculated Values $T(°C)$	Calculated Values $D(m^2/s)$
Fe	α-Fe (BCC)	2.8×10^{-4}	251	2.60	500	3.0×10^{-21}
					900	1.8×10^{-15}
Fe	γ-Fe (FCC)	5.0×10^{-5}	284	2.94	900	1.1×10^{-17}
					1100	7.8×10^{-16}
C	α-Fe	6.2×10^{-7}	80	0.83	500	2.4×10^{-12}
					900	1.7×10^{-10}
C	γ-Fe	2.3×10^{-5}	148	1.53	900	5.9×10^{-12}
					1100	5.3×10^{-11}
Cu	Cu	7.8×10^{-5}	211	2.19	500	4.2×10^{-19}
Zn	Cu	2.4×10^{-5}	189	1.96	500	4.0×10^{-18}
Al	Al	2.3×10^{-4}	144	1.49	500	4.2×10^{-14}
Cu	Al	6.5×10^{-5}	136	1.41	500	4.1×10^{-14}
Mg	Al	1.2×10^{-4}	131	1.35	500	1.9×10^{-13}
Cu	Ni	2.7×10^{-5}	256	2.65	500	1.3×10^{-22}

Source: E. A. Brandes and G. B. Brook (Editors), *Smithells Metals Reference Book,* 7th edition, Butterworth-Heinemann, Oxford, 1992.

FIGURE 5.7 Plot of the logarithm of the diffusion coefficient versus the reciprocal of absolute temperature for several metals. [Data taken from E. A. Brandes and G. B. Brook, (Editors), *Smithells Metals Reference Book,* 7th edition, Butterworth-Heinemann, Oxford, 1992.]

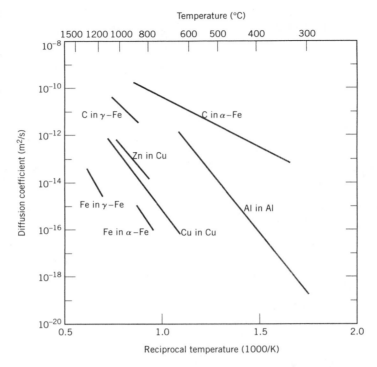

Since D_0, Q_d, and R are all constants, Equation 5.9b takes on the form of an equation of a straight line:

$$y = b + mx$$

where y and x are analogous, respectively, to the variables log D and $1/T$. Thus, if log D is plotted versus the reciprocal of the absolute temperature, a straight line should result, having slope and intercept of $-Q_d/2.3R$ and log D_0, respectively. This is, in fact, the manner in which the values of Q_d and D_0 are determined experimentally. From such a plot for several alloy systems (Figure 5.7), it may be noted that linear relationships exist for all cases shown.

EXAMPLE PROBLEM 5.4

Using the data in Table 5.2, compute the diffusion coefficient for magnesium in aluminum at 550°C.

SOLUTION

This diffusion coefficient may be determined by applying Equation 5.8; the values of D_0 and Q_d from Table 5.2 are 1.2×10^{-4} m²/s and 131 kJ/mol, respectively. Thus,

$$D = (1.2 \times 10^{-4}\,\text{m}^2/\text{s}) \exp\left[-\frac{(131{,}000\,\text{J/mol})}{(8.31\,\text{J/mol-K})(550 + 273\,\text{K})} \right]$$

$$= 5.8 \times 10^{-13}\,\text{m}^2/\text{s}$$

EXAMPLE PROBLEM 5.5

In Figure 5.8 is shown a plot of the logarithm (to the base 10) of the diffusion coefficient versus reciprocal of absolute temperature, for the diffusion of copper in gold. Determine values for the activation energy and the preexponential.

SOLUTION

From Equation 5.9b the slope of the line segment in Figure 5.8 is equal to $-Q_d/2.3R$, and the intercept at $1/T = 0$ gives the value of $\log D_0$. Thus, the activation energy may be determined as

$$Q_d = -2.3R \text{ (slope)} = -2.3R \left[\frac{\Delta (\log D)}{\Delta \left(\dfrac{1}{T} \right)} \right]$$

$$= -2.3R \left[\frac{\log D_1 - \log D_2}{\dfrac{1}{T_1} - \dfrac{1}{T_2}} \right]$$

where D_1 and D_2 are the diffusion coefficient values at $1/T_1$ and $1/T_2$, respectively. Let us arbitrarily take $1/T_1 = 0.8 \times 10^{-3}$ (K)$^{-1}$ and $1/T_2 = 1.1 \times 10^{-3}$ (K)$^{-1}$. We may now read the corresponding $\log D_1$ and $\log D_2$ values from the line segment in Figure 5.8.

[Before this is done, however, a parenthetic note of caution is offered. The vertical axis in Figure 5.8 is scaled logarithmically (to the base 10); however, the actual diffusion coefficient values are noted on this axis. For example, for $D = 10^{-14}$ m^2/s, the logarithm of D is -14.0 *not* 10^{-14}. Furthermore, this logarithmic scaling affects the readings between decade values; for example, at a location midway between 10^{-14} and 10^{-15}, the value is not 5×10^{-15}, but rather, $10^{-14.5} = 3.2 \times 10^{-15}$].

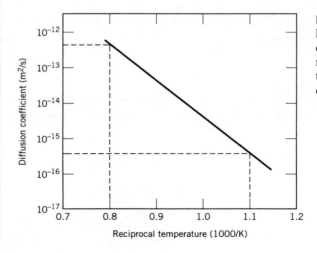

FIGURE 5.8 Plot of the logarithm of the diffusion coefficient versus the reciprocal of absolute temperature for the diffusion of copper in gold.

Thus, from Figure 5.8, at $1/T_1 = 0.8 \times 10^{-3}$ (K)$^{-1}$, log $D_1 = -12.40$, while for $1/T_2 = 1.1 \times 10^{-3}$ (K)$^{-1}$, log $D_2 = -15.45$, and the slope of the line segment in Figure 5.8 is

$$Q_d = -2.3R \left[\frac{\log D_1 - \log D_2}{\dfrac{1}{T_1} - \dfrac{1}{T_2}} \right]$$

$$= -2.3 \,(8.31 \text{ J/mol-K}) \left[\frac{-12.40 - (-15.45)}{0.8 \times 10^{-3} \text{ (K)}^{-1} - 1.1 \times 10^{-3} \text{ (K)}^{-1}} \right]$$

$$= 194{,}000 \text{ J/mol} = 194 \text{ kJ/mol}$$

Now, rather than trying to make a graphical extrapolation to determine D_0, a more accurate value is obtained analytically using Equation 5.9b, and a specific value of D (or log D) and its corresponding T (or $1/T$) from Figure 5.8. Since we know that log $D = -15.45$ at $1/T = 1.1 \times 10^{-3}$ (K)$^{-1}$, then

$$\log D_0 = \log D + \frac{Q_d}{2.3R} \left(\frac{1}{T} \right)$$

$$= -15.45 + \frac{(194{,}000 \text{ J/mol})(1.1 \times 10^{-3} \text{ [K]}^{-1})}{(2.3)(8.31 \text{ J/mol-K})}$$

$$= -4.28$$

Thus, $D_0 = 10^{-4.28} \text{ m}^2/\text{s} = 5.2 \times 10^{-5} \text{ m}^2/\text{s}$.

DESIGN EXAMPLE 5.1

The wear resistance of a steel gear is to be improved by hardening its surface. This is to be accomplished by increasing the carbon content within an outer surface layer as a result of carbon diffusion into the steel; the carbon is to be supplied from an external carbon-rich gaseous atmosphere at an elevated and constant temperature. The initial carbon content of the steel is 0.20 wt%, whereas the surface concentration is to be maintained at 1.00 wt%. In order for this treatment to be effective, a carbon content of 0.60 wt% must be established at a position 0.75 mm below the surface. Specify an appropriate heat treatment in terms of temperature and time for temperatures between 900°C and 1050°C. Use data in Table 5.2 for the diffusion of carbon in γ-iron.

SOLUTION

Since this is a nonsteady-state diffusion situation, let us first of all employ Equation 5.5, utilizing the following values for the concentration parameters:

$$C_0 = 0.20 \text{ wt\% C}$$

$$C_s = 1.00 \text{ wt\% C}$$

$$C_x = 0.60 \text{ wt\% C}$$

Therefore

$$\frac{C_x - C_0}{C_s - C_0} = \frac{0.60 - 0.20}{1.00 - 0.20} = 1 - \text{erf} \left(\frac{x}{2\sqrt{Dt}} \right)$$

And thus

$$0.5 = \operatorname{erf}\left(\frac{x}{2\sqrt{Dt}}\right)$$

Using an interpolation technique as demonstrated in Example Problem 5.2 and the data presented in Table 5.1

$$\frac{x}{2\sqrt{Dt}} = 0.4747 \qquad (5.10)$$

The problem stipulates that $x = 0.75$ mm $= 7.5 \times 10^{-4}$ m. Therefore

$$\frac{7.5 \times 10^{-4}\,\text{m}}{2\sqrt{Dt}} = 0.4747$$

Which leads to

$$Dt = 6.24 \times 10^{-7}\,\text{m}^2$$

Furthermore, the diffusion coefficient depends on temperature according to Equation 5.8; and, from Table 5.2 for the diffusion of carbon in γ-iron, $D_0 = 2.3 \times 10^{-5}$ m^2/s and $Q_d = 148{,}000$ J/mol. Hence

$$Dt = D_0 \exp\left(-\frac{Q_d}{RT}\right)(t) = 6.24 \times 10^{-7}\,\text{m}^2$$

$$(2.3 \times 10^{-5}\,\text{m}^2/\text{s}) \exp\left[-\frac{148{,}000\,\text{J/mol}}{(8.31\,\text{J/mol-K})(T)}\right](t) = 6.24 \times 10^{-7}\,\text{m}^2$$

And solving for the time t

$$t\,(\text{in s}) = \frac{0.0271}{\exp\left(-\dfrac{17{,}810}{T}\right)}$$

Thus, the required diffusion time may be computed for some specified temperature (in K). Below are tabulated t values for four different temperatures that lie within the range stipulated in the problem.

Temperature (°C)	Time	
	s	h
900	106,400	29.6
950	57,200	15.9
1000	32,300	9.0
1050	19,000	5.3

5.6 OTHER DIFFUSION PATHS

Atomic migration may also occur along dislocations, grain boundaries, and external surfaces. These are sometimes called *"short-circuit" diffusion paths* inasmuch as rates are much faster than for bulk diffusion. However, in most situations short-circuit contributions to the overall diffusion flux are insignificant because the cross-sectional areas of these paths are extremely small.

SUMMARY

Solid-state diffusion is a means of mass transport within solid materials by stepwise atomic motion. The term "self-diffusion" refers to the migration of host atoms; for impurity atoms, the term "interdiffusion" is used. Two mechanisms are possible: vacancy and interstitial. For a given host metal, interstitial atomic species generally diffuse more rapidly.

For steady-state diffusion, the concentration profile of the diffusing species is time independent, and the flux or rate is proportional to the negative of the concentration gradient according to Fick's first law. The mathematics for nonsteady state are described by Fick's second law, a partial differential equation. The solution for a constant surface composition boundary condition involves the Gaussian error function.

The magnitude of the diffusion coefficient is indicative of the rate of atomic motion, being strongly dependent on and increasing exponentially with increasing temperature.

IMPLICATIONS

Some properties of materials (e.g., hardness and strength) are subject to alteration and improvement as a result of transformations that involve atomic diffusion; diffusion path lengths are often microscopic in magnitude (i.e., on the order of microns). For these transformations to occur over reasonable time periods (usually on the order of hours), they are ordinarily carried out at elevated temperatures at which diffusion rates are comparatively rapid. An alteration of the microstructure attends many of these transformations, and, having a knowledge of the diffusion phenomenon, is essential in understanding the transformation mechanisms (e.g., see Sections 9.6, 9.7, and 9.14). These high-temperature procedures, often termed *heat treatments,* are utilized at least once during the production of almost all common metallic, ceramic, and polymeric materials. For example, the strength of some steels is reliant on appropriate heat treatments (Chapter 11), as is also the mechanical integrity of many ceramics (Section 14.15).

Furthermore, during the processing of some materials, compositional alterations may occur as a result of mass transport from external sources (e.g., case hardening, Section 8.11). Heat-treating temperatures and times may be predicted using the mathematics of diffusion (i.e., solutions to Fick's second law) in conjunction with appropriate diffusion coefficient values.

IMPORTANT TERMS AND CONCEPTS

Activation energy
Carburizing
Concentration gradient
Concentration profile
Diffusion
Diffusion coefficient

Diffusion flux
Driving force
Fick's first and second laws
Interdiffusion (impurity diffusion)

Interstitial diffusion
Nonsteady-state diffusion
Self-diffusion
Steady-state diffusion
Vacancy diffusion

REFERENCES

Borg, R. J. and G. J. Dienes (Editors), *An Introduction to Solid State Diffusion,* Academic Press, San Diego, 1988.

Brandes, E. A. and G. B. Brook (Editors), *Smithells Metals Reference Book,* 7th edition, Butterworth-Heinemann Ltd., Oxford, 1992.

Carslaw, H. S. and J. C. Jaeger, *Conduction of Heat in Solids,* 2nd edition, Clarendon Press, Oxford, 1986.

Crank, J., *The Mathematics of Diffusion,* 2nd edition, Clarendon Press, Oxford, 1980.

Girifalco, L. A., *Atomic Migration In Crystals,* Blaisdell Publishing Company, New York, 1964.

Shewmon, P. G., *Diffusion in Solids,* McGraw-Hill Book Company, New York, 1963. Reprinted by The Minerals, Metals and Materials Society, Warrendale, PA, 1989.

QUESTIONS AND PROBLEMS

5.1 Briefly explain the difference between self-diffusion and interdiffusion.

5.2 Self-diffusion involves the motion of atoms that are all of the same type; therefore it is not subject to observation by compositional changes, as with interdiffusion. Suggest one way in which self-diffusion may be monitored.

5.3 **(a)** Compare interstitial and vacancy atomic mechanisms for diffusion.

(b) Cite two reasons why interstitial diffusion is normally more rapid than vacancy diffusion.

5.4 Briefly explain the concept of steady state as it applies to diffusion.

5.5 **(a)** Briefly explain the concept of a driving force.

(b) What is the driving force for steady-state diffusion?

5.6 The purification of hydrogen gas by diffusion through a palladium sheet was discussed in Section 5.3. Compute the number of kilograms of hydrogen that pass per hour through a 6-mm-thick sheet of palladium having an area of 0.25 m^2 at 600°C. Assume a diffusion coefficient of 1.7×10^{-8} m^2/s, that the concentrations at the high- and low-pressure sides of the plate are 2.0 and 0.4 kg of hydrogen per cubic meter of palladium, and that steady-state conditions have been attained.

5.7 A sheet of steel 2.5 mm thick has nitrogen atmospheres on both sides at 900°C and is permitted to achieve a steady-state diffusion condition. The diffusion coefficient for nitrogen in steel at this temperature is 1.2×10^{-10} m^2/s, and the diffusion flux is found to be 1.0×10^{-7} kg/m^2-s. Also, it is known that the concentration of nitrogen in the steel at the high-pressure surface is 2 kg/m^3. How far into

the sheet from this high-pressure side will the concentration be 0.5 kg/m^3? Assume a linear concentration profile.

5.8 A sheet of BCC iron 2 mm thick was exposed to a carburizing gas atmosphere on one side and a decarburizing atmosphere on the other side at 675°C. After having reached steady state, the iron was quickly cooled to room temperature. The carbon concentrations at the two surfaces of the sheet were determined to be 0.015 and 0.0068 wt%. Compute the diffusion coefficient if the diffusion flux is 7.36×10^{-9} kg/m^2-s. *Hint:* Use Equation 4.9 to convert the concentrations from weight percent to kilograms of carbon per cubic meter of iron.

5.9 Show that Fick's second law (Equation 5.4b) takes on the form of Fick's first law (Equation 5.3) for conditions of steady state, that is,

$$\frac{\partial C}{\partial t} = 0$$

5.10 Show that

$$C_x = \frac{B}{\sqrt{Dt}} \exp\left(-\frac{x^2}{4Dt}\right)$$

is also a solution to Equation 5.4b. The parameter B is a constant, being independent of both x and t.

5.11 Determine the carburizing time necessary to achieve a carbon concentration of 0.30 wt% at a position 4 mm into an iron–carbon alloy that initially contains 0.10 wt% C. The surface concentration is to be maintained at 0.90 wt% C, and the treatment is to be conducted at 1100°C. Use the diffusion data for γ-Fe in Table 5.2.

5.12 An FCC iron–carbon alloy initially containing 0.35 wt% C is exposed to an oxygen-rich and virtually carbon-free atmosphere at 1400 K (1127°C). Under these circumstances the carbon diffuses from the alloy and reacts at the surface with the oxygen in the atmosphere; that is, the carbon concentration at the surface position is maintained essentially at 0 wt% C. (This process of carbon depletion is termed *decarburization.*) At what position will the carbon concentration be 0.15 wt% after a 10-h treatment? The value of D at 1400 K is 6.9×10^{-11} m²/s.

5.13 Nitrogen from a gaseous phase is to be diffused into pure iron at 675°C. If the surface concentration is maintained at 0.2 wt% N, what will be the concentration 2 mm from the surface after 25 h? The diffusion coefficient for nitrogen in iron at 675°C is 1.9×10^{-11} m²/s.

5.14 Simplify Equation 5.5 for the situation when C_x is halfway between C_s and C_0.

5.15 For a steel alloy it has been determined that a carburizing heat treatment of 15 h duration will raise the carbon concentration to 0.35 wt% at a point 2.0 mm from the surface. Estimate the time necessary to achieve the same concentration at a 6.0-mm position for an identical steel and at the same carburizing temperature.

5.16 Cite the values of the diffusion coefficients for the interdiffusion of carbon in both α-iron (BCC) and γ-iron (FCC) at 900°C. Which is larger? Explain why this is the case.

5.17 Using the data in Table 5.2, compute the value of D for the diffusion of magnesium in aluminum at 400°C.

5.18 At what temperature will the diffusion coefficient for the diffusion of zinc in copper have a value of 2.6×10^{-16} m²/s? Use the diffusion data in Table 5.2.

5.19 The preexponential and activation energy for the diffusion of iron in cobalt are 1.1×10^{-5} m²/s and 253,300 J/mol, respectively. At what temperature will the diffusion coefficient have a value of 2.1×10^{-14} m²/s?

5.20 The activation energy for the diffusion of carbon in chromium is 111,000 J/mol. Calculate the diffusion coefficient at 1100 K (827°C), given that D at 1400 K (1127°C) is 6.25×10^{-11} m²/s.

5.21 The diffusion coefficients for nickel in iron are given at two temperatures:

$T(K)$	$D(m^2/s)$
1473	2.2×10^{-15}
1673	4.8×10^{-14}

(a) Determine the values of D_0 and the activation energy Q_d.
(b) What is the magnitude of the D at 1300°C (1573 K)?

5.22 The diffusion coefficients for silver in copper are given at two temperatures:

$T(°C)$	$D(m^2/s)$
650	5.5×10^{-16}
900	1.3×10^{-13}

(a) Determine the values of D_0 and Q_d.
(b) What is the magnitude of D at 875°C?

5.23 Below is shown a plot of the logarithm (to the base 10) of the diffusion coefficient versus reciprocal of the absolute temperature, for the diffusion of iron in chromium. Determine values for the activation energy and preexponential.

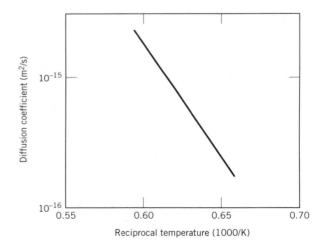

5.24 Carbon is allowed to diffuse through a steel plate 15 mm thick. The concentrations of carbon at the two faces are 0.65 and 0.30 kg C/m³ Fe, which are maintained constant. If the preexponential and activation energy are

6.2×10^{-7} m²/s and 80,000 J/mol, respectively, compute the temperature at which the diffusion flux is 1.43×10^{-9} kg/m²-s.

5.25 The steady-state diffusion flux through a metal plate is 5.4×10^{-10} kg/m²-s at a temperature of 727°C (1000 K) and when the concentration gradient is -350 kg/m⁴. Calculate the diffusion flux at 1027°C (1300 K) for the same concentration gradient and assuming an activation energy for diffusion of 125,000 J/mol.

5.26 At approximately what temperature would a specimen of γ-iron have to be carburized for 4 h to produce the same diffusion result as at 1000°C for 12 h?

5.27 (a) Calculate the diffusion coefficient for magnesium in aluminum at 450°C.
(b) What time will be required at 550°C to produce the same diffusion result (in terms of concentration at a specific point) as for 15 h at 450°C?

5.28 A copper-nickel diffusion couple similar to that shown in Figure 5.1a is fashioned. After a 700-h heat treatment at 1100°C (1373 K) the concentration of Cu is 2.5 wt% at the 3.0-mm position within the nickel. At what temperature must the diffusion couple need to be heated to produce this same concentration (i.e., 2.5 wt% Cu) at a 2.0 mm-position after 700 h? The preexponential and activation energy for the diffusion of Cu in Ni are given in Table 5.2.

5.29 A diffusion couple similar to that shown in Figure 5.1a is prepared using two hypothetical metals A and B. After a 30-h heat treatment at 1000 K (and subsequently cooling to room temperature) the concentration of A in B is 3.2 wt% at the 15.5-mm position within metal B. If another heat treatment is conducted on an identical diffusion couple, only at 800 K for 30 h, at what position will the composition be 3.2 wt% A? Assume that the preexponential and activation energy for the diffusion coefficient are 1.8×10^{-5} m²/s and 152,000 J/mol, respectively.

5.30 The outer surface of a steel gear is to be hardened by increasing its carbon content. The carbon is to be supplied from an external carbon-rich atmosphere, which is maintained at an elevated temperature. A diffusion heat treatment at 850°C (1123 K) for 10 min increases the carbon concentration to 0.90 wt% at a position 1.0 mm below the surface. Estimate the diffusion time required at 650°C (923 K) to achieve this same concentration also at a 1.0-mm position. Assume that the surface carbon content is the same for both heat treatments, which is maintained constant. Use the diffusion data in Table 5.2 for C diffusion in α-Fe.

5.31 An FCC iron-carbon alloy initially containing 0.20 wt% C is carburized at an elevated temperature and in an atmosphere wherein the surface carbon concentration is maintained at 1.0 wt%. If after 49.5 h the concentration of carbon is 0.35 wt% at a position 4.0 mm below the surface, determine the temperature at which the treatment was carried out.

Design Problem

5.D1 The wear resistance of a steel shaft is to be improved by hardening its surface. This is to be accomplished by increasing the nitrogen content within an outer surface layer as a result of nitrogen diffusion into the steel. The nitrogen is to be supplied from an external nitrogen-rich gas at an elevated and constant temperature. The initial nitrogen content of the steel is 0.002 wt%, whereas the surface concentration is to be maintained at 0.50 wt%. In order for this treatment to be effective, a nitrogen content of 0.10 wt% must be established at a position 0.40 mm below the surface. Specify appropriate heat treatments in terms of temperature and time for temperatures between 475°C and 625°C. The preexponential and activation energy for the diffusion of nitrogen in iron are 3×10^{-7} m²/s and 76,150 J/mol, respectively, over this temperature range.

6

Mechanical Properties of Metals

A modern Rockwell hardness tester. (Photograph courtesy of Wilson Instruments Division, Instron Corporation, originator of the Rockwell® Hardness Tester.)

6.1 INTRODUCTION

Many materials, when in service, are subjected to forces or loads; examples include the aluminum alloy from which an airplane wing is constructed and the steel in an automobile axle. In such situations it is necessary to know the characteristics of the material and to design the member from which it is made such that any resulting deformation will not be excessive and fracture will not occur. The mechanical behavior of a material reflects the relationship between its response or deformation to an applied load or force. Important mechanical properties are strength, hardness, ductility, and stiffness.

The mechanical properties of materials are ascertained by performing carefully designed laboratory experiments that replicate as nearly as possible the service conditions. Factors to be considered include the nature of the applied load and its duration, as well as the environmental conditions. It is possible for the load to be tensile, compressive, or shear, and its magnitude may be constant with time, or it may fluctuate continuously. Application time may be for only a fraction of a second, or it may extend over a period of many years. Service temperature may be an important factor.

Mechanical properties are of concern to a variety of parties (e.g., producers and consumers of materials, research organizations, government agencies) that have differing interests. Consequently, it is imperative that there be some consistency in the manner in which tests are conducted, and in the interpretation of their results. This consistency is accomplished by using standardized testing techniques. Establishment and publication of these standards are often coordinated by professional societies. In the United States the most active organization is the American Society for Testing and Materials (ASTM). Its *Annual Book of ASTM Standards* comprises numerous volumes, which are issued and updated yearly; a large number of these standards relate to mechanical testing techniques. Several of these are referenced by footnote in this and subsequent chapters.

The role of structural engineers is to determine stresses and stress distributions within members that are subjected to well-defined loads. This may be accomplished by experimental testing techniques and/or by theoretical and mathematical stress analyses. These topics are treated in traditional stress analysis and strength of materials texts.

Materials and metallurgical engineers, on the other hand, are concerned with producing and fabricating materials to meet service requirements as predicted by these stress analyses. This necessarily involves an understanding of the relationships between the microstructure (i.e., internal features) of materials and their mechanical properties.

Materials are frequently chosen for structural applications because they have desirable combinations of mechanical characteristics. The present discussion is confined primarily to the mechanical behavior of metals; polymers and ceramics are treated separately because they are, to a large degree, mechanically dissimilar to metals. This chapter discusses the stress–strain behavior of metals and the related mechanical properties, and also examines other important mechanical characteristics. Discussions of the microscopic aspects of deformation mechanisms and methods to strengthen and regulate the mechanical behavior of metals are deferred to later chapters.

6.2 CONCEPTS OF STRESS AND STRAIN

If a load is static or changes relatively slowly with time and is applied uniformly over a cross section or surface of a member, the mechanical behavior may be ascertained by a simple stress–strain test; these are most commonly conducted for metals at room temperature. There are three principal ways in which a load may be applied: namely, tension, compression, and shear (Figures 6.1a, b, c). In engineering practice many loads are torsional rather than pure shear; this type of loading is illustrated in Figure 6.1d.

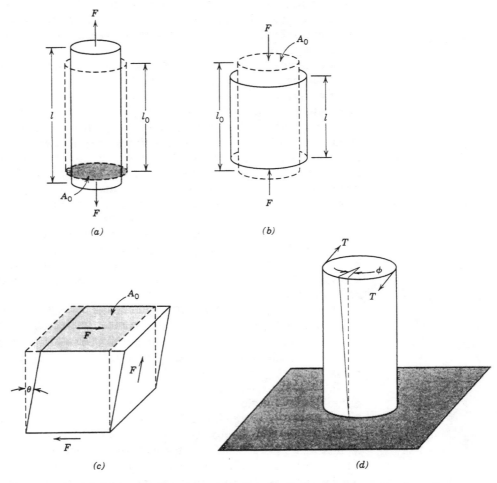

FIGURE 6.1   (a) Schematic illustration of how a tensile load produces an elongation and positive linear strain. Dashed lines represent the shape before deformation; solid lines, after deformation. (b) Schematic illustration of how a compressive load produces contraction and a negative linear strain. (c) Schematic representation of shear strain γ, where $\gamma = \tan \theta$. (d) Schematic representation of torsional deformation (i.e., angle of twist ϕ) produced by an applied torque T.

TENSION TESTS[1]

One of the most common mechanical stress–strain tests is performed in *tension*. As will be seen, the tension test can be used to ascertain several mechanical properties of materials that are important in design. A specimen is deformed, usually to fracture, with a gradually increasing tensile load that is applied uniaxially along the long axis of a specimen. A standard tensile specimen is shown in Figure 6.2. Normally, the cross section is circular, but rectangular specimens are also used. During testing, deformation is confined to the narrow center region, which has a uniform cross section along its length. The standard diameter is approximately 12.8 mm (0.5 in.), whereas the reduced section length should be at least four times this diameter; 60 mm (2¼ in.) is common. Gauge length is used in ductility computations, as discussed in Section 6.6; the standard value is 50 mm (2.0 in.). The specimen is mounted by its ends into the holding grips of the testing apparatus (Figure 6.3). The tensile testing machine is designed to elongate the specimen at a constant rate, and to continuously and simultaneously measure the instantaneous applied load (with a load cell) and the resulting elongations (using an extensometer). A stress–strain test typically takes several minutes to perform and is destructive; that is, the test specimen is permanently deformed and usually fractured.

The output of such a tensile test is recorded on a strip chart as load or force versus elongation. These load–deformation characteristics are dependent on the specimen size. For example, it will require twice the load to produce the same elongation if the cross-sectional area of the specimen is doubled. To minimize these geometrical factors, load and elongation are normalized to the respective parameters of **engineering stress** and **engineering strain.** Engineering stress σ is defined by the relationship

$$\sigma = \frac{F}{A_0} \tag{6.1}$$

in which F is the instantaneous load applied perpendicular to the specimen cross section, in units of newtons (N) or pounds force (lb$_f$), and A_0 is the original cross-sectional area before any load is applied (m^2 or in.^{2}). The units of engineering stress (referred to subsequently as just stress) are megapascals, MPa (SI) (where 1 MPa = 10^6 N/m^2), and pounds force per square inch, psi (Customary U.S.).[2]

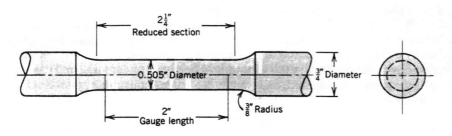

FIGURE 6.2 A standard tensile specimen with circular cross section.

---

[1] ASTM Standards E 8 and E 8M, "Standard Test Methods for Tension Testing of Metallic Materials."

[2] Conversion from one system of stress units to the other is accomplished by the relationship

145 psi = 1 MPa

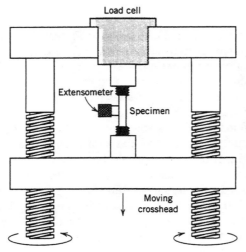

Load cell

Extensometer

Specimen

Moving
crosshead

FIGURE 6.3 Schematic representation of the apparatus used to conduct tensile stress–strain tests. The specimen is elongated by the moving crosshead; load cell and extensometer measure, respectively, the magnitude of the applied load and the elongation. (Adapted from H. W. Hayden, W. G. Moffatt, and J. Wulff, *The Structure and Properties of Materials,* Vol. III, *Mechanical Behavior,* p. 2. Copyright © 1965 by John Wiley & Sons, New York. Reprinted by permission of John Wiley & Sons, Inc.)

Engineering strain ϵ is defined according to

$$\epsilon = \frac{l_i - l_0}{l_0} = \frac{\Delta l}{l_0} \tag{6.2}$$

in which l_0 is the original length before any load is applied, and l_i is the instantaneous length. Sometimes the quantity $l_i - l_0$ is denoted as Δl, and is the deformation elongation or change in length at some instant, as referenced to the original length. Engineering strain (subsequently called just strain) is unitless, but meters per meter or inches per inch are often used; the value of strain is obviously independent of the unit system. Sometimes strain is also expressed as a percentage, in which the strain value is multiplied by 100.

COMPRESSION TESTS[3]

Compression stress–strain tests may be conducted if in-service forces are of this type. A compression test is conducted in a manner similar to the tensile test, except that the force is compressive and the specimen contracts along the direction of the stress. Equations 6.1 and 6.2 are utilized to compute compressive stress and strain, respectively. By convention, a compressive force is taken to be negative, which yields a negative stress. Furthermore, since l_0 is greater than l_i, compressive strains computed from Equation 6.2 are necessarily also negative. Tensile tests are more common because they are easier to perform; also, for most materials used in structural applications, very little additional information is obtained from compressive tests. Compressive tests are used when a material's behavior under large and permanent (i.e., plastic) strains is desired, as in manufacturing applications, or when the material is brittle in tension.

SHEAR AND TORSIONAL TESTS[4]

For tests performed using a pure shear force as shown in Figure 6.1c, the shear stress τ is computed according to

---

[3] ASTM Standard E 9, "Standard Test Methods of Compression Testing of Metallic Materials at Room Temperature."

[4] ASTM Standard E 143, "Standard Test for Shear Modulus."

$$\tau = \frac{F}{A_0} \tag{6.3}$$

where F is the load or force imposed parallel to the upper and lower faces, each of which has an area of A_0. The shear strain γ is defined as the tangent of the strain angle θ, as indicated in the figure. The units for shear stress and strain are the same as for their tensile counterparts.

Torsion is a variation of pure shear, wherein a structural member is twisted in the manner of Figure 6.1d; torsional forces produce a rotational motion about the longitudinal axis of one end of the member relative to the other end. Examples of torsion are found for machine axles and drive shafts, and also for twist drills. Torsional tests are normally performed on cylindrical solid shafts or tubes. A shear stress τ is a function of the applied torque T, whereas shear strain γ is related to the angle of twist, ϕ in Figure 6.1d.

ELASTIC DEFORMATION

6.3 STRESS–STRAIN BEHAVIOR

The degree to which a structure deforms or strains depends on the magnitude of an imposed stress. For most metals that are stressed in tension and at relatively low levels, stress and strain are proportional to each other through the relationship

$$\sigma = E\epsilon \tag{6.4}$$

This is known as Hooke's law, and the constant of proportionality E (GPa or psi)[5] is the **modulus of elasticity,** or *Young's modulus.* For most typical metals the magnitude of this modulus ranges between 45 GPa (6.5×10^6 psi), for magnesium, and 407 GPa (59×10^6 psi), for tungsten. Modulus of elasticity values for several metals at room temperature are presented in Table 6.1.

Deformation in which stress and strain are proportional is called **elastic deformation;** a plot of stress (ordinate) versus strain (abscissa) results in a linear relationship, as shown in Figure 6.4. The slope of this linear segment corresponds to the modulus of elasticity E. This modulus may be thought of as stiffness, or a material's

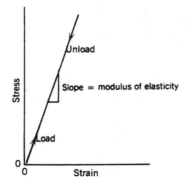

FIGURE 6.4 Schematic stress–strain diagram showing linear elastic deformation for loading and unloading cycles.

---

[5] The SI unit for the modulus of elasticity is gigapascal, GPa, where

$$1 \text{ GPa} = 10^9 \text{ N/m}^2 = 10^3 \text{ MPa}$$

Table 6.1 Room-Temperature Elastic and Shear Moduli, and Poisson's Ratio for Various Metal Alloys

Metal Alloy	Modulus of Elasticity E		Shear Modulus G		Poisson's Ratio
	GPa	10^6 psi	GPa	10^6 psi	
Aluminum	69	10	25	3.6	0.33
Brass	97	14	37	5.4	0.34
Copper	110	16	46	6.7	0.34
Magnesium	45	6.5	17	2.5	0.29
Nickel	207	30	76	11.0	0.31
Steel	207	30	83	12.0	0.30
Titanium	107	15.5	45	6.5	0.34
Tungsten	407	59	160	23.2	0.28

resistance to elastic deformation. The greater the modulus, the stiffer the material, or the smaller the elastic strain that results from the application of a given stress. The modulus is an important design parameter used for computing elastic deflections.

Elastic deformation is nonpermanent, which means that when the applied load is released, the piece returns to its original shape. As shown in the stress–strain plot (Figure 6.4), application of the load corresponds to moving from the origin up and along the straight line. Upon release of the load, the line is traversed in the opposite direction, back to the origin.

There are some materials (e.g., gray cast iron, concrete, and many polymers) for which this initial elastic portion of the stress–strain curve is not linear (Figure 6.5); hence, it is not possible to determine a modulus of elasticity as described above. For this nonlinear behavior, either *tangent* or *secant modulus* is normally used. Tangent modulus is taken as the slope of the stress–strain curve at some specified level of stress, while secant modulus represents the slope of a secant drawn from the origin to some given point of the σ–ϵ curve. The determination of these moduli is illustrated in Figure 6.5.

On an atomic scale, macroscopic elastic strain is manifested as small changes in the interatomic spacing and the stretching of interatomic bonds. As a conse-

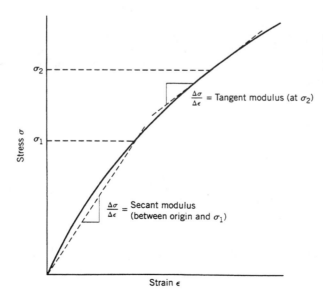

FIGURE 6.5 Schematic stress–strain diagram showing nonlinear elastic behavior, and how secant and tangent moduli are determined.

$\frac{\Delta\sigma}{\Delta\epsilon}$ = Tangent modulus (at σ_2)

$\frac{\Delta\sigma}{\Delta\epsilon}$ = Secant modulus (between origin and σ_1)

Stress σ

Strain ϵ

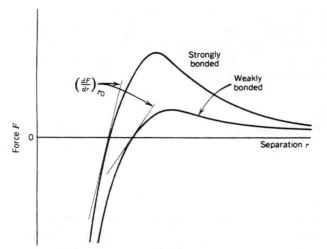

FIGURE 6.6 Force versus interatomic separation for weakly and strongly bonded atoms. The magnitude of the modulus of elasticity is proportional to the slope of each curve at the equilibrium interatomic separation r_0.

quence, the magnitude of the modulus of elasticity is a measure of the resistance to separation of adjacent atoms, that is, the interatomic bonding forces. Furthermore, this modulus is proportional to the slope of the interatomic force–separation curve (Figure 2.8a) at the equilibrium spacing:

$$E \propto \left(\frac{dF}{dr}\right)_{r_0} \tag{6.5}$$

Figure 6.6 shows the force–separation curves for materials having both strong and weak interatomic bonds; the slope at r_0 is indicated for each.

Values of the modulus of elasticity for ceramic materials are characteristically higher than for metals; for polymers, they are lower. These differences are a direct consequence of the different types of atomic bonding in the three materials types. Furthermore, with increasing temperature, the modulus of elasticity diminishes, as is shown for several metals in Figure 6.7.

FIGURE 6.7 Plot of modulus of elasticity versus temperature for tungsten, steel, and aluminum. (Adapted from K. M. Ralls, T. H. Courtney, and J. Wulff, *Introduction to Materials Science and Engineering.* Copyright © 1976 by John Wiley & Sons, New York. Reprinted by permission of John Wiley & Sons, Inc.)

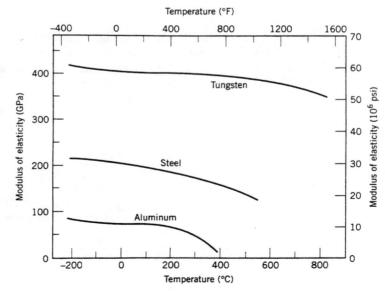

As would be expected, the imposition of compressive, shear, or torsional stresses also evokes elastic behavior. The stress–strain characteristics at low stress levels are virtually the same for both tensile and compressive situations, to include the magnitude of the modulus of elasticity. Shear stress and strain are proportional to each other through the expression

$$\tau = G\gamma \qquad (6.6)$$

where G is the *shear modulus,* the slope of the linear elastic region of the shear stress–strain curve. Table 6.1 gives the shear moduli for a number of the common metals.

6.4 ANELASTICITY

Up to this point, it has been assumed that elastic deformation is time independent, that is, that an applied stress produces an instantaneous elastic strain which remains constant over the period of time the stress is maintained. It has also been assumed that upon release of the load the strain is totally recovered, that is, that the strain immediately returns to zero. In most engineering materials, however, there will also exist a time-dependent elastic strain component. That is, elastic deformation will continue after the stress application, and upon load release some finite time is required for complete recovery. This time-dependent elastic behavior is known as **anelasticity,** and it is due to time-dependent microscopic and atomistic processes that are attendant to the deformation. For metals the anelastic component is normally small and is often neglected. However, for some polymeric materials its magnitude is significant; in this case it is termed *viscoelastic behavior,* which is the discussion topic of Section 16.6.

EXAMPLE PROBLEM 6.1

A piece of copper originally 305 mm (12 in.) long is pulled in tension with a stress of 276 MPa (40,000 psi). If the deformation is entirely elastic, what will be the resultant elongation?

SOLUTION

Since the deformation is elastic, strain is dependent on stress according to Equation 6.4. Furthermore, the elongation Δl is related to the original length l_0 through Equation 6.2. Combining these two expressions and solving for Δl yields

$$\sigma = \epsilon E = \left(\frac{\Delta l}{l_0}\right) E$$

$$\Delta l = \frac{\sigma l_0}{E}$$

The values of σ and l_0 are given as 276 MPa and 305 mm, respectively, and the magnitude of E for copper from Table 6.1 is 110 GPa (16×10^6 psi). Elongation is obtained by substitution into the expression above as

$$\Delta l = \frac{(276\,\text{MPa})(305\,\text{mm})}{110 \times 10^3\,\text{MPa}} = 0.77\,\text{mm}\ (0.30\,\text{in.})$$

6.5 ELASTIC PROPERTIES OF MATERIALS

When a tensile stress is imposed on a metal specimen, an elastic elongation and accompanying strain ϵ_z result in the direction of the applied stress (arbitrarily taken to be the z direction), as indicated in Figure 6.8. As a result of this elongation, there will be constrictions in the lateral (x and y) directions perpendicular to the applied stress; from these contractions, the compressive strains ϵ_x and ϵ_y may be determined. If the applied stress is uniaxial (only in the z direction), then $\epsilon_x = \epsilon_y$. A parameter termed **Poisson's ratio** ν is defined as the ratio of the lateral and axial strains, or

$$\nu = -\frac{\epsilon_x}{\epsilon_z} = -\frac{\epsilon_y}{\epsilon_z} \tag{6.7}$$

The negative sign is included in the expression so that ν will always be positive, since ϵ_x and ϵ_z will always be of opposite sign. Theoretically, Poisson's ratio for isotropic materials should be $\frac{1}{4}$; furthermore, the maximum value for ν (or that value for which there is no net volume change) is 0.50. For many metals and other alloys, values of Poisson's ratio range between 0.25 and 0.35. Table 6.1 shows ν values for several common metallic materials.

Shear and elastic moduli are related to each other and to Poisson's ratio according to

$$E = 2G(1 + \nu) \tag{6.8}$$

In most metals G is about $0.4E$; thus, if the value of one modulus is known, the other may be approximated.

Many materials are elastically anisotropic; that is, the elastic behavior (e.g., the magnitude of E) varies with crystallographic direction (see Table 3.3). For these materials the elastic properties are completely characterized only by the specification

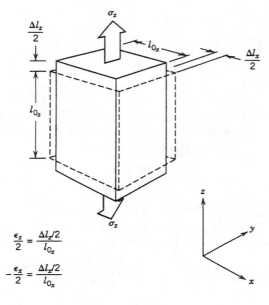

$$\frac{\epsilon_z}{2} = \frac{\Delta l_z/2}{l_{0_z}}$$

$$-\frac{\epsilon_x}{2} = \frac{\Delta l_x/2}{l_{0_x}}$$

FIGURE 6.8 Axial (z) elongation (positive strain) and lateral (x and y) contractions (negative strains) in response to an imposed tensile stress. Solid lines represent dimensions after stress application; dashed lines, before.

of several elastic constants, their number depending on characteristics of the crystal structure. Even for isotropic materials, for complete characterization of the elastic properties, at least two constants must be given. Since the grain orientation is random in most polycrystalline materials, these may be considered to be isotropic; inorganic ceramic glasses are also isotropic. The remaining discussion of mechanical behavior assumes isotropy and polycrystallinity because such is the character of most engineering materials.

EXAMPLE PROBLEM 6.2

A tensile stress is to be applied along the long axis of a cylindrical brass rod that has a diameter of 10 mm (0.4 in.). Determine the magnitude of the load required to produce a 2.5×10^{-3} mm (10^{-4} in.) change in diameter if the deformation is entirely elastic.

SOLUTION

This deformation situation is represented in the accompanying drawing.

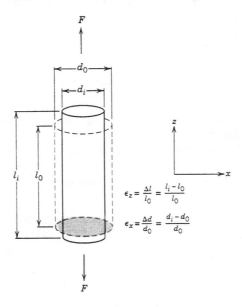

$$\epsilon_z = \frac{\Delta l}{l_0} = \frac{l_i - l_0}{l_0}$$

$$\epsilon_x = \frac{\Delta d}{d_0} = \frac{d_i - d_0}{d_0}$$

When the force F is applied, the specimen will elongate in the z direction and at the same time experience a reduction in diameter, Δd, of 2.5×10^{-3} mm in the x direction. For the strain in the x direction,

$$\epsilon_x = \frac{\Delta d}{d_0} = \frac{-2.5 \times 10^{-3} \text{ mm}}{10 \text{ mm}} = -2.5 \times 10^{-4}$$

which is negative, since the diameter is reduced.

It next becomes necessary to calculate the strain in the z direction using Equation 6.7. The value for Poisson's ratio for brass is 0.34 (Table 6.1), and thus

$$\epsilon_z = -\frac{\epsilon_x}{\nu} = -\frac{(-2.5 \times 10^{-4})}{0.34} = 7.35 \times 10^{-4}$$

The applied stress may now be computed using Equation 6.4 and the modulus of elasticity, given in Table 6.1 as 97 GPa (14×10^6 psi), as

$$\sigma = \epsilon_z E = (7.35 \times 10^{-4})(97 \times 10^3 \text{ MPa}) = 71.3 \text{ MPa}$$

Finally, from Equation 6.1, the applied force may be determined as

$$F = \sigma A_0 = \sigma \left(\frac{d_0}{2}\right)^2 \pi$$

$$= (71.3 \times 10^6 \text{ N/m}^2) \left(\frac{10 \times 10^{-3} \text{ m}}{2}\right)^2 \pi = 5600 \text{ N } (1293 \text{ lb}_f)$$

PLASTIC DEFORMATION

For most metallic materials, elastic deformation persists only to strains of about 0.005. As the material is deformed beyond this point, the stress is no longer proportional to strain (Hooke's law, Equation 6.4, ceases to be valid), and permanent, nonrecoverable, or **plastic deformation** occurs. Figure 6.9a plots schematically the tensile stress–strain behavior into the plastic region for a typical metal. The transition from elastic to plastic is a gradual one for most metals; some curvature results at the onset of plastic deformation, which increases more rapidly with rising stress.

From an atomic perspective, plastic deformation corresponds to the breaking of bonds with original atom neighbors and then reforming bonds with new neighbors as large numbers of atoms or molecules move relative to one another; upon removal of the stress they do not return to their original positions. The mechanism of this deformation is different for crystalline and amorphous materials. For crystalline solids, deformation is accomplished by means of a process called slip, which involves the motion of dislocations as discussed in Section 7.2. Plastic deformation in noncrys-

FIGURE 6.9 (a) Typical stress–strain behavior for a metal showing elastic and plastic deformations, the proportional limit P, and the yield strength σ_y, as determined using the 0.002 strain offset method. (b) Representative stress–strain behavior found for some steels demonstrating the yield point phenomenon.

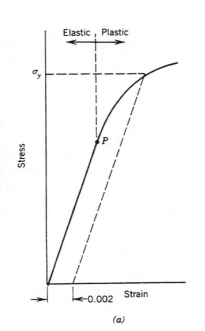

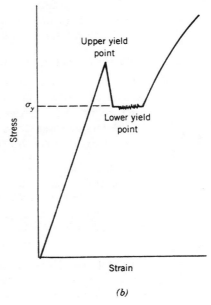

talline solids (as well as liquids) occurs by a viscous flow mechanism, which is outlined in Section 13.9.

6.6 TENSILE PROPERTIES

YIELDING AND YIELD STRENGTH

Most structures are designed to ensure that only elastic deformation will result when a stress is applied. It is therefore desirable to know the stress level at which plastic deformation begins, or where the phenomenon of **yielding** occurs. For metals that experience this gradual elastic–plastic transition, the point of yielding may be determined as the initial departure from linearity of the stress–strain curve; this is sometimes called the **proportional limit,** as indicated by point P in Figure 6.9a. In such cases the position of this point may not be determined precisely. As a consequence, a convention has been established wherein a straight line is constructed parallel to the elastic portion of the stress–strain curve at some specified strain offset, usually 0.002. The stress corresponding to the intersection of this line and the stress–strain curve as it bends over in the plastic region is defined as the **yield strength** σ_y.[6] This is demonstrated in Figure 6.9a. Of course, the units of yield strength are MPa or psi.[7]

For those materials having a nonlinear elastic region (Figure 6.5), use of the strain offset method is not possible, and the usual practice is to define the yield strength as the stress required to produce some amount of strain (e.g., $\epsilon = 0.005$).

Some steels and other materials exhibit the tensile stress–strain behavior as shown in Figure 6.9b. The elastic–plastic transition is very well defined and occurs abruptly in what is termed a *yield point phenomenon.* At the upper yield point, plastic deformation is initiated with an actual decrease in stress. Continued deformation fluctuates slightly about some constant stress value, termed the lower yield point; stress subsequently rises with increasing strain. For metals that display this effect, the yield strength is taken as the average stress that is associated with the lower yield point, since it is well defined and relatively insensitive to the testing procedure.[8] Thus, it is not necessary to employ the strain offset method for these materials.

The magnitude of the yield strength for a metal is a measure of its resistance to plastic deformation. Yield strengths may range from 35 MPa (5000 psi) for a low-strength aluminum to over 1400 MPa (200,000 psi) for high-strength steels.

TENSILE STRENGTH

After yielding, the stress necessary to continue plastic deformation in metals increases to a maximum, point M in Figure 6.10, and then decreases to the eventual fracture, point F. The **tensile strength** TS (MPa or psi) is the stress at the maximum on the engineering stress–strain curve (Figure 6.10). This corresponds to the maximum stress that can be sustained by a structure in tension; if this stress is applied

---

[6] "Strength" is used in lieu of "stress" because strength is a property of the metal, whereas stress is related to the magnitude of the applied load.

[7] For Customary U.S. units, the unit of kilopounds per square inch (ksi) is sometimes used for the sake of convenience where

$$1 \text{ ksi} = 1000 \text{ psi}$$

[8] It should be pointed out that to observe the yield point phenomenon, a "stiff" tensile-testing apparatus must be used; by stiff is meant that there is very little elastic deformation of the machine during loading.

FIGURE 6.10 Typical engineering stress–strain behavior to fracture, point *F*. The tensile strength *TS* is indicated at point *M*. The circular insets represent the geometry of the deformed specimen at various points along the curve.

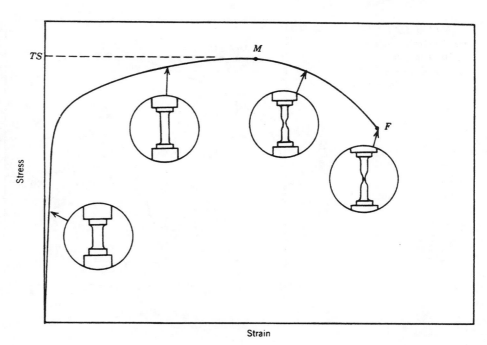

and maintained, fracture will result. All deformation up to this point is uniform throughout the narrow region of the tensile specimen. However, at this maximum stress, a small constriction or neck begins to form at some point, and all subsequent deformation is confined at this neck, as indicated by the schematic specimen insets in Figure 6.10. This phenomenon is termed "necking," and fracture ultimately occurs at the neck. The fracture strength corresponds to the stress at fracture.

Tensile strengths may vary anywhere from 50 MPa (7000 psi) for an aluminum to as high as 3000 MPa (450,000 psi) for the high-strength steels. Ordinarily, when the strength of a metal is cited for design purposes, the yield strength is used. This is because by the time a stress corresponding to the tensile strength has been applied, often a structure has experienced so much plastic deformation that it is useless. Furthermore, fracture strengths are not normally specified for engineering design purposes.

EXAMPLE PROBLEM 6.3

From the tensile stress–strain behavior for the brass specimen shown in Figure 6.11, determine the following:

(a) The modulus of elasticity.

(b) The yield strength at a strain offset of 0.002.

(c) The maximum load that can be sustained by a cylindrical specimen having an original diameter of 12.8 mm (0.505 in.).

(d) The change in length of a specimen originally 250 mm (10 in.) long which is subjected to a tensile stress of 345 MPa (50,000 psi).

FIGURE 6.11 The stress–strain behavior for the brass specimen discussed in Example Problem 6.3.

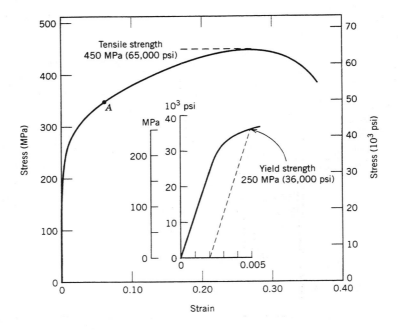

SOLUTION

(a) The modulus of elasticity is the slope of the elastic or initial linear portion of the stress–strain curve. The strain axis has been expanded in the inset, Figure 6.11, to facilitate this computation. The slope of this linear region is the rise over the run, or the change in stress divided by the corresponding change in strain; in mathematical terms,

$$E = \text{slope} = \frac{\Delta\sigma}{\Delta\epsilon} = \frac{\sigma_2 - \sigma_1}{\epsilon_2 - \epsilon_1} \tag{6.9}$$

Inasmuch as the line segment passes through the origin, it is convenient to take both σ_1 and ϵ_1 as zero. If σ_2 is arbitrarily taken as 150 MPa, then ϵ_2 will have a value of 0.0016. Therefore,

$$E = \frac{(150 - 0)\,\text{MPa}}{0.0016 - 0} = 93.8\,\text{GPa}\ (13.6 \times 10^6\,\text{psi})$$

which is very close to the value of 97 GPa (14×10^6 psi) given for brass in Table 6.1.

(b) The 0.002 strain offset line is constructed as shown in the inset; its intersection with the stress–strain curve is at approximately 250 MPa (36,000 psi), which is the yield strength of the brass.

(c) The maximum load that can be sustained by the specimen is calculated by using Equation 6.1, in which σ is taken to be the tensile strength, from Figure 6.11, 450 MPa (65,000 psi). Solving for F, the maximum load, yields

$$F = \sigma A_0 = \sigma \left(\frac{d_0}{2}\right)^2 \pi$$

$$= (450 \times 10^6\,\text{N/m}^2) \left(\frac{12.8 \times 10^{-3}\,\text{m}}{2}\right)^2 \pi = 57{,}900\,\text{N}\ (13{,}000\,\text{lb}_f)$$

(d) To compute the change in length, Δl, in Equation 6.2, it is first necessary to determine the strain that is produced by a stress of 345 MPa. This is accomplished by locating the stress point on the stress–strain curve, point A, and reading the corresponding strain from the strain axis, which is approximately 0.06. Inasmuch as $l_0 = 250$ mm, we have

$$\Delta l = \epsilon l_0 = (0.06)(250 \text{ mm}) = 15 \text{ mm } (0.6 \text{ in.})$$

DUCTILITY

Ductility is another important mechanical property. It is a measure of the degree of plastic deformation that has been sustained at fracture. A material that experiences very little or no plastic deformation upon fracture is termed *brittle*. The tensile stress–strain behaviors for both ductile and brittle materials are schematically illustrated in Figure 6.12.

Ductility may be expressed quantitatively as either *percent elongation* or *percent area reduction*. The percent elongation %EL is the percentage of plastic strain at fracture, or

$$\%EL = \left(\frac{l_f - l_0}{l_0}\right) \times 100 \tag{6.10}$$

where l_f is the fracture length[9] and l_0 is the original gauge length as above. Inasmuch as a significant proportion of the plastic deformation at fracture is confined to the neck region, the magnitude of %EL will depend on specimen gauge length. The shorter l_0, the greater is the fraction of total elongation from the neck and, consequently, the higher the value of %EL. Therefore, l_0 should be specified when percent elongation values are cited; it is commonly 50 mm (2 in.).

Percent area reduction %AR is defined as

$$\%AR = \left(\frac{A_0 - A_f}{A_0}\right) \times 100 \tag{6.11}$$

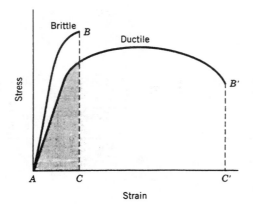

FIGURE 6.12 Schematic representations of tensile stress–strain behavior for brittle and ductile materials loaded to fracture.

---

[9] Both l_f and A_f are measured subsequent to fracture, and after the two broken ends have been repositioned back together.

where A_0 is the original cross-sectional area and A_f is the cross-sectional area at the point of fracture (refer to footnote 9 on page 123). Percent area reduction values are independent of both l_0 and A_0. Furthermore, for a given material the magnitudes of %EL and %AR will, in general, be different. Most metals possess at least a moderate degree of ductility at room temperature; however, some become brittle as the temperature is lowered (Section 8.6).

A knowledge of the ductility of materials is important for at least two reasons. First, it indicates to a designer the degree to which a structure will deform plastically before fracture. Second, it specifies the degree of allowable deformation during fabrication operations. We sometimes refer to relatively ductile materials as being "forgiving," in the sense that they may experience local deformation without fracture should there be an error in the magnitude of the design stress calculation.

Brittle materials are *approximately* considered to be those having a fracture strain of less than about 5%.

Thus, several important mechanical properties of metals may be determined from tensile stress–strain tests. Table 6.2 presents some typical room-temperature values of yield strength, tensile strength, and ductility for several of the common metals. These properties are sensitive to any prior deformation, the presence of impurities, and/or any heat treatment to which the metal has been subjected. The modulus of elasticity is one mechanical parameter that is insensitive to these treatments. As with modulus of elasticity, the magnitudes of both yield and tensile strengths decline with increasing temperature; just the reverse holds for ductility—it usually increases with temperature. Figure 6.13 shows how the stress–strain behavior of iron varies with temperature.

RESILIENCE

Resilience is the capacity of a material to absorb energy when it is deformed elastically and then, upon unloading, to have this energy recovered. The associated property is the *modulus of resilience, U_r*, which is the strain energy per unit volume required to stress a material from an unloaded state up to the point of yielding.

Computationally, the modulus of resilience for a specimen subjected to a uniaxial tension test is just the area under the engineering stress–strain curve taken to yielding (Figure 6.14), or

$$U_r = \int_0^{\epsilon_y} \sigma \, d\epsilon \tag{6.12a}$$

Table 6.2 **Typical Mechanical Properties of Several Metals and Alloys in an Annealed State**

Metal Alloy	Yield Strength MPa (ksi)	Tensile Strength MPa (ksi)	Ductility, %EL [in 50 mm (2 in.)]
Aluminum	35 (5)	90 (13)	40
Copper	69 (10)	200 (29)	45
Brass (70Cu–30Zn)	75 (11)	300 (44)	68
Iron	130 (19)	262 (38)	45
Nickel	138 (20)	480 (70)	40
Steel (1020)	180 (26)	380 (55)	25
Titanium	450 (65)	520 (75)	25
Molybdenum	565 (82)	655 (95)	35

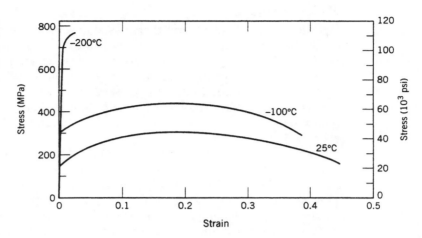

FIGURE 6.13 Engineering stress–strain behavior for iron at three temperatures.

Assuming a linear elastic region,

$$U_r = \tfrac{1}{2}\sigma_y\epsilon_y \qquad\qquad (6.12b)$$

in which ϵ_y is the strain at yielding.

The units of resilience are the product of the units from each of the two axes of the stress–strain plot. For SI units, this is joules per cubic meter (J/m^3, equivalent to Pa), whereas with Customary U.S. units it is inch-pounds force per cubic inch (in.-lb_f/in.^{3}, equivalent to psi). Both joules and inch-pounds force are units of energy, and thus this area under the stress–strain curve represents energy absorption per unit volume (in cubic inches or cubic meters) of material.

Incorporation of Equation 6.4 into Equation 6.12b yields

$$U_r = \tfrac{1}{2}\sigma_y\epsilon_y = \tfrac{1}{2}\sigma_y\left(\frac{\sigma_y}{E}\right) = \frac{\sigma_y^2}{2E} \qquad\qquad (6.13)$$

Thus, resilient materials are those having high yield strengths and low moduli of elasticity; such alloys would be used in spring applications.

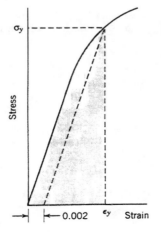

FIGURE 6.14 Schematic representation showing how modulus of resilience (corresponding to the shaded area) is determined from the tensile stress–strain behavior of a material.

TOUGHNESS

Toughness is a mechanical term that is used in several contexts; loosely speaking, it is a measure of the ability of a material to absorb energy up to fracture. Specimen geometry as well as the manner of load application are important in toughness determinations. For dynamic (high strain rate) loading conditions and when a notch (or point of stress concentration) is present, *notch toughness* is assessed by using an impact test, as discussed in Section 8.6. Furthermore, fracture toughness is a property indicative of a material's resistance to fracture when a crack is present (Section 8.5).

For the static (low strain rate) situation, toughness may be ascertained from the results of a tensile stress–strain test. It is the area under the σ–ϵ curve up to the point of fracture. The units for toughness are the same as for resilience (i.e., energy per unit volume of material). For a material to be tough, it must display both strength and ductility; and often, ductile materials are tougher than brittle ones. This is demonstrated in Figure 6.12, in which the stress–strain curves are plotted for both material types. Hence, even though the brittle material has higher yield and tensile strengths, it has a lower toughness than the ductile one, by virtue of lack of ductility; this is deduced by comparing the areas ABC and $AB'C'$ in Figure 6.12.

6.7 True Stress and Strain

From Figure 6.10, the decline in the stress necessary to continue deformation past the maximum, point M, seems to indicate that the material is becoming weaker. This is not at all the case; as a matter of fact, it is increasing in strength. However, the cross-sectional area is decreasing rapidly within the neck region, where deformation is occurring. This results in a reduction in the load-bearing capacity of the specimen. The stress, as computed from Equation 6.1, is on the basis of the original cross-sectional area before any deformation, and does not take into account this diminution in area at the neck.

Sometimes it is more meaningful to use a true stress–true strain scheme. **True stress** σ_T is defined as the load F divided by the instantaneous cross-sectional area A_i over which deformation is occurring (i.e., the neck, past the tensile point), or

$$\sigma_T = \frac{F}{A_i} \tag{6.14}$$

Furthermore, it is occasionally more convenient to represent strain as **true strain** ϵ_T, defined by

$$\epsilon_T = \ln \frac{l_i}{l_0} \tag{6.15}$$

If no volume change occurs during deformation, that is, if

$$A_i l_i = A_0 l_0 \tag{6.16}$$

true and engineering stress and strain are related according to

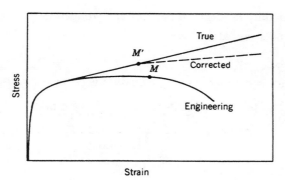

FIGURE 6.15 A comparison of typical tensile engineering stress–strain and true stress–strain behaviors. Necking begins at point M on the engineering curve, which corresponds to M' on the true curve. The "corrected" true stress–strain curve takes into account the complex stress state within the neck region.

$$\sigma_T = \sigma(1 + \epsilon) \tag{6.17a}$$

$$\epsilon_T = \ln(1 + \epsilon) \tag{6.17b}$$

Equations 6.17a and 6.17b are valid only to the onset of necking; beyond this point true stress and strain should be computed from actual load, cross-sectional area, and gauge length measurements.

A schematic comparison of engineering and true stress–strain behavior is made in Figure 6.15. It is worth noting that the true stress necessary to sustain increasing strain continues to rise past the tensile point M'.

Coincident with the formation of a neck is the introduction of a complex stress state within the neck region (i.e., the existence of other stress components in addition to the axial stress). As a consequence, the correct stress (*axial*) within the neck is slightly lower than the stress computed from the applied load and neck cross-sectional area. This leads to the "corrected" curve in Figure 6.15.

For some metals and alloys the region of the true stress-strain curve from the onset of plastic deformation to the point at which necking begins may be approximated by

$$\sigma_T = K\epsilon_T^n \tag{6.18}$$

In this expression, K and n are constants, which values will vary from alloy to alloy, and will also depend on the condition of the material (i.e., whether it has been plastically deformed, heat treated, etc.). The parameter n is often termed the *strain-hardening exponent* and has a value less than unity. Values of n and K for several alloys are contained in Table 6.3.

EXAMPLE PROBLEM 6.4

A cylindrical specimen of steel having an original diameter of 12.8 mm (0.505 in.) is tensile tested to fracture and found to have an engineering fracture strength σ_f of 460 MPa (67,000 psi). If its cross-sectional diameter at fracture is 10.7 mm (0.422 in.), determine:

(a) The ductility in terms of percent area reduction.

(b) The true stress at fracture.

SOLUTION

(a) Ductility is computed using Equation 6.11, as

$$\%AR = \frac{\left(\dfrac{12.8 \text{ mm}}{2}\right)^2 \pi - \left(\dfrac{10.7 \text{ mm}}{2}\right)^2 \pi}{\left(\dfrac{12.8 \text{ mm}}{2}\right)^2 \pi} \times 100$$

$$= \frac{128.7 \text{ mm}^2 - 89.9 \text{ mm}^2}{128.7 \text{ mm}^2} \times 100 = 30\%$$

(b) True stress is defined by Equation 6.14, where in this case the area is taken as the fracture area A_f. However, the load at fracture must first be computed from the fracture strength as

$$F = \sigma_f A_0 = (460 \times 10^6 \text{ N/m}^2)(128.7 \text{ mm}^2)\left(\frac{1 \text{ m}^2}{10^6 \text{ mm}^2}\right) = 59{,}200 \text{ N}$$

Thus, the true stress is calculated as

$$\sigma_T = \frac{F}{A_f} = \frac{59{,}200 \text{ N}}{(89.9 \text{ mm}^2)\left(\dfrac{1 \text{ m}^2}{10^6 \text{ mm}^2}\right)}$$

$$= 6.6 \times 10^8 \text{ N/m}^2 = 660 \text{ MPa } (95{,}700 \text{ psi})$$

Table 6.3 **Tabulation of n and K Values (Equation 6.18) for Several Alloys**

Material	n	K MPa	K psi
Low-carbon steel (annealed)	0.26	530	77,000
Alloy steel (Type 4340, annealed)	0.15	640	93,000
Stainless steel (Type 304, annealed)	0.45	1275	185,000
Aluminum (annealed)	0.20	180	26,000
Aluminum alloy (Type 2024, heat treated)	0.16	690	100,000
Copper (annealed)	0.54	315	46,000
Brass (70Cu–30Zn, annealed)	0.49	895	130,000

Source: S. Kalpakjian, *Manufacturing Processes for Engineering Materials,* © 1984 by Addison-Wesley Publishing Company, Inc. Reprinted by permission of Addison-Wesley Publishing Company, Inc.

EXAMPLE PROBLEM 6.5

Compute the strain-hardening exponent n in Equation 6.18 for an alloy in which a true stress of 415 MPa (60,000 psi) produces a true strain of 0.10; assume a value of 1035 MPa (150,000 psi) for K.

SOLUTION

This requires some algebraic manipulation of Equation 6.18 so that n becomes the dependent parameter. This is accomplished by taking logarithms and rearranging. Solving for n yields

$$n = \frac{\log \sigma_T - \log K}{\log \epsilon_T}$$

$$= \frac{\log(415 \text{ MPa}) - \log(1035 \text{ MPa})}{\log(0.1)} = 0.40$$

6.8 ELASTIC RECOVERY DURING PLASTIC DEFORMATION

Upon release of the load during the course of a stress–strain test, some fraction of the total deformation is recovered as elastic strain. This behavior is demonstrated in Figure 6.16, a schematic engineering stress–strain plot. During the unloading cycle, the curve traces a near straight-line path from the point of unloading (point D), and its slope is virtually identical to the modulus of elasticity, or parallel to the initial elastic portion of the curve. The magnitude of this elastic strain, which is regained during unloading, corresponds to the strain recovery, as shown in Figure 6.16. If the load is reapplied, the curve will traverse essentially the same linear portion in the direction opposite to unloading; yielding will again occur at the

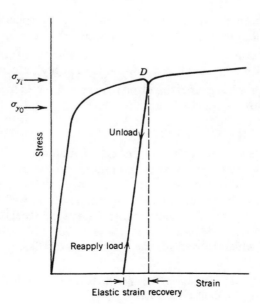

FIGURE 6.16 Schematic tensile stress–strain diagram showing the phenomena of elastic strain recovery and strain hardening. The initial yield strength is designated as σ_{y_0}; σ_{y_i} is the yield strength after releasing the load at point D, and then upon reloading.

unloading stress level where the unloading began. There will also be an elastic strain recovery associated with fracture.

6.9 COMPRESSIVE. SHEAR, AND TORSIONAL DEFORMATION

Of course, metals may experience plastic deformation under the influence of applied compressive, shear, and torsional loads. The resulting stress–strain behavior into the plastic region will be similar to the tensile counterpart (Figure 6.9a: yielding and the associated curvature). However, for compression, there will be no maximum, since necking does not occur; furthermore, the mode of fracture will be different from that for tension.

6.10 HARDNESS

Another mechanical property that may be important to consider is **hardness,** which is a measure of a material's resistance to localized plastic deformation (e.g., a small dent or a scratch). Early hardness tests were based on natural minerals with a scale constructed solely on the ability of one material to scratch another that was softer. A qualitative and somewhat arbitrary hardness indexing scheme was devised, termed the Mohs scale, which ranged from 1 on the soft end for talc to 10 for diamond. Quantitative hardness techniques have been developed over the years in which a small indenter is forced into the surface of a material to be tested, under controlled conditions of load and rate of application. The depth or size of the resulting indentation is measured, which in turn is related to a hardness number; the softer the material, the larger and deeper the indentation, and the lower the hardness index number. Measured hardnesses are only relative (rather than absolute), and care should be exercised when comparing values determined by different techniques.

Hardness tests are performed more frequently than any other mechanical test for several reasons:

1. They are simple and inexpensive—ordinarily no special specimen need be prepared, and the testing apparatus is relatively inexpensive.

2. The test is nondestructive—the specimen is neither fractured nor excessively deformed; a small indentation is the only deformation.

3. Other mechanical properties often may be estimated from hardness data, such as tensile strength (see Figure 6.18).

ROCKWELL HARDNESS TESTS[10]

The Rockwell tests constitute the most common method used to measure hardness because they are so simple to perform and require no special skills. Several different scales may be utilized from possible combinations of various indenters and different loads, which permit the testing of virtually all metals and alloys, from the hardest to the softest. Indenters include spherical and hardened steel balls having diameters of $\frac{1}{16}$, $\frac{1}{8}$, $\frac{1}{4}$, and $\frac{1}{2}$ in. (1.588, 3.175, 6.350, and 12.70 mm), and a conical diamond (Brale) indenter, which is used for the hardest materials.

---

[10] ASTM Standard E 18, "Standard Test Methods for Rockwell Hardness and Rockwell Superficial Hardness of Metallic Materials."

With this system, a hardness number is determined by the difference in depth of penetration resulting from the application of an initial minor load followed by a larger major load; utilization of a minor load enhances test accuracy. On the basis of the magnitude of both major and minor loads, there are two types of tests: Rockwell and superficial Rockwell. For Rockwell, the minor load is 10 kg, whereas major loads are 60, 100, and 150 kg. Each scale is represented by a letter of the alphabet; several are listed with the corresponding indenter and load in Tables 6.4 and 6.5a. For superficial tests, 3 kg is the minor load; 15, 30, and 45 kg are the possible major load values. These scales are identified by a 15, 30, or 45 (according to load), followed by N, T, W, X, or Y, depending on indenter. Superficial tests are frequently performed on thin specimens. Table 6.5b presents several superficial scales.

When specifying Rockwell and superficial hardnesses, both hardness number and scale symbol must be indicated. The scale is designated by the symbol HR followed by the appropriate scale identification.[11] For example, 80 HRB represents a Rockwell hardness of 80 on the B scale, and 60 HR30W indicates a superficial hardness of 60 on the 30W scale.

For each scale, hardnesses may range up to 130; however, as hardness values rise above 100 or drop below 20 on any scale, they become inaccurate; and because the scales have some overlap, in such a situation it is best to utilize the next harder or softer scale.

Inaccuracies also result if the test specimen is too thin, if an indentation is made too near a specimen edge, or if two indentations are made too close to one another. Specimen thickness should be at least ten times the indentation depth, whereas allowance should be made for at least three indentation diameters between the center of one indentation and the specimen edge, or to the center of a second indentation. Furthermore, testing of specimens stacked one on top of another is not recommended. Also, accuracy is dependent on the indentation being made into a smooth flat surface.

The modern apparatus for making Rockwell hardness measurements (page 108) is automated and very simple to use; hardness is read directly, and each measurement requires only a few seconds.

The modern testing apparatus also permits a variation in the time of load application. This variable must also be considered in interpreting hardness data.

BRINELL HARDNESS TESTS[12]

In Brinell tests, as in Rockwell measurements, a hard, spherical indenter is forced into the surface of the metal to be tested. The diameter of the hardened steel (or tungsten carbide) indenter is 10.00 mm (0.394 in.). Standard loads range between 500 and 3000 kg in 500-kg increments; during a test, the load is maintained constant for a specified time (between 10 and 30 s). Harder materials require greater applied loads. The Brinell hardness number, HB, is a function of both the magnitude of the load and the diameter of the resulting indentation (see Table 6.4).[13] This diameter is measured with a special low-power microscope, utilizing a scale that is etched on

---

[11] Rockwell scales are also frequently designated by an R with the appropriate scale letter as a subscript, for example, R_C denotes the Rockwell C scale.

[12] ASTM Standard E 10, "Standard Test Method for Brinell Hardness of Metallic Materials."

[13] The Brinell hardness number is also represented by BHN.

Table 6.4 Hardness Testing Techniques

Test	Indenter	Shape of Indentation Side View	Shape of Indentation Top View	Load	Formula for Hardness Number[a]
Brinell	10-mm sphere of steel or tungsten carbide	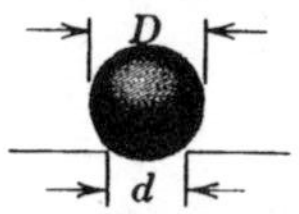	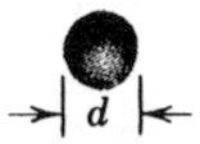	P	$HB = \dfrac{2P}{\pi D[D - \sqrt{D^2 - d^2}]}$
Vickers microhardness	Diamond pyramid	 136°		P	$HV = 1.854P/d_1^2$
Knoop microhardness	Diamond pyramid	 $l/b = 7.11$ $b/t = 4.00$	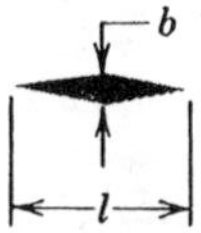	P	$HK = 14.2P/l^2$
Rockwell and Superficial Rockwell	Diamond cone $\frac{1}{16}, \frac{1}{8}, \frac{1}{4}, \frac{1}{2}$ in. diameter steel spheres	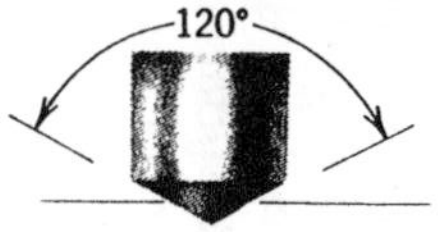 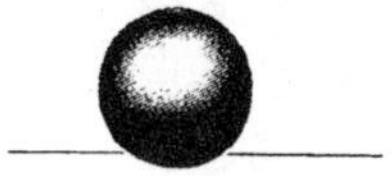	 	60 kg, 100 kg, 150 kg } Rockwell; 15 kg, 30 kg, 45 kg } Superficial Rockwell	

[a] For the hardness formulas given, P (the applied load) is in kg, while D, d, d_1, and l are all in mm.

Source: Adapted from H. W. Hayden, W. G. Moffatt, and J. Wulff, *The Structure and Properties of Materials*, Vol. III, *Mechanical Behavior*. Copyright © 1965 by John Wiley & Sons, New York. Reprinted by permission of John Wiley & Sons, Inc.

Table 6.5a **Rockwell Hardness Scales**

Scale Symbol	Indenter	Major Load (kg)
A	Diamond	60
B	$\frac{1}{16}$ in. ball	100
C	Diamond	150
D	Diamond	100
E	$\frac{1}{8}$ in. ball	100
F	$\frac{1}{16}$ in. ball	60
G	$\frac{1}{16}$ in. ball	150
H	$\frac{1}{8}$ in. ball	60
K	$\frac{1}{8}$ in. ball	150

Table 6.5b **Superficial Rockwell Hardness Scales**

Scale Symbol	Indenter	Major Load (kg)
15N	Diamond	15
30N	Diamond	30
45N	Diamond	45
15T	$\frac{1}{16}$ in. ball	15
30T	$\frac{1}{16}$ in. ball	30
45T	$\frac{1}{16}$ in. ball	45
15W	$\frac{1}{8}$ in. ball	15
30W	$\frac{1}{8}$ in. ball	30
45W	$\frac{1}{8}$ in. ball	45

the eyepiece. The measured diameter is then converted to the appropriate HB number using a chart; only one scale is employed with this technique.

Maximum specimen thickness as well as indentation position (relative to specimen edges) and minimum indentation spacing requirements are the same as for Rockwell tests. In addition, a well-defined indentation is required; this necessitates a smooth flat surface in which the indentation is made.

KNOOP AND VICKERS MICROHARDNESS TESTS[14]

Two other hardness testing techniques are Knoop (pronounced *nūp*) and Vickers (sometimes also called diamond pyramid). For each test a very small diamond indenter having pyramidal geometry is forced into the surface of the specimen. Applied loads are much smaller than for Rockwell and Brinell, ranging between 1 and 1000 g. The resulting impression is observed under a microscope and measured; this measurement is then converted into a hardness number (Table 6.4). Careful specimen surface preparation (grinding and polishing) may be necessary to ensure a well-defined indentation that may be accurately measured. The Knoop and Vickers hardness numbers are designated by HK and HV, respectively,[15] and hardness scales for both techniques are approximately equivalent. Knoop and Vickers are referred to as microhardness testing methods on the basis of load and indenter size. Both are well suited for measuring the hardness of small, selected specimen regions; furthermore, Knoop is used for testing brittle materials such as ceramics.

---

[14] ASTM Standard E 92, "Standard Test Method for Vickers Hardness of Metallic Materials," and ASTM Standard E 384, "Standard Test for Microhardness of Materials."

[15] Sometimes KHN and VHN are used to denote Knoop and Vickers hardness numbers, respectively.

There are other hardness-testing techniques that are frequently employed, but which will not be discussed here; these include ultrasonic microhardness, dynamic (Scleroscope), durometer (for plastic and elastomeric materials), and scratch hardness tests. These are described in references provided at the end of the chapter.

HARDNESS CONVERSION

The facility to convert the hardness measured on one scale to that of another is most desirable. However, since hardness is not a well-defined material property, and because of the experimental dissimilarities among the various techniques, a comprehensive conversion scheme has not been devised. Hardness conversion data have been determined experimentally and found to be dependent on material type and characteristics. The most reliable conversion data exist for steels, some of which are presented in Figure 6.17 for Knoop, Brinell, and two Rockwell scales; the Mohs scale is also included. Detailed conversion tables for various other metals and alloys are contained in ASTM Standard E 140, "Standard Hardness Conversion Tables for Metals." In light of the preceding discussion, care should be exercised in extrapolation of conversion data from one alloy system to another.

FIGURE 6.17 Comparison of several hardness scales. (Adapted from G. F. Kinney, *Engineering Properties and Applications of Plastics*, p. 202. Copyright © 1957 by John Wiley & Sons, New York. Reprinted by permission of John Wiley & Sons, Inc.)

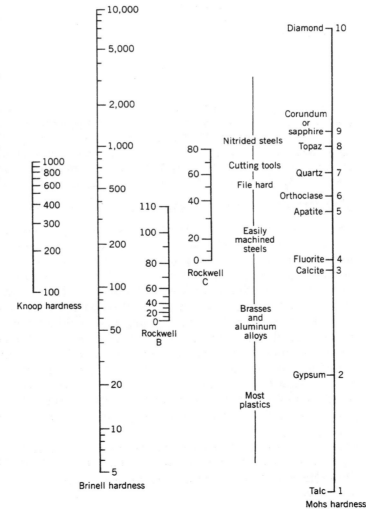

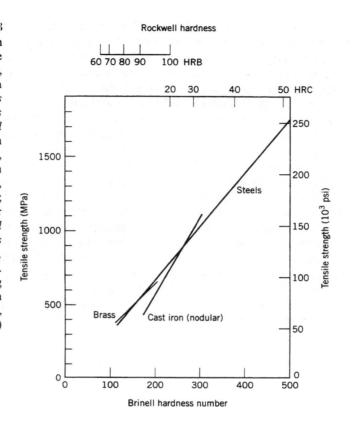

FIGURE 6.18
Relationships between hardness and tensile strength for steel, brass, and cast iron. (Data taken from *Metals Handbook: Properties and Selection: Irons and Steels,* Vol. 1, 9th edition, B. Bardes, Editor, American Society for Metals, 1978, pp. 36 and 461; and *Metals Handbook: Properties and Selection: Nonferrous Alloys and Pure Metals,* Vol. 2, 9th edition, H. Baker, Managing Editor, American Society for Metals, 1979, p. 327.)

CORRELATION BETWEEN HARDNESS AND TENSILE STRENGTH

Both tensile strength and hardness are indicators of a metal's resistance to plastic deformation. Consequently, they are roughly proportional, as shown in Figure 6.18, for tensile strength as a function of the HB for cast iron, steel, and brass. The same proportionality relationship does not hold for all metals, as Figure 6.18 indicates. As a rule of thumb for most steels, the HB and the tensile strength are related according to

$$TS(\text{MPa}) = 3.45 \times \text{HB} \tag{6.19a}$$

$$TS(\text{psi}) = 500 \times \text{HB} \tag{6.19b}$$

6.11 VARIABILITY OF MATERIAL PROPERTIES

At this point it is worthwhile to discuss an issue that sometimes proves troublesome to many engineering students, namely, that measured material properties are not exact quantities. That is, even if we have a most precise measuring apparatus and a highly controlled test procedure, there will always be some scatter or variability in the data that are collected from specimens of the same material. For example, consider a number of identical tensile samples that are prepared from a single bar of some metal alloy, which samples are subsequently stress–strain tested in the same apparatus. We would most likely observe that each resulting stress–strain plot is slightly different than the others. This would lead to a variety of modulus of elasticity, yield strength, and tensile strength values. A number of factors lead to uncertainties in measured data. These include the test method, variations in specimen fabrication procedures, operator bias, and apparatus calibration. Furthermore, inhomogeneities may exist within the same lot of material, and/or slight compositional and other differences from lot to lot. Of course, appropriate measures should be taken to minimize the possibility of measurement error, and also to mitigate those factors which lead to data variability.

It should also be mentioned that scatter exists for other measured material properties such as density, electrical conductivity, and coefficient of thermal expansion.

It is important for the design engineer to realize that scatter and variability of materials properties are inevitable and must be dealt with appropriately. On occasion, data must be subjected to statistical treatments and probabilities determined. For example, instead of asking the question, "What is the fracture strength of this alloy?" the engineer should become accustomed to asking the question, "What is the probability of failure of this alloy under these given circumstances?"

In spite of the variation of some measured property, specification of a "typical" value is still desirable. Most commonly, the typical value is described by taking an average of the data. This is obtained by dividing the sum of all measured values by the number of measurements taken. In mathematical terms, the average $\bar{x}$ of some parameter x is

$$\bar{x} = \frac{\sum_{i=1}^{n} x_i}{n} \tag{6.20}$$

where n is the number of observations or measurements and x_i is the value of a discrete measurement.

Sometimes it is also desirable to quantify the degree of dispersion, or scatter, of the measured data. The most common measure of this variability is the standard deviation s, which is determined using the following expression:

$$s = \left[\frac{\sum_{i=1}^{n} (x_i - \bar{x})^2}{n - 1} \right]^{1/2} \tag{6.21}$$

where x_i, $\bar{x}$, and n are defined above. A large value of the standard deviation corresponds to a high degree of scatter.

EXAMPLE PROBLEM 6.6

The following tensile strengths were measured for four specimens of the same steel alloy:

Sample Number	Tensile Strength (MPa)
1	520
2	512
3	515
4	522

FIGURE 6.19 (a) Tensile strength data associated with Example Problem 6.6. (b) The manner in which these data could be plotted. The data point corresponds to the average value of the tensile strength ($\overline{TS}$); error bars which indicate the degree of scatter correspond to the average value plus and minus the standard deviation ($\overline{TS} \pm s$).

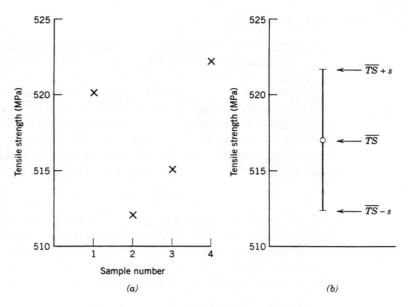

(a)

(b)

(a) Compute the average tensile strength.

(b) Determine the standard deviation.

SOLUTION

(a) The average tensile strength ($\overline{TS}$) is computed using Equation 6.20 with $n = 4$:

$$\overline{TS} = \frac{\sum_{i=1}^{4} (TS)_i}{4}$$

$$= \frac{520 + 512 + 515 + 522}{4}$$

$$= 517 \text{ MPa}$$

(b) And for the standard deviation, using Equation 6.21,

$$s = \left[\frac{\sum_{i=1}^{4} \{(TS)_i - \overline{TS}\}^2}{4 - 1} \right]^{1/2}$$

$$= \left(\frac{(520 - 517)^2 + (512 - 517)^2 + (515 - 517)^2 + (522 - 517)^2}{4 - 1} \right)^{1/2}$$

$$= 4.6 \text{ MPa}$$

Figure 6.19 presents the tensile strength by specimen number for this example problem, and also how the data may be represented in graphical form. The tensile strength data point (Figure 6.19b) corresponds to the average value $\overline{TS}$, whereas scatter is depicted by error bars (short horizontal lines) situated above and below the data point symbol and connected to this symbol by vertical lines. The upper error bar is positioned at a value of the average value plus the standard deviation ($\overline{TS} + s$), whereas the lower error bar corresponds to the average minus the standard deviation ($\overline{TS} - s$).

6.12 DESIGN/SAFETY FACTORS

There will always be uncertainties in characterizing the magnitude of applied loads and their associated stress levels for in-service applications; ordinarily load calculations are only approximate. Furthermore, as noted in the previous section, virtually all engineering materials exhibit a variability in their measured mechanical properties. Consequently, design allowances must be made to protect against unanticipated failure. One way this may be accomplished is by establishing, for the particular application, a **design stress,** denoted as σ_d. For static situations and when ductile materials are used, σ_d is taken as the calculated stress level σ_c, (on the basis of the estimated maximum load) multiplied by a *design factor, N'*, that is

$$\sigma_d = N'\sigma_c \qquad (6.22)$$

where N' is greater than unity. Thus, the material to be used for the particular application is chosen so as to have a yield strength at least as high as this value of σ_d.

Alternatively, a **safe stress** or *working stress, σ_w*, is used instead of design stress. This safe stress is based on the yield strength of the material and is defined as the yield strength divided by a *factor of safety, N,* or

$$\sigma_w = \frac{\sigma_y}{N} \qquad (6.23)$$

Utilization of design stress (Equation 6.22) is usually preferred since it is based on the anticipated maximum applied stress instead of the yield strength of the material; normally there is a greater uncertainty in estimating this stress level than in the specification of the yield strength. However, in the discussion of this text, we are concerned with factors that influence the yield strengths of metal alloys, and not in the determination of applied stresses; therefore, the succeeding discussion will deal with working stresses and factors of safety.

The choice of an appropriate value of N is necessary. If N is too large, then component overdesign will result, that is, either too much material or an alloy having a higher-than-necessary strength will be used. Values normally range between 1.2 and 4.0. Selection of N will depend on a number of factors, including economics, previous experience, the accuracy with which mechanical forces and material properties may be determined, and, most important, the consequences of failure in terms of loss of life and/or property damage.

DESIGN EXAMPLE 6.1

A tensile-testing apparatus is to be constructed which must withstand a maximum load of 220,000 N (50,000 lb$_f$). The design calls for two cylindrical support posts, each of which is to support half of the maximum load. Furthermore, plain-carbon (1045) steel ground and polished shafting rounds are to be used; the minimum yield and tensile strengths of this alloy are 310 MPa (45,000 psi) and 565 MPa (82,000 psi), respectively. Specify a suitable diameter for these support posts.

SOLUTION

The first step in this design process is to decide on a factor safety, N, which then allows determination of a working stress according to Equation 6.23. In addition to ensure that the apparatus will be safe to operate, we also want to minimize any elastic deflection of the rods during testing; therefore, a relatively conservative factor of safety is to be used, say $N = 5$. Thus, the working stress σ_w is just

$$\sigma_w = \frac{\sigma_y}{N}$$

$$= \frac{310 \, \text{MPa}}{5} = 62 \, \text{MPa} \, (9000 \, \text{psi})$$

From the definition of stress, Equation 6.1

$$A_0 = \left(\frac{d}{2}\right)^2 \pi = \frac{F}{\sigma_w}$$

where d is the rod diameter and F is the applied force; furthermore, each of the two rods must support half of the total force or 110,000 N (25,000 psi). Solving for d leads to

$$d = 2\sqrt{\frac{F}{\pi \sigma_w}}$$

$$= 2\sqrt{\frac{110,000 \, \text{N}}{\pi \, (62 \times 10^6 \, \text{N/m}^2)}}$$

$$= 4.75 \times 10^{-2} \, \text{m} = 47.5 \, \text{mm} \, (1.87 \, \text{in.})$$

Therefore, the diameter of each of the two rods should be 47.5 mm or 1.87 in.

SUMMARY

A number of the important mechanical properties of materials, predominantly metals, have been discussed in this chapter. Concepts of stress and strain were first introduced. Stress is a measure of an applied mechanical load or force, normalized to take into account cross-sectional area. Two different stress parameters were defined—engineering stress and true stress. Strain represents the amount of deformation induced by a stress; both engineering and true strains are used.

Some of the mechanical characteristics of metals can be ascertained by simple stress–strain tests. There are four test types: tension, compression, torsion, and shear. Tensile are the most common. A material that is stressed first undergoes elastic, or nonpermanent, deformation, wherein stress and strain are proportional. The constant of proportionality is the modulus of elasticity for tension and compression, and is the shear modulus when the stress is shear.

The phenomenon of yielding occurs at the onset of plastic or permanent deformation; yield strength is determined by a strain offset method from the stress–strain behavior, which is indicative of the stress at which plastic deformation begins. Tensile strength corresponds to the maximum tensile stress that may be sustained by a specimen, whereas percents elongation and area reduction are measures of ductility—the amount of plastic deformation that has occurred at fracture. Resilience is the capacity of a material to absorb energy during elastic deformation; modulus of resilience is the area beneath the engineering stress–strain curve up to the yield point. Also, static toughness represents the energy absorbed during the fracture of a material, and is taken as the area under the entire engineering stress–strain curve. Ductile materials are normally tougher than brittle ones.

Hardness is a measure of the resistance to localized plastic deformation. In several popular hardness-testing techniques (Rockwell, Brinell, Knoop, and Vickers) a small indenter is forced into the surface of the material, and an index number is determined on the basis of the size or depth of the resulting indentation. For many metals, hardness and tensile strength are approximately proportional to each other.

Measured mechanical properties (as well as other material properties) are not exact and precise quantities, in that there will always be some scatter for the measured data. Typical material property values are commonly specified in terms of averages, whereas magnitudes of scatter may be expressed as standard deviations.

As a result of uncertainties in both measured mechanical properties and inservice applied stresses, design or safe stresses are normally utilized for design purposes. For ductile materials, safe stress is the ratio of the yield strength and the factor of safety.

IMPORTANT TERMS AND CONCEPTS

Anelasticity	Hardness	Shear
Design stress	Modulus of elasticity	Tensile strength
Ductility	Plastic deformation	Toughness
Elastic deformation	Poisson's ratio	True strain
Elastic recovery	Proportional limit	True stress
Engineering strain	Resilience	Yielding
Engineering stress	Safe stress	Yield strength

REFERENCES

ASM Handbook, Vol. 8, *Mechanical Testing*, ASM International, Materials Park, OH, 1985.

Boyer, H. E. (Editor), *Atlas of Stress–Strain Curves*, ASM International, Materials Park, OH, 1986.

Boyer, H. E. (Editor), *Hardness Testing*, ASM International, Metals Park, OH, 1987.

Dieter, G. E., *Mechanical Metallurgy*, 3rd edition, McGraw-Hill Book Co., New York, 1986.

Dowling, N. E., *Mechanical Behavior of Materials*, Prentice Hall, Inc., Englewood Cliffs, NJ, 1993.

Han, P. (Editor), *Tensile Testing*, ASM International, Materials Park, OH, 1992.

Hayden, H. W., W. G. Moffatt, and J. Wulff, *The Structure and Properties of Materials*, Vol. III, *Mechanical Behavior*, John Wiley & Sons, New York, 1965.

McClintock, F. A. and A. S. Argon, *Mechanical Behavior of Materials*, Addison–Wesley Publishing Co., Reading, MA, 1966.

Meyers, M. A. and K. K. Chawla, *Mechanical Metallurgy, Principles and Applications*, Prentice Hall, Inc., Englewood Cliffs, NJ, 1984.

Tegart, W. J. M., *Elements of Mechanical Metallurgy*, The Macmillan Company, New York, 1966.

QUESTIONS AND PROBLEMS

6.1 A specimen of copper having a rectangular cross section of 15.2 mm × 19.1 mm (0.6 in. × 0.75 in.) is pulled in tension with 44,500 N (10,000 lb$_f$) force, producing only elastic deformation. Calculate the resulting strain.

6.2 A cylindrical specimen of a nickel alloy having a modulus of elasticity of 207 GPa (30 × 10^6 psi) and an original diameter of 10.2 mm (0.40 in.) will experience only elastic deformation when a tensile load of 8900 N (2000 lb$_f$) is applied. Compute the maximum length of the specimen before deformation if the maximum allowable elongation is 0.25 mm (0.010 in.).

6.3 An aluminum bar 125 mm (5.0 in.) long and having a square cross section 16.5 mm (0.65 in.) on an edge is pulled in tension with a load of 66,700 N (15,000 lb$_f$) and experiences an elongation of 0.43 mm (1.7 × 10^{-2} in.). Assuming that the deformation is entirely elastic, calculate the modulus of elasticity of the aluminum.

6.4 Consider a cylindrical titanium wire 3.0 mm (0.12 in.) in diameter and 2.5×10^4 mm (1000 in.) long. Calculate its elongation when a load of 500 N (112 lb$_f$) is applied. Assume that the deformation is totally elastic.

6.5 For a bronze alloy, the stress at which plastic deformation begins is 275 MPa (40,000 psi), and the modulus of elasticity is 115 GPa (16.7×10^6 psi).

(a) What is the maximum load that may be applied to a specimen with a cross-sectional area of 325 mm^2 (0.5 in.^{2}) without plastic deformation?

(b) If the original specimen length is 115 mm (4.5 in.), what is the maximum length to which it may be stretched without causing plastic deformation?

6.6 A cylindrical rod of steel ($E = 207$ GPa, 30×10^6 psi) having a yield strength of 310 MPa (45,000 psi) is to be subjected to a load of 11,100 N (2500 lb$_f$). If the length of the rod is 500 mm (20 in.), what must be the diameter to allow an elongation of 0.38 mm (0.015 in.)?

6.7 Consider a cylindrical specimen of an aluminum alloy (Figure 6.20) 10 mm (0.39 in.) in diameter and 75 mm (3.0 in.) long which is

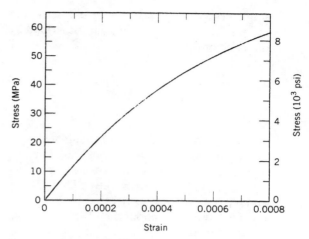

Fιϭυʀɛ 6.21 Tensile stress–strain behavior for a gray cast iron.

pulled in tension. Determine its elongation when a load of 13,500 N (3035 lb$_f$) is applied.

6.8 Figure 6.21 shows, for a gray cast iron, the tensile engineering stress–strain curve in the elastic region. Determine (a) the secant modulus taken to 35 MPa (5000 psi), and (b) the tangent modulus taken from the origin.

6.9 As was noted in Section 3.14, for single crystals of some substances, the physical properties are anisotropic, that is, they are dependent on crystallographic direction. One such property is the modulus of elasticity. For cubic

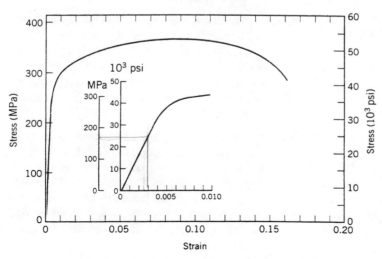

Fιϭυʀɛ 6.20 Tensile stress–strain behavior for an aluminum alloy.

single crystals, the modulus of elasticity in a general $[uvw]$ direction, E_{uvw}, is described by the relationship

$$\frac{1}{E_{uvw}} = \frac{1}{E_{\langle 100 \rangle}} - 3 \left(\frac{1}{E_{\langle 100 \rangle}} - \frac{1}{E_{\langle 111 \rangle}} \right)$$
$$(\alpha^2 \beta^2 + \beta^2 \gamma^2 + \gamma^2 \alpha^2)$$

where $E_{\langle 100 \rangle}$ and $E_{\langle 111 \rangle}$ are the moduli of elasticity in [100] and [111] directions, respectively; α, β, and γ are the cosines of the angles between $[uvw]$ and the respective [100], [010], and [001] directions. Verify that the $E_{\langle 110 \rangle}$ values for aluminum, copper, and iron in Table 3.3 are correct.

6.10 In Section 2.6 it was noted that the net bonding energy E_N between two isolated positive and negative ions is a function of interionic distance r as follows:

$$E_N = -\frac{A}{r} + \frac{B}{r^n} \qquad (6.24)$$

where A, B, and n are constants for the particular ion pair. Equation 6.24 is also valid for the bonding energy between adjacent ions in solid materials. The modulus of elasticity E is proportional to the slope of the interionic force-separation curve at the equilibrium interionic separation; that is,

$$E \propto \left(\frac{dF}{dr} \right)_{r_0}$$

Derive an expression for the dependence of the modulus of elasticity on these A, B, and n parameters (for the two-ion system) using the following procedure:

1. Establish a relationship for the force F as a function of r, realizing that

$$F = \frac{dE_N}{dr}$$

2. Now take the derivative dF/dr.

3. Develop an expression for r_0, the equilibrium separation. Since r_0 corresponds to the value of r at the minimum of the E_N-versus-r-curve (Figure 2.8b), take the derivative dE_N/dr, set it equal to zero, and solve for r, which corresponds to r_0.

4. Finally, substitute this expression for r_0 into the relationship obtained by taking dF/dr.

6.11 Using the solution to Problem 6.10, rank the magnitudes of the moduli of elasticity for the following hypothetical X, Y, and Z materials from the greatest to the least. The appropriate A, B, and n parameters (Equation 6.24) for these three materials are tabulated below; they yield E_N in units of electron volts and r in nanometers:

Material	A	B	n
X	2.5	2×10^{-5}	8
Y	2.3	8×10^{-6}	10.5
Z	3.0	1.5×10^{-5}	9

6.12 A cylindrical specimen of steel having a diameter of 15.2 mm (0.6 in.) and a length of 250 mm (10 in.) is deformed elastically in tension with a force of 48,900 N (11,000 lb$_f$). Using the data contained in Table 6.1, determine the following:

(a) The amount by which this specimen will elongate in the direction of the applied stress.

(b) The change in diameter of the specimen. Will the diameter increase or decrease?

6.13 A cylindrical bar of aluminum 19 mm (0.75 in.) in diameter is to be deformed elastically by application of a force along the bar axis. Using the data in Table 6.1, determine the force that will produce an elastic reduction of 2.5×10^{-3} mm (1.0×10^{-4} in.) in the diameter.

6.14 A cylindrical specimen of some alloy 8 mm (0.31 in.) in diameter is stressed elastically in tension. A force of 15,700 N (3530 lb$_f$) produces a reduction in specimen diameter of 5×10^{-3} mm (2×10^{-4} in.). Compute Poisson's ratio for this material if its modulus of elasticity is 140 GPa (20.3×10^6 psi).

6.15 A cylindrical specimen of a hypothetical metal alloy is stressed in compression. If its original and final diameters are 20.000 and 20.025 mm, respectively, and its final length is 74.96 mm, compute its original length if the deformation is totally elastic. The elastic and shear moduli for this alloy are 105 GPa and 39.7 GPa, respectively.

6.16 Consider a cylindrical specimen of some hypothetical metal alloy that has a diameter of 8.0 mm (0.31 in.). A tensile force of 1000 N (225 lb$_f$) produces an elastic reduction in diameter of 2.8×10^{-4} mm (1.10×10^{-5} in.). Compute the modulus of elasticity for this alloy, given that Poisson's ratio is 0.30.

6.17 A brass alloy is known to have a yield strength of 240 MPa (35,000 psi), a tensile strength of 310 MPa (45,000 psi), and a modulus of elasticity of 110 GPa (16×10^6 psi). A cylindrical specimen of this alloy 15.2 mm (0.60 in.) in diameter and 380 mm (15 in.) long is stressed in tension and found to elongate 1.9 mm (0.075 in.). On the basis of the information given, is it possible to compute the magnitude of the load that is necessary to produce this change in length? If so, calculate the load. If not, explain why.

6.18 A cylindrical metal specimen 15.0 mm (0.59 in.) in diameter and 150 mm (5.9 in.) long is to be subjected to a tensile stress of 50 MPa (7250 psi); at this stress level the resulting deformation will be totally elastic.

(a) If the elongation must be less than 0.072 mm (2.83×10^{-3} in.), which of the metals in Table 6.1 are suitable candidates? Why?

(b) If, in addition, the maximum permissible diameter decrease is 2.3×10^{-3} mm (9.1×10^{-5} in.), which of the metals in Table 6.1 may be used? Why?

6.19 Consider the brass alloy with stress–strain behavior shown in Figure 6.11. A cylindrical specimen of this material 6 mm (0.24 in.) in diameter and 50 mm (2 in.) long is pulled in tension with a force of 5000 N (1125 lb$_f$). If it is known that this alloy has a Poisson's ratio of 0.30, compute: (a) the specimen elongation, and (b) the reduction in specimen diameter.

6.20 Cite the primary differences between elastic, anelastic, and plastic deformation behaviors.

6.21 A cylindrical rod 100 mm long and having a diameter of 10.0 mm is to be deformed using a tensile load of 27,500 N. It must not experience either plastic deformation or a diameter reduction of more than 7.5×10^{-3} mm. Of the materials listed as follows, which are possible candidates? Justify your choice(s).

Material	Modulus of Elasticity (GPa)	Yield Strength (MPa)	Poisson's Ratio
Aluminum alloy	70	200	0.33
Brass alloy	101	300	0.35
Steel alloy	207	400	0.27
Titanium alloy	107	650	0.36

6.22 A cylindrical rod 20 in. (500 mm) long, having a diameter of 0.5 in. (12.7 mm), is to be subjected to a tensile load. If the rod is to experience neither plastic deformation nor an elongation of more than 0.05 in. (1.3 mm) when the applied load is 6500 lb$_f$ (29,000 N), which of the four metals or alloys listed below are possible candidates? Justify your choice(s).

Material	Modulus of Elasticity (psi)	Yield Strength (psi)	Tensile Strength (psi)
Aluminum alloy	10×10^6	37,000	61,000
Brass alloy	14.6×10^6	50,000	61,000
Copper	16×10^6	30,000	40,000
Steel	30×10^6	65,000	80,000

6.23 Figure 6.20 shows the tensile engineering stress–strain behavior for an aluminum alloy.

(a) What is the modulus of elasticity?

(b) What is the proportional limit?

(c) What is the yield strength at a strain offset of 0.002?

(d) What is the tensile strength?

6.24 A cylindrical specimen of a brass alloy having a length of 60 mm (2.36 in.) must elongate only 10.8 mm (0.425 in.) when a tensile load of 50,000 N (11,240 lb$_f$) is applied. Under these circumstances, what must be the radius of the specimen? Consider this brass alloy to have the stress–strain behavior shown in Figure 6.11.

6.25 A load of 56,600 N (12,500 lb$_f$) is applied to a cylindrical specimen of an aluminum alloy (displaying the stress–strain behavior shown in Figure 6.20) that has a cross-sectional diameter of 15.2 mm (0.60 in.).

(a) Will the specimen experience elastic or plastic deformation? Why?

(b) If the original specimen length is 250 mm (10 in.), how much will it increase in length when this load is applied?

6.26 A bar of an aluminum alloy exhibiting the stress–strain behavior shown in Figure 6.20 is subjected to a tensile load; the specimen is 400 mm (16 in.) long and of square cross section 6.4 mm (0.25 in.) on a side.

(a) Compute the magnitude of the load necessary to produce an elongation of 0.81 mm (0.032 in.).

(b) What will be the deformation after the load is released?

6.27 A cylindrical specimen of stainless steel having a diameter of 0.505 in. (12.8 mm) and a gauge length of 2.000 in. (50.800 mm) is pulled in tension. Use the load–elongation characteristics tabulated below to complete problems a through f.

Load		Length	
lb_f	N	in.	mm
2850	12,700	2.001	50.825
5710	25,400	2.002	50.851
8560	38,100	2.003	50.876
11,400	50,800	2.004	50.902
17,100	76,200	2.006	50.952
20,000	89,100	2.008	51.003
20,800	92,700	2.010	51.054
23,000	102,500	2.015	51.181
24,200	107,800	2.020	51.308
26,800	119,400	2.030	51.562
28,800	128,300	2.040	51.816
33,650	149,700	2.080	52.832
35,750	159,000	2.120	53.848
36,000	160,400	2.140	54.356
35,850	159,500	2.160	54.864
34,050	151,500	2.200	55.880
28,000	124,700	2.230	56.642
	Fracture		

(a) Plot the data as engineering stress versus engineering strain.

(b) Compute the modulus of elasticity.

(c) Determine the yield strength at a strain offset of 0.002.

(d) Determine the tensile strength of this alloy.

(e) What is the approximate ductility, in percent elongation?

(f) Compute the modulus of resilience.

6.28 A specimen of ductile cast iron having a rectangular cross section of dimensions 4.8 mm × 15.9 mm ($\frac{3}{16}$ in. × $\frac{5}{8}$ in.) is deformed in tension. Using the load-elongation data tabulated below, complete problems a through f.

Load		Length	
N	lb_f	mm	in.
0	0	75.000	2.953
4,740	1065	75.025	2.954
9,140	2055	75.050	2.955
12,920	2900	75.075	2.956
16,540	3720	75.113	2.957
18,300	4110	75.150	2.959
20,170	4530	75.225	2.962
22,900	5145	75.375	2.968
25,070	5635	75.525	2.973
26,800	6025	75.750	2.982
28,640	6440	76.500	3.012
30,240	6800	78.000	3.071
31,100	7000	79.500	3.130
31,280	7030	81.000	3.189
30,820	6930	82.500	3.248
29,180	6560	84.000	3.307
27,190	6110	85.500	3.366
24,140	5430	87.000	3.425
18,970	4265	88.725	3.493
	Fracture		

(a) Plot the data as engineering stress versus engineering strain.

(b) Compute the modulus of elasticity.

(c) Determine the yield strength at a strain offset of 0.002.

(d) Determine the tensile strength of this alloy.

(e) Compute the modulus of resilience.

(f) What is the ductility, in percent elongation?

6.29 A cylindrical metal specimen having an original diameter of 12.8 mm (0.505 in.) and gauge length of 50.80 mm (2.000 in.) is pulled in tension until fracture occurs. The diameter at the point of fracture is 8.13 mm (0.320 in.), and the fractured gauge length is 74.17 mm (2.920 in.). Calculate the ductility in terms of percent area reduction and percent elongation.

6.30 Calculate the moduli of resilience for the materials having the stress–strain behaviors shown in Figures 6.11 and 6.20.

6.31 Determine the modulus of resilience for each of the following alloys:

Material	Yield Strength MPa	psi
Steel alloy	550	80,000
Brass alloy	350	50,750
Aluminum alloy	250	36,250
Titanium alloy	800	116,000

Use modulus of elasticity values in Table 6.1.

6.32 A brass alloy to be used for a spring application must have a modulus of resilience of at least 0.75 MPa (110 psi). What must be its minimum yield strength?

6.33 (a) Make a schematic plot showing the tensile true stress–strain behavior for a typical metal alloy.

(b) Superimpose on this plot a schematic curve for the compressive true stress–strain behavior for the same alloy. Explain any difference between this curve and the one in part a.

(c) Now superimpose a schematic curve for the compressive engineering stress–strain behavior for this same alloy, and explain any difference between this curve and the one in part b.

6.34 Show that Equations 6.17a and 6.17b are valid when there is no volume change during deformation.

6.35 Demonstrate that Equation 6.15, the expression defining true strain, may also be represented by

$$\epsilon_T = \ln\left(\frac{A_0}{A_i}\right)$$

when specimen volume remains constant during deformation. Which of these two expressions is more valid during necking? Why?

6.36 Using the data in Problem 6.27 and Equations 6.14, 6.15, and 6.17a, generate a true stress–true strain plot for stainless steel. Equation 6.17a becomes invalid past the point at which necking begins; therefore, measured diameters are given below for the last four data

points, which should be used in true stress computations.

Load		Length		Diameter	
lb_f	N	in.	mm	in.	mm
35,850	159,500	2.160	54.864	0.481	12.22
34,050	151,500	2.200	55.880	0.464	11.80
28,000	124,700	2.230	56.642	0.419	10.65

6.37 A tensile test is performed on a metal specimen, and it is found that a true plastic strain of 0.16 is produced when a true stress of 500 MPa (72,500 psi) is applied; for the same metal, the value of K in Equation 6.18 is 825 MPa (120,000 psi). Calculate the true strain that results from the application of a true stress of 600 MPa (87,000 psi).

6.38 For some metal alloy, a true stress of 415 MPa (60,175 psi) produces a plastic true strain of 0.475. How much will a specimen of this material elongate when a true stress of 325 MPa (46,125 psi) is applied if the original length is 300 mm (11.8 in.)? Assume a value of 0.25 for the strain-hardening exponent n.

6.39 The following true stresses produce the corresponding true plastic strains for a brass alloy:

σ_T (psi)	ϵ_T
60,000	0.15
70,000	0.25

What true stress is necessary to produce a true plastic strain of 0.21?

6.40 For a brass alloy, the following engineering stresses produce the corresponding plastic engineering strains, prior to necking:

Engineering Stress (MPa)	Engineering Strain
235	0.194
250	0.296

On the basis of this information, compute the *engineering* stress necessary to produce an *engineering* strain of 0.25.

6.41 Find the toughness (or energy to cause fracture) for a metal that experiences both elastic and plastic deformation. Assume Equation 6.4 for elastic deformation, that the modulus of elasticity is 103 GPa (15 × 10⁶ psi), and that elastic deformation terminates at a strain of 0.007. For plastic deformation, assume that the relationship between stress and strain is described by Equation 6.18, in which the values for K and n are 1520 MPa (221,000 psi) and 0.15, respectively. Furthermore, plastic deformation occurs between strain values of 0.007 and 0.60, at which point fracture occurs.

6.42 For a tensile test, it can be demonstrated that necking begins when

$$\frac{d\sigma_T}{d\epsilon_T} = \sigma_T \qquad (6.25)$$

Using Equation 6.18, determine the value of the true strain at this onset of necking.

6.43 Taking the logarithm of both sides of Equation 6.18 yields

$$\log \sigma_T = \log K + n \log \epsilon_T \qquad (6.26)$$

Thus, a plot of $\log \sigma_T$ versus $\log \epsilon_T$ in the plastic region to the point of necking should yield a straight line having a slope of n and an intercept (at $\log \sigma_T = 0$) of $\log K$.

Using the appropriate data tabulated in Problem 6.27, make a plot of $\log \sigma_T$ versus $\log \epsilon_T$ and determine the values of n and K. It will be necessary to convert engineering stresses and strains to true stresses and strains using Equations 6.17a and 6.17b.

6.44 A cylindrical specimen of a brass alloy 7.5 mm (0.30 in.) in diameter and 90.0 mm (3.54 in.) long is pulled in tension with a force of 6000 N (1350 lb$_f$); the force is subsequently released.

(a) Compute the final length of the specimen at this time. The tensile stress–strain behavior for this alloy is shown in Figure 6.11.

(b) Compute the final specimen length when the load is increased to 16,500 N (3700 lb$_f$) and then released.

6.45 An aluminum alloy specimen having a rectangular cross section of dimensions 19 mm × 3.2 mm ($\frac{3}{4}$ in. × $\frac{1}{8}$ in.) has the stress–strain behavior shown in Figure 6.20. If this specimen is subjected to a tensile force of 20,000 N (4500 lb$_f$), then

(a) Determine the elastic and plastic strain values once the load is completely released.

(b) If its original length is 460 mm (18 in.), what will be its final length after the load in part a is applied and then released?

6.46 (a) A 10-mm-diameter Brinell hardness indenter produced an indentation 1.62 mm in diameter in a steel alloy when a load of 500 kg was used. Compute the HB of this material.

(b) What will be the diameter of an indentation to yield a hardness of 450 HB when a 500 kg load is used?

6.47 Estimate the Brinell and Rockwell hardnesses for the following:

(a) The naval brass for which the stress–strain behavior is shown in Figure 6.11.

(b) The stainless steel for which the stress–strain behavior is given in Problem 6.27.

6.48 Using the data represented in Figure 6.18, specify equations relating tensile strength and Brinell hardness for brass and nodular cast iron, similar to Equations 6.19a and 6.19b for steels.

6.49 Cite five factors that lead to scatter in measured material properties.

6.50 Below are tabulated a number of Rockwell B hardness values, which were measured on a single steel specimen. Compute average and standard deviation hardness values.

83.3	80.7	86.4
88.3	84.7	85.2
82.8	87.8	86.9
86.2	83.5	84.4
87.2	85.5	86.3

6.51 Upon what three criteria are factors of safety based?

6.52 Determine the working stresses for the two alloys the stress–strain behaviors of which are shown in Figures 6.11 and 6.20.

Design Problem

6.D1 A large tower is to be supported by a series of steel wires. It is estimated that the load on each wire will be 11,100 N (2500 lb$_f$). Determine the minimum required wire diameter assuming a factor of safety of 2 and a yield strength of 1030 MPa (150,000 psi).

9

Phase Diagrams

scanning electron micrograph which shows the microstructure of a plain carbon steel that contains 0.44 wt% C. The large dark areas are proeutectoid ferrite. Regions having the alternating light and dark lamellar structure are pearlite; the dark and light layers in the pearlite correspond, respectively, to ferrite and cementite phases. During etching of the surface prior to examination, the ferrite phase was preferentially dissolved; thus, the pearlite appears in topographical relief with cementite layers being elevated above the ferrite layers. 3000x. (Micrograph courtesy of Republic Steel Corporation.)

9.1 INTRODUCTION

The understanding of phase diagrams for alloy systems is extremely important because there is a strong correlation between microstructure and mechanical properties, and the development of microstructure of an alloy is related to the characteristics of its phase diagram. In addition, phase diagrams provide valuable information about melting, casting, crystallization, and other phenomena.

This chapter presents and discusses the following topics: (1) terminology associated with phase diagrams and phase transformations; (2) the interpretation of phase diagrams; (3) some of the common and relatively simple binary phase diagrams, including that for the iron–carbon system; and (4) the development of equilibrium microstructures, upon cooling, for several situations.

DEFINITIONS AND BASIC CONCEPTS

It is necessary to establish a foundation of definitions and basic concepts relating to alloys, phases, and equilibrium before delving into the interpretation and utilization of phase diagrams. The term **component** is frequently used in this discussion; components are pure metals and/or compounds of which an alloy is composed. For example, in a copper–zinc brass, the components are Cu and Zn. *Solute* and *solvent,* which are also common terms, were defined in Section 4.3. Another term used in this context is **system,** which has two meanings. First, "system" may refer to a specific body of material under consideration (e.g., a ladle of molten steel). Or, it may relate to the series of possible alloys consisting of the same components, but without regard to alloy composition (e.g., the iron–carbon system).

The concept of a solid solution was introduced in Section 4.3. By way of review, a solid solution consists of atoms of at least two different types; the solute atoms occupy either substitutional or interstitial positions in the solvent lattice, and the crystal structure of the solvent is maintained.

9.2 SOLUBILITY LIMIT

For many alloy systems and at some specific temperature, there is a maximum concentration of solute atoms that may dissolve in the solvent to form a solid solution; this is called a **solubility limit.** The addition of solute in excess of this solubility limit results in the formation of another solid solution or compound that has a distinctly different composition. To illustrate this concept, consider the sugar–water ($C_{12}H_{22}O_{11}$–H_2O) system. Initially, as sugar is added to water, a sugar–water solution or syrup forms. As more sugar is introduced, the solution becomes more concentrated, until the solubility limit is reached, or the solution becomes saturated with sugar. At this time the solution is not capable of dissolving any more sugar, and further additions simply settle to the bottom of the container. Thus, the system now consists of two separate substances: a sugar–water syrup liquid solution and solid crystals of undissolved sugar.

This solubility limit of sugar in water depends on the temperature of the water and may be represented in graphical form on a plot of temperature along the ordinate and composition (in weight percent sugar) along the abscissa, as shown in Figure 9.1. Along the composition axis, increasing sugar concentration is from left to right, and percentage of water is read from right to left. Since only two components are involved (sugar and water), the sum of the concentrations at any

FIGURE 9.1 The solubility of sugar ($C_{12}H_{22}O_{11}$) in a sugar–water syrup.

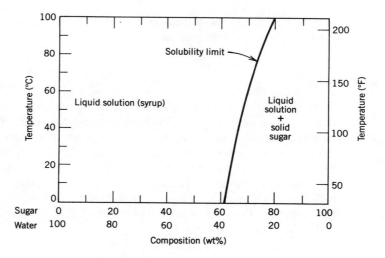

composition will equal 100 wt%. The solubility limit is represented as the nearly vertical line in the figure. For compositions and temperatures to the left of the solubility line, only the syrup liquid solution exists; to the right of the line, syrup and solid sugar coexist. The solubility limit at some temperature is the composition that corresponds to the intersection of the given temperature coordinate and the solubility limit line. For example, at 20°C the maximum solubility of sugar in water is 65 wt%. As Figure 9.1 indicates, the solubility limit increases slightly with rising temperature.

9.3 PHASES

Also critical to the understanding of phase diagrams is the concept of a **phase.** A phase may be defined as a homogeneous portion of a system that has uniform physical and chemical characteristics. Every pure material is considered to be a phase; so also is every solid, liquid, and gaseous solution. For example, the sugar–water syrup solution just discussed is one phase, and solid sugar is another. Each has different physical properties (one is a liquid, the other is a solid); furthermore, each is different chemically (i.e., has a different chemical composition); one is virtually pure sugar, the other is a solution of H_2O and $C_{12}H_{22}O_{11}$. If more than one phase is present in a given system, each will have its own distinct properties, and a boundary separating the phases will exist across which there will be a discontinuous and abrupt change in physical and/or chemical characteristics. When two phases are present in a system, it is not necessary that there be a difference in both physical and chemical properties; a disparity in one or the other set of properties is sufficient. When water and ice are present in a container, two separate phases exist; they are physically dissimilar (one is a solid, the other is a liquid) but identical in chemical makeup. Also, when a substance can exist in two or more polymorphic forms (e.g., having both FCC and BCC structures), each of these structures is a separate phase because their respective physical characteristics differ.

Sometimes, a single-phase system is termed "homogeneous." Systems composed of two or more phases are termed "mixtures" or "heterogeneous systems." Most metallic alloys, and, for that matter, ceramic, polymeric, and composite systems are heterogeneous. Ordinarily, the phases interact in such a way that the property combination of the multiphase system is different from, and more attractive than, either of the individual phases.

9.4 MICROSTRUCTURE

Many times, the physical properties and, in particular, the mechanical behavior of a material depend on the microstructure. Microstructure is subject to direct microscopic observation, using optical or electron microscopes; this topic was touched on in Section 4.9. In metal alloys, microstructure is characterized by the number of phases present, their proportions, and the manner in which they are distributed or arranged. The microstructure of an alloy depends on such variables as the alloying elements present, their concentrations, and the heat treatment of the alloy (i.e., the temperature, the heating time at temperature, and the rate of cooling to room temperature).

The procedure of specimen preparation for microscopic examination was briefly outlined in Section 4.9. After appropriate polishing and etching, the different phases may be distinguished by their appearance. For example, for a two-phase alloy, one phase may appear light, and the other phase dark, as on page 236. When only a single phase or solid solution is present, the texture will be uniform, except for grain boundaries that may be revealed (Figure 4.12b).

9.5 PHASE EQUILIBRIA

Equilibrium is another essential concept. It is best described in terms of a thermodynamic quantity called the **free energy.** In brief, free energy is a function of the internal energy of a system, and also the randomness or disorder of the atoms or molecules (or entropy). A system is at equilibrium if its free energy is at a minimum under some specified combination of temperature, pressure, and composition. In a macroscopic sense, this means that the characteristics of the system do not change with time but persist indefinitely; that is, the system is stable. A change in temperature, pressure, and/or composition for a system in equilibrium will result in an increase in the free energy and in a possible spontaneous change to another state whereby the free energy is lowered.

The term **phase equilibrium,** often used in the context of this discussion, refers to equilibrium as it applies to systems in which more than one phase may exist. Phase equilibrium is reflected by a constancy with time in the phase characteristics of a system. Perhaps an example best illustrates this concept. Suppose that a sugar–water syrup is contained in a closed vessel and the solution is in contact with solid sugar at 20°C. If the system is at equilibrium, the composition of the syrup is 65 wt% $C_{12}H_{22}O_{11}$–35 wt% H_2O (Figure 9.1), and the amounts and compositions of the syrup and solid sugar will remain constant with time. If the temperature of the system is suddenly raised—say, to 100°C—this equilibrium or balance is temporarily upset in that the solubility limit has been increased to 80 wt% $C_{12}H_{22}O_{11}$ (Figure 9.1). Thus, some of the solid sugar will go into solution in the syrup. This will continue until the new equilibrium syrup concentration is established at the higher temperature.

This sugar–syrup example has illustrated the principle of phase equilibrium using a liquid–solid system. In many metallurgical and materials systems of interest, phase equilibrium involves just solid phases. In this regard the state of the system is reflected in the characteristics of the microstructure, which necessarily include not only the phases present and their compositions but, in addition, the relative phase amounts and their spatial arrangement or distribution.

Free energy considerations and diagrams similar to Figure 9.1 provide information about the equilibrium characteristics of a particular system, which is important; but they do not indicate the time period necessary for the attainment of a new equilibrium state. It is often the case, especially in solid systems, that a state of equilibrium is never completely achieved because the rate of approach to equilibrium is extremely slow; such a system is said to be in a nonequilibrium or **metastable** state. A metastable state or microstructure may persist indefinitely, experiencing only extremely slight and almost imperceptible changes as time progresses. Often, metastable structures are of more practical significance than equilibrium ones. For example, some steel and aluminum alloys rely for their strength on the development of metastable microstructures during carefully designed heat treatments (Sections 10.5 and 11.7).

Thus not only is an understanding of equilibrium states and structures important, but the speed or rate at which they are established and, in addition, the factors that affect the rate must be considered. This chapter is devoted almost exclusively to equilibrium structures; the treatment of reaction rates and nonequilibrium structures is deferred to Chapters 10 and 11.

EQUILIBRIUM PHASE DIAGRAMS

Much of the information about the control of microstructure or phase structure of a particular alloy system is conveniently and concisely displayed in what is called a **phase diagram,** also often termed an *equilibrium* or *constitutional diagram*. Many microstructures develop from phase transformations, the changes that occur between phases when the temperature is altered (ordinarily upon cooling). This may involve the transition from one phase to another, or the appearance or disappearance of a phase. Phase diagrams are helpful in predicting phase transformations and the resulting microstructures, which may have equilibrium or nonequilibrium character.

Equilibrium phase diagrams represent the relationships between temperature and the compositions and the quantities of phases at equilibrium. There are several different varieties; but in the present discussion, temperature and composition are the variable parameters, for binary alloys. A binary alloy is one that contains two components. If more than two components are present, phase diagrams become extremely complicated and difficult to represent. The principles of microstructural control with the aid of phase diagrams can be illustrated with binary alloys even though, in reality, most alloys contain more than two components. External pressure is also a parameter that influences the phase structure. However, in practicality, pressure remains virtually constant in most applications; thus, the phase diagrams presented here are for a constant pressure of one atmosphere (1 atm).

9.6 BINARY ISOMORPHOUS SYSTEMS

Possibly the easiest type of binary phase diagram to understand and interpret is that which is characterized by the copper–nickel system (Figure 9.2a). Temperature is plotted along the ordinate, and the abscissa represents the composition of the alloy, in weight percent (bottom) and atomic percent (top) of nickel. The composition ranges from 0 wt% Ni (100 wt% Cu) on the left horizontal extremity to 100

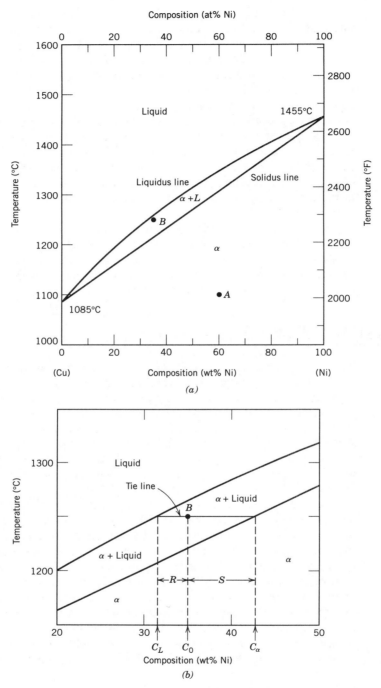

FIGURE 9.2 (a) The copper–nickel phase diagram. (Adapted from *Phase Diagrams of Binary Nickel Alloys,* P. Nash, Editor, 1991. Reprinted by permission of ASM International, Materials Park, OH 44073-0002.) (b) A portion of the copper–nickel phase diagram for which compositions and phase amounts are determined at point *B*.

wt% Ni (0 wt% Cu) on the right. Three different phase regions, or fields, appear on the diagram, an alpha (α) field, a liquid (L) field, and a two-phase $\alpha + L$ field. Each region is defined by the phase or phases that exist over the range of temperatures and compositions delimited by the phase boundary lines.

The liquid L is a homogeneous liquid solution composed of both copper and nickel. The α phase is a substitutional solid solution consisting of both Cu and Ni atoms, and having an FCC crystal structure. At temperatures below about 1080°C, copper and nickel are mutually soluble in each other in the solid state for all compositions. This complete solubility is explained by the fact that both Cu and Ni have the same crystal structure (FCC), nearly identical atomic radii and electronegativities, and similar valences, as discussed in Section 4.3. The copper–nickel system is termed **isomorphous** because of this complete liquid and solid solubility of the two components.

A couple of comments are in order regarding nomenclature. First, for metallic alloys, solid solutions are commonly designated by lowercase Greek letters (α, β, γ, etc.). Furthermore, with regard to phase boundaries, the line separating the L and $\alpha + L$ phase fields is termed the *liquidus line,* as indicated in Figure 9.2a; the liquid phase is present at all temperatures and compositions above this line. The *solidus line* is located between the α and $\alpha + L$ regions, below which only the solid α phase exists.

For Figure 9.2a, the solidus and liquidus lines intersect at the two composition extremities; these correspond to the melting temperatures of the pure components. For example, the melting temperatures of pure copper and nickel are 1085°C and 1453°C, respectively. Heating pure copper corresponds to moving vertically up the left-hand temperature axis. Copper remains solid until its melting temperature is reached. The solid-to-liquid transformation takes place at the melting temperature, and no further heating is possible until this transformation has been completed.

For any composition other than pure components, this melting phenomenon will occur over the range of temperatures between the solidus and liquidus lines; both solid α and liquid phases will be in equilibrium within this temperature range. For example, upon heating an alloy of composition 50 wt% Ni–50 wt% Cu (Figure 9.2a), melting begins at approximately 1280°C (2340°F); the amount of liquid phase continuously increases with temperature until about 1320°C (2410°F), at which the alloy is completely liquid.

INTERPRETATION OF PHASE DIAGRAMS

For a binary system of known composition and temperature that is at equilibrium, at least three kinds of information are available: (1) the phases that are present, (2) the compositions of these phases, and (3) the percentages or fractions of the phases. The procedures for making these determinations will be demonstrated using the copper–nickel system.

Phases Present

The establishment of what phases are present is relatively simple. One just locates the temperature–composition point on the diagram and notes the phase(s) with which the corresponding phase field is labeled. For example, an alloy of composition 60 wt% Ni–40 wt% Cu at 1100°C would be located at point A in Figure 9.2a; since this is within the α region, only the single α phase will be present. On the other hand, a 35 wt% Ni–65 wt% Cu alloy at 1250°C (point B) will consist of both α and liquid phases at equilibrium.

Determination of Phase Compositions

The first step in the determination of phase compositions (in terms of the concentrations of the components) is to locate the temperature–composition point on the phase diagram. Different methods are used for single- and two-phase regions. If only one phase is present, the procedure is trivial: the composition of this phase is simply the same as the overall composition of the alloy. For example, consider the 60 wt% Ni–40 wt% Cu alloy at 1100°C (point *A*, Figure 9.2*a*). At this composition and temperature, only the α phase is present, having a composition of 60 wt% Ni–40 wt% Cu.

For an alloy having composition and temperature located in a two-phase region, the situation is more complicated. In all two-phase regions (and in two-phase regions only), one may imagine a series of horizontal lines, one at every temperature; each of these is known as a **tie line,** or sometimes as an isotherm. These tie lines extend across the two-phase region and terminate at the phase boundary lines on either side. To compute the equilibrium concentrations of the two phases, the following procedure is used:

1. A tie line is constructed across the two-phase region at the temperature of the alloy.

2. The intersections of the tie line and the phase boundaries on either side are noted.

3. Perpendiculars are dropped from these intersections to the horizontal composition axis, from which the composition of each of the respective phases is read.

For example, consider again the 35 wt% Ni–65 wt% Cu alloy at 1250°C, located at point *B* in Figure 9.2*b* and lying within the $\alpha + L$ region. Thus, the problem is to determine the composition (in wt% Ni and Cu) for both the α and liquid phases. The tie line has been constructed across the $\alpha + L$ phase region, as shown in Figure 9.2*b*. The perpendicular from the intersection of the tie line with the liquidus boundary meets the composition axis at 31.5 wt% Ni–68.5 wt% Cu, which is the composition of the liquid phase, C_L. Likewise, for the solidus–tie line intersection, we find a composition for the α solid-solution phase, C_α, of 42.5 wt% Ni–57.5 wt% Cu.

Determination of Phase Amounts

The relative amounts (as fraction or as percentage) of the phases present at equilibrium may also be computed with the aid of phase diagrams. Again, the single- and two-phase situations must be treated separately. The solution is obvious in the single-phase region: Since only one phase is present, the alloy is composed entirely of that phase; that is, the phase fraction is 1.0 or, alternately, the percentage is 100%. From the previous example for the 60 wt% Ni–40 wt% Cu alloy at 1100°C (point *A* in Figure 9.2*a*), only the α phase is present; hence, the alloy is completely or 100% α.

If the composition and temperature position is located within a two-phase region, things are more complex. The tie line must be utilized in conjunction with a procedure that is often called the **lever rule** (or the *inverse lever rule*), which is applied as follows:

1. The tie line is constructed across the two-phase region at the temperature of the alloy.

2. The overall alloy composition is located on the tie line.

3. The fraction of one phase is computed by taking the length of tie line from the overall alloy composition to the phase boundary for the *other* phase, and dividing by the total tie line length.

4. The fraction of the other phase is determined in the same manner.

5. If phase percentages are desired, each phase fraction is multiplied by 100. When the composition axis is scaled in weight percent, the phase fractions computed using the lever rule are mass fractions—the mass (or weight) of a specific phase divided by the total alloy mass (or weight). The mass of each phase is computed from the product of each phase fraction and the total alloy mass.

In the employment of the lever rule, tie line segment lengths may be determined either by direct measurement from the phase diagram using a linear scale, preferrably graduated in millimeters, or by subtracting compositions as taken from the composition axis.

Consider again the example shown in Figure 9.2b, in which at 1250°C both α and liquid phases are present for a 35 wt% Ni–65 wt% Cu alloy. The problem is to compute the fraction of each of the α and liquid phases. The tie line has been constructed that was used for the determination of α and L phase compositions. Let the overall alloy composition be located along the tie line and denoted as C_0, and mass fractions be represented by W_L and W_α for the respective phases. From the lever rule, W_L may be computed according to

$$W_L = \frac{S}{R + S} \tag{9.1a}$$

or, by subtracting compositions,

$$W_L = \frac{C_\alpha - C_0}{C_\alpha - C_L} \tag{9.1b}$$

Composition need be specified only in terms of one of the constituents for a binary alloy; for the computation above, weight percent nickel will be used (i.e., $C_0 = 35$ wt% Ni, $C_\alpha = 42.5$ wt% Ni, and $C_L = 31.5$ wt% Ni), and

$$W_L = \frac{42.5 - 35}{42.5 - 31.5} = 0.68$$

Similarly, for the α phase,

$$W_\alpha = \frac{R}{R + S} \tag{9.2a}$$

$$= \frac{C_0 - C_L}{C_\alpha - C_L} \tag{9.2b}$$

$$= \frac{35 - 31.5}{42.5 - 31.5} = 0.32$$

Of course, identical answers are obtained if compositions are expressed in weight percent copper instead of nickel.

Thus, the lever rule may be employed to determine the relative amounts or fractions of phases in any two-phase region for a binary alloy if the temperature and composition are known and if equilibrium has been established. Its derivation is presented as an example problem.

It is easy to confuse the foregoing procedures for the determination of phase compositions and fractional phase amounts; thus, a brief summary is warranted. *Compositions* of phases are expressed in terms of weight percents of the components (e.g., wt% Cu, wt% Ni). For any alloy consisting of a single phase, the composition of that phase is the same as the total alloy composition. If two phases are present, the tie line must be employed, the extremities of which determine the compositions of the respective phases. With regard to *fractional phase amounts* (e.g., mass fraction of the α or liquid phase), when a single phase exists, the alloy is completely that phase. For a two-phase alloy, on the other hand, the lever rule is utilized, in which a ratio of tie line segment lengths is taken.

EXAMPLE PROBLEM 9.1

Derive the lever rule.

SOLUTION

Consider the phase diagram for copper and nickel (Figure 9.2b) and alloy of composition C_0 at 1250°C, and let C_α, C_L, W_α, and W_L represent the same parameters as above. This derivation is accomplished through two conservation-of-mass expressions. With the first, since only two phases are present, the sum of their mass fractions must be equal to unity, that is,

$$W_\alpha + W_L = 1 \tag{9.3}$$

For the second, the mass of one of the components (either Cu or Ni) that is present in both of the phases must be equal to the mass of that component in the total alloy, or

$$W_\alpha C_\alpha + W_L C_L = C_0 \tag{9.4}$$

Simultaneous solution of these two equations leads to the lever rule expressions for this particular situation, Equations 9.1b and 9.2b:

$$W_L = \frac{C_\alpha - C_0}{C_\alpha - C_L} \tag{9.1b}$$

$$W_\alpha = \frac{C_0 - C_L}{C_\alpha - C_L} \tag{9.2b}$$

For multiphase alloys, it is often more convenient to specify relative phase amount in terms of volume fraction rather than mass fraction. Phase volume fractions are preferred because they (rather than mass fractions) may be determined from examination of the microstructure; furthermore, the properties of a multiphase alloy may be estimated on the basis of volume fractions.

For an alloy consisting of α and β phases, the volume fraction of the α phase, V_α, is defined as

$$V_\alpha = \frac{v_\alpha}{v_\alpha + v_\beta} \tag{9.5}$$

where v_α and v_β denote the volumes of the respective phases in the alloy. Of course, an analogous expression exists for V_β; and, for an alloy consisting of just two phases, it is the case that $V_\alpha + V_\beta = 1$.

On occasion conversion from mass fraction to volume fraction (or vice versa) is desired. Equations that facilitate these conversions are as follows:

$$V_\alpha = \frac{\dfrac{W_\alpha}{\rho_\alpha}}{\dfrac{W_\alpha}{\rho_\alpha} + \dfrac{W_\beta}{\rho_\beta}} \tag{9.6a}$$

$$V_\beta = \frac{\dfrac{W_\beta}{\rho_\beta}}{\dfrac{W_\alpha}{\rho_\alpha} + \dfrac{W_\beta}{\rho_\beta}} \tag{9.6b}$$

and

$$W_\alpha = \frac{V_\alpha \rho_\alpha}{V_\alpha \rho_\alpha + V_\beta \rho_\beta} \tag{9.7a}$$

$$W_\beta = \frac{V_\beta \rho_\beta}{V_\alpha \rho_\alpha + V_\beta \rho_\beta} \tag{9.7b}$$

In these expressions, ρ_α and ρ_β are the densities of the respective phases; these may be determined approximately using Equations 4.10a and 4.10b.

When the densities of the phases in a two-phase alloy differ significantly, there will be quite a disparity between mass and volume fractions; conversely, if the phase densities are the same, weight and volume fractions are identical.

DEVELOPMENT OF MICROSTRUCTURE IN ISOMORPHOUS ALLOYS—EQUILIBRIUM COOLING

At this point it is instructive to examine the development of microstructure that occurs for isomorphous alloys during solidification. We first treat the situation in which the cooling occurs very slowly, in that phase equilibrium is continuously maintained.

Let us consider the copper–nickel system (Figure 9.2a), specifically an alloy of composition 35 wt% Ni–65 wt% Cu as it is cooled from 1300°C. The region of the Cu–Ni phase diagram in the vicinity of this composition is shown in Figure 9.3. Cooling of an alloy of the above composition corresponds to moving down the vertical dashed line. At 1300°C, point a, the alloy is completely liquid (of composition 35 wt% Ni–65 wt% Cu) and has the microstructure represented by the circle inset in the figure. As cooling begins, no microstructural or compositional changes will be realized until we reach the liquidus line (point b, ~1260°C). At this point, the first solid α begins to form, which has a composition dictated by the tie line drawn at this temperature [i.e., 46 wt% Ni–54 wt% Cu, noted as α(46 Ni)]; the composition of liquid is still approximately 35 wt% Ni–65 wt% Cu [L(35 Ni)], which is different than that of the solid α. With continued cooling, both compositions and relative amounts of each of the phases will change. The compositions of the liquid and α phases will follow the liquidus and solidus lines, respectively. Furthermore, the

FIGURE 9.3 Schematic representation of the development of microstructure during the equilibrium solidification of a 35 wt% Ni–65 wt% Cu alloy.

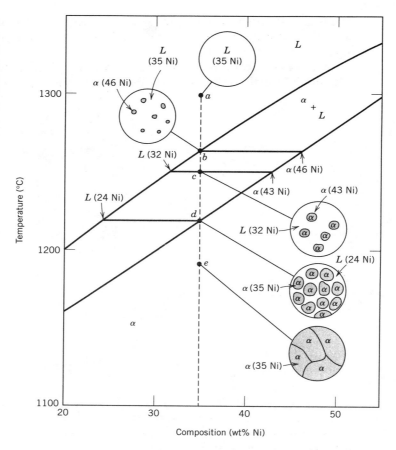

fraction of the α phase will increase with continued cooling. Note that the overall alloy composition (35 wt% Ni–65 wt% Cu) remains unchanged during cooling even though there is a redistribution of copper and nickel between the phases.

At 1250°C, point c in Figure 9.3, the compositions of the liquid and α phases are 32 wt% Ni–68 wt% Cu [L (32 Ni)] and 43 wt% Ni–57 wt% Cu [α(43 Ni)], respectively.

The solidification process is virtually complete at about 1220°C, point d; the composition of the solid α is approximately 35 wt% Ni–65 wt% Cu (the overall alloy composition) while that of the last remaining liquid is 24 wt% Ni–76 wt% Cu. Upon crossing the solidus line, this remaining liquid solidifies; the final product then is a polycrystalline α-phase solid solution that has a uniform 35 wt% Ni–65 wt% Cu composition (point e, Figure 9.3). Subsequent cooling will produce no microstructural or compositional alterations.

DEVELOPMENT OF MICROSTRUCTURE— NONEQUILIBRIUM COOLING

Conditions of equilibrium solidification and the development of microstructures, as described in the previous section, are realized only for extremely slow cooling rates. The reason for this is that with changes in temperature, there must be readjustments in the compositions of the liquid and solid phases in accordance with the phase diagram (i.e., with the liquidus and solidus lines), as discussed. These readjustments are accomplished by diffusional processes, that is, diffusion in both solid and liquid phases and also across the solid–liquid interface. Inasmuch as diffusion is a time-dependent phenomenon (Section 5.3), to maintain equilibrium during cooling, sufficient time must be allowed at each temperature for the appropriate compositional readjustments. Diffusion rates (i.e., the magnitudes of the diffusion coefficients) are especially low for the solid phase and, for both phases, decrease with diminishing temperature. In virtually all practical solidification situations, cooling rates are much too rapid to allow these compositional readjustments and maintenance of equilibrium; consequently, microstructures other than those previously described develop.

Some of the consequences of nonequilibrium solidification for isomorphous alloys will now be discussed by considering a 35 wt% Ni–65 wt% Cu alloy, the same composition that was used for equilibrium cooling in the previous section. The portion of the phase diagram near this composition is shown in Figure 9.4; in addition, microstructures and associated phase compositions at various temperatures upon cooling are noted in the circular insets. In order to simplify this discussion it will be assumed that diffusion rates in the liquid phase are sufficiently rapid such that equilibrium is maintained in the liquid.

FIGURE 9.4 Schematic representation of the development of microstructure during the nonequilibrium solidification of a 35 wt% Ni–65 wt% Cu alloy.

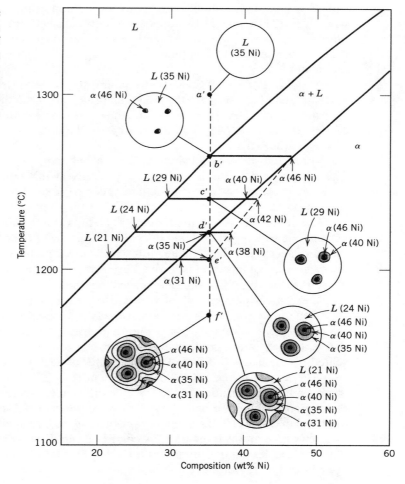

Let us begin cooling from a temperature of about 1300°C; this is indicated by point a' in the liquid region. This liquid has a composition of 35 wt% Ni–65 wt% Cu [noted as $L(35 \text{ Ni})$ in the figure], and no changes occur while cooling through the liquid phase region (moving down vertically from point a'). At point b' (approximately 1260°C), α phase particles begin to form, which, from the tie line constructed, have a composition of 46 wt% Ni–54 wt% Cu [$\alpha(46 \text{ Ni})$].

Upon further cooling to point c' (about 1240°C), the liquid composition has shifted to 29 wt% Ni–71 wt% Cu; furthermore, at this temperature the composition of the α phase that solidified is 40 wt% Ni–60 wt% Cu [$\alpha(40 \text{ Ni})$]. However, since diffusion in the solid α phase is relatively slow, the α phase that formed at point b' has not changed composition appreciably—i.e., it is still about 46 wt% Ni—and the composition of the α grains has continuously changed with radial position, from 46 wt% Ni at grain centers to 40 wt% Ni at the outer grain perimeters. Thus, at point c', the *average composition* of the solid α grains that have formed would be some volume weighted average composition, lying between 46 and 40 wt% Ni; for the sake of argument, let us take this average composition to be 42 wt% Ni–58 wt% Cu [$\alpha(42 \text{ Ni})$]. Furthermore, we would also find that, on the basis of lever-rule computations, a greater proportion of liquid is present for these nonequilibrium conditions than for equilibrium cooling. The implication of this nonequilibrium solidification phenomenon is that the solidus line on the phase diagram has been shifted to higher Ni contents—to the average compositions of the α phase (e.g., 42 wt% Ni at 1240°C)—and is represented by the dashed line in Figure 9.4. There is no comparable alteration of the liquidus line inasmuch as it is assumed that equilibrium is maintained in the liquid phase during cooling because of sufficiently rapid diffusion rates.

At point d', (~1220°C) and for equilibrium cooling rates, solidification should be completed. However, for this nonequilibrium situation, there is still an appreciable proportion of liquid remaining, and the α phase that is forming has a composition of 35 wt% Ni [$\alpha(35 \text{ Ni})$]; also the *average* α-phase composition at this point is 38 wt% Ni [$\alpha(38 \text{ Ni})$].

Nonequilibrium solidification finally reaches completion at point e' (~1205°C). The composition of the last α phase to solidify at this point is about 31 wt% Ni; the *average* composition of the α phase at complete solidification is 35 wt% Ni. The inset at point f' shows the microstructure of the totally solid material.

The degree of displacement of the nonequilibrium solidus curve from the equilibrium one will depend on rate of cooling. The slower the cooling rate, the smaller this displacement—that is, the difference between the equilibrium solidus and average solid composition is lower. Furthermore, if the diffusion rate in the solid phase is increased, this displacement will be diminished.

There are some important consequences for isomorphous alloys that have solidified under nonequilibrium conditions. As discussed above, the distribution of the two elements within the grains is nonuniform, a phenomenon termed *segregation;* that is, concentration gradients are established across the grains, which are represented by the insets of Figure 9.4. The center of each grain, which is the first part to freeze, is rich in the high-melting element (e.g., nickel for this Cu–Ni system), whereas the concentration of the low-melting element increases with position from this region to the grain boundary. This is termed a *cored* structure, which may be observed in Color Plate D, a micrograph of a cast bronze alloy; variation of composition across the grains is manifest by color hue variations. The properties of a cored structure are less than optimal; as a casting having a cored structure is reheated, grain boundary regions will melt first inasmuch as they are richer in the low-melting

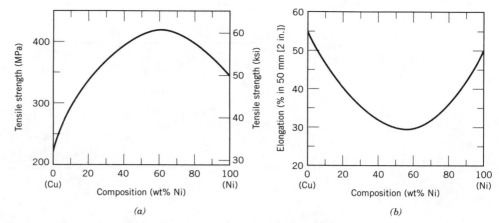

FIGURE 9.5   For the copper–nickel system, (a) tensile strength versus composition, and (b) ductility (%EL) versus composition at room temperature. A solid solution exists over all compositions for this system.

component. This produces a sudden loss in mechanical integrity due to the thin liquid film that separates the grains. Furthermore, this melting may begin at a temperature below the equilibrium solidus temperature of the alloy. Coring may be eliminated by a homogenization heat treatment carried out at a temperature below the solidus point for the particular alloy composition. During this process, atomic diffusion occurs, which produces compositionally homogeneous grains.

MECHANICAL PROPERTIES OF ISOMORPHOUS ALLOYS

We shall now briefly explore how the mechanical properties of solid isomorphous alloys are affected by composition as other structural variables (e.g., grain size) are held constant. For all temperatures and compositions below the melting temperature of the lowest-melting component, only a single solid phase will exist. Therefore, each component will experience solid-solution strengthening (Section 7.9), or an increase in strength and hardness by additions of the other component. This effect is demonstrated in Figure 9.5a as tensile strength versus composition for the copper–nickel system at room temperature; at some intermediate composition, the curve necessarily passes through a maximum. Plotted in Figure 9.5b is the ductility (%EL)–composition behavior, which is just the opposite of tensile strength; that is, ductility decreases with additions of the second component, and the curve exhibits a minimum.

9.7 BINARY EUTECTIC SYSTEMS

Another type of common and relatively simple phase diagram found for binary alloys is shown in Figure 9.6 for the copper–silver system; this is known as a binary eutectic phase diagram. A number of features of this phase diagram are important and worth noting. First of all, three single-phase regions are found on the diagram: α, β, and liquid. The α phase is a solid solution rich in copper; it has silver as the solute component and an FCC crystal structure. The β phase solid solution also has an FCC structure, but copper is the solute. Technically, pure copper and pure silver are considered to be α and β phases, respectively.

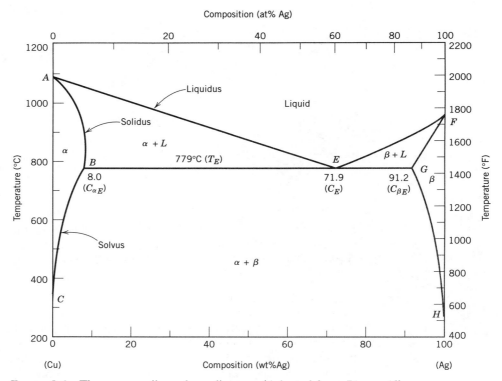

Composition (at% Ag)

FIGURE 9.6   The copper–silver phase diagram. (Adapted from *Binary Alloy Phase Diagrams,* 2nd edition, Vol. 1, T. B. Massalski, Editor-in-Chief, 1990. Reprinted by permission of ASM International, Materials Park, OH 44073-0002.)

Thus, the solubility in each of these solid phases is limited, in that at any temperature below line *BEG* only a limited concentration of silver will dissolve in copper (for the α phase), and similarly for copper in silver (for the β phase). The solubility limit for the α phase corresponds to the boundary line, labeled *CBA*, between the $\alpha/(\alpha + \beta)$ and $\alpha/(\alpha + L)$ phase regions; it increases with temperature to a maximum [8.0 wt% Ag at 779°C (1434°F)] at point *B*, and decreases back to zero at the melting temperature of pure copper, point *A* [1085°C (1985°F)]. At temperatures below 779°C (1434°F), the solid solubility limit line separating the α and $\alpha + \beta$ phase regions is termed a **solvus line;** the boundary *AB* between the α and *L* fields is the **solidus line,** as indicated in Figure 9.6. For the β phase, both solvus and solidus lines also exist, *HG* and *GF*, respectively, as shown. The maximum solubility of copper in the β phase, point *G* (8.8 wt% Cu), also occurs at 779°C (1434°F). This horizontal line *BEG*, which is parallel to the composition axis and extends between these maximum solubility positions, may also be considered to be a solidus line; it represents the lowest temperature at which a liquid phase may exist for any copper–silver alloy that is at equilibrium.

There are also three two-phase regions found for the copper–silver system (Figure 9.6): $\alpha + L$, $\beta + L$, and $\alpha + \beta$. The α and β phase solid solutions coexist for all compositions and temperatures within the $\alpha + \beta$ phase field; the α + liquid and β + liquid phases also coexist in their respective phase regions. Furthermore, compositions and relative amounts for the phases may be determined using tie lines and the lever rule as outlined in the preceding section.

As silver is added to copper, the temperature at which the alloys become totally liquid decreases along the liquidus line, line AE; thus, the melting temperature of copper is lowered by silver additions. The same may be said for silver: the introduction of copper reduces the temperature of complete melting along the other liquidus line, FE. These liquidus lines meet at the point E on the phase diagram, through which also passes the horizontal isotherm line BEG. Point E is called an **invariant point,** which is designated by the composition C_E and temperature T_E; for the copper–silver system, the values of C_E and T_E are 71.9 wt% Ag and 779°C (1434°F), respectively.

An important reaction occurs for an alloy of composition C_E as it changes temperature in passing through T_E; this reaction may be written as follows:

$$L(C_E) \underset{\text{heating}}{\overset{\text{cooling}}{\rightleftharpoons}} \alpha(C_{\alpha E}) + \beta(C_{\beta E}) \tag{9.8}$$

Or, upon cooling, a liquid phase is transformed into the two solid α and β phases at the temperature T_E; the opposite reaction occurs upon heating. This is called a **eutectic reaction** (eutectic means easily melted), and C_E and T_E represent the eutectic composition and temperature, respectively; $C_{\alpha E}$ and $C_{\beta E}$ are the respective compositions of the α and β phases at T_E. Thus, for the copper–silver system, the eutectic reaction, Equation 9.8, may be written as follows:

$$L(71.9\,\text{wt\% Ag}) \underset{\text{heating}}{\overset{\text{cooling}}{\rightleftharpoons}} \alpha(8.0\,\text{wt\% Ag}) + \beta(91.2\,\text{wt\% Ag})$$

Often, the horizontal solidus line at T_E is called the *eutectic isotherm.*

The eutectic reaction, upon cooling, is similar to solidification for pure components in that the reaction proceeds to completion at a constant temperature, or isothermally, at T_E. However, the solid product of eutectic solidification is always two solid phases, whereas for a pure component only a single phase forms. Because of this eutectic reaction, phase diagrams similar to that in Figure 9.6 are termed eutectic phase diagrams; components exhibiting this behavior comprise a eutectic system.

In the construction of binary phase diagrams, it is important to understand that one or at most two phases may be in equilibrium within a phase field. This holds true for the phase diagrams in Figures 9.2a and 9.6. For a eutectic system, three phases (α, β, and L) may be in equilibrium, but only at points along the eutectic isotherm. Another general rule is that single-phase regions are always separated from each other by a two-phase region which consists of the two single phases that it separates. For example, the $\alpha + \beta$ field is situated between the α and β single-phase regions in Figure 9.6.

Another common eutectic system is that for lead and tin; the phase diagram (Figure 9.7) has a general shape similar to that for copper–silver. For the lead–tin system the solid solution phases are also designated by α and β; in this case, α represents a solid solution of tin in lead, and for β, tin is the solvent and lead is the solute. The eutectic invariant point is located at 61.9 wt% Sn and 183°C (361°F). Of course, maximum solid solubility compositions as well as component melting temperatures will be different for the copper–silver and lead–tin systems, as may be observed by comparing their phase diagrams.

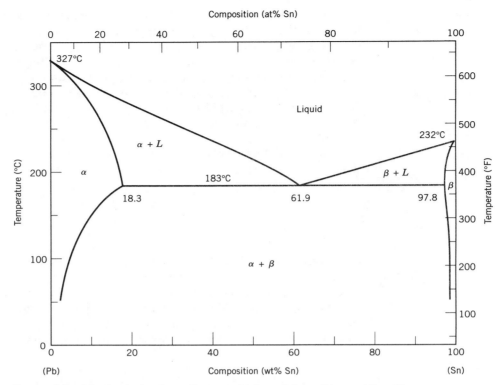

FIGURE 9.7   The lead–tin phase diagram. (Adapted from *Binary Alloy Phase Diagrams,* 2nd edition, Vol. 3, T. B. Massalski, Editor-in-Chief, 1990. Reprinted by permission of ASM International, Materials Park, OH 44073-0002.)

On occasion, low-melting-temperature alloys are prepared having near-eutectic compositions. A familiar example is the 60–40 solder, containing 60 wt% Sn and 40 wt% Pb. Figure 9.7 indicates that an alloy of this composition is completely molten at about 185°C (365°F), which makes this material especially attractive as a low-temperature solder, since it is easily melted.

EXAMPLE PROBLEM 9.2

For a 40 wt% Sn–60 wt% Pb alloy at 150°C (300°F), **(a)** What phase(s) is (are) present? **(b)** What is (are) the composition(s) of the phase(s)?

SOLUTION

(a) Locate this temperature–composition point on the phase diagram (point *B* in Figure 9.8). Inasmuch as it is within the $\alpha + \beta$ region, both α and β phases will coexist.

(b) Since two phases are present, it becomes necessary to construct a tie line across the $\alpha + \beta$ phase field at 150°C, as indicated in Figure 9.8. The composition of the α phase corresponds to the tie line intersection with the $\alpha/(\alpha + \beta)$ solvus

FIGURE 9.8 The lead–tin phase diagram. For a 40 wt% Sn–60 wt% Pb alloy at 150°C (point B), phase compositions and relative amounts are computed in Example Problems 9.2 and 9.3.

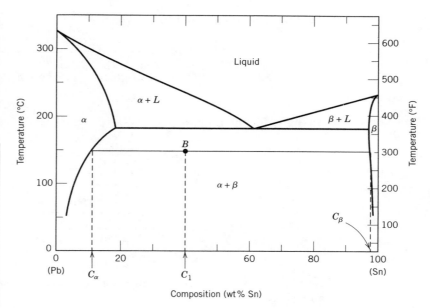

phase boundary—about 10 wt% Sn–90 wt% Pb, denoted as C_α. Similarly for the β phase, which will have a composition approximately 98 wt% Sn–2 wt% Pb (C_β).

EXAMPLE PROBLEM 9.3

For the lead-tin alloy in Example Problem 9.2, calculate the relative amount of each phase present in terms of (a) mass fraction and (b) volume fraction. At 150°C take the densities of Pb and Sn to be 11.23 and 7.24 g/cm³, respectively.

SOLUTION

(a) Since the alloy consists of two phases, it is necessary to employ the lever rule. If C_1 denotes the overall alloy composition, mass fractions may be computed by subtracting compositions, in terms of weight percent tin, as follows:

$$W_\alpha = \frac{C_\beta - C_1}{C_\beta - C_\alpha} = \frac{98 - 40}{98 - 10} = 0.66$$

$$W_\beta = \frac{C_1 - C_\alpha}{C_\beta - C_\alpha} = \frac{40 - 10}{98 - 10} = 0.34$$

(b) To compute volume fractions it is first necessary to determine the density of each phase using Equation 4.10a. Thus

$$\rho_\alpha = \frac{100}{\dfrac{C_{Sn(\alpha)}}{\rho_{Sn}} + \dfrac{C_{Pb(\alpha)}}{\rho_{Pb}}}$$

where $C_{Sn(\alpha)}$ and $C_{Pb(\alpha)}$ denote the concentrations in weight percent of tin and lead, respectively, in the α phase. From Example Problem 9.2, these values are 10 wt% and 90 wt%. Incorporation of these values along with the densities of the two components lead to

$$\rho_\alpha = \cfrac{100}{\cfrac{10}{7.24 \text{ g/cm}^3} + \cfrac{90}{11.23 \text{ g/cm}^3}}$$

$$= 10.64 \text{ g/cm}^3$$

Similarly for the β phase

$$\rho_\beta = \cfrac{100}{\cfrac{C_{\text{Sn}(\beta)}}{\rho_{\text{Sn}}} + \cfrac{C_{\text{Pb}(\beta)}}{\rho_{\text{Pb}}}}$$

$$= \cfrac{100}{\cfrac{98}{7.24 \text{ g/cm}^3} + \cfrac{2}{11.23 \text{ g/cm}^3}}$$

$$= 7.29 \text{ g/cm}^3$$

Now it becomes necessary to employ Equations 9.6a and 9.6b to determine V_α and V_β as

$$V_\alpha = \cfrac{\cfrac{W_\alpha}{\rho_\alpha}}{\cfrac{W_\alpha}{\rho_\alpha} + \cfrac{W_\beta}{\rho_\beta}}$$

$$= \cfrac{\cfrac{0.66}{10.64 \text{ g/cm}^3}}{\cfrac{0.66}{10.64 \text{ g/cm}^3} + \cfrac{0.34}{7.29 \text{ g/cm}^3}} = 0.57$$

$$V_\beta = \cfrac{\cfrac{W_\beta}{\rho_\beta}}{\cfrac{W_\alpha}{\rho_\alpha} + \cfrac{W_\beta}{\rho_\beta}}$$

$$= \cfrac{\cfrac{0.34}{7.29 \text{ g/cm}^3}}{\cfrac{0.66}{10.64 \text{ g/cm}^3} + \cfrac{0.34}{7.29 \text{ g/cm}^3}} = 0.43$$

DEVELOPMENT OF MICROSTRUCTURE IN EUTECTIC ALLOYS

Depending on composition, several different types of microstructures are possible for the slow cooling of alloys belonging to binary eutectic systems. These possibilities will be considered in terms of the lead–tin phase diagram, Figure 9.7.

The first case is for compositions ranging between a pure component and the maximum solid solubility for that component at room temperature [20°C (70°F)]. For the lead–tin system, this includes lead-rich alloys containing between 0 and about 2 wt% Sn (for the α phase solid solution), and also between approximately 99 wt% Sn and pure tin (for the β phase). For example, consider an alloy of

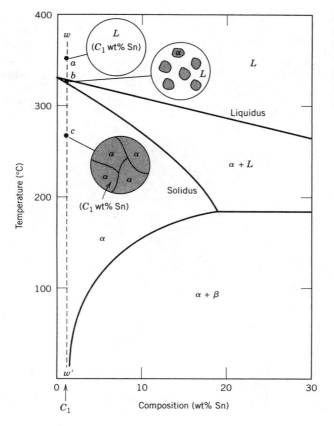

FIGURE 9.9 Schematic representations of the equilibrium microstructures for a lead–tin alloy of composition C_1 as it is cooled from the liquid-phase region.

composition C_1 (Figure 9.9) as it is slowly cooled from a temperature within the liquid-phase region, say, 350°C; this corresponds to moving down the dashed vertical line ww' in the figure. The alloy remains totally liquid and of composition C_1 until we cross the liquidus line at approximately 330°C, at which time the solid α phase begins to form. While passing through this narrow $\alpha + L$ phase region, solidification proceeds in the same manner as was described for the copper–nickel alloy in the preceding section; that is, with continued cooling more of the solid α forms. Furthermore, liquid- and solid-phase compositions are different, which follow along the liquidus and solidus phase boundaries, respectively. Solidification reaches completion at the point where ww' crosses the solidus line. The resulting alloy is polycrystalline with a uniform composition of C_1, and no subsequent changes will occur upon cooling to room temperature. This microstructure is represented schematically by the inset at point c in Figure 9.9.

The second case considered is for compositions that range between the room temperature solubility limit and the maximum solid solubility at the eutectic temperature. For the lead–tin system (Figure 9.7), these compositions extend from about 2 wt% Sn to 18.3 wt% Sn (for lead-rich alloys) and from 97.8 wt% Sn to approximately 99 wt% Sn (for tin-rich alloys). Let us examine an alloy of composition C_2 as it is cooled along the vertical line xx' in Figure 9.10. Down to the intersection of xx' and the solvus line, changes that occur are similar to the previous case, as we pass through the corresponding phase regions (as demonstrated by the insets at points

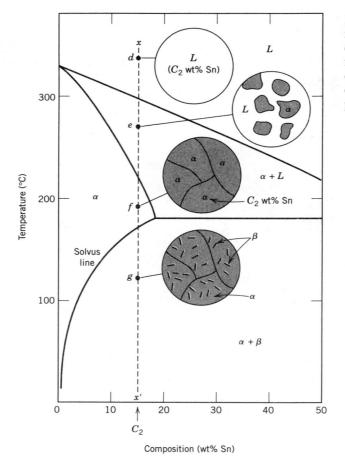

FIGURE 9.10 Schematic representations of the equilibrium microstructures for a lead–tin alloy of composition C_2 as it is cooled from the liquid-phase region.

d, e, and f). Just above the solvus intersection, point f, the microstructure consists of α grains of composition C_2. Upon crossing the solvus line, the α solid solubility is exceeded, which results in the formation of small β phase particles; these are indicated in the microstructure inset at point g. With continued cooling, these particles will grow in size because the mass fraction of the β phase increases slightly with decreasing temperature.

The third case involves solidification of the eutectic composition, 61.9 wt% Sn (C_3 in Figure 9.11). Consider an alloy having this composition that is cooled from a temperature within the liquid-phase region (e.g., 250°C) down the vertical line yy' in Figure 9.11. As the temperature is lowered, no changes occur until we reach the eutectic temperature, 183°C. Upon crossing the eutectic isotherm, the liquid transforms to the two α and β phases. This transformation may be represented by the reaction

$$L(61.9 \text{ wt\% Sn}) \underset{\text{heating}}{\overset{\text{cooling}}{\rightleftarrows}} \alpha(18.3 \text{ wt\% Sn}) + \beta(97.8 \text{ wt\% Sn}) \qquad (9.9)$$

in which the α and β phase compositions are dictated by the eutectic isotherm end points.

During this transformation, there must necessarily be a redistribution of the lead and tin components, inasmuch as the α and β phases have different composi-

FIGURE 9.11
Schematic
representations of the
equilibrium
microstructures for a
lead–tin alloy of
eutectic composition C_3
above and below the
eutectic temperature.

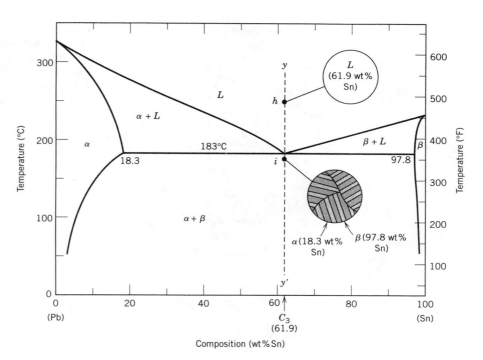

tions neither of which is the same as that of the liquid (as indicated in Equation 9.9). This redistribution is accomplished by atomic diffusion. The microstructure of the solid that results from this transformation consists of alternating layers (sometimes called lamellae) of the α and β phases that form simultaneously during the transformation. This microstructure, represented schematically in Figure 9.11, point i, is called a **eutectic structure,** and is characteristic of this reaction. A photomicrograph of this structure for the lead–tin eutectic is shown in Figure 9.12. Subsequent cooling of the alloy from just below the eutectic to room temperature will result in only minor microstructural alterations.

The microstructural change that accompanies this eutectic transformation is represented schematically in Figure 9.13; here is shown the α-β layered eutectic growing into and replacing the liquid phase. The process of the redistribution of lead and tin occurs by diffusion in the liquid just ahead of the eutectic-liquid interface. The arrows indicate the directions of diffusion of lead and tin atoms;

FIGURE 9.12 Photomicrograph showing the microstructure of a lead–tin alloy of eutectic composition. This microstructure consists of alternating layers of a lead-rich α-phase solid solution (dark layers), and a tin-rich β-phase solid solution (light layers). 375×. (Reproduced with permission from *Metals Handbook,* Vol. 9, 9th edition, *Metallography and Microstructures,* American Society for Metals, Materials Park, OH, 1985.)

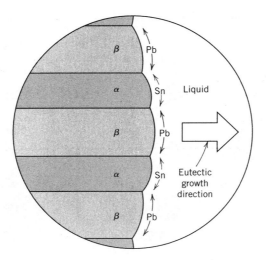

FIGURE 9.13 Schematic representation of the formation of the eutectic structure for the lead–tin system. Directions of diffusion of tin and lead atoms indicated by colored and black arrows, respectively.

lead atoms diffuse toward the α-phase layers since this α phase is lead-rich (18.3 wt% Sn–81.7 wt% Pb); conversely, the direction of diffusion of tin is in the direction of the β, tin-rich (97.8 wt% Sn–2.2 wt% Pb) layers. The eutectic structure forms in these alternating layers because, for this lamellar configuration, atomic diffusion of lead and tin need only occur over relatively short distances.

The fourth and final microstructural case for this system includes all compositions other than the eutectic that, when cooled, cross the eutectic isotherm. Consider, for example, the composition C_4, Figure 9.14, which lies to the left of the eutectic; as the temperature is lowered, we move down the line zz', beginning at point j. The microstructural development between points j and l is similar to that for the second case, such that just prior to crossing the eutectic isotherm (point l), the α and liquid phases are present having compositions of approximately 18.3 and 61.9 wt% Sn, respectively, as determined from the appropriate tie line. As the temperature is lowered to just below the eutectic, the liquid phase, which is of the eutectic composition, will transform to the eutectic structure (i.e., alternating α and β lamellae); insignificant changes will occur with the α phase which formed during cooling through the $\alpha + L$ region. This microstructure is represented schematically by the inset at point m in Figure 9.14. Thus, the α phase will be present both in the eutectic structure and also as that phase that formed while cooling through the $\alpha + L$ phase field. To distinguish one α from the other, that which resides in the eutectic structure is called **eutectic** α, while the other that formed prior to crossing the eutectic isotherm is termed **primary** α; both are labeled in Figure 9.14. The photomicrograph in Figure 9.15 is of a lead–tin alloy in which both primary α and eutectic structures are shown.

In dealing with microstructures, it is sometimes convenient to use the term **microconstituent,** that is, an element of the microstructure having an identifiable and characteristic structure. For example, in the point m inset, Figure 9.14, there are two microconstituents, namely, primary α and the eutectic structure. Thus, the eutectic structure is a microconstituent even though it is a mixture of two phases, because it has a distinct lamellar structure, with a fixed ratio of the two phases.

It is possible to compute the relative amounts of both eutectic and primary α microconstituents. Since the eutectic microconstituent always forms from the liquid having the eutectic composition, this microconstituent may be assumed to have a

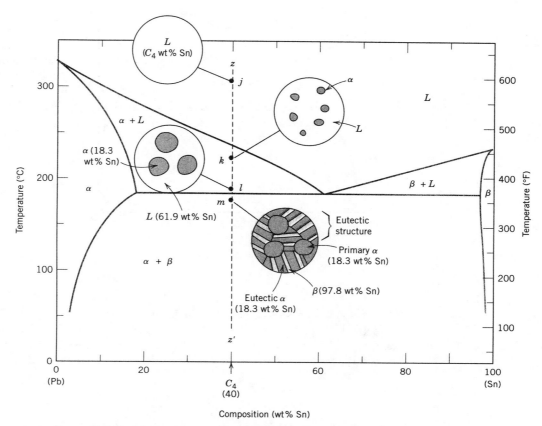

FIGURE 9.14   Schematic representations of the equilibrium microstructures for a lead–tin alloy of composition C_4 as it is cooled from the liquid-phase region.

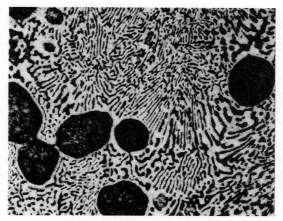

FIGURE 9.15   Photomicrograph showing the microstructure of a lead–tin alloy of composition 50 wt% Sn–50 wt% Pb. This microstructure is composed of a primary lead-rich α phase (large dark regions) within a lamellar eutectic structure consisting of a tin-rich β phase (light layers) and a lead-rich α phase (dark layers). 400×. (Reproduced with permission from *Metals Handbook,* Vol. 9, 9th edition, *Metallography and Microstructures,* American Society for Metals, Materials Park, OH, 1985.)

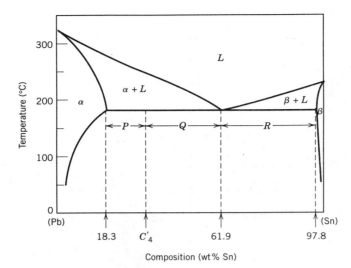

FIGURE 9.16 The lead–tin phase diagram used in computations for relative amounts of primary α and eutectic microconstituents for an alloy of composition C_4'.

composition of 61.9 wt% Sn. Hence, the lever rule is applied using a tie line between the α–($\alpha + \beta$) phase boundary (18.3 wt% Sn) and the eutectic composition. For example, consider the alloy of composition C_4' in Figure 9.16. The fraction of the eutectic microconstituent W_e is just the same as the fraction of liquid W_L from which it transforms, or

$$W_e = W_L = \frac{P}{P+Q}$$

$$= \frac{C_4' - 18.3}{61.9 - 18.3} = \frac{C_4' - 18.3}{43.6} \tag{9.10}$$

Furthermore, the fraction of primary α, $W_{\alpha'}$, is just the fraction of the α phase that existed prior to the eutectic transformation; or, from Figure 9.16,

$$W_{\alpha'} = \frac{Q}{P+Q}$$

$$= \frac{61.9 - C_4'}{61.9 - 18.3} = \frac{61.9 - C_4'}{43.6} \tag{9.11}$$

The fractions of *total* α, W_α (both eutectic and primary), and also of total β, W_β, are determined by use of the lever rule and a tie line that extends *entirely across the* $\alpha + \beta$ *phase field*. Again, for an alloy having composition C_4',

$$W_\alpha = \frac{Q+R}{P+Q+R}$$

$$= \frac{97.8 - C_4'}{97.8 - 18.3} = \frac{97.8 - C_4'}{79.5} \tag{9.12}$$

and

$$W_\beta = \frac{P}{P + Q + R}$$

$$= \frac{C_4' - 18.3}{97.8 - 18.3} = \frac{C_4' - 18.3}{79.5} \tag{9.13}$$

Analogous transformations and microstructures result for alloys having compositions to the right of the eutectic (i.e., between 61.9 and 97.8 wt% Sn). However, below the eutectic temperature, the microstructure will consist of the eutectic and primary β microconstituents because, upon cooling from the liquid, we pass through the β + liquid phase field.

When, for case 4 (represented in Figure 9.14), conditions of equilibrium are not maintained while passing through the α (or β) + liquid phase region, the following consequences will be realized for the microstructure upon crossing the eutectic isotherm: (1) grains of the primary microconstituent will be cored, that is, have a nonuniform distribution of solute across the grains; and (2) the fraction of the eutectic microconstituent formed will be greater than for the equilibrium situation.

9.8 EQUILIBRIUM DIAGRAMS HAVING INTERMEDIATE PHASES OR COMPOUNDS

The isomorphous and eutectic phase diagrams discussed thus far are relatively simple, but those for many binary alloy systems are much more complex. The eutectic copper–silver and lead–tin phase diagrams (Figures 9.6 and 9.7) have only two solid phases, α and β; these are sometimes termed **terminal solid solutions,** because they exist over composition ranges near the concentration extremities of the phase diagram. For other alloy systems, **intermediate solid solutions** (or *intermediate phases*) may be found at other than the two composition extremes. Such is the case for the copper–zinc system. Its phase diagram (Figure 9.17) may at first appear formidable because there are some invariant points and reactions similar to the eutectic that have not yet been discussed. In addition, there are six different solid solutions—two terminal (α and η) and four intermediate (β, γ, δ, and ϵ). (The β' phase is termed an ordered solid solution, one in which the copper and zinc atoms are situated in a specific and ordered arrangement within each unit cell.) Some phase boundary lines near the bottom of Figure 9.17 are dashed to indicate that their positions have not been exactly determined. The reason for this is that at low temperatures, diffusion rates are very slow and inordinately long times are required for the attainment of equilibrium. Again, only single- and two-phase regions are found on the diagram, and the same rules outlined in Section 9.6 are utilized for computing phase compositions and relative amounts. The commercial brasses are copper-rich copper-zinc alloys; for example, cartridge brass has a composition of 70 wt% Cu–30 wt% Zn and a microstructure consisting of a single α phase.

For some systems, discrete intermediate compounds rather than solid solutions may be found on the phase diagram, and these compounds have distinct chemical formulas; for metal–metal systems, they are called **intermetallic compounds.** For example, consider the magnesium–lead system (Figure 9.18). The compound Mg_2Pb has a composition of 19 wt% Mg–81 wt% Pb (33 at% Pb), and is represented as a

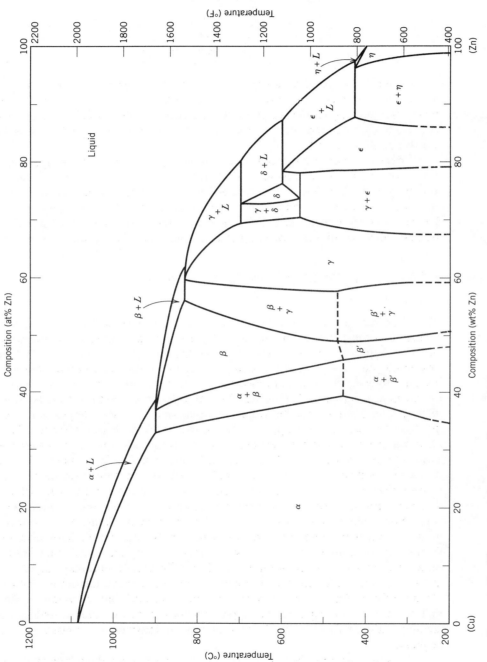

FIGURE 9.17 The copper–zinc phase diagram. (Adapted from *Binary Alloy Phase Diagrams*, 2nd edition, Vol. 2, T. B. Massalski, Editor-in-Chief, 1990. Reprinted by permission of ASM International, Materials Park, OH 44073-0002.)

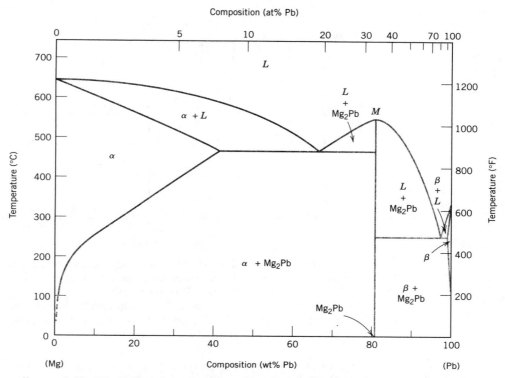

Composition (at% Pb)

FIGURE 9.18 The magnesium–lead phase diagram. (Adapted from *Phase Diagrams of Binary Magnesium Alloys*, A. A. Nayeb-Hashemi and J. B. Clark, Editors, 1988. Reprinted by permission of ASM International, Materials Park, OH 44073-0002.)

vertical line on the diagram, rather than as a phase region of finite width; hence, Mg_2Pb can exist by itself only at this precise composition.

Several other characteristics are worth noting for this magnesium–lead system. First, the compound Mg_2Pb melts at approximately 550°C (1020°F), as indicated by point *M* in Figure 9.18. Also, the solubility of lead in magnesium is rather extensive, as indicated by the relatively large composition span for the α phase field. On the other hand, the solubility of magnesium in lead is extremely limited. This is evident from the very narrow β terminal solid-solution region on the right or lead-rich side of the diagram. Finally, this phase diagram may be thought of as two simple eutectic diagrams joined back to back, one for the Mg–Mg_2Pb system, the other for Mg_2Pb–Pb; as such, the compound Mg_2Pb is really considered to be a component. This separation of complex phase diagrams into smaller-component units may simplify them and, furthermore, expedite their interpretation.

9.9 EUTECTOID AND PERITECTIC REACTIONS

In addition to the eutectic, other invariant points involving three different phases are found for some alloy systems. One of these occurs for the copper–zinc system (Figure 9.17) at 560°C (1040°F) and 74 wt% Zn–26 wt% Cu. A portion of the phase

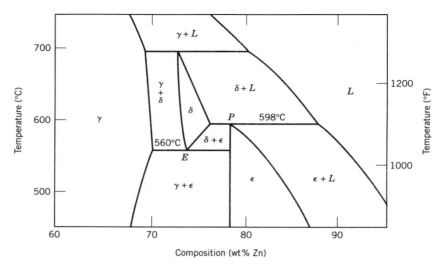

FIGURE 9.19 A region of the copper–zinc phase diagram which has been enlarged to show eutectoid and peritectic invariant points, labeled E (560°C, 74 wt% Zn) and P (598°C, 78.6 wt% Zn), respectively. (Adapted from *Binary Alloy Phase Diagrams,* 2nd edition, Vol. 2, T. B. Massalski, Editor-in-Chief, 1990. Reprinted by permission of ASM International, Materials Park, OH 44073-0002.)

diagram in this vicinity appears enlarged in Figure 9.19. Upon cooling, a solid δ phase transforms into two other solid phases (γ and ϵ) according to the reaction

$$\delta \underset{\text{heating}}{\overset{\text{cooling}}{\rightleftharpoons}} \gamma + \epsilon \tag{9.14}$$

The reverse reaction occurs upon heating. It is called a **eutectoid** (or eutecticlike) **reaction,** and the invariant point (point E, Figure 9.19) and the horizontal tie line at 560°C are termed the *eutectoid* and *eutectoid isotherm,* respectively. The feature distinguishing "eutectoid" from "eutectic" is that one solid phase instead of a liquid transforms into two other solid phases at a single temperature. A eutectoid reaction is found in the iron–carbon system (Section 9.13), which is very important in the heat treating of steels.

The **peritectic reaction** is yet another invariant reaction involving three phases at equilibrium. With this reaction, upon heating, one solid phase transforms into a liquid phase and another solid phase. A peritectic exists for the copper–zinc system (Figure 9.19, point P) at 598°C (1108°F) and 78.6 wt% Zn–21.4 wt% Cu; this reaction is as follows:

$$\delta + L \underset{\text{heating}}{\overset{\text{cooling}}{\rightleftharpoons}} \epsilon \tag{9.15}$$

The low-temperature solid phase may be an intermediate solid solution (e.g., ϵ in the above reaction), or it may be a terminal solid solution. One of the latter peritectics exists at about 97 wt% Zn and 435°C (815°F), (see Figure 9.17), wherein the η phase, when heated, transforms to ϵ and liquid phases. Three other peritectics are found for the Cu–Zn system, the reactions of which involve β, δ, and γ intermediate solid solutions as the low-temperature phases that transform upon heating.

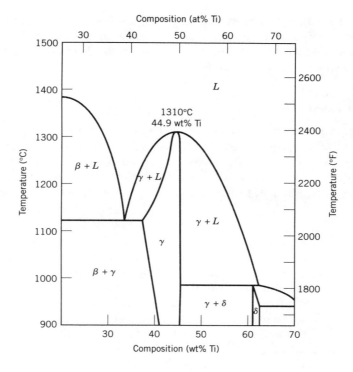

FIGURE 9.20 A portion of the nickel–titanium phase diagram on which is shown a congruent melting point for the γ phase solid solution at 1310°C and 44.9 wt% Ti. (Adapted from *Phase Diagrams of Binary Nickel Alloys*, P. Nash, Editor, 1991. Reprinted by permission of ASM International, Materials Park, OH 44073-0002.)

9.10 CONGRUENT PHASE TRANSFORMATIONS

Phase transformations may be classified according to whether or not there is any change in composition for the phases involved. Those for which there are no compositional alterations are said to be **congruent transformations.** Conversely, for *incongruent transformations,* at least one of the phases will experience a change in composition. Examples of congruent transformations include allotropic transformations (Section 3.6) and melting of pure materials. Eutectic and eutectoid reactions, as well as the melting of an alloy that belongs to an isomorphous system, all represent incongruent transformations.

Intermediate phases are sometimes classified on the basis of whether they melt congruently or incongruently. The intermetallic compound Mg_2Pb melts congruently at the point designated *M* on the magnesium–lead phase diagram, Figure 9.18. Also, for the nickel–titanium system, Figure 9.20, there is a congruent melting point for the γ solid solution which corresponds to the point of tangency for the pairs of liquidus and solidus lines, at 1310°C and 44.9 wt% Ti. Furthermore, the peritectic reaction is an example of incongruent melting for an intermediate phase.

9.11 CERAMIC AND TERNARY PHASE DIAGRAMS

It need not be assumed that phase diagrams exist only for metal–metal systems; in fact, phase diagrams that are very useful in the design and processing of ceramic systems have been experimentally determined for quite a number of these materials. Ceramic phase diagrams are discussed in Section 13.6.

Phase diagrams have also been determined for metallic (as well as ceramic) systems containing more than two components; however, their representation and interpretation may be exceedingly complex. For example, a ternary, or three-component, composition–temperature phase diagram in its entirety is depicted by a three-dimensional model. Portrayal of features of the diagram or model in two dimensions is possible but somewhat difficult.

9.12 THE GIBBS PHASE RULE

The construction of phase diagrams as well as some of the principles governing the conditions for phase equilibria are dictated by laws of thermodynamics. One of these is the **Gibbs phase rule,** proposed by the nineteenth century physicist J. Willard Gibbs. This rule represents a criterion for the number of phases that will coexist within a system at equilibrium, and is expressed by the simple equation

$$P + F = C + N \tag{9.16}$$

where P is the number of phases present (the phase concept is discussed in Section 9.3). The parameter F is termed the *number of degrees of freedom* or the number of externally controlled variables (e.g., temperature, pressure, composition) which must be specified to completely define the state of the system. Or, expressed another way, F is the number of these variables that can be changed independently without altering the number of phases that coexist at equilibrium. The parameter C in Equation 9.16 represents the number of components in the system. Components are normally elements or stable compounds and, in the case of phase diagrams, are the materials at the two extremities of the horizontal compositional axis (e.g., H_2O and $C_{12}H_{22}O_{11}$, and Cu and Ni for the phase diagrams shown in Figures 9.1 and 9.2a, respectively). Finally, N in Equation 9.16 is the number of noncompositional variables (e.g., temperature and pressure).

Let us demonstrate the phase rule by applying it to binary temperature–composition phase diagrams, specifically the copper–silver system, Figure 9.6. Since pressure is constant (1 atm), the parameter N is 1—temperature is the only noncompositional variable. Equation 9.16 now takes the form

$$P + F = C + 1 \tag{9.17}$$

Furthermore, the number of components C is 2 (viz Cu and Ag), and

$$P + F = 2 + 1 = 3$$

or

$$F = 3 - P$$

Consider the case of single-phase fields on the phase diagram (e.g., α, β, and liquid regions). Since only one phase is present, $P = 1$ and

$$F = 3 - P$$
$$= 3 - 1 = 2$$

This means that to completely describe the characteristics of any alloy which exists within one of these phase fields, we must specify two parameters; these are composition and temperature, which locate, respectively, the horizontal and vertical positions of the alloy on the phase diagram.

For the situation wherein two phases coexist, for example, $\alpha + L$, $\beta + L$, and

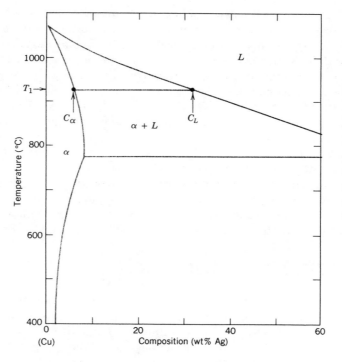

Fɪɢᴜʀᴇ 9.21 Enlarged copper-rich section of the Cu–Ag phase diagram in which the Gibbs phase rule for the coexistence of two phases (i.e., α and L) is demonstrated. Once the composition of either phase (i.e., C_α or C_L) or the temperature (i.e., T_1) is specified, values for the two remaining parameters are established by construction of the appropriate tie line.

$\alpha + \beta$ phase regions, Figure 9.6, the phase rule stipulates that we have but one degree of freedom since

$$F = 3 - P$$

$$= 3 - 2 = 1$$

Thus, it is necessary to specify either temperature or the composition of one of the phases to completely define the system. For example, suppose that we decide to specify temperature for the $\alpha + L$ phase region, say, T_1 in Figure 9.21. The compositions of the α and liquid phases (C_α and C_L) are thus dictated by the extremities of the tie line constructed at T_1 across the $\alpha + L$ field. It should be noted that only the nature of the phases is important in this treatment and not the relative phase amounts. This is to say that the overall alloy composition could lie anywhere along this tie line constructed at temperature T_1 and still give C_α and C_L compositions for the respective α and liquid phases.

The second alternative is to stipulate the composition of one of the phases for this two-phase situation, which thereby fixes completely the state of the system. For example, if we specified C_α as the composition of the α phase that is in equilibrium with the liquid (Figure 9.21), then both the temperature of the alloy (T_1) and the composition of the liquid phase (C_L) are established, again by the tie line drawn across the $\alpha + L$ phase field so as to give this C_α composition.

For binary systems, when three phases are present, there are no degrees of freedom, since

$$F = 3 - P$$

$$= 3 - 3 = 0$$

This means that the compositions of all three phases as well as the temperature are fixed. This condition is met for a eutectic system by the eutectic isotherm; for the Cu–Ag system (Figure 9.6), it is the horizontal line that extends between points *B* and *G*. At this temperature, 779°C, the points at which each of the α, *L*, and β phase fields touch the isotherm line correspond to the respective phase compositions; namely, the composition of the α phase is fixed at 8.0 wt% Ag, that of the liquid at 71.9 wt% Ag, and that of the β phase at 91.2 wt% Ag. Thus, three-phase equilibrium will not be represented by a phase field, but rather by the unique horizontal isotherm line. Furthermore, all three phases will be in equilibrium for any alloy composition that lies along the length of the eutectic isotherm (e.g., for the Cu–Ag system at 779°C and compositions between 8.0 and 91.2 wt% Ag).

One use of the Gibbs phase rule is in analyzing for nonequilibrium conditions. For example, a microstructure for a binary alloy which developed over a range of temperatures and consisting of three phases is a nonequilibrium one; under these circumstances, three phases will exist only at a single temperature.

THE IRON–CARBON SYSTEM

Of all binary alloy systems, the one that is possibly the most important is that for iron and carbon. Both steels and cast irons, primary structural materials in every technologically advanced culture, are essentially iron–carbon alloys. This section is devoted to a study of the phase diagram for this system and the development of several of the possible microstructures. The relationships between heat treatment, microstructure, and mechanical properties are explored in Chapters 10 and 11.

9.13 THE IRON–IRON CARBIDE (Fe–Fe₃C) PHASE DIAGRAM

A portion of the iron–carbon phase diagram is presented in Figure 9.22. Pure iron, upon heating, experiences two changes in crystal structure before it melts. At room temperature the stable form, called **ferrite**, or α iron, has a BCC crystal structure. Ferrite experiences a polymorphic transformation to FCC **austenite**, or γ iron, at 912°C (1674°F). This austenite persists to 1394°C (2541°F), at which temperature the FCC austenite reverts back to a BCC phase known as δ ferrite, which finally melts at 1538°C (2800°F). All these changes are apparent along the left vertical axis of the phase diagram.

The composition axis in Figure 9.22 extends only to 6.70 wt% C; at this concentration the intermediate compound iron carbide, or **cementite** (Fe₃C), is formed, which is represented by a vertical line on the phase diagram. Thus, the iron–carbon system may be divided into two parts: an iron-rich portion, as in Figure 9.22; and the other (not shown) for compositions between 6.70 and 100 wt% C (pure graphite). In practice, all steels and cast irons have carbon contents less than 6.70 wt% C; therefore, we consider only the iron–iron carbide system. Figure 9.22 would be more appropriately labeled the Fe–Fe₃C phase diagram, since Fe₃C is now considered to be a component. Convention and convenience dictate that composition still be expressed in "wt% C" rather than "wt% Fe₃C"; 6.70 wt% C corresponds to 100 wt% Fe₃C.

Carbon is an interstitial impurity in iron and forms a solid solution with each of α and δ ferrites, and also with austenite, as indicated by the α, δ, and γ single-

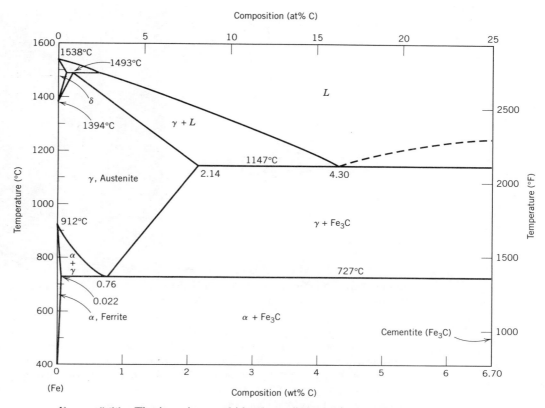

FIGURE 9.22 The iron–iron carbide phase diagram. (Adapted from *Binary Alloy Phase Diagrams,* 2nd edition, Vol. 1, T. B. Massalski, Editor-in-Chief, 1990. Reprinted by permission of ASM International, Materials Park, OH 44073–0002.)

phase fields in Figure 9.22. In the BCC α ferrite, only small concentrations of carbon are soluble; the maximum solubility is 0.022 wt% at 727°C (1341°F). The limited solubility is explained by the shape and size of the BCC interstitial positions, which make it difficult to accommodate the carbon atoms. Even though present in relatively low concentrations, carbon significantly influences the mechanical properties of ferrite. This particular iron–carbon phase is relatively soft, may be made magnetic at temperatures below 768°C (1414°F), and has a density of 7.88 g/cm³. Figure 9.23a is a photomicrograph of α ferrite.

The austenite, or γ phase of iron, when alloyed with just carbon, is not stable below 727°C (1341°F), as indicated in Figure 9.22. The maximum solubility of carbon in austenite, 2.14 wt%, occurs at 1147°C (2097°F). This solubility is approximately 100 times greater than the maximum for BCC ferrite, since the FCC interstitial positions are larger (see the results of Problem 4.5), and, therefore, the strains imposed on the surrounding iron atoms are much lower. As the discussions that follow demonstrate, phase transformations involving austenite are very important in the heat treating of steels. In passing, it should be mentioned that austenite is nonmagnetic. Figure 9.23b shows a photomicrograph of this austenite phase.

The δ ferrite is virtually the same as α ferrite, except for the range of tempera-

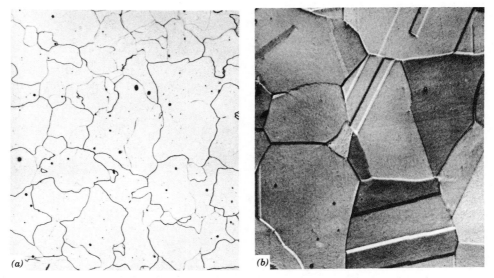

FIGURE 9.23   Photomicrographs of (a) α ferrite (90×) and (b) austenite (325×). (Copyright 1971 by United States Steel Corporation.)

tures over which each exists. Since the δ ferrite is stable only at relatively high temperatures, it is of no technological importance and is not discussed further.

Cementite (Fe_3C) forms when the solubility limit of carbon in α ferrite is exceeded below 727°C (1341°F) (for compositions within the α + Fe_3C phase region). As indicated in Figure 9.22, Fe_3C will also coexist with the γ phase between 727 and 1147°C (1341 and 2097°F). Mechanically, cementite is very hard and brittle; the strength of some steels is greatly enhanced by its presence.

Strictly speaking, cementite is only metastable; that is, it will remain as a compound indefinitely at room temperature. But if heated to between 650 and 700°C (1200 and 1300°F) for several years, it will gradually change or transform into α iron and carbon, in the form of graphite, which will remain upon subsequent cooling to room temperature. Thus, the phase diagram in Figure 9.22 is not a true equilibrium one because cementite is not an equilibrium compound. However, inasmuch as the decomposition rate of cementite is extremely sluggish, virtually all the carbon in steel will be as Fe_3C instead of graphite, and the iron–iron carbide phase diagram is, for all practical purposes, valid. As will be seen in Section 12.6, addition of silicon to cast irons greatly accelerates this cementite decomposition reaction to form graphite.

The two-phase regions are labeled in Figure 9.22. It may be noted that one eutectic exists for the iron–iron carbide system, at 4.30 wt% C and 1147°C (2097°F); for this eutectic reaction,

$$L \underset{\text{heating}}{\overset{\text{cooling}}{\rightleftharpoons}} \gamma + Fe_3C \qquad (9.18)$$

the liquid solidifies to form austenite and cementite phases. Of course, subsequent cooling to room temperature will promote additional phase changes.

It may be noted that a eutectoid invariant point exists at a composition of

0.76 wt% C and a temperature of 727°C (1341°F). This eutectoid reaction may be represented by

$$\gamma(0.76 \text{ wt\% C}) \underset{\text{heating}}{\overset{\text{cooling}}{\rightleftharpoons}} \alpha(0.022 \text{ wt\% C}) + \text{Fe}_3\text{C} \ (6.7 \text{ wt\% C}) \qquad (9.19)$$

or, upon cooling, the solid γ phase is transformed into α iron and cementite. (Eutectoid phase transformations were addressed in Section 9.9.) The eutectoid phase changes described by Equation 9.19 are very important, being fundamental to the heat treatment of steels, as explained in subsequent discussions.

Ferrous alloys are those in which iron is the prime component, but carbon as well as other alloying elements may be present. In the classification scheme of ferrous alloys based on carbon content, there are three types: iron, steel, and cast iron. Commercially pure iron contains less than 0.008 wt% C and, from the phase diagram, is composed almost exclusively of the ferrite phase at room temperature. The iron–carbon alloys that contain between 0.008 and 2.14 wt% C are classified as steels. In most steels the microstructure consists of both α and Fe_3C phases. Upon cooling to room temperature, an alloy within this composition range must pass through at least a portion of the γ phase field; distinctive microstructures are subsequently produced, as discussed below. Although a steel alloy may contain as much as 2.14 wt% C, in practice, carbon concentrations rarely exceed 1.0 wt%. The properties and various classifications of steels are treated in Section 12.5. Cast irons are classified as ferrous alloys that contain between 2.14 and 6.70 wt% C. However, commercial cast irons normally contain less than 4.5 wt% C. These alloys are discussed further in Section 12.6.

9.14 DEVELOPMENT OF MICROSTRUCTURES IN IRON–CARBON ALLOYS

Several of the various microstructures that may be produced in steel alloys and their relationships to the iron–iron carbon phase diagram are now discussed, and it is shown that the microstructure that develops depends on both the carbon content and heat treatment. The discussion is confined to very slow cooling of steel alloys, in which equilibrium is continuously maintained. A more detailed exploration of the influence of heat treatment on microstructure, and ultimately on the mechanical properties of steels, is contained in Chapter 10.

Phase changes that occur upon passing from the γ region into the $\alpha + \text{Fe}_3\text{C}$ phase field (Figure 9.22) are relatively complex and similar to those described for the eutectic systems in Section 9.7. Consider, for example, an alloy of eutectoid composition (0.76 wt% C) as it is cooled from a temperature within the γ phase region, say, 800°C, that is, beginning at point a in Figure 9.24 and moving down the vertical line xx'. Initially, the alloy is composed entirely of the austenite phase having a composition of 0.76 wt% C and corresponding microstructure, also indicated in Figure 9.24. As the alloy is cooled, there will occur no changes until the eutectoid temperature (727°C) is reached. Upon crossing this temperature to point b, the austenite transforms according to Equation 9.19.

The microstructure for this eutectoid steel that is slowly cooled through the eutectoid temperature consists of alternating layers or lamellae of the two phases (α and Fe_3C) that form simultaneously during the transformation. In this case, the relative layer thickness is approximately 8 to 1. This microstructure, represented schematically in Figure 9.24, point b, is called **pearlite** because it has the appearance

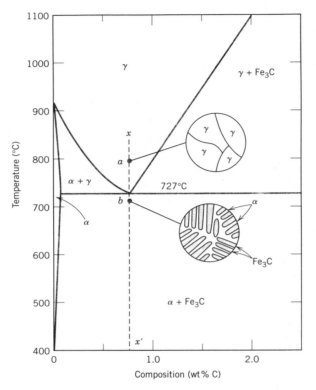

FIGURE 9.24 Schematic representations of the microstructures for an iron–carbon alloy of eutectoid composition (0.76 wt% C) above and below the eutectoid temperature.

of mother of pearl when viewed under the microscope at low magnifications. Figure 9.25 is a photomicrograph of a eutectoid steel showing the pearlite. The pearlite exists as grains, often termed "colonies"; within each colony the layers are oriented in essentially the same direction, which varies from one colony to another. The thick light layers are the ferrite phase, and the cementite phase appears as thin lamellae most of which appear dark. Many cementite layers are so thin that adjacent phase boundaries are indistinguishable, which layers appear dark at this magnification. Mechanically, pearlite has properties intermediate between the soft, ductile ferrite and the hard, brittle cementite.

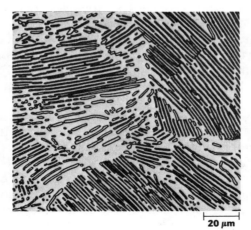

20 μm

FIGURE 9.25 Photomicrograph of a eutectoid steel showing the pearlite microstructure consisting of alternating layers of α ferrite (the light phase) and Fe_3C (thin layers most of which appear dark). 500×. (Reproduced with permission from *Metals Handbook,* Vol. 9, 9th edition, *Metallography and Microstructures,* American Society for Metals, Materials Park, OH, 1985.)

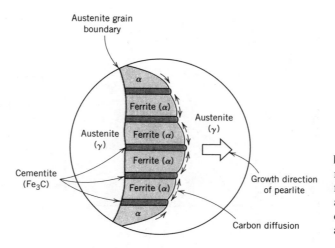

FIGURE 9.26 Schematic representation of the formation of pearlite from austenite; direction of carbon diffusion indicated by arrows.

The alternating α and Fe_3C layers in pearlite form as such for the same reason that the eutectoid structure (Figures 9.11 and 9.12) forms—because the composition of the parent phase [in this case austenite (0.76 wt% C)] is different than either of the product phases [ferrite (0.022 wt% C) and cementite (6.7 wt% C)], and the phase transformation requires that there be a redistribution of the carbon by diffusion. Figure 9.26 illustrates schematically microstructural changes that accompany this eutectoid reaction; here the directions of carbon diffusion are indicated by arrows. Carbon atoms diffuse away from the 0.022 wt% ferrite regions and to the 6.7 wt% cementite layers, as the pearlite extends from the grain boundary into the unreacted austenite grain. The layered pearlite forms because carbon atoms need diffuse only minimal distances with the formation of this structure.

Furthermore, subsequent cooling of the pearlite from point *b* in Figure 9.24 will produce relatively insignificant microstructural changes.

HYPOEUTECTOID ALLOYS

Microstructures for iron–iron carbide alloys having other than the eutectoid composition are now explored; these are analogous to the fourth case described in Section 9.7 and illustrated in Figure 9.14 for the eutectic system. Consider a composition C_0 to the left of the eutectoid, between 0.022 and 0.76 wt% C; this is termed a **hypoeutectoid** (less than eutectoid) **alloy.** Cooling an alloy of this composition is represented by moving down the vertical line *yy'* in Figure 9.27. At about 875°C, point *c*, the microstructure will consist entirely of grains of the γ phase, as shown schematically in the figure. In cooling to point *d*, about 775°C, which is within the $\alpha + \gamma$ phase region, both these phases will coexist as in the schematic microstructure. Most of the small α particles will form along the original γ grain boundaries. The compositions of both α and γ phases may be determined using the appropriate tie line; these compositions correspond, respectively, to about 0.020 and 0.40 wt% C.

While cooling an alloy through the $\alpha + \gamma$ phase region, the composition of the ferrite phase changes with temperature along the $\alpha - (\alpha + \gamma)$ phase boundary, line *MN*, becoming slightly richer in carbon. On the other hand, the change in composition of the austenite is more dramatic, proceeding along the $(\alpha + \gamma) - \gamma$ boundary, line *MO*, as the temperature is reduced.

Cooling from point *d* to *e*, just above the eutectoid but still in the $\alpha + \gamma$ region, will produce an increased fraction of the α phase and a microstructure similar to that

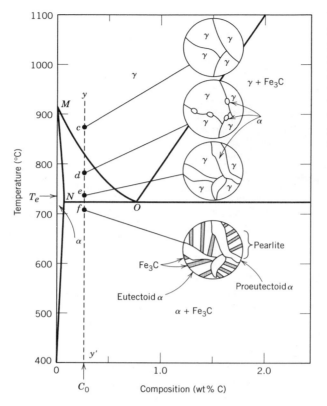

FIGURE 9.27 Schematic representations of the microstructures for an iron–carbon alloy of hypoeutectoid composition C_0 (containing less than 0.76 wt% C) as it is cooled from within the austenite phase region to below the eutectoid temperature.

also shown: the α particles will have grown larger. At this point, the compositions of the α and γ phases are determined by constructing a tie line at the temperature T_e; the α phase will contain 0.022 wt% C, while the γ phase will be of the eutectoid composition, 0.76 wt% C.

As the temperature is lowered just below the eutectoid, to point f, all the γ phase that was present at temperature T_e (and having the eutectoid composition) will transform to pearlite, according to the reaction in Equation 9.19. There will be virtually no change in the α phase that existed at point e in crossing the eutectoid temperature—it will normally be present as a continuous matrix phase surrounding the isolated pearlite colonies. The microstructure at point f will appear as the corresponding schematic inset of Figure 9.27. Thus the ferrite phase will be present both in the pearlite and also as the phase that formed while cooling through the $\alpha + \gamma$ phase region. The ferrite that is present in the pearlite is called *eutectoid ferrite*, whereas the other, that formed above T_e, is termed **proeutectoid** (meaning pre- or before eutectoid) **ferrite**, as labeled in Figure 9.27. Figure 9.28 is a photomicrograph of a 0.38 wt% C steel; large, white regions correspond to the proeutectoid ferrite. For pearlite, the spacing between the α and Fe_3C layers varies from grain to grain; some of the pearlite appears dark because the many close-spaced layers are unresolved at the magnification of the photomicrograph. On page 236 is shown a scanning electron micrograph of a hypoeutectoid (0.44 wt% C) steel in which may also be seen both pearlite and proeutectoid ferrite, only at a higher magnification. It should also be noted that two microconstituents are present in these micrographs—proeutectoid ferrite and pearlite—and which will appear in all hypoeutectoid iron–carbon alloys that are slowly cooled to a temperature below the eutectoid.

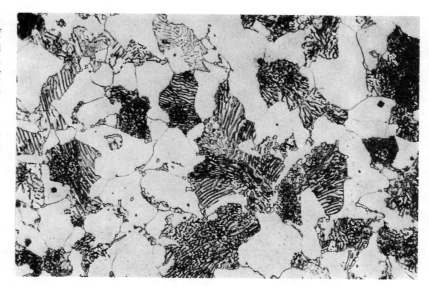

The relative amounts of the proeutectoid α and pearlite may be determined in a manner similar to that described in Section 9.7 for primary and eutectic micro-constituents. We use the lever rule in conjunction with a tie line that extends from the $\alpha - (\alpha + Fe_3C)$ phase boundary (0.022 wt% C) to the eutectoid composition (0.76 wt% C), inasmuch as pearlite is the transformation product of austenite having this composition. For example, let us consider an alloy of composition C_0' in Figure 9.29. Thus, the fraction of pearlite, W_p, may be determined according to

$$W_p = \frac{T}{T + U}$$

$$= \frac{C_0' - 0.022}{0.76 - 0.022} = \frac{C_0' - 0.022}{0.74} \tag{9.20}$$

FIGURE 9.29
A portion of the
Fe–Fe$_3$C phase
diagram used in
computations for
relative amounts of
proeutectoid and
pearlite
microconstituents for
hypoeutectoid (C_0')
and hypereutectoid
(C_1') compositions.

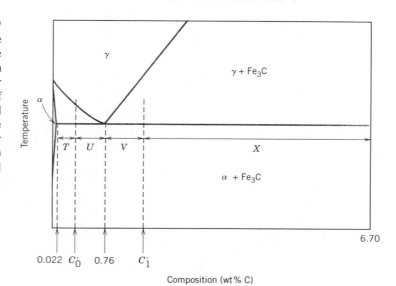

Furthermore, the fraction of proeutectoid α, $W_{\alpha'}$, is computed as follows:

$$W_{\alpha'} = \frac{U}{T + U}$$

$$= \frac{0.76 - C_0'}{0.76 - 0.022} = \frac{0.76 - C_0'}{0.74} \tag{9.21}$$

Of course, fractions of both total α (eutectoid and proeutectoid) and cementite are determined using the lever rule and a tie line that extends across the entirety of the α + Fe$_3$C phase region, from 0.022 to 6.7 wt% C.

HYPEREUTECTOID ALLOYS

Analogous transformations and microstructures result for **hypereutectoid alloys,** those containing between 0.76 and 2.14 wt% C, which are cooled from temperatures within the γ phase field. Consider an alloy of composition C_1 in Figure 9.30 which, upon cooling, moves down the line zz'. At point g only the γ phase will be present with a composition of C_1; the microstructure will appear as shown, having only γ grains. Upon cooling into the γ + Fe$_3$C phase field, say, to point h, the cementite phase will begin to form along the initial γ grain boundaries, similar to the α phase in Figure 9.27, point d. This cementite is called **proeutectoid cementite**—that which forms before the eutectoid reaction. Of course, the cementite composition remains

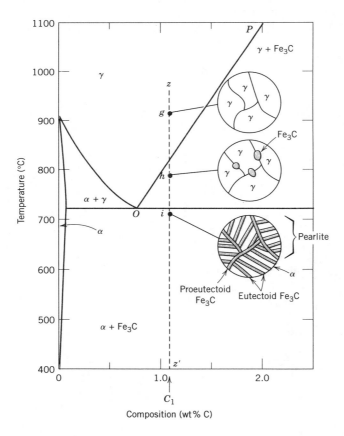

FIGURE 9.30 Schematic representations of the microstructures for an iron–carbon alloy of hypereutectoid composition C_1 (containing between 0.76 and 2.14 wt% C), as it is cooled from within the austenite phase region to below the eutectoid temperature.

FIGURE 9.31 Photomicrograph of a 1.4 wt% C steel having a microstructure consisting of a white proeutectoid cementite network surrounding the pearlite colonies. 1000×. (Copyright 1971 by United States Steel Corporation.)

constant (6.70 wt% C) as the temperature changes. However, the composition of the austenite phase will move along line PO toward the eutectoid. As the temperature is lowered through the eutectoid to point i, all remaining austenite of eutectoid composition is converted into pearlite; thus, the resulting microstructure consists of pearlite and proeutectoid cementite as microconstituents (Figure 9.30). In the photomicrograph of a 1.4 wt% C steel (Figure 9.31), note that the proeutectoid cementite appears light. Since it has much the same appearance as proeutectoid ferrite (Figure 9.28), there is some difficulty in distinguishing between hypoeutectoid and hypereutectoid steels on the basis of microstructure.

Relative amounts of both pearlite and proeutectoid Fe_3C microconstituents may be computed for hypereutectoid steel alloys in a manner analogous to that for hypoeutectoid materials; the appropriate tie line extends between 0.76 and 6.70 wt% C. Thus, for an alloy having composition C_1' in Figure 9.29, fractions of pearlite W_p and proeutectoid cementite $W_{Fe_3C'}$ are determined from the following lever rule expressions:

$$W_p = \frac{X}{V + X} = \frac{6.70 - C_1'}{6.70 - 0.76} = \frac{6.70 - C_1'}{5.94} \qquad (9.22)$$

and

$$W_{Fe_3C'} = \frac{V}{V + X} = \frac{C_1' - 0.76}{6.70 - 0.76} = \frac{C_1' - 0.76}{5.94} \qquad (9.23)$$

EXAMPLE PROBLEM 9.4

For a 99.65 wt% Fe–0.35 wt% C alloy at a temperature just below the eutectoid, determine the following:

(a) The fractions of total ferrite and cementite phases.

(b) The fractions of the proeutectoid ferrite and pearlite.

(c) The fraction of eutectoid ferrite.

SOLUTION

(a) This part of the problem is solved by application of the lever rule expressions employing a tie line that extends all the way across the $\alpha + Fe_3C$ phase field. Thus, C_0' is 0.35 wt% C, and

$$W_\alpha = \frac{6.70 - 0.35}{6.70 - 0.022} = 0.95$$

and

$$W_{Fe_3C} = \frac{0.35 - 0.022}{6.70 - 0.022} = 0.05$$

(b) The fractions of proeutectoid ferrite and pearlite are determined by using the lever rule, and a tie line that extends only to the eutectoid composition (i.e., Equations 9.20 and 9.21). Or

$$W_p = \frac{0.35 - 0.022}{0.76 - 0.022} = 0.44$$

and

$$W_{\alpha'} = \frac{0.76 - 0.35}{0.76 - 0.022} = 0.56$$

(c) All ferrite is either as proeutectoid or eutectoid (in the pearlite). Therefore, the sum of these two ferrite fractions will equal the fraction of total ferrite, that is,

$$W_{\alpha'} + W_{\alpha e} = W_\alpha$$

where $W_{\alpha e}$ denotes the fraction of the total alloy that is eutectoid ferrite. Values for W_α and $W_{\alpha'}$ were determined in parts a and b as 0.95 and 0.56, respectively. Therefore,

$$W_{\alpha e} = W_\alpha - W_{\alpha'} = 0.95 - 0.56 = 0.39$$

NONEQUILIBRIUM COOLING

In this discussion on the microstructural development of iron–carbon alloys it has been assumed that, upon cooling, conditions of metastable equilibrium[1] have been continuously maintained; that is, sufficient time has been allowed at each new temperature for any necessary adjustment in phase compositions and relative amounts as predicted from the Fe–Fe₃C phase diagram. In most situations these cooling rates are impractically slow and really unnecessary; in fact, on many occasions nonequilibrium conditions are desirable. Two nonequilibrium effects of practical importance are (1) the occurrence of phase changes or transformations at temperatures other than those predicted by phase boundary lines on the phase diagram, and (2) the existence at room temperature of nonequilibrium phases that do not appear on the phase diagram. Both are discussed in the next chapter.

---

[1] The term "metastable equilibrium" is used in this discussion inasmuch as Fe₃C is only a metastable compound.

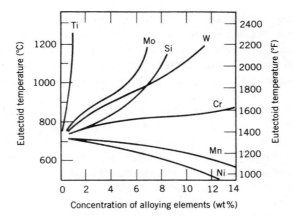

FIGURE 9.32 The dependence of eutectoid temperature on alloy concentration for several alloying elements in steel. (From Dr. Edgar C. Bain, *Functions of the Alloying Elements in Steel*, American Society for Metals, 1939, p. 127.)

9.15 THE INFLUENCE OF OTHER ALLOYING ELEMENTS

Additions of other alloying elements (Cr, Ni, Ti, etc.) bring about rather dramatic changes in the binary iron–iron carbide phase diagram, Figure 9.22. The extent of these alterations of the positions of phase boundaries and the shapes of the phase fields depends on the particular alloying element and its concentration. One of the important changes is the shift in position of the eutectoid with respect to temperature and to carbon concentration. These effects are illustrated in Figures 9.32 and 9.33, which plot the eutectoid temperature and composition (in wt% C) as a function of concentration for several other alloying elements. Thus, other alloy additions alter not only the temperature of the eutectoid reaction but also the relative fractions of pearlite and the proeutectoid phase that form. Steels are normally alloyed for other reasons, however—usually to either improve their corrosion resistance or to render them amenable to heat treatment (see Chapter 11).

SUMMARY

Equilibrium phase diagrams are a convenient and concise way of representing the most stable relationships between phases in alloy systems. This discussion considered binary phase diagrams for which temperature and composition are variables.

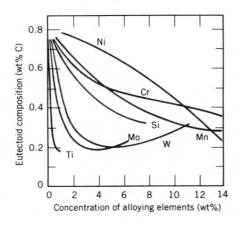

FIGURE 9.33 The dependence of eutectoid composition (wt% C) on alloy concentration for several alloying elements in steel. (From Dr. Edgar C. Bain, *Functions of the Alloying Elements in Steel*, American Society for Metals, 1939, p. 127.)

Areas, or phase regions, are defined on these temperature-versus-composition plots within which either one or two phases exist. For an alloy of specified composition and at a known temperature, the phases present, their compositions, and relative amounts under equilibrium conditions may be determined. Within two-phase regions, tie lines and the lever rule must be used for phase composition and mass fraction computations, respectively.

Several different kinds of phase diagram were discussed for metallic systems. Isomorphous diagrams are those for which there is complete solubility in the solid phase; the copper–nickel system displays this behavior. Also discussed for alloys belonging to isomorphous systems were the development of microstructure for both cases of equilibrium and nonequilibrium cooling, and also the dependence of mechanical characteristics on composition.

In a eutectic reaction, as found in some alloy systems, a liquid phase transforms isothermally to two different solid phases upon cooling. Such a reaction is noted on the copper–silver and lead–tin phase diagrams. Complete solid solubility for all compositions does not exist; instead, solid solutions are terminal—there is only a limited solubility of each component in the other. Four different kinds of microstructures that may develop for the equilibrium cooling of alloys belonging to eutectic systems were discussed.

Other equilibrium phase diagrams are more complex, having intermediate compounds and/or phases, possibly more than a single eutectic, and other reactions including eutectoid, peritectic, and congruent phase transformations. These are found for copper–zinc and magnesium–lead systems.

The Gibbs phase rule was introduced; it is a simple equation that relates the number of phases present in a system at equilibrium with the number of degrees of freedom, the number of components, and the number of noncompositional variables.

Considerable attention was given to the iron–carbon system, and specifically, the iron–iron carbide phase diagram, which technologically is one of the most important. The development of microstructure in many iron–carbon alloys and steels depends on the eutectoid reaction in which the FCC austenite phase of composition 0.76 wt% C transforms isothermally to the BCC α ferrite phase (0.022 wt% C) and the intermetallic compound, cementite (Fe_3C). The microstructural product of an iron–carbon alloy of eutectoid composition is pearlite, a microconstituent consisting of alternating layers of ferrite and cementite. The microstructures of alloys having carbon contents less than the eutectoid (hypoeutectoid) are comprised of a proeutectoid ferrite phase in addition to pearlite. On the other hand, pearlite and proeutectoid cementite constitute the microconstituents for hypereutectoid alloys—those with carbon contents in excess of the eutectoid composition.

IMPLICATIONS

At this point, one may question the relevance of phase diagrams in the real world of engineering. Phase diagrams are indeed very useful tools to materials engineers and scientists; examples are provided in succeeding chapters. In essence, they are a convenient way of representing phase relationships—i.e., how materials change when they are heated, cooled, alloyed, or subjected to pressures. They are frequently consulted when designing materials for existing or new applications. Many times, this results in alternative materials which are less expensive, or by the replacement of constituents which are toxic or hazardous.

In addition, phase diagrams are useful in the design of fabrication procedures. For example, for metal alloys, the causes of and cures for fabrication-induced defects that impair performance are often determined with the aid of phase diagrams; typical defects include microporosity and cracks that form in castings and welds.

Another important area of relevance includes the design and control of material heat-treating procedures. Mechanical and other properties of materials are dependent on their thermal histories. In this regard, phase diagrams are valuable in understanding how microstructures and properties may be tailored by thermal processing; this knowledge often leads to the development of new processing technologies. Furthermore, formation of even minute amounts of a liquid phase during high-temperature exposures often leads to a deterioration of material performance. Solidus temperatures (even under nonequilibrium conditions) may be determined using appropriate phase diagrams.

In-service materials performance problems are often solved by consulting phase diagrams; this leads to improved product reliability. Problems of this type include intergranular corrosion (Section 18.7), hydrogen damage, and hot corrosion. Also, with respect to product performance and reliability, phase diagrams give some indication of the phase situation for equilibrium conditions; using this information, extrapolations may be made relative to expected phase and property changes over extended service periods.

IMPORTANT TERMS AND CONCEPTS

Austenite	Hypereutectoid alloy	Phase
Cementite	Hypoeutectoid alloy	Phase diagram
Component	Intermediate solid solution	Phase equilibrium
Congruent transformation	Intermetallic compound	Primary phase
Equilibrium	Invariant point	Proeutectoid cementite
Eutectic phase	Isomorphous	Proeutectoid ferrite
Eutectic reaction	Lever rule	Solidus line
Eutectic structure	Liquidus line	Solubility limit
Eutectoid reaction	Metastable	Solvus line
Ferrite	Microconstituent	System
Free energy	Pearlite	Terminal solid solution
Gibbs phase rule	Peritectic reaction	Tie line

REFERENCES

ASM Handbook, Vol. 3, *Alloy Phase Diagrams,* ASM International, Materials Park, OH, 1992.

ASM Handbook, Vol. 9, *Metallography and Microstructures,* ASM International, Materials Park, OH, 1985.

Gordon, P., *Principles of Phase Diagrams in Materials Systems,* McGraw-Hill Book Company, New York, 1968. Reprinted by Krieger Publishing Company, Melbourne, FL, 1983.

Hansen, M. and K. Anderko, *Constitution of Binary Alloys,* 2nd edition, McGraw-Hill Book Company, New York, 1958. *First Supplement* (R. P. Elliott), 1965. *Second Supplement* (F. A.

Shunk), 1969. Reprinted by Genium Publishing Corp., Schenectady, NY.

Massalski, T. B. (Editor), *Binary Phase Diagrams,* 2nd edition, ASM International, Materials Park, OH, 1990. Three volumes.

Petzow, G. and G. Effenberg, *Ternary Alloys, A Comprehensive Compendium of Evaluated Constitutional Data and Phase Diagrams,* VCH Publishers, New York, 1988. Eight volumes.

Rhines, F. N., *Phase Diagrams in Metallurgy— Their Development and Application,* McGraw-Hill Book Company, Inc., New York, 1956.

QUESTIONS AND PROBLEMS

9.1 Cite three variables that determine the microstructure of an alloy.

9.2 What thermodynamic condition must be met for a state of equilibrium to exist?

9.3 For metal alloys, the development of microstructure depends on the phenomenon of diffusion (Figures 9.13 and 9.26). It was noted in Section 5.3 that the driving force for steady-state diffusion is a concentration gradient. However, concentration gradients are normally absent in regions where diffusion is occurring, as represented in Figures 9.13 and 9.26; for these situations, what is the driving force?

9.4 What is the difference between the states of phase equilibrium and metastability?

9.5 Cite the phases that are present and the phase compositions for the following alloys:

(a) 90 wt% Zn–10 wt% Cu at 400°C (750°F).

(b) 75 wt% Sn–25 wt% Pb at 175°C (345°F).

(c) 55 wt% Ag–45 wt% Cu at 900°C (1650°F).

(d) 30 wt% Pb–70 wt% Mg at 425°C (795°F).

(e) 2.12 kg Zn and 1.88 kg Cu at 500°C (930°F).

(f) 37 lb$_m$ Pb and 6.5 lb$_m$ Mg at 400°C (750°F).

(g) 8.2 mol Ni and 4.3 mol Cu at 1250°C (2280°F).

(h) 4.5 mol Sn and 0.45 mol Pb at 200°C (390°F).

9.6 For an alloy of composition 74 wt% Zn–26 wt% Cu, cite the phases present and their compositions at the following temperatures: 850°C, 750°C, 680°C, 600°C, and 500°C.

9.7 Determine the relative amounts (in terms of mass fractions) of the phases for the alloys and temperatures given in Problem 9.5.

9.8 Derive Equations 9.6a and 9.7a, which may be used to convert mass fraction to volume fraction, and vice versa.

9.9 Determine the relative amounts (in terms of volume fractions) of the phases for the alloys and temperatures given in Problem 9.5a, b, and c. Below are given the approximate densities of the various metals at the alloy temperatures:

Metal	Temperature (°C)	Density (g/cm³)
Ag	900	9.97
Cu	400	8.77
Cu	900	8.56
Pb	175	11.20
Sn	175	7.22
Zn	400	6.83

9.10 Below is a portion of the H$_2$O–NaCl phase diagram:

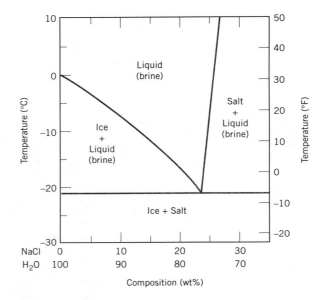

(a) Using this diagram, briefly explain how spreading salt on ice that is at a temperature below 0°C (32°F) can cause the ice to melt.

(b) What concentration of salt is necessary to have a 75% ice–25% liquid brine at −15°C (5°F)?

9.11 A 2.0-kg specimen of an 85 wt% Pb–15 wt% Sn alloy is heated to 200°C (390°F), at which temperature it is entirely an α phase solid solution (Figure 9.7). The alloy is to be melted to the extent that 50% of the specimen is liquid, the remainder being the α phase. This may be accomplished either by heating the alloy or changing its composition while holding the temperature constant.

(a) To what temperature must the specimen be heated?

(b) How much tin must be added to the 2.0-kg specimen at 200°C to achieve this state?

9.12 Consider the sugar–water phase diagram of Figure 9.1.

(a) How much sugar will dissolve in 1500 g water at 90°C (194°F)?

(b) If the saturated liquid solution in part a is cooled to 20°C (68°F), some of the sugar will precipitate out as a solid. What will be the composition of the saturated liquid solution (in wt% sugar) at 20°C?

(c) How much of the solid sugar will come out of solution upon cooling to 20°C?

9.13 A magnesium-lead alloy of mass 5.5 kg consists of a solid α phase which has a composition that is just slightly below the solubility limit at 200°C (390°F).

(a) What mass of lead is in the alloy?

(b) If the alloy is heated to 350°C (660°F), how much more lead may be dissolved in the α phase without exceeding the solubility limit of this phase?

9.14 (a) Briefly describe the phenomenon of coring and why it occurs.

(b) Cite one undesirable consequence of coring.

9.15 It is desired to produce a copper–nickel alloy that has a minimum noncold-worked tensile strength of 350 MPa (50,750 psi) and a ductility of at least 48%EL. Is such an alloy possible? If so, what must be its composition? If this is not possible, then explain why.

9.16 Is it possible to have a copper–silver alloy which, at equilibrium, consists of a β phase of composition 92 wt% Ag–8 wt% Cu, and also a liquid phase of composition 76 wt% Ag–24 wt% Cu? If so, what will be the approximate temperature of the alloy? If this is not possible, explain why.

9.17 Is it possible to have a copper–zinc alloy which, at equilibrium, consists of an ϵ phase of composition 80 wt% Zn–20 wt% Cu, and also a liquid phase of composition 95 wt% Zn–5 wt% Cu? If so, what will be the approximate temperature of the alloy? If this is not possible, explain why.

9.18 A copper–nickel alloy of composition 70 wt% Ni–30 wt% Cu is slowly heated from a temperature of 1300°C (2370°F).

(a) At what temperature does the first liquid phase form?

(b) What is the composition of this liquid phase?

(c) At what temperature does complete melting of the alloy occur?

(d) What is the composition of the last solid remaining prior to complete melting?

9.19 A 50 wt% Pb–50 wt% Mg alloy is slowly cooled from 700°C (1290°F) to 400°C (750°F).

(a) At what temperature does the first solid phase form?

(b) What is the composition of this solid phase?

(c) At what temperature does the liquid solidify?

(d) What is the composition of this last remaining liquid phase?

9.20 A 90 wt% Ag–10 wt% Cu alloy is heated to a temperature within the β + liquid phase region. If the composition of the liquid phase is 85 wt% Ag, determine (a) the temperature of the alloy, (b) the composition of the β phase, and (c) the mass fractions of both phases.

9.21 Below are given the solidus and liquidus temperatures for the germanium–silicon system. Construct the phase diagram for this system and label each region.

Composition (wt% Si)	Solidus Temperature (°C)	Liquidus Temperature (°C)
0	938	938
10	1005	1147
20	1065	1226
30	1123	1278
40	1178	1315
50	1232	1346
60	1282	1367
70	1326	1385
80	1359	1397
90	1390	1408
100	1414	1414

9.22 A 30 wt% Sn–70 wt% Pb alloy is heated to a temperature within the α + liquid phase region. If the mass fraction of each phase is 0.5, estimate **(a)** the temperature of the alloy, and **(b)** the compositions of the two phases.

9.23 For alloys of two hypothetical metals A and B, there exist an α, A-rich phase and a β, B-rich phase. From the mass fractions of both phases for two different alloys, which are at the same temperature, determine the composition of the phase boundary (or solubility limit) for both α and β phases at this temperature.

Alloy Composition	Fraction α Phase	Fraction β Phase
70 wt% A–30 wt% B	0.78	0.22
35 wt% A–65 wt% B	0.36	0.64

9.24 A hypothetical A–B alloy of composition 40 wt% B–60 wt% A at some temperature is found to consist of mass fractions of 0.66 and 0.34 for the α and β phases, respectively. If the composition of the α phase is 13 wt% B–87 wt% A, what is the composition of the β phase?

9.25 Is it possible to have a copper–silver alloy of composition 50 wt% Ag–50 wt% Cu, which, at equilibrium, consists of α and β phases having mass fractions $W_\alpha = 0.60$ and $W_\beta = 0.40$? If so, what will be the approximate temperature of the alloy? If such an alloy is not possible, explain why.

9.26 For 11.20 kg of a magnesium–lead alloy of composition 30 wt% Pb–70 wt% Mg, is it possible, at equilibrium, to have α and Mg_2Pb phases having respective masses of 7.39 kg and 3.81 kg? If so, what will be the approximate temperature of the alloy? If such an alloy is not possible, explain why.

9.27 At 200°C (390°F), what is the maximum solubility **(a)** of Pb in Sn? **(b)** of Sn in Pb?

9.28 A 60 wt% Pb–40 wt% Mg alloy is rapidly quenched to room temperature from an elevated temperature in such a way that the high-temperature microstructure is preserved. This microstructure is found to consist of the α phase and Mg_2Pb, having respective mass fractions of 0.42 and 0.58. Determine the approximate temperature from which the alloy was quenched.

9.29 Is it possible to have a copper–silver alloy in

which the mass fractions of primary β and total β are 0.68 and 0.925, respectively, at 775°C (1425°F)? Why or why not?

9.30 For 6.70 kg of a magnesium-lead alloy, is it possible to have the masses of primary α and total α of 4.23 kg and 6.00 kg, respectively, at 460°C (860°F)? Why or why not?

9.31 For a copper–silver alloy of composition 25 wt% Ag–75 wt% Cu and at 775°C (1425°F) do the following:

(a) Determine the mass fractions of the α and β phases.

(b) Determine the mass fractions of primary α and eutectic microconstituents.

(c) Determine the mass fraction of eutectic α.

9.32 The microstructure of a lead–tin alloy at 180°C (355°F) consists of primary β and eutectic structures. If the mass fractions of these two microconstituents are 0.57 and 0.43, respectively, determine the composition of the alloy.

9.33 Consider the hypothetical eutectic phase diagram for metals A and B, which is similar to that for the lead–tin system, Figure 9.7. Assume that (1) α and β phases exist at the A and B extremities of the phase diagram, respectively; (2) the eutectic composition is 47 wt% B–53 wt% A; and (3) the composition of the β phase at the eutectic temperature is 92.6 wt% B–7.4 wt% A. Determine the composition of an alloy that will yield primary α and total α mass fractions of 0.356 and 0.693, respectively.

9.34 Briefly explain why, upon solidification, an alloy of eutectic composition forms a microstructure consisting of alternating layers of the two solid phases.

9.35 For an 85 wt% Pb–15 wt% Mg alloy, make schematic sketches of the microstructure that would be observed for conditions of very slow cooling at the following temperatures: 600°C (1110°F), 500°C (930°F), 270°C (520°F), and 200°C (390°F). Label all phases and indicate their approximate compositions.

9.36 For a 68 wt% Zn–32 wt% Cu alloy, make schematic sketches of the microstructure that would be observed for conditions of very slow cooling at the following temperatures: 1000°C

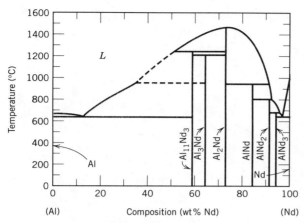

FIGURE 9.34 The aluminum–neodymium phase diagram. (Adapted from *ASM Handbook,* Vol. 3, *Alloy Phase Diagrams,* H. Baker, Editor, 1992. Reprinted by permission of ASM International, Materials Park, OH 44073-0002.)

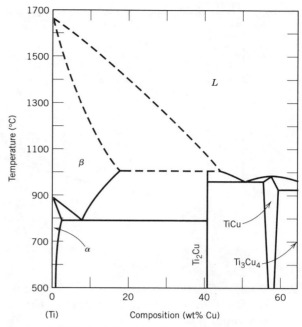

FIGURE 9.35 The titanium–copper phase diagram. (Adapted from *Phase Diagrams of Binary Titanium Alloys,* J. L. Murray, Editor, 1987. Reprinted by permission of ASM International, Materials Park, OH 44073-0002.)

(1830°F), 760°C (1400°F), 600°C (1110°F), and 400°C (750°F). Label all phases and indicate their approximate compositions.

9.37 For a 30 wt% Zn–70 wt% Cu alloy, make schematic sketches of the microstructure that would be observed for conditions of very slow cooling at the following temperatures: 1100°C (2010°F), 950°C (1740°F), 900°C (1650°F), and 700°C (1290°F). Label all phases and indicate their approximate compositions.

9.38 What is the principal difference between congruent and incongruent phase transformations?

9.39 Figure 9.34 is the aluminum–neodymium phase diagram, for which only single-phase regions are labeled. Specify temperature–composition points at which all eutectics, eutectoids, peritectics, and congruent phase transformations occur. Also, for each, write the reaction upon cooling.

9.40 Figure 9.35 is a portion of the titanium–copper phase diagram for which only single-phase regions are labeled. Specify all temperature–composition points at which eutectics, eutectoids, peritectics, and congruent phase transformations occur. Also, for each, write the reaction upon cooling.

9.41 For a ternary system, three components are present; temperature is also a variable. Com-

pute the maximum number of phases that may be present for a ternary system, assuming that pressure is held constant.

9.42 On the following page is shown the pressure–temperature phase diagram for H_2O. Apply the Gibbs phase rule at points A, B, and C; that is, specify the number of degrees of freedom at each of the points, that is, the number of externally controllable variables that need be specified to completely define the system.

9.43 Compute the mass fractions of α ferrite and cementite in pearlite.

9.44 What is the difference between a phase and a microconstituent?

9.45 (a) What is the distinction between hypoeutectoid and hypereutectoid steels?

(b) In a hypoeutectoid steel, both eutectoid and proeutectoid ferrite exist. Explain the difference between them. What will be the carbon concentration in each?

9.46 Briefly explain why a proeutectoid phase forms along austenite grain boundaries. *Hint:* Consult Section 4.5.

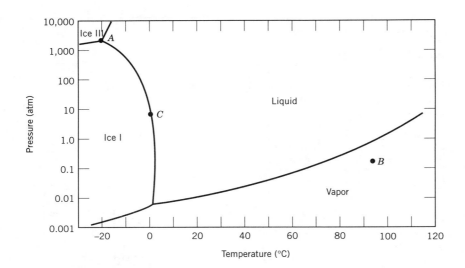

9.47 What is the carbon concentration of an iron–carbon alloy for which the fraction of total cementite is 0.10?

9.48 What is the proeutectoid phase for an iron–carbon alloy in which the mass fractions of total ferrite and total cementite are 0.92 and 0.08, respectively? Why?

9.49 Consider 3.5 kg of austenite containing 0.95 wt% C, cooled to below 727°C (1341°F).

(a) What is the proeutectoid phase?

(b) How many kilograms each of total ferrite and cementite form?

(c) How many kilograms each of pearlite and the proeutectoid phase form?

(d) Schematically sketch and label the resulting microstructure.

9.50 Consider 6.0 kg of austenite containing 0.45 wt% C, cooled to below 727°C (1341°F).

(a) What is the proeutectoid phase?

(b) How many kilograms each of total ferrite and cementite form?

(c) How many kilograms each of pearlite and the proeutectoid phase form?

(d) Schematically sketch and label the resulting microstructure.

9.51 Compute the mass fractions of proeutectoid ferrite and pearlite that form in an iron–carbon alloy containing 0.35 wt% C.

9.52 The microstructure of an iron–carbon alloy consists of proeutectoid ferrite and pearlite; the mass fractions of these two microconstituents are 0.174 and 0.826, respectively. Determine the concentration of carbon in this alloy.

9.53 The mass fractions of total ferrite and total cementite in an iron–carbon alloy are 0.88 and 0.12, respectively. Is this a hypoeutectoid or hypereutectoid alloy? Why?

9.54 The microstructure of an iron–carbon alloy consists of proeutectoid ferrite and pearlite; the mass fractions of these microconstituents are 0.20 and 0.80, respectively. Determine the concentration of carbon in this alloy.

9.55 Consider 1.5 kg of a 99.7 wt% Fe–0.3 wt% C alloy that is cooled to a temperature just below the eutectoid.

(a) How many kilograms of proeutectoid ferrite form?

(b) How many kilograms of eutectoid ferrite form?

(c) How many kilograms of cementite form?

9.56 Compute the maximum mass fraction of proeutectoid cementite possible for a hypereutectoid iron–carbon alloy.

9.57 Is it possible to have an iron–carbon alloy for which the mass fractions of total ferrite and proeutectoid cementite are 0.846 and 0.049, respectively? Why or why not?

9.58 Is it possible to have an iron–carbon alloy for which the mass fractions of total cementite and pearlite are 0.039 and 0.417, respectively? Why or why not?

9.59 Compute the mass fraction of eutectoid ferrite in an iron–carbon alloy that contains 0.43 wt% C.

9.60 The mass fraction of *eutectoid* cementite in an iron–carbon alloy is 0.104. On the basis of this information, is it possible to determine the composition of the alloy? If so, what is its composition? If this is not possible, explain why.

9.61 The mass fraction of *eutectoid* ferrite in an iron–carbon alloy is 0.82. On the basis of this information, is it possible to determine the composition of the alloy? If so, what is its composition? If this is not possible, explain why.

9.62 For an iron–carbon alloy of composition 5 wt% C–95 wt% Fe, make schematic sketches of the microstructure that would be observed for conditions of very slow cooling at the following temperatures: 1175°C (2150°F), 1145°C (2095°F), and 700°C (1290°F). Label the phases and indicate their compositions (approximate).

9.63 Often, the properties of multiphase alloys may be approximated by the relationship

$$E \text{ (alloy)} = E_\alpha V_\alpha + E_\beta V_\beta$$

where E represents a specific property (modulus of elasticity, hardness, etc.), and V is the volume fraction. The subscripts α and β denote the existing phases or microconstituents. Employ the relationship above to determine the approximate Brinell hardness of a 99.75 wt% Fe–0.25 wt% C alloy. Assume Brinell hardnesses of 80 and 280 for ferrite and pearlite, respectively, and that volume fractions may be approximated by mass fractions.

9.64 On the basis of the photomicrograph (i.e., the relative amounts of the microconstituents) for the lead–tin alloy shown in Figure 9.15 and the Pb–Sn phase diagram (Figure 9.7), estimate the composition of the alloy, and then compare this estimate with the composition given in the figure legend of Figure 9.15. Make the following assumptions: (1) the area fraction of each phase and microconstituent in the photomicrograph is equal to its volume fraction; (2) the densities of the α and β phases as well as the eutectic structure are 11.2, 7.3, and 8.7 g/cm^3, respectively; and (3) this photomicrograph represents the equilibrium microstructure at 180°C (356°F).

9.65 A steel alloy contains 95.7 wt% Fe, 4.0 wt% W, and 0.3 wt% C.

(a) What is the eutectoid temperature of this alloy?

(b) What is the eutectoid composition?

(c) What is the proeutectoid phase?

Assume that there are no changes in the positions of other phase boundaries with the addition of W.

9.66 A steel alloy is known to contain 93.65 wt% Fe, 6.0 wt% Mn, and 0.35 wt% C.

(a) What is the approximate eutectoid temperature of this alloy?

(b) What is the proeutectoid phase when this alloy is cooled to a temperature just below the eutectoid?

(c) Compute the relative amounts of the proeutectoid phase and pearlite. Assume that there are no alterations in the positions of other phase boundaries with the addition of Mn.

13

Structures and Properties of Ceramics

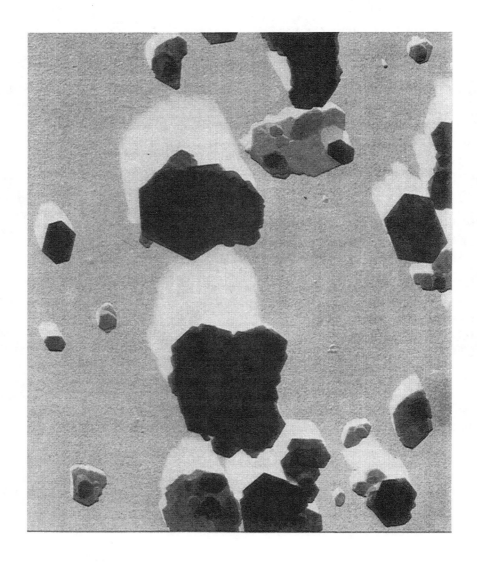

Electron micrograph of kaolinite crystals. They are in the form of hexagonal plates, some of which are stacked on top of one another. 21,000×. (Photograph courtesy of Georgia Kaolin Co., Inc.)

13.1 INTRODUCTION

Ceramic materials were discussed briefly in Chapter 1, which noted that they are inorganic and nonmetallic materials. Most ceramics are compounds between metallic and nonmetallic elements for which the interatomic bonds are either totally ionic, or predominantly ionic but having some covalent character. The term "ceramic" comes from the Greek word *keramikos*, which means "burnt stuff," indicating that desirable properties of these materials are normally achieved through a high-temperature heat treatment process called firing.

Up until the past 50 or so years, the most important materials in this class were termed the "traditional ceramics," those for which the primary raw material is clay; products considered to be traditional ceramics are china, porcelain, bricks, tiles, and, in addition, glasses and high-temperature ceramics. Of late, significant progress has been made in understanding the fundamental character of these materials and of the phenomena that occur in them that are responsible for their unique properties. Consequently, a new generation of these materials has evolved, and the term "ceramic" has taken on a much broader meaning. To one degree or another, these new materials have a rather dramatic effect on our lives; electronic, computer, communication, aerospace, and a host of other industries rely on their use.

This chapter discusses the types of crystal structure and atomic point defect that are found in ceramic materials and, in addition, some of their mechanical characteristics. Applications and fabrication techniques for this class of materials are treated in the next chapter.

CERAMIC STRUCTURES

Because ceramics are composed of at least two elements, and often more, their crystal structures are generally more complex than those for metals. The atomic bonding in these materials ranges from purely ionic to totally covalent; many ceramics exhibit a combination of these two bonding types, the degree of ionic character being dependent on the electronegativities of the atoms. Table 13.1 presents the percent ionic character for several common ceramic materials; these values were determined using Equation 2.12 and the electronegativities in Figure 2.7.

Table 13.1 **For Several Ceramic Materials, Percent Ionic Character of the Interatomic Bonds**

Material	Percent Ionic Character
CaF_2	89
MgO	73
$NaCl$	67
Al_2O_3	63
SiO_2	51
Si_3N_4	30
ZnS	18
SiC	12

13.2 CRYSTAL STRUCTURES

For those ceramic materials for which the atomic bonding is predominantly ionic, the crystal structures may be thought of as being composed of electrically charged ions instead of atoms. The metallic ions, or **cations,** are positively charged, because they have given up their valence electrons to the nonmetallic ions, or **anions,** which are negatively charged. Two characteristics of the component ions in crystalline ceramic materials influence the crystal structure: the magnitude of the electrical charge on each of the component ions, and the relative sizes of the cations and anions. With regard to the first characteristic, the crystal must be electrically neutral; that is, all the cation positive charges must be balanced by an equal number of anion negative charges. The chemical formula of a compound indicates the ratio of cations to anions, or the composition that achieves this charge balance. For example, in calcium fluoride, each calcium ion has a +2 charge (Ca^{2+}), and associated with each fluorine ion is a single negative charge (F^-). Thus, there must be twice as many F^- as Ca^{2+} ions, which is reflected in the chemical formula CaF_2.

The second criterion involves the sizes or ionic radii of the cations and anions, r_C and r_A, respectively. Because the metallic elements give up electrons when ionized, cations are ordinarily smaller than anions, and, consequently, the ratio r_C/r_A is less than unity. Each cation prefers to have as many nearest-neighbor anions as possible. The anions also desire a maximum number of cation nearest neighbors.

Stable ceramic crystal structures form when those anions surrounding a cation are all in contact with that cation, as illustrated in Figure 13.1. The coordination number (i.e., number of anion nearest neighbors for a cation) is related to the cation–anion radius ratio. For a specific coordination number, there is a critical or minimum r_C/r_A ratio for which this cation–anion contact is established (Figure 13.1), which ratio may be determined from pure geometrical considerations (see Example Problem 13.1).

The coordination numbers and nearest-neighbor geometries for various r_C/r_A ratios are presented in Table 13.2. For r_C/r_A ratios less than 0.155, the very small cation is bonded to two anions in a linear manner. If r_C/r_A has a value between 0.155 and 0.225, the coordination number for the cation is 3. This means each cation is surrounded by three anions in the form of a planar equilateral triangle, with the cation located in the center. The coordination number is 4 for r_C/r_A between 0.225 and 0.414; the cation is located at the center of a tetrahedron, with anions at each of the four corners. For r_C/r_A between 0.414 and 0.732, the cation may be thought of as being situated at the center of an octahedron surrounded by six anions, one at each corner, as also shown in the table. The coordination number is 8 for r_C/r_A between 0.732 and 1.0, with anions at all corners of a cube and a cation positioned at the center. For a radius ratio greater than unity, the coordination number is 12. The most common coordination numbers for ceramic materials are 4, 6, and 8. Table 13.3 gives the ionic radii for several anions and cations that are common to ceramic materials.

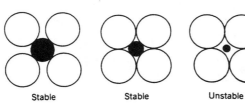

Stable   Stable   Unstable

FIGURE 13.1 Stable and unstable anion–cation coordination configurations. Open circles represent anions; closed circles denote cations.

Table 13.2 Coordination Numbers and Geometries for Various Cation–Anion Radius Ratios (r_C/r_A)

Coordination Number	Cation–Anion Radius Ratio	Coordination Geometry
2	<0.155	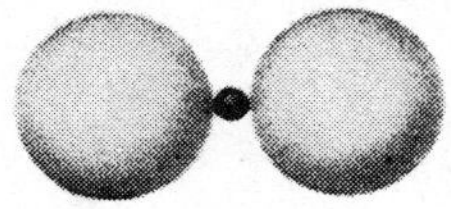
3	0.155–0.225	
4	0.225–0.414	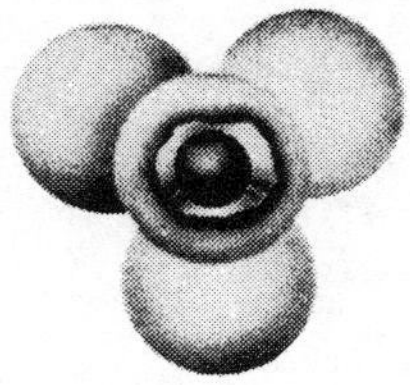
6	0.414–0.732	
8	0.732–1.0	

Source: W. D. Kingery, H. K. Bowen, and D. R. Uhlmann, *Introduction to Ceramics,* 2nd edition. Copyright © 1976 by John Wiley & Sons, New York. Reprinted by permission of John Wiley & Sons, Inc.

EXAMPLE PROBLEM 13.1

Show that the minimum cation-to-anion radius ratio for the coordination number 3 is 0.155.

SOLUTION

For this coordination, the small cation is surrounded by three anions to form an equilateral triangle as shown below—triangle *ABC;* the centers of all four ions are coplanar.

Table 13.3 Ionic Radii for Several Cations and Anions (for a Coordination Number of 6)

Cation	Ionic Radius (nm)	Anion	Ionic Radius (nm)
Al^{3+}	0.053	Br^-	0.196
Ba^{2+}	0.136	Cl^-	0.181
Ca^{2+}	0.100	F^-	0.133
Cs^+	0.170	I^-	0.220
Fe^{2+}	0.077	O^{2-}	0.140
Fe^{3+}	0.069	S^{2-}	0.184
K^+	0.138		
Mg^{2+}	0.072		
Mn^{2+}	0.067		
Na^+	0.102		
Ni^{2+}	0.069		
Si^{4+}	0.040		
Ti^{4+}	0.061		

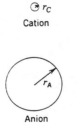

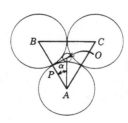

This boils down to a relatively simple plane trigonometry problem. Consideration of the right triangle APO makes it clear that the side lengths are related to the anion and cation radii r_A and r_C as

$$\overline{AP} = r_A$$

and

$$\overline{AO} = r_A + r_C$$

Furthermore, the side length ratio $\overline{AP}/\overline{AO}$ is a function of the angle α as

$$\frac{\overline{AP}}{\overline{AO}} = \cos \alpha$$

The magnitude of α is 30°, since line $\overline{AO}$ bisects the 60° angle BAC. Thus,

$$\frac{\overline{AP}}{\overline{AO}} = \frac{r_A}{r_A + r_C} = \cos 30° = \frac{\sqrt{3}}{2}$$

Or, solving for the cation–anion radius ratio,

$$\frac{r_C}{r_A} = \frac{1 - \sqrt{3}/2}{\sqrt{3}/2} = 0.155$$

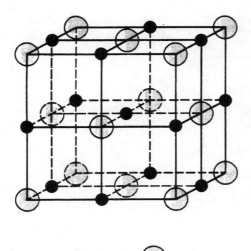

FIGURE 13.2 A unit cell for the rock salt, or sodium chloride (NaCl), crystal structure.

● Na⁺   ○ Cl⁻

AX-TYPE CRYSTAL STRUCTURES

Some of the common ceramic materials are those in which there are equal numbers of cations and anions. These are often referred to as AX compounds, where A denotes the cation and X the anion. There are several different crystal structures for AX compounds; each is normally named after a common material that assumes the particular structure.

Rock Salt Structure

Perhaps the most common AX crystal structure is the *sodium chloride* (NaCl), or *rock salt,* type. The coordination number for both cations and anions is 6, and therefore the cation–anion radius ratio is between approximately 0.414 and 0.732. A unit cell for this crystal structure (Figure 13.2) is generated from an FCC arrangement of anions with one cation situated at the cube center and one at the center of each of the 12 cube edges. An equivalent crystal structure results from a face-centered arrangement of cations. Thus, the rock salt crystal structure may be thought of as two interpenetrating FCC lattices, one composed of the cations, the other of anions. Some of the common ceramic materials that form with this crystal structure are NaCl, MgO, MnS, LiF, and FeO.

Cesium Chloride Structure

Figure 13.3 shows a unit cell for the *cesium chloride* (CsCl) crystal structure; the coordination number is 8 for both ion types. The anions are located at each of the corners of a cube, whereas the cube center is a single cation. Interchange of anions with cations, and vice versa, produces the same crystal structure. This is *not* a BCC crystal structure because ions of two different kinds are involved.

Zinc Blende Structure

A third AX structure is one in which the coordination number is 4; that is, all ions are tetrahedrally coordinated. This is called the *zinc blende,* or *sphalerite,* structure, after the mineralogical term for zinc sulfide (ZnS). A unit cell is presented in Figure 13.4; all corner and face positions of the cubic cell are occupied by S atoms, while

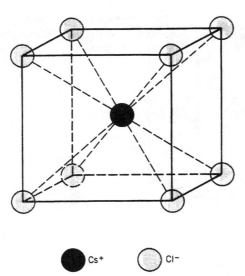

FIGURE 13.3 A unit cell for the cesium chloride (CsCl) crystal structure.

● Cs⁺   ○ Cl⁻

the Zn atoms fill interior tetrahedral positions. An equivalent structure results if Zn and S atom positions are reversed. Thus, each Zn atom is bonded to four S atoms, and vice versa. Most often the atomic bonding is highly covalent in compounds exhibiting this crystal structure (Table 13.1), which include ZnS, ZnTe, and SiC.

$A_m X_p$-TYPE CRYSTAL STRUCTURES

If the charges on the cations and anions are not the same, a compound can exist with the chemical formula $A_m X_p$, where m and/or $p \neq 1$. An example would be AX_2, for which a common crystal structure is found in *fluorite* (CaF_2). The ionic radii ratio r_C/r_A for CaF_2 is about 0.8 which, according to Table 13.2, gives a coordination number of 8. Calcium ions are positioned at the centers of cubes, with fluorine ions at the corners. The chemical formula shows that there are only half as many Ca^{2+} ions as F^- ions, and therefore the crystal structure would be similar

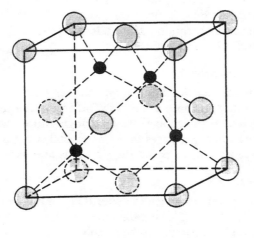

FIGURE 13.4 A unit cell for the zinc blende (ZnS) crystal structure.

● Zn   ○ S

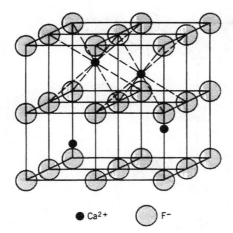

FIGURE 13.5   A unit cell for the fluorite (CaF_2) crystal structure.

● Ca^{2+} ◯ F^-

to CsCl (Figure 13.3), except that only half the center cube positions are occupied by Ca^{2+} ions. One unit cell consists of eight cubes, as indicated in Figure 13.5. Other compounds that have this crystal structure include UO_2, PuO_2, and ThO_2.

$A_mB_nX_p$-TYPE CRYSTAL STRUCTURES

It is also possible for ceramic compounds to have more than one type of cation; for two types of cations (represented by A and B), their chemical formula may be designated as $A_mB_nX_p$. Barium titanate ($BaTiO_3$), having both Ba^{2+} and Ti^{4+} cations, falls into this classification. This material has a *perovskite crystal structure* and rather interesting electromechanical properties to be discussed later. At temperatures above 120°C (248°F), the crystal structure is cubic. A unit cell of this structure is shown in Figure 13.6; Ba^{2+} ions are situated at all eight corners of the cube and a single Ti^{4+} is at the cube center, with O^{2-} ions located at the center of each of the six faces.

Table 13.4 summarizes the rock salt, cesium chloride, zinc blende, fluorite, and perovskite crystal structures in terms of cation–anion ratios and coordination numbers, and gives examples for each. Of course, many other ceramic crystal structures are possible.

Table 13.4   Summary of Some Common Ceramic Crystal Structures

Structure Name	Structure Type	Anion Packing	Coordination Numbers		Examples
			Cation	Anion	
Rock salt (sodium chloride)	AX	FCC	6	6	NaCl, MgO, FeO
Cesium chloride	AX	Simple cubic	8	8	CsCl
Zinc blende (sphalerite)	AX	FCC	4	4	ZnS, SiC
Fluorite	AX_2	Simple cubic	8	4	CaF_2, UO_2, ThO_2
Perovskite	ABX_3	FCC	12(A) 6(B)	6	$BaTiO_3$, $SrZrO_3$, $SrSnO_3$
Spinel	AB_2X_4	FCC	4(A) 6(B)	4	$MgAl_2O_4$, $FeAl_2O_4$

Source: W. D. Kingery, H. K. Bowen, and D. R. Uhlmann, *Introduction to Ceramics,* 2nd edition. Copyright © 1976 by John Wiley & Sons, New York. Reprinted by permission of John Wiley & Sons, Inc.

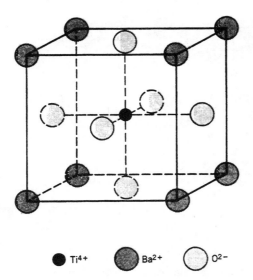

FIGURE 13.6   A unit cell for the perovskite crystal structure.

● Ti^{4+} ● Ba^{2+} ○ O^{2-}

CRYSTAL STRUCTURES FROM THE CLOSE PACKING OF ANIONS

It may be recalled (Section 3.11) that for metals, close-packed planes of atoms stacked on one another generate both FCC and HCP crystal structures. Similarly, a number of ceramic crystal structures may be considered in terms of close-packed planes of ions, as well as by unit cells. Ordinarily, the close-packed planes are composed of the large anions. As these planes are stacked atop each other, small interstitial sites are created between them in which the cations may reside.

These interstitial positions exist in two different types, as illustrated in Figure 13.7. Four atoms (three in one plane, and a single one in the adjacent plane) surround one type, labeled T in the figure; this is termed a **tetrahedral position,** since straight lines drawn from the centers of the surrounding spheres form a four-sided tetrahedron. The other site type, denoted as O in Figure 13.7, involves six ion spheres, three in each of the two planes. Because an octahedron is produced by joining these six sphere centers, this site is called an **octahedral position.** Thus, the coordination numbers for cations filling tetrahedral and octahedral positions

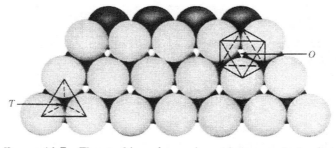

FIGURE 13.7   The stacking of one plane of close-packed spheres (anions) on top of another; tetrahedral and octahedral positions between the planes are designated by T and O, respectively. (From W. G. Moffatt, G. W. Pearsall, and J. Wulff, *The Structure and Properties of Materials,* Vol. 1, *Structure.* Copyright © 1964 by John Wiley & Sons, New York. Reprinted by permission of John Wiley & Sons, Inc.)

Figure 13.8 A section of the rock salt crystal structure from which a corner has been removed. The exposed plane of anions (light spheres inside the triangle) is a {111}-type plane; the cations (dark spheres) occupy the interstitial octahedral positions.

are 4 and 6, respectively. Furthermore, for each of these anion spheres, one octahedral and two tetrahedral positions will exist.

Ceramic crystal structures of this type depend on two factors: (1) the stacking of the close-packed anion layers (both FCC and HCP arrangements are possible, which correspond to *ABCABC* . . . and *ABABAB* . . . sequences, respectively), and (2) the manner in which the interstitial sites are filled with cations. For example, consider the rock salt crystal structure discussed above. The unit cell has cubic symmetry, and each cation (Na^+ ion) has six Cl^- ion nearest neighbors, as may be verified from Figure 13.2. That is, the Na^+ ion at the center has as nearest neighbors the six Cl^- ions that reside at the centers of each of the cube faces. The crystal structure, having cubic symmetry, may be considered in terms of an FCC array of close-packed planes of anions, and all planes are of the {111} type. The cations reside in octahedral positions because they have as nearest neighbors six anions. Furthermore, all octahedral positions are filled, since there is a single octahedral site per anion, and the ratio of anions to cations is 1:1. For this crystal structure, the relationship between the unit cell and close-packed anion plane stacking schemes is illustrated in Figure 13.8.

Other, but not all, ceramic crystal structures may be treated in a similar manner; included are the zinc blende and perovskite structures. The *spinel structure* is one of the $A_mB_nX_p$ types, which is found for magnesium aluminate or spinel ($MgAl_2O_4$). With this structure, the O^{2-} ions form an FCC lattice, whereas Mg^{2+} ions fill tetrahedral sites and Al^{3+} reside in octahedral positions. Magnetic ceramics, or ferrites, have a crystal structure that is a slight variant of this spinel structure; and the magnetic characteristics are affected by the occupancy of tetrahedral and octahedral positions (see Section 21.5).

EXAMPLE PROBLEM 13.2

On the basis of ionic radii, what crystal structure would you predict for FeO?

SOLUTION

First, note that FeO is an AX-type compound. Next, determine the cation–anion radius ratio, which from Table 13.3 is

$$\frac{r_{Fe^{2+}}}{r_{O^{2-}}} = \frac{0.077 \text{ nm}}{0.140 \text{ nm}} = 0.550$$

This value lies between 0.414 and 0.732, and, therefore, from Table 13.2 the coordination number for the Fe^{2+} ion is 6; this is also the coordination number of O^{2-}, since there are equal numbers of cations and anions. The predicted crystal structure will be rock salt, which is the AX crystal structure having a coordination number of 6, as given in Table 13.4.

CERAMIC DENSITY COMPUTATIONS

It is possible to compute the theoretical density of a crystalline ceramic material from unit cell data in a manner similar to that described in Section 3.5 for metals. In this case the density ρ may be determined using a modified form of Equation 3.5, as follows:

$$\rho = \frac{n'(\Sigma A_C + \Sigma A_A)}{V_C N_A} \tag{13.1}$$

where

n' = the number of formula units[1] within the unit cell

ΣA_C = the sum of the atomic weights of all cations in the formula unit

ΣA_A = the sum of the atomic weights of all anions in the formula unit

V_C = the unit cell volume

N_A = Avogadro's number, 6.023×10^{23} formula units/mol

EXAMPLE PROBLEM 13.3

On the basis of crystal structure, compute the theoretical density for sodium chloride. How does this compare with its measured density?

SOLUTION

The density may be determined using Equation 13.1, where n', the number of NaCl units per unit cell, is 4 because both sodium and chloride ions form FCC lattices. Furthermore,

$$\Sigma A_C = A_{Na} = 22.99 \text{ g/mol}$$

$$\Sigma A_A = A_{Cl} = 35.45 \text{ g/mol}$$

Since the unit cell is cubic, $V_C = a^3$, a being the unit cell edge length. For the face of the cubic unit cell shown on the next page,

$$a = 2r_{Na^+} + 2r_{Cl^-}$$

r_{Na^+} and r_{Cl^-} being the sodium and chlorine ionic radii, given in Table 13.3 as 0.102 and 0.181 nm, respectively.

---

[1] By "formula unit" we mean all the ions that are included in the chemical formula unit. For example, for $BaTiO_3$, a formula unit consists of one barium ion, a titanium ion, and three oxygen ions.

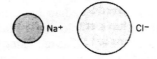

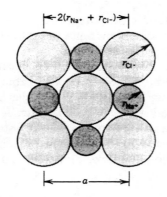

Thus,

$$V_C = a^3 = (2r_{Na^+} + 2r_{Cl^-})^3$$

And finally,

$$\rho = \frac{n'(A_{Na} + A_{Cl})}{(2r_{Na^+} + 2r_{Cl^-})^3 N_A}$$

$$= \frac{4(22.99 + 35.45)}{[2(0.102 \times 10^{-7}) + 2(0.181 \times 10^{-7})]^3(6.023 \times 10^{23})}$$

$$= 2.14 \text{ g/cm}^3$$

This compares very favorably with the experimental value of 2.16 g/cm^3.

13.3 SILICATE CERAMICS

Silicates are materials composed primarily of silicon and oxygen, the two most abundant elements in the earth's crust; consequently, the bulk of soils, rocks, clays, and sand come under the silicate classification. Rather than characterizing the crystal structures of these materials in terms of unit cells, it is more convenient to use various arrangements of an SiO$_4^{4-}$ tetrahedron (Figure 13.9). Each atom of silicon

FIGURE 13.9 A silicon–oxygen (SiO$_4^{4-}$) tetrahedron.

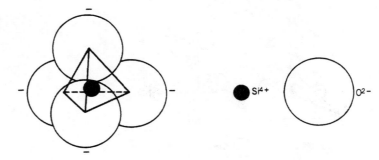

is bonded to four oxygen atoms, which are situated at the corners of the tetrahedron; the silicon atom is positioned at the center. Since this is the basic unit of the silicates, it is often treated as a negatively charged entity.

Often the silicates are not considered to be ionic because there is a significant covalent character to the interatomic Si–O bonds (Table 13.1), which bonds are directional and relatively strong. Regardless of the character of the Si–O bond, there is a −4 charge associated with every SiO_4^{4-} tetrahedron, since each of the four oxygen atoms requires an extra electron to achieve a stable electronic structure. Various silicate structures arise from the different ways in which the SiO_4^{4-} units can be combined into one-, two-, and three-dimensional arrangements.

SILICA

Chemically, the most simple silicate material is silicon dioxide, or silica (SiO_2). Structurally, it is a three-dimensional network that is generated when every corner oxygen atom in each tetrahedron is shared by adjacent tetrahedra. Thus, the material is electrically neutral and all atoms have stable electronic structures. Under these circumstances the ratio of Si to O atoms is 1:2, as indicated by the chemical formula.

If these tetrahedra are arrayed in a regular and ordered manner, a crystalline structure is formed. There are three primary polymorphic crystalline forms of silica: quartz, cristobalite (Figure 13.10), and tridymite. Their structures are relatively complicated, and comparatively open; that is, the atoms are not closely packed together. As a consequence, these crystalline silicas have relatively low densities; for example, at room temperature quartz has a density of only 2.65 g/cm³. The strength of the Si–O interatomic bonds is reflected in a relatively high melting temperature, 1710°C (3110°F).

SILICA GLASSES

Silica can also be made to exist as a noncrystalline solid or glass, having a high degree of atomic randomness, which is characteristic of the liquid; such a material is called *fused silica*, or *vitreous silica*. As with crystalline silica, the SiO_4^{4-} tetrahedron is the basic unit; beyond this structure, considerable disorder exists. The structures for crystalline and noncrystalline silica are compared schematically in Figure 3.21. Other oxides (e.g., B_2O_3 and GeO_2) may also form glassy structures (and polyhedral oxide structures similar to that shown in Figure 13.9); these materials, as well as SiO_2, are termed *network formers*.

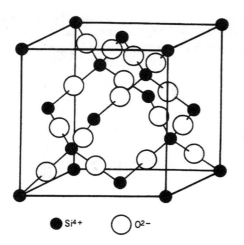

Figure 13.10 The arrangement of silicon and oxygen atoms in a unit cell of cristobalite, a polymorph of SiO_2.

● Si^{4+} ○ O^{2-}

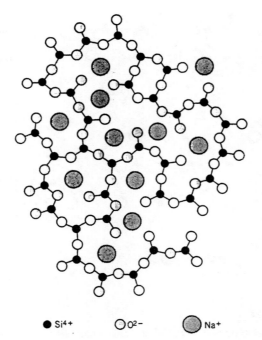

FIGURE 13.11 Schematic representation of ion positions in a sodium–silicate glass.

● Si^{4+} ○ O^{2-} ◉ Na^+

The common inorganic glasses that are used for containers, windows, and so on are silica glasses to which have been added other oxides such as CaO and Na_2O. These oxides do not form polyhedral networks. Rather, their cations are incorporated within and modify the SiO_4^{4-} network; for this reason, these oxide additives are termed *network modifiers*. For example, Figure 13.11 is a schematic representation of the structure of a sodium-silicate glass. Still other oxides, such as TiO_2 and Al_2O_3, while not network formers, substitute for silicon and become part of and stabilize the network; these are called *intermediates*. From a practical perspective, the addition of these modifiers and intermediates lowers the melting point and viscosity of a glass, and makes it easier to form at lower temperatures (Section 14.2).

THE SILICATES

For the various silicate minerals, one, two, or three of the corner oxygen atoms of the SiO_4^{4-} tetrahedra are shared by other tetrahedra to form some rather complex structures. Some of these, represented in Figure 13.12, have formulas SiO_4^{4-}, $Si_2O_7^{6-}$, $Si_3O_9^{6-}$, and so on; single-chain structures are also possible, as in Figure 13.12e. Positively charged cations such as Ca^{2+}, Mg^{2+}, and Al^{3+} serve two roles. First, they compensate the negative charges from the SiO_4^{4-} units so that charge neutrality is achieved; and second, these cations ionically bond the SiO_4^{4-} tetrahedra together.

Simple Silicates

Of these silicates, the most structurally simple ones involve isolated tetrahedra (Figure 13.12a). For example, forsterite (Mg_2SiO_4) has the equivalent of two Mg^{2+} ions associated with each tetrahedron in such a way that every Mg^{2+} ion has six oxygen nearest neighbors.

The $Si_2O_7^{6-}$ ion is formed when two tetrahedra share a common oxygen atom (Figure 13.12b). Akermanite ($Ca_2MgSi_2O_7$) is a mineral having the equivalent of two Ca^{2+} ions and one Mg^{2+} ion bonded to each $Si_2O_7^{6-}$ unit.

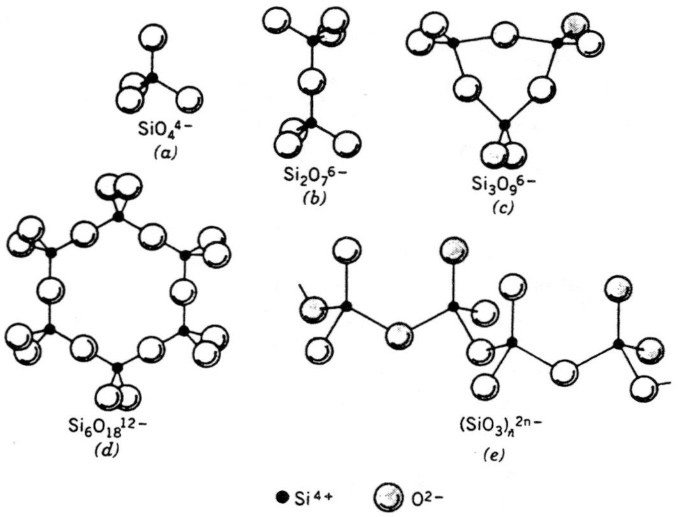

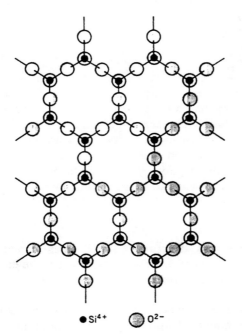

FIGURE 13.12 Five silicate ion structures formed from SiO_4^{4-} tetrahedra.

SiO_4^{4-}
(a)

$Si_2O_7^{6-}$
(b)

$Si_3O_9^{6-}$
(c)

$Si_6O_{18}^{12-}$
(d)

$(SiO_3)_n^{2n-}$
(e)

● Si^{4+} ◯ O^{2-}

Layered Silicates

A two-dimensional sheet or layered structure can also be produced by the sharing of three oxygen ions in each of the tetrahedra (Figure 13.13); for this structure the repeating unit formula may be represented by $(Si_2O_5)^{2-}$. The net negative charge is associated with the unbonded oxygen atoms projecting out of the plane of the page. Electroneutrality is ordinarily established by a second planar sheet structure having an excess of cations, which bond to these unbonded oxygen atoms from the Si_2O_5 sheet. Such materials are called the sheet or layered silicates, and their basic structure is characteristic of the clays and other minerals.

FIGURE 13.13 Schematic representation of the two-dimensional silicate sheet structure having a repeat unit formula of $(Si_2O_5)^{2-}$.

● Si^{4+} ◯ O^{2-}

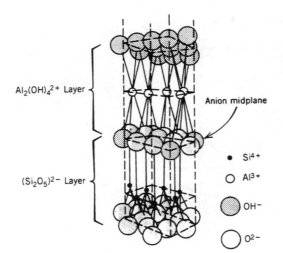

$Al_2(OH)_4^{2+}$ Layer

Anion midplane

$(Si_2O_5)^{2-}$ Layer

• Si^{4+}

○ Al^{3+}

⬤ OH^-

◯ O^{2-}

FIGURE 13.14   The structure of kaolinite clay. (Adapted from W. E. Hauth, "Crystal Chemistry of Ceramics," *American Ceramic Society Bulletin,* Vol. 30, No. 4, 1951, p. 140.)

One of the most common clay minerals, kaolinite, has a relatively simple two-layer silicate sheet structure. Kaolinite clay has the formula $Al_2(Si_2O_5)(OH)_4$ in which the silica tetrahedral layer, represented by $(Si_2O_5)^{2-}$, is made electrically neutral by an adjacent $Al_2(OH)_4^{2+}$ layer. A single sheet of this structure is shown in Figure 13.14, which is exploded in the vertical direction to provide a better perspective of the ion positions; the two distinct layers are indicated in the figure. The midplane of anions consists of O^{2-} ions from the $(Si_2O_5)^{2-}$ layer, as well as OH^- ions that are a part of the $Al_2(OH)_4^{2+}$ layer. Whereas the bonding within this two-layered sheet is strong and intermediate ionic-covalent, adjacent sheets are only loosely bound to one another by weak van der Waals forces.

A crystal of kaolinite is made of a series of these double layers or sheets stacked parallel to each other, which form small flat plates typically less than 1 μm in diameter and nearly hexagonal. On page 372 is an electron micrograph of kaolinite crystals at a high magnification, showing the hexagonal crystal plates some of which are piled one on top of the other.

These silicate sheet structures are not confined to the clays; other minerals also in this group are talc $[Mg_3(Si_2O_5)_2(OH)_2]$ and the micas [e.g., muscovite, $KAl_3Si_3O_{10}(OH)_2$], which are important ceramic raw materials. As might be deduced from the chemical formulas, the structures for some silicates are among the most complex of all the inorganic materials.

13.4 CARBON

Carbon is an element that exists in various polymorphic forms, as well as in the amorphous state. This group of materials does not really fall within any one of the traditional metal, ceramic, polymer classification schemes. However, it has been decided to discuss these materials in this chapter since graphite, one of the polymorphic forms, is sometimes classified as a ceramic, and, in addition, the crystal structure of diamond, another polymorph, is similar to that of zinc blende, discussed in Section 13.2. Treatment of the carbon materials will focus on the structures and characteristics of graphite, diamond, and the new fullerenes, and, in addition, on their current and potential uses.

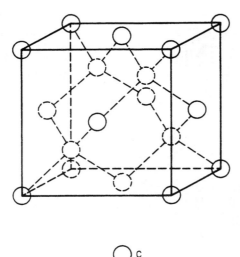

FIGURE 13.15 A unit cell for the diamond cubic crystal structure.

○ c

DIAMOND

Diamond is a metastable carbon polymorph at room temperature and atmospheric pressure. Its crystal structure is a variant of the zinc blende, in which carbon atoms occupy all positions (both Zn and S), as indicated in the unit cell shown in Figure 13.15. Thus, each carbon bonds to four other carbons, and these bonds are totally covalent. This is appropriately called the *diamond cubic* crystal structure, which is also found for other Group IVA elements in the periodic table [e.g., germanium, silicon, and gray tin, below 13°C (55°F)].

The physical properties of diamond make it an extremely attractive material. It is extremely hard (the hardest known material) and has a very low electrical conductivity; these characteristics are due to its crystal structure and the strong interatomic covalent bonds. Furthermore, it has an unusually high thermal conductivity for a nonmetallic material, is optically transparent in the visible and infrared regions of the electromagnetic spectrum, and has a high index of refraction. Relatively large diamond single crystals are used as gem stones. Industrially, diamonds are utilized to grind or cut other softer materials (Section 14.14). Techniques to produce synthetic diamonds have been developed, beginning in the mid-1950s, which have been refined to the degree that today a large proportion of the industrial-quality materials are man-made, in addition to some of those of gem quality.

Over the last several years, diamond in the form of thin films has been produced. Film growth techniques involve vapor-phase chemical reactions followed by the film deposition. Maximum film thicknesses are on the order of a millimeter. Furthermore, none of the films yet produced has the long-range crystalline regularity of natural diamond. The diamond is polycrystalline and may consist of very small and/or relatively large grains; in addition, amorphous carbon and graphite may be present. A scanning electron micrograph of the surface of a diamond thin film is shown in Figure 13.16. The mechanical, electrical, and optical properties of diamond films approach those of the bulk diamond material. These desirable properties have been and will continue to be exploited so as to create new and better products. For example, the surfaces of drills, dies, bearings, knives, and other tools have been coated with diamond films to increase surface hardness; some lenses and radomes have been made stronger while remaining transparent by the application of diamond coatings; coatings have also been applied to loudspeaker tweeters and to high-

FIGURE 13.16 **Scanning** electron micrograph of a diamond thin film in which is shown numerous multifaceted microcrystals. 1000×. (Photograph courtesy of the Norton Company.)

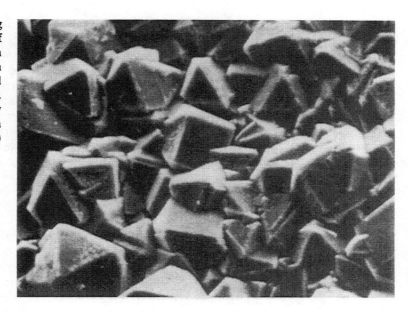

precision micrometers. Potential applications for these films include application to the surface of machine components such as gears, to optical recording heads and disks, and as substrates for semiconductor devices.

GRAPHITE

Another polymorph of carbon is graphite; it has a crystal structure (Figure 13.17) distinctly different from that of diamond and is also more stable than diamond at ambient temperature and pressure. The graphite structure is composed of layers of hexagonally arranged carbon atoms; within the layers, each carbon atom is bonded to three coplanar neighbor atoms by strong covalent bonds. The fourth bonding electron participates in a weak van der Waals type of bond between the layers. As a consequence of these weak interplanar bonds, interplanar cleavage is facile, which gives rise to the excellent lubricative properties of graphite. Also, the

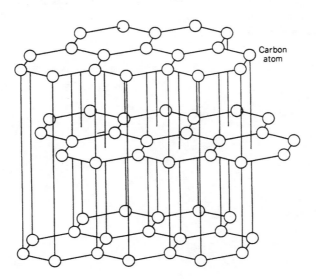

Carbon atom

FIGURE 13.17 The structure of **graphite.**

electrical conductivity is relatively high in crystallographic directions parallel to the hexagonal sheets.

Other desirable properties of graphite include the following: high strength and good chemical stability at elevated temperatures and in nonoxidizing atmospheres, high thermal conductivity, low coefficient of thermal expansion and high resistance to thermal shock, high adsorption of gases, and good machinability. Graphite is commonly used as heating elements for electric furnaces, as electrodes for arc welding, in metallurgical crucibles, in casting molds for metal alloys and ceramics, for high-temperature refractories and insulations, in rocket nozzles, in chemical reactor vessels, for electrical contacts, brushes and resistors, as electrodes in batteries, and in air purification devices.

FULLERENES

Another polymorphic form of carbon was discovered in 1985. It exists in discrete molecular form, and consists of a hollow spherical cluster of sixty carbon atoms; a single molecule is denoted by C_{60}. Each molecule is composed of groups of carbon atoms that are bonded to one another to form both hexagon (six-carbon atom) and pentagon (five-carbon atom) geometrical configurations. One such molecule, shown in Figure 13.18, is found to consist of 20 hexagons and 12 pentagons, which are arrayed such that no two pentagons share a common side; the molecular surface thus exhibits the symmetry of a soccer ball. The material composed of C_{60} molecules is known as *buckministerfullerene,* named in honor of R. Buckminister Fuller, who invented the geodesic dome; each C_{60} is simply a molecular replica of such a dome, which is often referred to as "buckyball" for short. The term *fullerene* is used to denote the class of materials that are composed of this type of molecule.

Diamond and graphite are what may be termed *network solids,* in that all of the carbon atoms form primary bonds with adjacent atoms throughout the entirety of the solid. By way of contrast, the carbon atoms in buckminsterfullerene bond together so as to form these spherical molecules. In the solid state, the C_{60} units form a crystalline structure and pack together in a face-centered cubic array.

As a pure crystalline solid, this material is electrically insulating. However, with proper impurity additions, it can be made highly conductive and semiconductive. As a final note, molecular shapes other than the ball clusters recently have been discovered; these include nanoscale tubular and polyhedral structures. It is anticipated that, with further developments, the fullerenes will become technologically important materials.

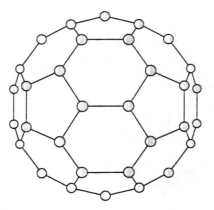

FIGURE 13.18 The structure of a C_{60} molecule.

FIGURE 13.19
Schematic
representations of
cation and anion
vacancies and a cation
interstitial. (From W.
G. Moffatt, G. W.
Pearsall, and J. Wulff,
*The Structure and
Properties of Materials,*
Vol. 1, *Structure,* p. 78.
Copyright © 1964 by
John Wiley & Sons,
New York. Reprinted
by permission of John
Wiley & Sons, Inc.)

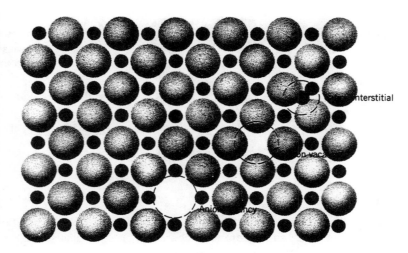

13.5 IMPERFECTIONS IN CERAMICS

ATOMIC POINT DEFECTS

Atomic defects involving host atoms may exist in ceramic compounds. As with metals, both vacancies and interstitials are possible; however, since ceramic materials contain ions of at least two kinds, defects for each ion type may occur. For example, in NaCl, Na interstitials and vacancies and Cl interstitials and vacancies may exist. It is highly improbable that there would be appreciable concentrations of anion interstitials. The anion is relatively large, and to fit into a small interstitial position, substantial strains on the surrounding ions must be introduced. Anion and cation vacancies and a cation interstitial are represented in Figure 13.19.

The expression **defect structure** is often used to designate the types and concentrations of atomic defects in ceramics. Because the atoms exist as charged ions, when defect structures are considered, conditions of electroneutrality must be maintained. **Electroneutrality** is the state that exists when there are equal numbers of positive and negative charges from the ions. As a consequence, defects in ceramics do not occur alone. One such type of defect involves a cation-vacancy and a cation–interstitial pair. This is called a **Frenkel defect** (Figure 13.20). It might be thought

FIGURE 13.20
Schematic diagram
showing Frenkel and
Schottky defects in
ionic solids. (From W.
G. Moffatt, G. W.
Pearsall, and J. Wulff,
*The Structure and
Properties of Materials,*
Vol. 1, *Structure,* p. 78.
Copyright © 1964 by
John Wiley & Sons,
New York. Reprinted
by permission of John
Wiley & Sons, Inc.)

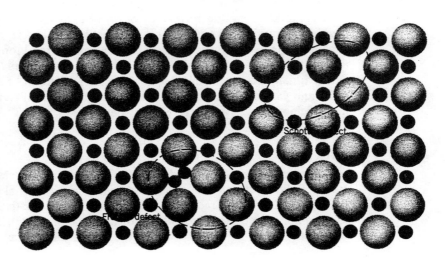

FIGURE 13.21 Schematic representation of an Fe^{2+} vacancy in FeO that results from the formation of two Fe^{3+} ions.

of as being formed by a cation leaving its normal position and moving into an interstitial site. There is no change in charge because the cation maintains the same positive charge as an interstitial.

Another type of defect found in AX materials is a cation vacancy–anion vacancy pair known as a **Schottky defect,** also schematically diagrammed in Figure 13.20. This defect might be thought of as being created by removing one cation and one anion from the interior of the crystal and then placing them both at an external surface. Since both cations and anions have the same charge, and since for every anion vacancy there exists a cation vacancy, the charge neutrality of the crystal is maintained.

The ratio of cations to anions is not altered by the formation of either a Frenkel or a Schottky defect. If no other defects are present, the material is said to be stoichiometric. **Stoichiometry** may be defined as a state for ionic compounds wherein there is the exact ratio of cations to anions as predicted by the chemical formula. For example, NaCl is stoichiometric if the ratio of Na^+ ions to Cl^- ions is exactly 1:1. A ceramic compound is *nonstoichiometric* if there is any deviation from this exact ratio.

Nonstoichiometry may occur for some ceramic materials in which two valence (or ionic) states exist for one of the ion types. Iron oxide (wüstite, FeO), is one such material, for the iron can be present in both Fe^{2+} and Fe^{3+} states; the number of each of these ion types depends on temperature and the ambient oxygen pressure. The formation of an Fe^{3+} ion disrupts the electroneutrality of the crystal by introducing an excess +1 charge, which must be offset by some type of defect. This may be accomplished by the formation of one Fe^{2+} vacancy (or the removal of two positive charges) for every two Fe^{3+} ions that are formed (Figure 13.21). The crystal is no longer stoichiometric because there is one more O ion than Fe ion; however, the crystal remains electrically neutral. This phenomenon is fairly common in iron oxide, and, in fact, its chemical formula is often written as $Fe_{1-x}O$ (where x is some small and variable fraction substantially less than unity) to indicate a condition of nonstoichiometry with a deficiency of Fe.

IMPURITIES IN CERAMICS

Impurity atoms can form solid solutions in ceramic materials much as they do in metals. Solid solutions of both substitutional and interstitial types are possible. For an interstitial, the ionic radius of the impurity must be relatively small in comparison to the anion. Since there are both anions and cations, a substitutional impurity will substitute for the host ion to which it is most similar in an electrical sense: if the

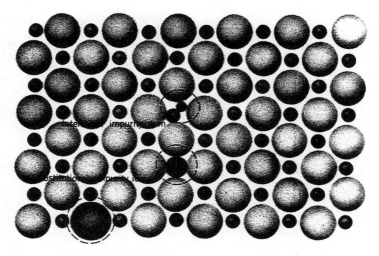

FIGURE 13.22 Schematic representations of interstitial, anion-substitutional, and cation-substitutional impurity atoms in an ionic compound. (Adapted from W. G. Moffatt, G. W. Pearsall, and J. Wulff, *The Structure and Properties of Materials,* Vol. 1, *Structure,* p. 78. Copyright © 1964 by John Wiley & Sons, New York. Reprinted by permission of John Wiley & Sons, Inc.)

impurity atom normally forms a cation in a ceramic material, it most probably will substitute for a host cation. For example, in sodium chloride, impurity Ca^{2+} and O^{2-} ions would most likely substitute for Na^+ and Cl^- ions, respectively. Schematic representations for cation and anion substitutional as well as interstitial impurities are shown in Figure 13.22. To achieve any appreciable solid solubility of substituting impurity atoms, the ionic size and charge must be very nearly the same as those of one of the host ions. For an impurity ion having a charge different from the host ion for which it substitutes, the crystal must compensate for this difference in charge so that electroneutrality is maintained with the solid. One way this is accomplished is by the formation of lattice defects—vacancies or interstitials of both ion types, as discussed above.

EXAMPLE PROBLEM 13.4

If electroneutrality is to be preserved, what point defects are possible in NaCl when a Ca^{2+} substitutes for an Na^+ ion? How many of these defects exist for every Ca^{2+} ion?

SOLUTION

Replacement of an Na^+ by a Ca^{2+} ion introduces one extra positive charge. Electroneutrality is maintained when either a single positive charge is eliminated or another single negative charge is added. Removal of a positive charge is accomplished by the formation of one Na^+ vacancy. Alternatively, a Cl^- interstitial will supply an additional negative charge, negating the effect of each Ca^{2+} ion. However, as mentioned above, the formation of this defect is highly unlikely.

FIGURE 13.23
The aluminum
oxide–chromium oxide
phase diagram.
(Adapted from E. N.
Bunting, "Phase
Equilibria in the
System Cr_2O_3–Al_2O_3,"
*Bur. Standards J.
Research,* **6,** 1931,
p. 948.)

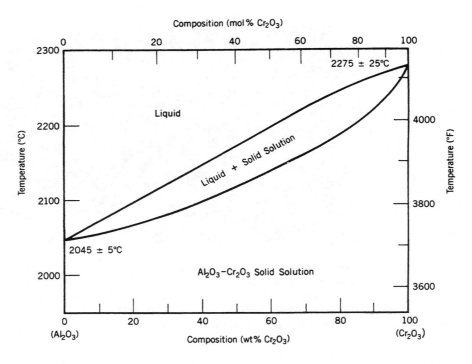

13.6 CERAMIC PHASE DIAGRAMS

Phase diagrams have been experimentally determined for a large number of ceramic systems. For binary or two-component phase diagrams, it is frequently the case that the two components are compounds that share a common element, often oxygen. These diagrams may have configurations similar to metal–metal systems, and they are interpreted in the same way. For a review of the interpretation of phase diagrams, the reader is referred to Section 9.6.

THE Al_2O_3–Cr_2O_3 SYSTEM

One of the relatively simple ceramic phase diagrams is that found for the aluminum oxide–chromium oxide system, Figure 13.23. This diagram has the same form as the isomorphous copper–nickel phase diagram (Figure 9.2a), consisting of single liquid and single solid phase regions separated by a two-phase solid–liquid region having the shape of a blade. The Al_2O_3–Cr_2O_3 solid solution is a substitutional one in which Al^{3+} substitutes for Cr^{3+}, and vice versa. It exists for all compositions below the melting point of Al_2O_3 inasmuch as both aluminum and chromium ions have the same charge as well as similar radii (0.053 and 0.062 nm, respectively). Furthermore, both Al_2O_3 and Cr_2O_3 have the same crystal structure.

THE MgO–Al_2O_3 SYSTEM

The phase diagram for the magnesium oxide–aluminum oxide system (Figure 13.24) is similar in many respects to the lead–magnesium diagram (Figure 9.18). There exists an intermediate phase, or better, a compound called *spinel,* which has the chemical formula $MgAl_2O_4$ (or MgO–Al_2O_3). Even though spinel is a distinct compound [of composition 50 mol% Al_2O_3–50 mol% MgO (72 wt% Al_2O_3–28 wt% MgO)], it is represented on the phase diagram as a single-phase field rather than

FIGURE 13.24
The magnesium
oxide–aluminum oxide
phase diagram; *ss*
denotes solid solution.
(Adapted from B.
Hallstedt,
"Thermodynamic
Assessment of the
System MgO–Al₂O₃,"
J. Am. Ceram. Soc., **75**
[6] 1502 (1992).
Reprinted by
permission of the
American Ceramic
Society.)

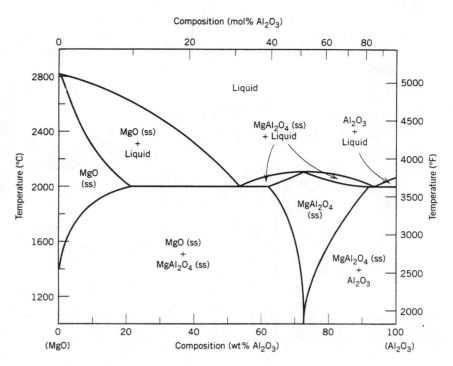

as a vertical line, as for Mg_2Pb (Figure 9.18); that is, there is a range of compositions over which spinel is a stable compound. Thus, spinel is nonstoichiometric for other than the 50 mol% Al_2O_3–50 mol% MgO composition. Furthermore, there is limited solubility of Al_2O_3 in MgO below about 1400°C (2550°F) at the left-hand extremity of Figure 13.24, which is due primarily to the differences in charge and radii of the Mg^{2+} and Al^{3+} ions (0.072 versus 0.053 nm). For the same reasons, MgO is virtually insoluble in Al_2O_3, as evidenced by a lack of a terminal solid solution on the right-hand side of the phase diagram. Also, two eutectics are found, one on either side of the spinel phase field, and stoichiometric spinel melts congruently at about 2100°C (3800°F).

THE ZrO₂–CaO SYSTEM

Another important binary ceramic system is that for zirconium oxide (zirconia) and calcium oxide (calcia); a portion of this phase diagram is shown in Figure 13.25. The horizontal axis extends to only about 31 wt% CaO (50 mol% CaO), at which composition the compound $CaZrO_3$ forms. It is worth noting that one eutectic (2250°C and 23 wt% CaO) and two eutectoid (1000°C and 2.5 wt% CaO, and 850°C and 7.5 wt% CaO) reactions are found for this system.

It may also be observed from Figure 13.25 that ZrO_2 phases having three different crystal structures exist in this system, namely tetragonal, monoclinic, and cubic. Pure ZrO_2 experiences a tetragonal-to-monoclinic phase transformation at about 1150°C (2102°F). A relatively large volume change accompanies this transformation, resulting in the formation of cracks, which renders a ceramic ware useless. This problem is overcome by "stabilizing" the zirconia by adding between about 3 and 7 wt% CaO. Over this composition range and at temperatures above about 1000°C both cubic and tetragonal phases will be present. Upon cooling to room

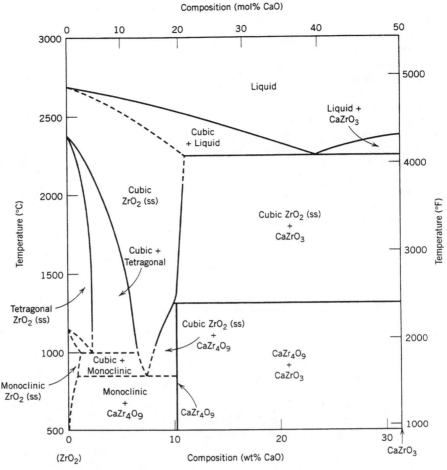

FIGURE 13.25 A portion of the zirconia–calcia phase diagram; *ss* denotes solid solution. (Adapted from V. S. Stubican and S. P. Ray, "Phase Equilibria and Ordering in the System ZrO_2-CaO," *J. Am. Ceram. Soc.*, **60** [11–12] 535 (1977). Reprinted by permission of the American Ceramic Society.)

temperature under normal cooling conditions, the monoclinic and $CaZr_4O_9$ phases do not form (as predicted from the phase diagram); consequently, the cubic and tetragonal phases are retained, and crack formation is circumvented. A zirconia material having a calcia content within the range cited above is termed a *partially stabilized zirconia*, or *PSZ*. Yttrium oxide (Y_2O_3) and magnesium oxide are also used as stabilizing agents. Furthermore, for higher stabilizer contents, only the cubic phase may be retained at room temperature; such a material is fully stabilized.

THE SiO_2–Al_2O_3 SYSTEM

Commercially, the silica-alumina system is an important one since the principal constituents of many ceramic refractories are these two materials. Figure 13.26 shows the SiO_2–Al_2O_3 phase diagram. The polymorphic form of silica that is stable at these temperatures is termed *cristobalite*, the unit cell for which is shown in Figure 13.10. Silica and alumina are not mutually soluble in one another, which is

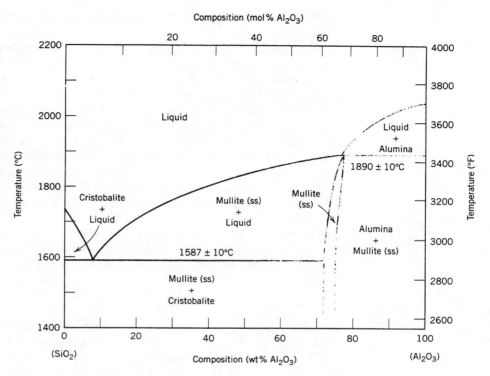

FIGURE 13.26
The silica–alumina phase diagram. (Adapted from F. J. Klug, S. Prochazka, and R. H. Doremus, "Alumina-Silica Phase Diagram in the Mullite Region," *J. Am. Ceram. Soc.*, **70** [10] 758 (1987). Reprinted by permission of the American Ceramic Society.)

evidenced by the absence of terminal solid solutions at both extremities of the phase diagram. Also, it may be noted that the intermediate compound *mullite*, $3Al_2O_3$–$2SiO_2$, exists, which is represented as a narrow phase field in Figure 13.26; furthermore, mullite melts incongruently at 1890°C (3435°F). A single eutectic exists at 1587°C (2890°F) and 7.7 wt% Al_2O_3. In Sections 14.10 and 14.11, refractory ceramic materials, the prime constituents for which are silica and alumina, are discussed.

MECHANICAL PROPERTIES

Ceramic materials are somewhat limited in applicability by their mechanical properties, which in many respects are inferior to those of metals. The principal drawback is a disposition to catastrophic fracture in a brittle manner with very little energy absorption.

13.7 BRITTLE FRACTURE OF CERAMICS

At room temperature, both crystalline and noncrystalline ceramics almost always fracture before any plastic deformation can occur in response to an applied tensile load. The topics of brittle fracture and fracture mechanics, as discussed previously in Sections 8.4 and 8.5, also relate to the fracture of ceramic materials; they will be reviewed briefly in this context.

The brittle fracture process consists of the formation and propagation of cracks through the cross section of material in a direction perpendicular to the applied load. Crack growth in crystalline ceramics is usually through the grains (i.e., transgranular) and along specific crystallographic (or cleavage) planes, planes of high atomic density.

The measured fracture strengths of ceramic materials are substantially lower than predicted by theory from interatomic bonding forces. This may be explained by very small and omnipresent flaws in the material which serve as stress raisers—points at which the magnitude of an applied tensile stress is amplified. The degree of stress amplification depends on crack length and tip radius of curvature according to Equation 8.1b, being greatest for long and pointed flaws. These stress raisers may be minute surface or interior cracks (microcracks), internal pores, and grain corners, which are virtually impossible to eliminate or control. For example, even moisture and contaminants in the atmosphere can introduce surface cracks in freshly drawn glass fibers; these cracks deleteriously affect the strength. A stress concentration at a flaw tip can cause a crack to form, which may propagate until the eventual failure.

The measure of a ceramic material's ability to resist fracture when a crack is present is specified in terms of fracture toughness. The plane strain fracture toughness K_{Ic}, as discussed in Section 8.5, is defined according to the expression

$$K_{Ic} = Y\sigma\sqrt{\pi a} \tag{13.2}$$

where Y is a dimensionless parameter or function which depends on both specimen and crack geometries, σ is the applied stress, and a is the length of a surface crack or half of the length of an internal crack. Crack propagation will not occur as long as the right-hand side of Equation 13.2 is less than the plane strain fracture toughness of the material. Plane strain fracture toughness values for ceramic materials are smaller than for metals; typically they are below 10 MPa$\sqrt{m}$ (9 ksi$\sqrt{in.}$). Values of K_{Ic} for several ceramic materials are included in Table 8.1 and Appendix C.5.

Under some circumstances, fracture of ceramic materials will occur by the slow propagation of cracks, when stresses are static in nature, and the right-hand side of Equation 13.2 is less than K_{Ic}. This phenomenon is called *static fatigue*, or *delayed fracture;* use of the term "fatigue" is somewhat misleading inasmuch as fracture may occur in the absence of cyclic stresses (metal fatigue was discussed in Chapter 8). It has been observed that this type of fracture is especially sensitive to environmental conditions, specifically when moisture is present in the atmosphere. Relative to mechanism, a stress–corrosion process probably occurs at the crack tips; that is, the combination of an applied tensile stress and material dissolution leads to a sharpening and lengthening of the cracks until, ultimately, one crack grows to a size capable of rapid propagation according to Equation 8.3. Furthermore, the duration of stress application preceding fracture diminishes with increasing stress. Consequently, when specifying the static fatigue strength, the time of stress application should also be stipulated. Silicate glasses are especially susceptible to this type of fracture; it has also been observed in other ceramic materials to include porcelain, portland cement, high-alumina ceramics, barium titanate, and silicon nitride.

There is usually considerable variation and scatter in the fracture strength for many specimens of a specific brittle ceramic material. A distribution of fracture strengths for portland cement is shown in Figure 13.27. This phenomenon may be explained by the dependence of fracture strength on the probability of the existence of a flaw that is capable of initiating a crack. This probability varies from specimen to specimen of the same material and depends on fabrication technique and any subsequent treatment. Specimen size or volume also influences fracture strength; the larger the specimen, the greater this flaw existence probability, and the lower the fracture strength.

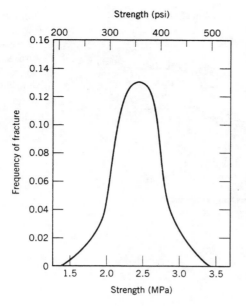

FIGURE 13.27 The frequency distribution of observed fracture strengths for a portland cement. (From W. Weibull, *Ing. Vetensk. Akad.,* Proc. 151, No. 153, 1939.)

For compressive stresses, there is no stress amplification associated with any existent flaws. For this reason, brittle ceramics display much higher strengths in compression than in tension (on the order of a factor of 10), and they are generally utilized when load conditions are compressive. Also, the fracture strength of a brittle ceramic may be enhanced dramatically by imposing residual compressive stresses at its surface. One way this may be accomplished is by thermal tempering (see Section 14.4).

Statistical theories have been developed which in conjunction with experimental data are used to determine the risk of fracture for a given material; a discussion of these is beyond the scope of the present treatment. However, due to the dispersion in the measured fracture strengths of brittle ceramic materials, the use of average values and factors of safety as discussed in Section 6.12 are not normally employed for design purposes.

13.8 STRESS–STRAIN BEHAVIOR

FLEXURAL STRENGTH

The stress–strain behavior of brittle ceramics is not usually ascertained by a tensile test as outlined in Section 6.2, for three reasons. First, it is difficult to prepare and test specimens having the required geometry. Second, it is difficult to grip brittle materials without fracturing them; and third, ceramics fail after only about 0.1% strain, which necessitates that tensile specimens be perfectly aligned in order to avoid the presence of bending stresses, which are not easily calculated. Therefore, a more suitable transverse bending test is most frequently employed, in which a rod specimen having either a circular or rectangular cross section is bent until fracture using a three- or four-point loading technique;[2] the three-point loading scheme is illustrated in Figure 13.28. At the point of loading, the top surface of the

---

[2] ASTM Standard C 1161, "Standard Test Method for Flexural Strength of Advanced Ceramics at Ambient Temperature."

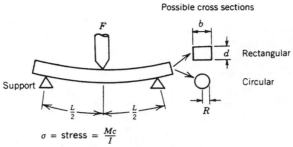

Possible cross sections

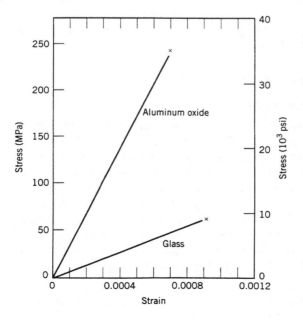

σ = stress = $\frac{Mc}{I}$

where M = maximum bending moment

c = distance from center of specimen to outer fibers

I = moment of inertia of cross section

F = applied load

	M	c	I	σ
Rectangular	$\frac{FL}{4}$	$\frac{d}{2}$	$\frac{bd^3}{12}$	$\frac{3FL}{2bd^2}$
Circular	$\frac{FL}{4}$	R	$\frac{\pi R^4}{4}$	$\frac{FL}{\pi R^3}$

FIGURE 13.28 A three-point loading scheme for measuring the stress–strain behavior and flexural strength of brittle ceramics, including expressions for computing stress for rectangular and circular cross sections.

specimen is placed in a state of compression, whereas the bottom surface is in tension. Stress is computed from the specimen thickness, the bending moment, and the moment of inertia of the cross section; these parameters are noted in Figure 13.28 for rectangular and circular cross sections. The maximum tensile stress (as determined using these stress expressions) exists at the bottom specimen surface directly below the point of load application. Since the tensile strengths of ceramics are about one-tenth of their compressive strengths, and since fracture occurs on the tensile specimen face, the flexure test is a reasonable substitute for the tensile test.

The stress at fracture using this flexure test, is known as the **flexural strength,**

FIGURE 13.29 Typical stress–strain behavior to fracture for aluminum oxide and glass.

Table 13.5 Tabulation of Flexural Strength (Modulus of Rupture) and Modulus of Elasticity for Ten Common Ceramic Materials

Material	Flexural Strength		Modulus of Elasticity	
	MPa	ksi	GPa	10^6 psi
Silicon nitride (Si_3N_4)	700–1000	100–145	304	44
Zirconia[a] (ZrO_2)	634	92	200	29
Silicon carbide (SiC)	552–862	80–125	430	62
Aluminum oxide (Al_2O_3)	275–550	40–80	393	57
Glass-ceramic (Pyroceram)	241	35	120	17
Mullite ($3Al_2O_3$-$2SiO_2$)	185	27	145	21
Spinel ($MgAl_2O_4$)	110–245	16–35.5	260	38
Fused silica (SiO_2)	110	16	73	11
Magnesium oxide (MgO)	105[b]	15[b]	225	33
Soda-lime glass	69	10	69	10

[a] Partially stabilized with 3 wt% MgO.
[b] Sintered and containing approximately 5% porosity.

modulus of rupture, fracture strength, or the *bend strength,* an important mechanical parameter for brittle ceramics. For a rectangular cross section, the flexural strength σ_{fs} is equal to

$$\sigma_{fs} = \frac{3F_fL}{2bd^2} \tag{13.3a}$$

where F_f is the load at fracture, L is the distance between support points, and the other parameters are as indicated in Figure 13.28. When the cross section is circular, then

$$\sigma_{fs} = \frac{F_fL}{\pi R^3} \tag{13.3b}$$

R being the specimen radius.

Characteristic flexural strength values for several ceramic materials are given in Table 13.5. Since, during bending, a specimen is subjected to both compressive and tensile stresses, the magnitude of its flexural strength is greater than the tensile fracture strength. Furthermore, σ_{fs} will depend on specimen size; as explained in the preceding section, with increasing specimen volume (under stress) there is an increase in flaw severity and, consequently, a decrease in flexural strength.

ELASTIC BEHAVIOR

The elastic stress–strain behavior for ceramic materials using these flexure tests is similar to the tensile test results for metals: a linear relationship exists between stress and strain. Figure 13.29 compares the stress–strain behavior to fracture for aluminum oxide (alumina) and glass. Again, the slope in the elastic region is the modulus of elasticity; the range of moduli of elasticity for ceramic materials is between about 70 and 500 GPa (10×10^6 and 70×10^6 psi), being slightly higher than for metals. Table 13.5 lists values for several ceramic materials. A more comprehensive tabulation is contained in Appendix C.2.

13.9 MECHANISMS OF PLASTIC DEFORMATION

Although at room temperature most ceramic materials suffer fracture before the onset of plastic deformation, a brief exploration into the possible mechanisms is worthwhile. Plastic deformation is different for crystalline and noncrystalline ceramics; however, each is discussed.

CRYSTALLINE CERAMICS

For crystalline ceramics, plastic deformation occurs, as with metals, by the motion of dislocations (Chapter 7). One reason for the hardness and brittleness of these materials is the difficulty of slip (or dislocation motion). For crystalline ceramic materials for which the bonding is predominantly ionic, there are very few slip systems (crystallographic planes and directions within those planes) along which dislocations may move. This is a consequence of the electrically charged nature of the ions. For slip in some directions, ions of like charge are brought into close proximity to one another; because of electrostatic repulsion, this mode of slip is very restricted. This is not a problem in metals, since all atoms are electrically neutral.

On the other hand, for ceramics in which the bonding is highly covalent, slip is also difficult and they are brittle for the following reasons: (1) the covalent bonds are relatively strong; (2) there are also limited numbers of slip systems; and (3) dislocation structures are complex.

NONCRYSTALLINE CERAMICS

Plastic deformation does not occur by dislocation motion for noncrystalline ceramics because there is no regular atomic structure. Rather, these materials deform by *viscous flow*, the same manner in which liquids deform; the rate of deformation is proportional to the applied stress. In response to an applied shear stress, atoms or ions slide past one another by the breaking and reforming of interatomic bonds. However, there is no prescribed manner or direction in which this occurs, as with dislocations. Viscous flow on a macroscopic scale is demonstrated in Figure 13.30.

The characteristic property for viscous flow, **viscosity,** is a measure of a noncrystalline material's resistance to deformation. For viscous flow in a liquid, which originates from shear stresses imposed by two flat and parallel plates, the viscosity η is the ratio of the applied shear stress τ and the change in velocity dv with distance

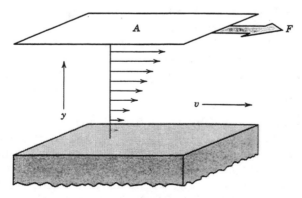

FIGURE 13.30 Representation of the viscous flow of a liquid or fluid glass in response to an applied shear force.

dy in a direction perpendicular to and away from the plates, or

$$\eta = \frac{\tau}{dv/dy} = \frac{F/A}{dv/dy} \tag{13.4}$$

This scheme is represented in Figure 13.30.

The units for viscosity are poises (P) and pascal-seconds (Pa-s); 1 P = 1 dyne-s/cm^2, and 1 Pa-s = 1 N-s/m^2. Conversion from one system of units to the other is according to

$$10 \text{ P} = 1 \text{ Pa-s}$$

Liquids have relatively low viscosities; for example, the viscosity of water at room temperature is about 10^{-3} Pa-s. On the other hand, glasses have extremely large viscosities at ambient temperatures, which is accounted for by strong interatomic bonding. As the temperature is raised, the magnitude of the bonding is diminished, the sliding motion or flow of the atoms or ions is facilitated, and subsequently there is an attendant decrease in viscosity. A discussion of the temperature dependence of viscosity for glasses is deferred to Section 14.2.

13.10 MISCELLANEOUS MECHANICAL CONSIDERATIONS

INFLUENCE OF POROSITY

As discussed in Sections 14.8 and 14.15, for some ceramic fabrication techniques, the precursor material is in the form of a powder. Subsequent to compaction or forming of these powder particles into the desired shape, pores or void spaces will exist between the powder particles. During the ensuing heat treatment, much of this porosity will be eliminated; however, it is often the case that this pore elimination process is incomplete and some residual porosity will remain (Figure 14.14). Any residual porosity will have a deleterious influence on both the elastic properties and strength. For example, it has been observed for some ceramic materials that the magnitude of the modulus of elasticity E decreases with volume fraction porosity P according to

$$E = E_0(1 - 1.9P + 0.9P^2) \tag{13.5}$$

where E_0 is the modulus of elasticity of the nonporous material. The influence of volume fraction porosity on the modulus of elasticity for aluminum oxide is shown in Figure 13.31; the curve represented in the figure is according to Equation 13.5.

Porosity is deleterious to the flexural strength for two reasons: (1) pores reduce the cross-sectional area across which a load is applied, and (2) they also act as stress concentrators—for an isolated spherical pore, an applied tensile stress is amplified by a factor of 2. The influence of porosity on strength is rather dramatic; for example, it is not uncommon that 10 vol% porosity will decrease the flexural strength by 50% from the measured value for the nonporous material. The degree of the influence of pore volume on flexural strength is demonstrated in Figure 13.32, again for aluminum oxide. Experimentally it has been shown that the flexural strength decreases exponentially with volume fraction porosity (P) as

$$\sigma_{fs} = \sigma_0 \exp(-nP) \tag{13.6}$$

In this expression σ_0 and n are experimental constants.

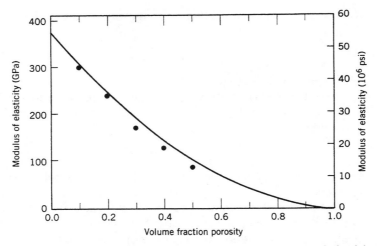

FIGURE 13.31   The influence of porosity on the modulus of elasticity for aluminum oxide at room temperature. The curve drawn is according to Equation 13.5. (From R. L. Coble and W. D. Kingery, "Effect of Porosity on Physical Properties of Sintered Alumina," *J. Am. Ceram. Soc.,* **39,** 11, Nov. 1956, p. 381. Reprinted by permission of the American Ceramic Society.)

HARDNESS

One beneficial mechanical property of ceramics is their hardness, which is often utilized when an abrasive or grinding action is required; in fact, the hardest known materials are ceramics. A listing of a number of different ceramic materials according to Knoop hardness is contained in Table 13.6. Only ceramics having Knoop hardnesses of about 1000 or greater are utilized for their abrasive characteristics.

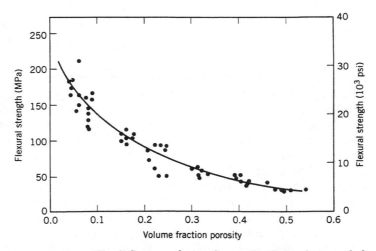

FIGURE 13.32   The influence of porosity on the flexural strength for aluminum oxide at room temperature. (From R. L. Coble and W. D. Kingery, "Effect of Porosity on Physical Properties of Sintered Alumina," *J. Am. Ceram. Soc.,* **39,** 11, Nov. 1956, p. 382. Reprinted by permission of the American Ceramic Society.)

Table 13.6 **Approximate Knoop Hardness (100 g load) for Seven Ceramic Materials**

Material	Approximate Knoop Hardness
Diamond (carbon)	7000
Boron carbide (B_4C)	2800
Silicon carbide (SiC)	2500
Tungsten carbide (WC)	2100
Aluminum oxide (Al_2O_3)	2100
Quartz (SiO_2)	800
Glass	550

CREEP

Often ceramic materials experience creep deformation as a result of exposure to stresses (usually compressive) at elevated temperatures. In general, the time-deformation creep behavior of ceramics is similar to that for metals (Section 8.13); however, creep occurs at higher temperatures in ceramics. High-temperature compressive creep tests are conducted on ceramic materials to ascertain creep deformation as a function of temperature and stress level.

SUMMARY

Both crystalline and noncrystalline states are possible for ceramics. Those materials for which the atomic bonding is predominantly ionic, crystal structure is determined by the charge magnitude and the radius of each kind of ion. Some of the simpler crystal structures are described in terms of unit cells; several of these were discussed (rock salt, cesium chloride, zinc blende, diamond cubic, graphite, fluorite, perovskite, and spinel structures).

For the silicates, structure is more conveniently represented by means of interconnecting SiO_4^{4-} tetrahedra. Relatively complex structures may result when other cations (e.g., Ca^{2+}, Mg^{2+}, Al^{3+}) and anions (e.g., OH^-) are added. The structures of silica (SiO_2), silica glass, and several of the simple and layered silicates were presented.

The various forms of carbon—diamond, graphite, and the fullerenes—were also discussed. Diamond is a gem stone and, because of its hardness, is used to cut and grind softer materials. Furthermore, it is now being produced and utilized in thin films. The layered structure of graphite gives rise to its excellent lubricative properties and a relatively high electrical conductivity. Graphite is also known for its high strength and chemical stability at elevated temperatures and in nonoxidizing atmospheres. The recently discovered fullerenes exist as hollow and spherical molecules composed of sixty carbon atoms. In the crystalline state these C_{60} molecules pack together in a face-centered cubic array. The pure material is electrically insulative, whereas metallic, semiconductive, and superconductive behavior may be induced by appropriate impurity additions.

With regard to atomic point defects, interstitials and vacancies for each anion and cation type are possible. These imperfections often occur in pairs as Frenkel and Schottky defects to ensure that crystal electroneutrality is maintained. Addition of impurity atoms may result in the formation of substitutional or interstitial solid solutions. Any charge imbalance created by the impurity ions may be compensated by the generation of host ion vacancies or interstitials.

Phase diagrams for the Al_2O_3–Cr_2O_3, MgO–Al_2O_3, ZrO_2–CaO, and SiO_2–Al_2O_3 systems were discussed. These diagrams are especially useful in assessing the high-temperature performance of ceramic materials.

At room temperature, virtually all ceramics are brittle. Microcracks, the presence of which is very difficult to control, result in amplification of applied tensile stresses and account for relatively low fracture strengths (flexural strengths). This amplification does not occur with compressive loads, and, consequently, ceramics are stronger in compression. Representative strengths of ceramic materials are determined by performing transverse bending tests to fracture.

Any plastic deformation of crystalline ceramics is a result of dislocation motion; the brittleness of these materials is, in part, explained by the limited number of operable slip systems. The mode of plastic deformation for noncrystalline materials is by viscous flow; a material's resistance to deformation is expressed as viscosity. At room temperature, the viscosity of many noncrystalline ceramics is extremely high.

Many ceramic bodies contain residual porosity, which is deleterious to both their moduli of elasticity and fracture strengths. In addition to their inherent brittleness, ceramic materials are distinctively hard. Also, since these materials are frequently utilized at elevated temperatures and under applied loads, creep characteristics are important.

IMPORTANT TERMS AND CONCEPTS

Anion	Flexural strength	Stoichiometry
Cation	Frenkel defect	Tetrahedral position
Defect structure	Octahedral position	Viscosity
Electroneutrality	Schottky defect	

REFERENCES

Bergeron, C. G. and S. H. Risbud, *Introduction to Phase Equilibria in Ceramics,* American Ceramic Society, Columbus, OH, 1984.

Bowen, H. K., "Advanced Ceramics," *Scientific American,* Vol. 255, No. 4, October 1986, pp. 168–176.

Budworth, D. W., *An Introduction to Ceramic Science,* Pergamon Press, Oxford, 1970.

Charles, R. J., "The Nature of Glasses," *Scientific American,* Vol. 217, No. 3, September 1967, pp. 126–136.

Cook, L. P. and H. F. McMurdie (Editors), *Phase Diagrams for Ceramists,* Vol. VII, American Ceramic Society, Columbus, OH, 1989.

Curl, R. F. and R. E. Smalley, "Fullerenes," *Scientific American,* Vol. 265, No. 4, October 1991, pp. 54–63.

Davidge, R. W., *Mechanical Behaviour of Ceramics,* Cambridge University Press, Cambridge, 1979. Reprinted by TechBooks, Fairfax, VA.

Engineered Materials Handbook, Vol. 4, *Ceramics and Glasses,* ASM International, Materials Park, OH, 1991.

Gilman, J. J., "The Nature of Ceramics," *Scientific American,* Vol. 217, No. 3, September 1967, pp. 112–124.

Hauth, W. E., "Crystal Chemistry in Ceramics," *American Ceramic Society Bulletin,* Vol. 30, 1951: No. 1, pp. 5–7; No. 2, pp. 47–49; No. 3, pp. 76–77; No. 4, pp. 137–142; No. 5, pp. 165–167; No. 6, pp. 203–205. A good overview of silicate structures.

Kingery, W. D., H. K. Bowen, and D. R. Uhlmann, *Introduction to Ceramics,* 2nd edition, John Wiley & Sons, New York, 1976. Chapters 1–4, 14, and 15.

Levin, E. M., C. R. Robbins, and H. F. McMurdie (Editors), *Phase Diagrams for Ceramists,* Vol. I, American Ceramic Society, Columbus, OH, 1964. Also supplementary Volumes II, III, IV, V and VI, published in 1969, 1973, 1981, 1983 and 1987, respectively.

Mysen, B. O. (Editor), *Phase Diagrams for Ceramists,* Vol. VIII, American Ceramic Society, Columbus, OH, 1990.

Norton, F. H., *Elements of Ceramics,* 2nd edition, Addison-Wesley Publishing Company, Reading, MA, 1974. Chapters 2 and 23.

Richerson, D. W., *Modern Ceramic Engineering,* 2nd edition, Marcel Dekker, New York, 1992.

Van Vlack, L. H., *Physical Ceramics for Engineers,* Addison-Wesley Publishing Company, Reading, MA, 1964. Chapters 1–4 and 6–8.

QUESTIONS AND PROBLEMS

13.1 For a ceramic compound, what are the two characteristics of the component ions that determine the crystal structure?

13.2 Show that the minimum cation-to-anion radius ratio for a coordination number of 4 is 0.225.

13.3 Show that the minimum cation-to-anion radius ratio for a coordination number of 6 is 0.414. *Hint:* Use the NaCl crystal structure (Figure 13.2), and assume that anions and cations are just touching along cube edges and across face diagonals.

13.4 Demonstrate that the minimum cation-to-anion radius ratio for a coordination number of 8 is 0.732.

13.5 On the basis of ionic charge and ionic radii, predict the crystal structures for the following materials: **(a)** CaO, **(b)** MnS, **(c)** KBr, and **(d)** CsBr. Justify your selections.

13.6 Which of the cations in Table 13.3 would you predict to form iodides having the cesium chloride crystal structure? Justify your choices.

13.7 Compute the atomic packing factor for the cesium chloride crystal structure in which $r_C/r_A = 0.732$.

13.8 Table 13.3 gives the ionic radii for K^+ and O^{2-} as 0.138 and 0.140 nm, respectively. What would be the coordination number for each O^{2-} ion? Briefly describe the resulting crystal structure for K_2O. Explain why this is called the antifluorite structure.

13.9 The zinc blende crystal structure is one that may be generated from close-packed planes of anions.

(a) Will the stacking sequence for this structure be FCC or HCP? Why?

(b) Will cations fill tetrahedral or octahedral positions? Why?

(c) What fraction of the positions will be occupied?

13.10 The corundum crystal structure, found for Al_2O_3, consists of an HCP arrangement of O^{2-} ions; the Al^{3+} ions occupy octahedral positions.

(a) What fraction of the available octahedral positions are filled with Al^{3+} ions?

(b) Sketch two close-packed O^{2-} planes stacked in an *AB* sequence, and note octahedral positions that will be filled with the Al^{3+} ions.

13.11 Iron sulfide (FeS) may form a crystal structure that consists of an HCP arrangement of S^{2-} ions.

(a) Which type of interstitial site will the Fe^{2+} ions occupy?

(b) What fraction of these available interstitial sites will be occupied by Fe^{2+} ions?

13.12 Magnesium silicate, Mg_2SiO_4, forms in the olivine crystal structure which consists of an HCP arrangement of O^{2-} ions.

(a) Which type of interstitial site will the Mg^{2+} ions occupy? Why?

(b) Which type of interstitial site will the Si^{4+} ions occupy? Why?

(c) What fraction of the total tetrahedral sites will be occupied?

(d) What fraction of the total octahedral sites will be occupied?

13.13 Calculate the density of NiO, given that it has the rock salt crystal structure.

13.14 Iron oxide (FeO) has the rock salt crystal structure and a density of 5.70 g/cm^3.

(a) Determine the unit cell edge length.

(b) How does this result compare with the edge length as determined from the radii in Table 13.3, assuming that the Fe^{2+} and O^{2-} ions just touch each other along the edges?

13.15 Compute the theoretical density of diamond given that the C—C distance and bond angle are 0.154 nm and 109.5°, respectively. How does this value compare with the measured density?

13.16 Compute the theoretical density of ZnS given that the Zn—S distance and bond angle are 0.234 nm and 109.5°, respectively. How does this value compare with the measured density?

13.17 One crystalline form of silica (SiO_2) has a cubic unit cell, and from x-ray diffraction data it is known that the cell edge length is 0.700 nm. If the measured density is 2.32 g/cm^3, how many Si^{4+} and O^{2-} ions are there per unit cell?

13.18 (a) Using the ionic radii in Table 13.3, compute the density of CsCl. *Hint:* Use a modification of the result of Problem 3.4.

(b) The measured density is 3.99 g/cm^3. How do you explain the slight discrepancy between your calculated value and the measured one?

13.19 From the data in Table 13.3, compute the density of CaF_2, which has the fluorite structure.

13.20 A hypothetical AX type of ceramic material is known to have a density of 2.65 g/cm^3 and a unit cell of cubic symmetry with a cell edge length of 0.43 nm. The atomic weights of the A and X elements are 86.6 and 40.3 g/mol, respectively. On the basis of this information, which of the following crystal structures is (are) possible for this material: rock salt, cesium chloride, or zinc blende? Justify your choice(s).

13.21 The unit cell for $MgFe_2O_4$ ($MgO\text{-}Fe_2O_3$) has cubic symmetry with a unit cell edge length

of 0.836 nm. If the density of this material is 4.52 g/cm^3, compute its atomic packing factor. For this computation, you will need to use ionic radii listed in Table 13.3.

13.22 The unit cell for Al_2O_3 has hexagonal symmetry with lattice parameters $a = 0.4759$ nm and $c = 1.2989$ nm. If the density of this material is 3.99 g/cm^3, calculate its atomic packing factor. For this computation use ionic radii listed in Table 13.3.

13.23 Compute the atomic packing factor for the diamond cubic crystal structure (Figure 13.15). Assume that bonding atoms touch one another, that the angle between adjacent bonds is 109.5°, and that each atom internal to the unit cell is positioned $a/4$ of the distance away from the two nearest cell faces (a is the unit cell edge length).

13.24 Compute the atomic packing factor for cesium chloride using the ionic radii in Table 13.3 and assuming that the ions touch along the cube diagonals.

13.25 For each of the following crystal structures, represent the indicated plane in the manner of Figures 3.9 and 3.10, showing both anions and cations: (a) (100) plane for the cesium chloride crystal structure, (b) (200) plane for the cesium chloride crystal structure, (c) (111) plane for the diamond cubic crystal structure, and (d) (110) plane for the fluorite crystal structure.

13.26 In terms of bonding, explain why silicate materials have relatively low densities.

13.27 Determine the angle between covalent bonds in an SiO_4^{4-} tetrahedron.

13.28 When kaolinite clay $[Al_2(Si_2O_5)(OH)_4]$ is heated to a sufficiently high temperature, chemical water is driven off.

(a) Under these circumstances what is the composition of the remaining product?

(b) What are the liquidus and solidus temperatures of this material?

13.29 Would you expect Frenkel defects for anions to exist in ionic ceramics in relatively large concentrations? Why or why not?

13.30 In your own words, briefly define the term "stoichiometric."

13.31 If cupric oxide (CuO) is exposed to reducing atmospheres at elevated temperatures, some of the Cu^{2+} ions will become Cu^+.

(a) Under these conditions, name one crystalline defect that you would expect to form in order to maintain charge neutrality.

(b) How many Cu^+ ions are required for the creation of each defect?

(c) How would you express the chemical formula for this nonstoichiometric material?

13.32 (a) Suppose that CaO is added as an impurity to Li_2O. If the Ca^{2+} substitutes for Li^+, what kind of vacancies would you expect to form? How many of these vacancies are created for every Ca^{2+} added?

(b) Suppose that CaO is added as an impurity to $CaCl_2$. If the O^{2-} substitutes for Cl^-, what kind of vacancies would you expect to form? How many of the vacancies are created for every O^{2-} added?

13.33 What point defects are possible for Al_2O_3 as an impurity in MgO? How many Al^{3+} ions must be added to form each of these defects?

13.34 For the ZrO_2-CaO system (Figure 13.25), write all eutectic and eutectoid reactions for cooling.

13.35 From Figure 13.24, the phase diagram for the $MgO-Al_2O_3$ system, it may be noted that the spinel solid solution exists over a range of compositions, which means that it is nonstoichiometric at compositions other than 50 mol% MgO–50 mol% Al_2O_3.

(a) The maximum nonstoichiometry on the Al_2O_3-rich side of the spinel phase field exists at about 2000°C (3630°F) corresponding to approximately 82 mol% (92 wt%) Al_2O_3. Determine the type of vacancy defect that is produced and the percentage of vacancies that exist at this composition.

(b) The maximum nonstoichiometry on the MgO-rich side of the spinel phase field exists at about 2000°C (3630°F) corresponding to approximately 39 mol% (62 wt%) Al_2O_3. Determine the type of vacancy defect that is produced and the percentage of vacancies that exist at this composition.

13.36 Briefly explain (a) why there may be significant scatter in the fracture strength for some given ceramic material, and (b) why fracture strength increases with decreasing specimen size.

13.37 The tensile strength of brittle materials may be determined using a variation of Equation 8.1b. Compute the critical crack tip radius for a glass specimen that experiences tensile fracture at an applied stress of 70 MPa (10,000 psi). Assume a critical surface crack length of 10^{-2} mm and a theoretical fracture strength of $E/10$, where E is the modulus of elasticity.

13.38 The fracture strength of glass may be increased by etching away a thin surface layer. It is believed that the etching may alter surface crack geometry (i.e., reduce crack length and increase the tip radius). Compute the ratio of the original and etched crack tip radii for an eightfold increase in fracture strength if two-thirds of the crack length is removed.

13.39 A three-point bending test is performed on a spinel ($MgAl_2O_4$) specimen having a rectangular cross section of height d 3.8 mm (0.15 in.) and width b 9.0 mm (0.35 in.); the distance between support points is 25 mm (1.0 in.):

(a) Compute the flexural strength if the load at fracture is 350 N (80 lb$_f$).

(b) The point of maximum deflection Δy occurs at the center of the specimen and is described by

$$\Delta y = \frac{FL^3}{48EI}$$

where E is the modulus of elasticity and I the cross-sectional moment of inertia. Compute Δy at a load of 310 N (70 lb$_f$).

13.40 A circular specimen of MgO is loaded using a three-point bending mode. Compute the minimum possible radius of the specimen without fracture, given that the applied load is 5560 N (1250 lb$_f$), the flexural strength is 105 MPa (15,000 psi), and the separation between load points is 45 mm (1.75 in.).

13.41 A three-point bending test was performed on an aluminum oxide specimen having a circular cross section of radius 3.5 mm (0.14 in.); the specimen fractured at a load of 950 N (215 lb$_f$) when the distance between the support points was 50 mm (2.0 in.). Another test is to be performed on a specimen of this same material, but one that has a square cross section of 12 mm (0.47 in.) length on each edge. At what load would you expect this specimen to fracture if the support point separation is 40 mm (1.6 in.)?

13.42 (a) A three-point transverse bending test is conducted on a cylindrical specimen of aluminum oxide having a reported flexural strength of 390 MPa (56,600 psi). If the specimen radius is 2.5 mm (0.10 in.) and the support point separation distance is 30 mm (1.2 in.), predict whether or not you would expect the specimen to fracture when a load of 620 N (140 lb$_f$) is applied. Justify your prediction.

(b) Would you be 100% certain of the prediction in part a? Why or why not?

13.43 Cite one reason why ceramic materials are, in general, harder yet more brittle than metals.

13.44 The modulus of elasticity for beryllium oxide (BeO) having 5 vol% porosity is 310 GPa (45 × 10^6 psi).

(a) Compute the modulus of elasticity for the nonporous material.

(b) Compute the modulus of elasticity for 10 vol% porosity.

13.45 The modulus of elasticity for boron carbide (B$_4$C) having 5 vol% porosity is 290 GPa (42 × 10^6 psi).

(a) Compute the modulus of elasticity for the nonporous material.

(b) At what volume percent porosity will

the modulus of elasticity be 235 GPa (34 × 10^6 psi)?

13.46 Using the data in Table 13.5, do the following:

(a) Determine the flexural strength for nonporous MgO assuming a value of 3.75 for n in Equation 13.6.

(b) Compute the volume fraction porosity at which the flexural strength for MgO is 62 MPa (9000 psi).

13.47 The flexural strength and associated volume fraction porosity for two specimens of the same ceramic material are as follows:

σ_{fs} (MPa)	P
70	0.10
60	0.15

(a) Compute the flexural strength for a completely nonporous specimen of this material.

(b) Compute the flexural strength for a 0.2 volume fraction porosity.

Design Problem

13.D1 It is necessary to select a ceramic material to be stressed using a three-point loading scheme (Figure 13.28). The specimen must have a circular cross section and a radius of 2.5 mm (0.10 in.), and must not experience fracture nor a deflection of more than 6.2 × 10^{-2} mm (2.4 × 10^{-3} in.) at its center when a load of 275 N (62 lb$_f$) is applied. If the distance between support points is 45 mm (1.77 in.), which of the materials in Table 13.5 are candidates? The magnitude of the centerpoint deflection may be computed using the equation supplied in Problem 13.39.

Polymer Structures

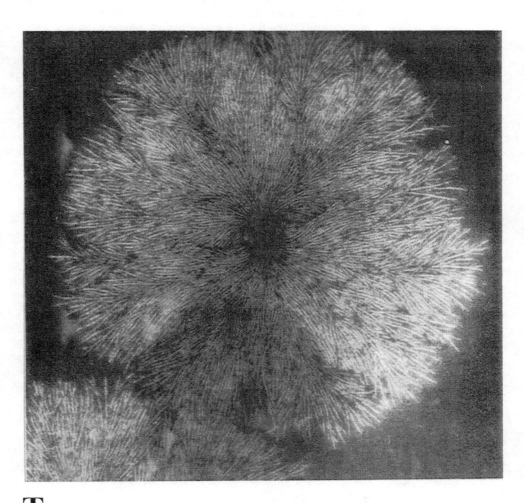

Transmission electron micrograph showing the spherulite structure in a natural rubber specimen. Chain-folded lamellar crystallites approximately 10 nm thick extend in radial directions from the center; they appear as white lines in the micrograph. 30,000×. (Photograph supplied by P. J. Phillips. First published in R. Bartnikas and R. M. Eichhorn, *Engineering Dielectrics*, Vol. IIA, *Electrical Properties of Solid Insulating Materials: Molecular Structure and Electrical Behavior.* Copyright ASTM, 1916 Race Street, Philadelphia, PA 19103. Reprinted with permission.)

15.1 INTRODUCTION

Naturally occurring polymers—those derived from plants and animals—have been used for many centuries; these materials include wood, rubber, cotton, wool, leather, and silk. Other natural polymers such as proteins, enzymes, starches, and cellulose are important in biological and physiological processes in plants and animals. Modern scientific research tools have made possible the determination of the molecular structures of this group of materials, and the development of numerous polymers, which are synthesized from small organic molecules. Many of our useful plastics, rubbers, and fiber materials are synthetic polymers. In fact, since the conclusion of World War II, the field of materials has been virtually revolutionized by the advent of synthetic polymers. The synthetics can be produced inexpensively, and their properties may be managed to the degree that many are superior to their natural counterparts. In some applications metal and wood parts have been replaced by plastics, which have satisfactory properties and may be produced at a lower cost.

As with metals and ceramics, the properties of polymers are intricately related to the structural elements of the material. This chapter explores molecular and crystal structures of polymers; Chapter 16 discusses the relationships between structure and some of the physical and chemical properties, along with typical applications and forming methods.

15.2 HYDROCARBON MOLECULES

Since most polymers are organic in origin, we briefly review some of the basic concepts relating to the structure of their molecules. First, many organic materials are *hydrocarbons;* that is, they are composed of hydrogen and carbon. Furthermore, the intramolecular bonds are covalent. Each carbon atom has four electrons that may participate in covalent bonding, whereas every hydrogen atom has only one bonding electron. A single covalent bond exists when each of the two bonding atoms contributes one electron, as represented schematically in Figure 2.10 for a molecule of methane (CH_4). Double and triple bonds between two carbon atoms involve the sharing of two and three pairs of electrons, respectively. For example, in ethylene, which has the chemical formula C_2H_4, the two carbon atoms are doubly bonded together, and each is also singly bonded to two hydrogen atoms, as represented by the structural formula

$$\begin{array}{cc} H & H \\ | & | \\ C & = C \\ | & | \\ H & H \end{array}$$

where — and = denote single and double covalent bonds, respectively. An example of a triple bond is found in acetylene, C_2H_2:

$$H - C \equiv C - H$$

Molecules that have double and triple covalent bonds are termed **unsaturated;** that is, each carbon atom is not bonded to the maximum (or four) other atoms. For an unsaturated molecule, a double bond may be thought of as consisting of two single bonds. A transfer in position around the carbon atom of one of these single bonds permits the addition of another atom or group of atoms to the original

Table 15.1 Compositions and Molecular Structures for Some of the Paraffin Compounds: C_nH_{2n+2}

Name	Composition	Structure	Boiling Point (°C)
Methane	CH_4	$\begin{array}{c} H \\ | \\ H-C-H \\ | \\ H \end{array}$	−164
Ethane	C_2H_6	$\begin{array}{c} H\ \ H \\ |\ \ \ \ | \\ H-C-C-H \\ |\ \ \ \ | \\ H\ \ H \end{array}$	−88.6
Propane	C_3H_8	$\begin{array}{c} H\ \ H\ \ H \\ |\ \ \ |\ \ \ | \\ H-C-C-C-H \\ |\ \ \ |\ \ \ | \\ H\ \ H\ \ H \end{array}$	−42.1
Butane	C_4H_{10}	·	−0.5
Pentane	C_5H_{12}	·	36.1
Hexane	C_6H_{14}	·	69.0

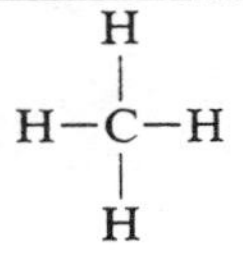

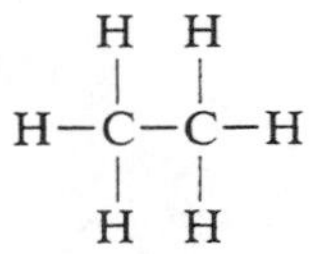

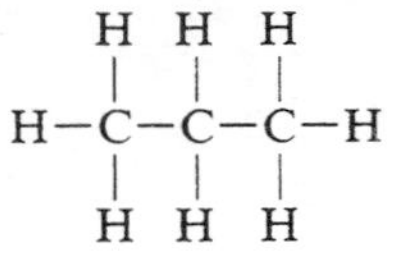

molecule. Of course, in a **saturated** hydrocarbon, all bonds are single ones (and saturated), and no new atoms may be joined without the removal of others that are already bonded.

Some of the simple hydrocarbons belong to the paraffin family; the chainlike paraffin molecules include methane (CH_4), ethane (C_2H_6), propane (C_3H_8), and butane (C_4H_{10}). Compositions and molecular structures for paraffin molecules are contained in Table 15.1. The covalent bonds in each molecule are strong, but only weak hydrogen and van der Waals bonds exist between molecules, and thus these hydrocarbons have relatively low melting and boiling points. However, boiling temperatures rise with increasing molecular weight (Table 15.1).

Hydrocarbon compounds with the same composition may have different atomic arrangements, a phenomenon termed **isomerism.** For example, there are two isomers for butane; normal butane has the structure

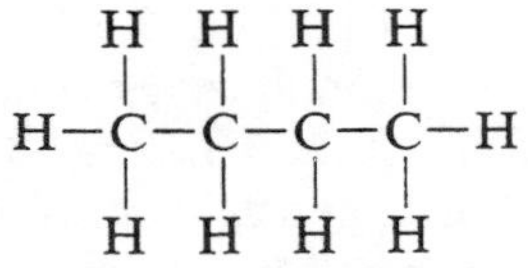

$$\begin{array}{c} H\ \ H\ \ H\ \ H \\ |\ \ \ |\ \ \ |\ \ \ | \\ H-C-C-C-C-H \\ |\ \ \ |\ \ \ |\ \ \ | \\ H\ \ H\ \ H\ \ H \end{array}$$

whereas a molecule of isobutane is represented as follows:

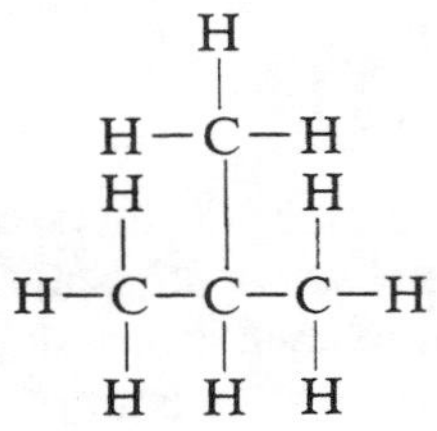

$$\begin{array}{c} H \\ | \\ H-C-H \\ H\ \ \ |\ \ \ H \\ |\ \ \ \ \ \ |\ \ \ \ \ \ | \\ H-C-C-C-H \\ |\ \ \ \ |\ \ \ \ | \\ H\ \ H\ \ H \end{array}$$

Table 15.2 **Some Common Hydrocarbon Groups**

Family	Characteristic Unit	Representative Compound	
Alcohols	R—OH	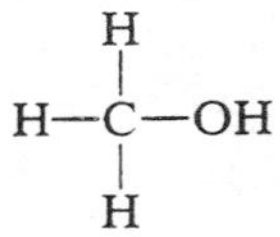 H—C—OH (with H above and below C)	Methyl alcohol
Ethers	R—O—R′	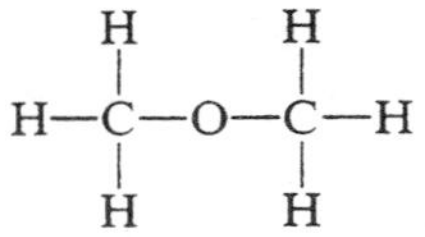 H—C—O—C—H (with H above and below each C)	Dimethyl ether
Acids	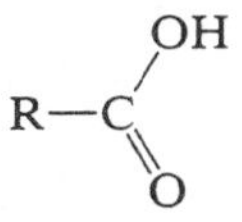 R—C(=O)OH	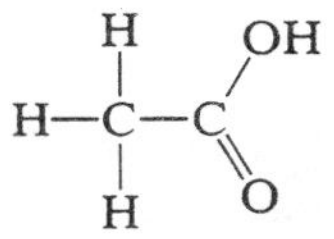 H—C—C(=O)OH (with H above and below first C)	Acetic acid
Aldehydes	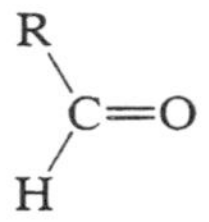 R—C(H)=O	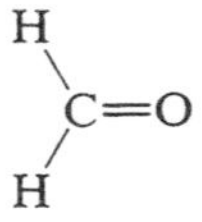 H—C(H)=O	Formaldehyde
Aromatic hydrocarbons	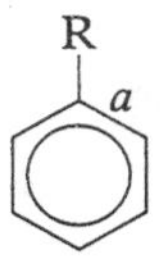 (phenyl ring with R, marked a)	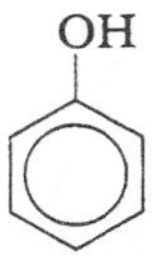 (phenyl ring with OH)	Phenol

a The simplified structure ⬡ denotes a phenyl group,

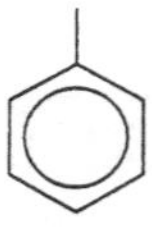

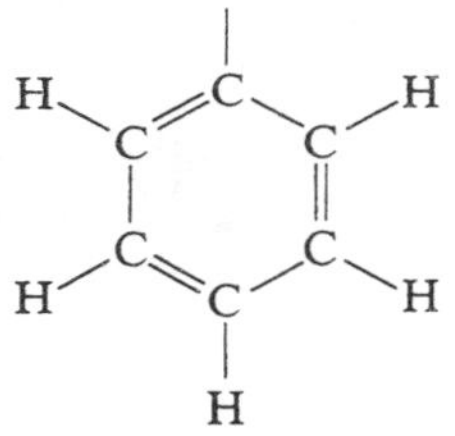

(benzene ring structure with six C atoms and H atoms shown)

Some of the physical properties of hydrocarbons will depend on the isomeric state; for example, the boiling temperatures for normal butane and isobutane are −0.5 and −12.3°C (31.1 and 9.9°F), respectively.

There are numerous other organic groups, many of which are involved in polymer structures. Several of the more common groups are presented in Table 15.2, where R and R′ represent organic radicals—groups of atoms that remain as a single unit and maintain their identity during chemical reactions. Examples of singly bonded hydrocarbon radicals include the CH_3, C_2H_5, and C_6H_5 (methyl, ethyl, and phenyl) groups.

15.3 POLYMER MOLECULES

The molecules in polymers are gigantic in comparison to the hydrocarbon molecules heretofore discussed; because of their size they are often referred to as **macromolecules.** Within each molecule, the atoms are bound together by covalent interatomic bonds. For most polymers, these molecules are in the form of long and flexible chains, the backbone of which is a string of carbon atoms; many times each carbon atom singly bonds to two adjacent carbons atoms on either side, represented schematically in two dimensions as follows:

$$-\overset{|}{\underset{|}{C}}-\overset{|}{\underset{|}{C}}-\overset{|}{\underset{|}{C}}-\overset{|}{\underset{|}{C}}-\overset{|}{\underset{|}{C}}-\overset{|}{\underset{|}{C}}-\overset{|}{\underset{|}{C}}-$$

Each of the two remaining valence electrons for every carbon atom may be involved in side-bonding with atoms or radicals that are positioned adjacent to the chain. Of course, both chain and side double bonds are also possible.

These long molecules are composed of structural entities called **mer** units, which are successively repeated along the chain. "Mer" originates from the Greek word *meros,* which means part; a single mer is called a **monomer;** the term **polymer** was coined to mean many mers. "Mer" denotes the repeat unit in a polymer chain, whereas, "monomer" is used in the context of a molecule consisting of a single mer.

15.4 THE CHEMISTRY OF POLYMER MOLECULES

Consider again the hydrocarbon ethylene (C_2H_4), which is a gas at ambient temperature and pressure, and has the following molecular structure:

$$\overset{H}{\underset{H}{\overset{|}{C}}}=\overset{H}{\underset{H}{\overset{|}{C}}}$$

If the ethylene gas is subjected catalytically to appropriate conditions of temperature and pressure, it will transform to polyethylene (PE), which is a solid polymeric material. This process begins when an active mer is formed by the reaction between an initiator or catalyst species (R·) and the ethylene mer unit, as follows:

$$R\cdot + \overset{H\ \ H}{\underset{H\ \ H}{C=C}} \longrightarrow R-\overset{H\ \ H}{\underset{H\ \ H}{C-C}}\cdot \tag{15.1}$$

The polymer chain then forms by the sequential addition of polyethylene monomer units to this active initiator-mer center. The active site, or unpaired electron (denoted by ·), is transferred to each successive end monomer as it is linked to the chain. This may be represented schematically as follows:

$$R-\overset{H\ \ H}{\underset{H\ \ H}{C-C}}\cdot + \overset{H\ \ H}{\underset{H\ \ H}{C=C}} \longrightarrow R-\overset{H\ \ H\ \ H\ \ H}{\underset{H\ \ H\ \ H\ \ H}{C-C-C-C}}\cdot \tag{15.2}$$

The final result, after the addition of many ethylene monomer units, is the polyethylene molecule, a portion of which is shown in Figure 15.1*a.* This representation is not strictly correct in that the angle between the singly bonded carbon atoms is not 180° as shown, but rather close to 109°. A more accurate three-dimensional model is one in which the carbon atoms form a zigzag pattern (Figure 15.1*b*), the

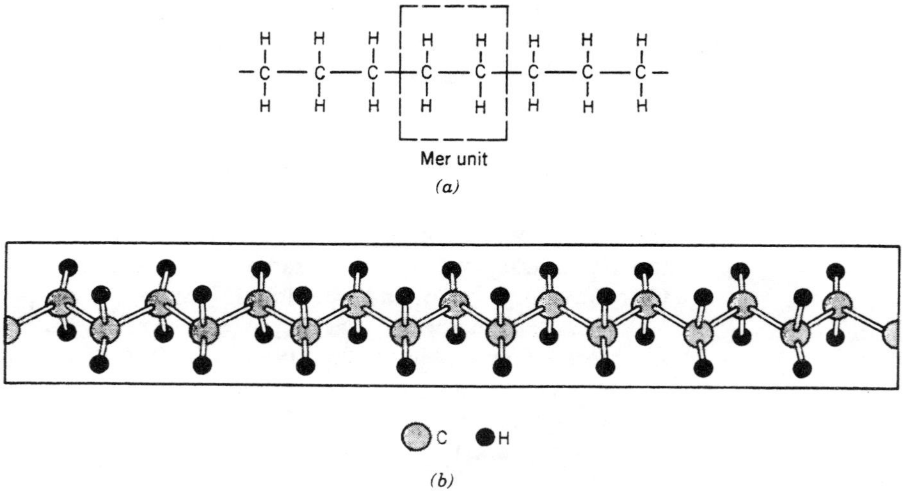

FIGURE 15.1 For polyethylene, (a) a schematic representation of mer and chain structures, and (b) a perspective of the molecule, indicating the zigzag backbone structure.

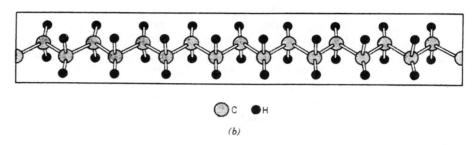

Mer unit

(a)

○ C ● H

(b)

C—C bond length being 0.154 nm. In this discussion, depiction of polymer molecules is frequently simplified using the linear chain model.

If all the hydrogen atoms in polyethylene are replaced by fluorine, the resulting polymer is *polytetrafluoroethylene* (PTFE); its mer and chain structures are shown in Figure 15.2a. Polytetrafluoroethylene (having the trade name Teflon) belongs to a family of polymers called the fluorocarbons.

Polyvinyl chloride (PVC), another common polymer, has a structure that is a

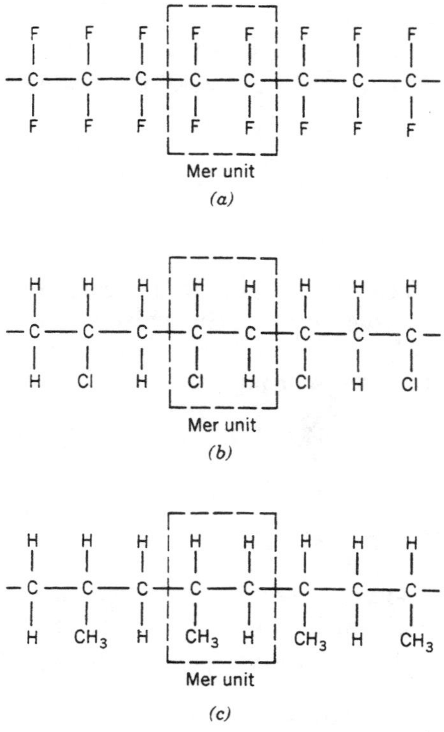

Mer unit

(a)

FIGURE 15.2 Mer and chain structures for (a) polytetrafluoroethylene, (b) polyvinyl chloride, and (c) polypropylene.

Mer unit

(b)

Mer unit

(c)

Table 15.3 A Listing of Mer Structures for 10 of the More Common Polymeric Materials

Polymer	Repeating (Mer) Structure
Polyethylene (PE)	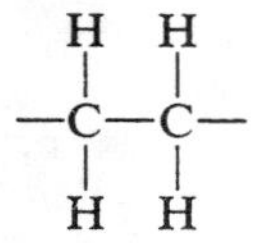
Polyvinyl chloride (PVC)	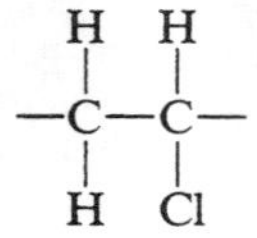
Polytetrafluoroethylene (PTFE)	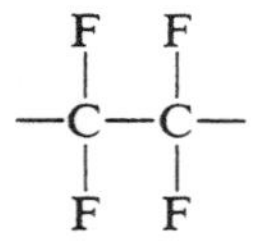
Polypropylene (PP)	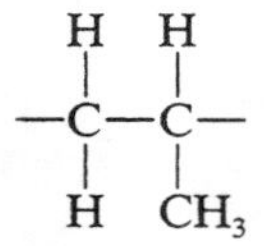
Polystyrene (PS)	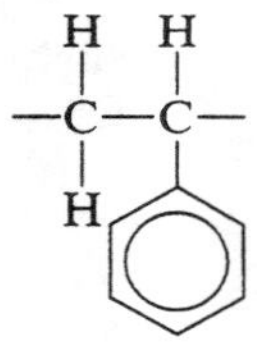
Polymethyl methacrylate (PMMA)	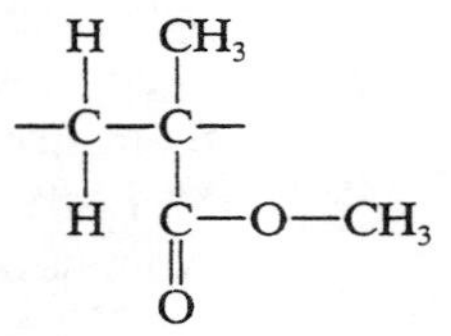
Phenol-formaldehyde (Bakelite)	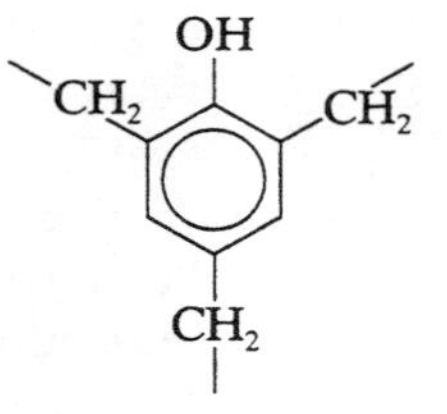
Polyhexamethylene adipamide (nylon 6,6)	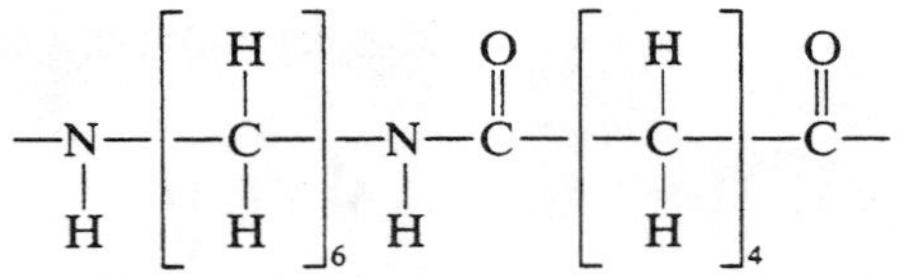

Table 15.3 (Continued)

Polymer	Repeating (Mer) Structure
Polyethylene terephthalate (PET, a polyester)	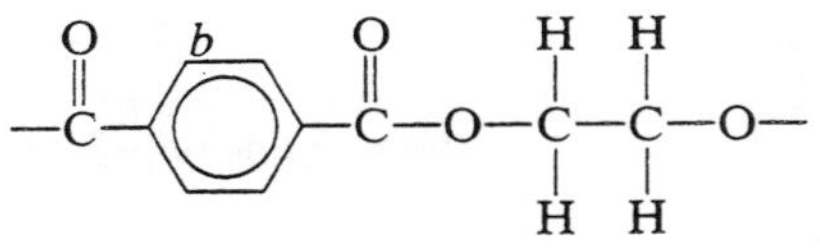
Polycarbonate	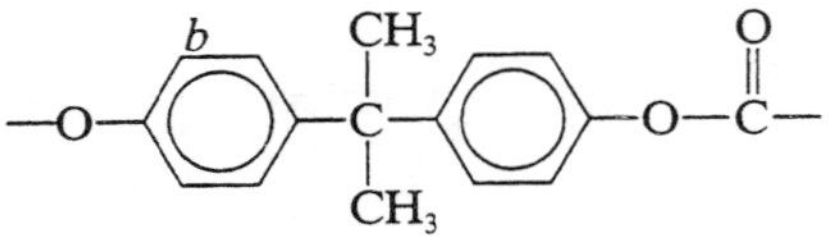

ᵇ The 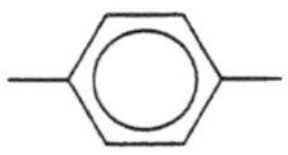 symbol in the backbone chain denotes an aromatic ring as

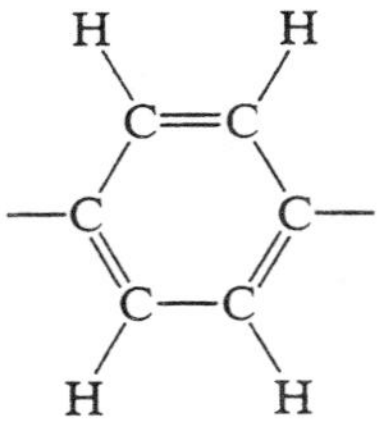

slight variant of that for polyethylene, in which every fourth hydrogen is replaced with a Cl atom. Furthermore, substitution of the CH_3 methyl group

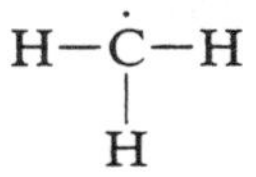

$$H-\overset{\cdot}{\underset{H}{C}}-H$$

for each Cl atom in PVC yields *polypropylene* (PP). Polyvinyl chloride and polypropylene chain structures are also represented in Figure 15.2. Table 15.3 lists mer structures for some of the more common polymers; as may be noted, some of them, for example, nylon, polyester, and polycarbonate, are relatively complex. Mer structures for a large number of relatively common polymers are given in Appendix D.

When all the repeating units along a chain are of the same type, the resulting polymer is called a **homopolymer.** There is no restriction in polymer synthesis that prevents the formation of compounds other than homopolymers; and, in fact, chains may be composed of two or more different mer units, in what are termed **copolymers** (see Section 15.9).

The mer units discussed thus far have two active bonds that may covalently bond with other mers, as indicated above for ethylene; such a mer is termed **bifunctional;** that is, it may bond with two other units in forming the two-dimensional chainlike molecular structure. However, other mers, such as phenol-formaldehyde (Table 15.3), are **trifunctional;** they have three active bonds, from which a three-dimensional molecular network structure results, as discussed later in this chapter.

15.5 MOLECULAR WEIGHT

Extremely large molecular weights are to be found in polymers with very long chains. During the polymerization process in which these large macromolecules are synthesized from smaller molecules, not all polymer chains will grow to the same length; this results in a distribution of chain lengths or molecular weights. Ordinarily,

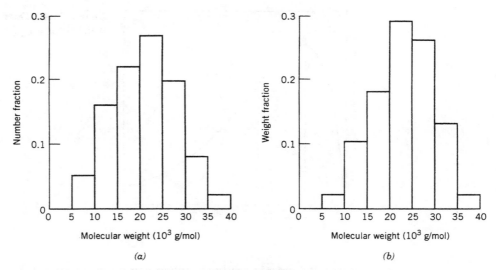

Figure 15.3 Hypothetical polymer molecule size distributions on the basis of (a) number and (b) weight fractions of molecules.

an average molecular weight is specified, which may be determined by the measurement of various physical properties such as viscosity and osmotic pressure.

There are several ways of defining average molecular weight. The number-average molecular weight $\overline{M}_n$ is obtained by dividing the chains into a series of size ranges and then determining the number fraction of chains with each size range (Figure 15.3a). This number-average molecular weight is expressed as

$$\overline{M}_n = \Sigma x_i M_i \qquad (15.3a)$$

where M_i represents the mean (middle) molecular weight of size range i, and x_i is the fraction of the total number of chains within the corresponding size range.

A weight-average molecular weight $\overline{M}_w$ is based on the weight fraction of molecules within the various size ranges (Figure 15.3b). It is calculated according to

$$\overline{M}_w = \Sigma w_i M_i \qquad (15.3b)$$

where, again, M_i is the mean molecular weight within a size range, whereas w_i denotes the weight fraction of molecules within the same size interval. Computations for both number-average and weight-average molecular weights are carried out in Example Problem 15.1. A typical molecular weight distribution along with these molecular weight averages are shown in Figure 15.4.

An alternate way of expressing average chain size of a polymer is as the **degree of polymerization** n, which represents the average number of mer units in a chain. Both number-average (n_n) and weight-average (n_w) degrees of polymerization are possible, as follows:

$$n_n = \frac{\overline{M}_n}{\overline{m}} \qquad (15.4a)$$

$$n_w = \frac{\overline{M}_w}{\overline{m}} \qquad (15.4b)$$

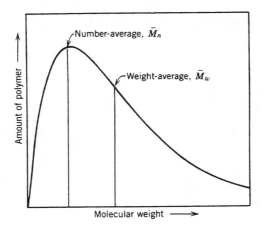

FIGURE 15.4 Distribution of molecular weights for a typical polymer.

where $\overline{M}_n$ and $\overline{M}_w$ are the number-average and weight-average molecular weights as defined above, while $\overline{m}$ is the mer molecular weight. For a copolymer (having two or more different mer units), $\overline{m}$ is determined from

$$\overline{m} = \Sigma f_j m_j \tag{15.5}$$

In this expression, f_j and m_j are, respectively, the chain fraction and molecular weight of mer j.

EXAMPLE PROBLEM 15.1

Assume that the molecular weight distributions shown in Figure 15.3 are for polyvinyl chloride. For this material, compute (a) the number-average molecular weight; (b) the number-average degree of polymerization; and (c) the weight-average molecular weight.

SOLUTION

(a) The data necessary for this computation, as taken from Figure 15.3a, are presented in Table 15.4a. According to Equation 15.3a, summation of all the $x_i M_i$ products (from the right-hand column) yields the number-average molecular weight, which in this case is 21,150 g/mol.

(b) To determine the number-average degree of polymerization (Equation 15.4a), it first becomes necessary to compute the mer molecular weight. For PVC, each mer consists of two carbon atoms, three hydrogen atoms, and a single chlorine atom (Table 15.3). Furthermore, the atomic weights of C, H, and Cl are, respectively, 12.01, 1.01, and 35.45 g/mol. Thus, for PVC

$$\overline{m} = 2(12.01 \text{ g/mol}) + 3(1.01 \text{ g/mol}) + 35.45 \text{ g/mol}$$

$$= 62.50 \text{ g/mol}$$

and

$$n_n = \frac{\overline{M}_n}{\overline{m}} = \frac{21{,}150 \text{ g/mol}}{62.50 \text{ g/mol}} = 338$$

Table 15.4a Data Used for Number-Average Molecular Weight Computations in Example Problem 15.1

Molecular Weight Range (g/mol)	Mean M_i (g/mol)	x_i	$x_i M_i$
5,000–10,000	7,500	0.05	375
10,000–15,000	12,500	0.16	2000
15,000–20,000	17,500	0.22	3850
20,000–25,000	22,500	0.27	6075
25,000–30,000	27,500	0.20	5500
30,000–35,000	32,500	0.08	2600
35,000–40,000	37,500	0.02	750
			$\overline{M}_n = 21,150$

Table 15.4b Data Used for Weight-Average Molecular Weight Computations in Example Problem 15.1

Molecular Weight Range (g/mol)	Mean M_i (g/mol)	w_i	$w_i M_i$
5,000–10,000	7,500	0.02	150
10,000–15,000	12,500	0.10	1250
15,000–20,000	17,500	0.18	3150
20,000–25,000	22,500	0.29	6525
25,000–30,000	27,500	0.26	7150
30,000–35,000	32,500	0.13	4225
35,000–40,000	37,500	0.02	750
			$\overline{M}_w = 23,200$

(c) Table 15.4b shows the data for the weight-average molecular weight, as taken from Figure 15.3b. The $w_i M_i$ products for the several size intervals are tabulated in the right-hand column. The sum of these products (Equation 15.3b) yields a value of 23,200 g/mol for $\overline{M}_w$.

Various polymer characteristics are affected by the magnitude of the molecular weight. One of these is the melting or softening temperature; melting temperature is raised with increasing molecular weight (for $\overline{M}$ up to about 100,000 g/mol). At room temperature, polymers with very short chains (having molecular weights on the order of 100 g/mol) exist as liquids or gases. Those with molecular weights of approximately 1000 g/mol are waxy solids (such as paraffin wax) and soft resins. Solid polymers (sometimes termed *high polymers*), which are of prime interest here, commonly have molecular weights ranging between 10,000 and several million g/mol.

15.6 MOLECULAR SHAPE

There is no reason to suppose that polymer chain molecules are strictly straight, straight in the sense that the zigzag arrangement of the backbone atoms (Figure 15.1b) is disregarded. Single chain bonds are capable of rotation and bending in three dimensions. Consider the chain atoms in Figure 15.5a; a third carbon atom may lie at any point on the cone of revolution and still subtend about a 109° angle

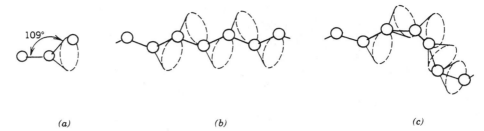

(a)   *(b)*   *(c)*

FIGURE 15.5   Schematic representations of how polymer chain shape is influenced by the positioning of backbone carbon atoms (solid circles). For (*a*), the right-most atom may lie anywhere on the dashed circle and still subtend a 109° angle with the bond between the other two atoms. Straight and twisted chain segments are generated when the backbone atoms are situated as in (*b*) and (*c*), respectively. (Adapted from Askeland, Donald R., *The Science and Engineering of Materials,* 3rd edition. PWS Publishing Company, Boston, 1994.)

with the bond between the other two atoms. A straight chain segment results when successive chain atoms are positioned as in Figure 15.5*b*. On the other hand, chain bending and twisting are possible when there is a rotation of the chain atoms into other positions, as illustrated in Figure 15.5*c*.[1] Thus, a single chain molecule composed of many chain atoms might assume a shape similar to that represented schematically in Figure 15.6, having a multitude of bends, twists, and kinks.[2] Also indicated in this figure is the end-to-end distance of the polymer chain *r*; this distance is much smaller than the total chain length.

Some polymers consist of large numbers of molecular chains, each of which may bend, coil, and kink in the manner of Figure 15.6. This leads to extensive intertwining and entanglement of neighboring chain molecules, a situation similar to that of a fishing line that has experienced backlash from a fishing reel. These random coils and molecular entanglements are responsible for a number of important characteristics of polymers, to include the large elastic extensions displayed by the rubber materials.

Some of the mechanical and thermal characteristics of polymers are a function of the ability of chain segments to experience rotation in response to applied stresses or thermal vibrations. Rotational flexibility is dependent on mer structure and chemistry. For example, the region of a chain segment that has a double bond (C=C) is rotationally rigid. Also, introduction of a bulky or large side group of atoms restricts rotational movement. For example, polystyrene molecules, which have a phenyl side group (Table 15.3), are more resistant to rotational motion than are polyethylene chains.

15.7 MOLECULAR STRUCTURE

The physical characteristics of a polymer depend not only on its molecular weight and shape, but also on differences in the structure of the molecular chains. Modern

---

[1] For some polymers, rotation of carbon backbone atoms within the cone may be hindered by bulky side group elements on neighboring chains.

[2] The term *conformation* is often used in reference to the physical outline of a molecule, or molecular shape, that can only be altered by rotation of chain atoms about single bonds.

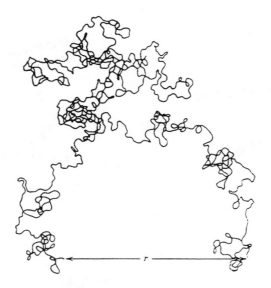

FIGURE 15.6 Schematic representation of a single polymer chain molecule that has numerous random kinks and coils produced by chain bond rotations. (From L. R. G. Treloar, *The Physics of Rubber Elasticity,* 2nd edition, Oxford University Press, Oxford, 1958, p. 47.)

polymer synthesis techniques permit considerable control over various structural possibilities. This section discusses several molecular structures including linear, branched, crosslinked, and network, in addition to various isomeric configurations.

LINEAR POLYMERS

Linear polymers are those in which the mer units are joined together end to end in single chains. These long chains are flexible and may be thought of as a mass of spaghetti, as represented schematically in Figure 15.7a, where each circle represents a mer unit. For linear polymers, there may be extensive van der Waals bonding between the chains. Some of the common polymers that form with linear structures are polyethylene, polyvinyl chloride, polystyrene, polymethyl methacrylate, nylon, and the fluorocarbons.

BRANCHED POLYMERS

Polymers may be synthesized in which side-branch chains are connected to the main ones, as indicated schematically in Figure 15.7b; these are fittingly called **branched polymers.** The branches, considered to be part of the main-chain molecule, result from side reactions that occur during the synthesis of the polymer. The chain packing efficiency is reduced with the formation of side branches, which results in a lowering of the polymer density. Those polymers that form linear structures may also be branched.

CROSSLINKED POLYMERS

In **crosslinked polymers,** adjacent linear chains are joined one to another at various positions by covalent bonds, as represented in Figure 15.7c. The process of crosslink-

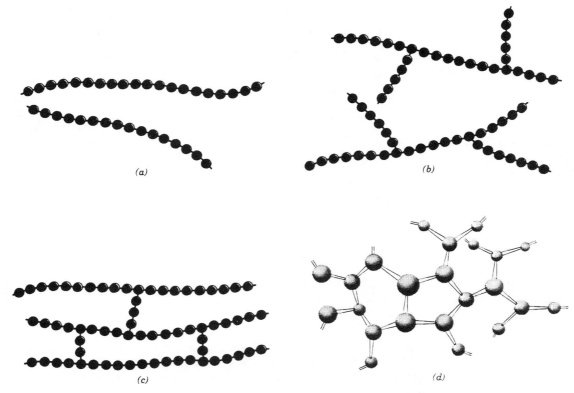

FIGURE 15.7   Schematic representations of (a) linear, (b) branched, (c) crosslinked, and (d) network (three-dimensional) molecular structures. Circles designate individual mer units.

ing is achieved either during synthesis or by a nonreversible chemical reaction that is usually carried out at an elevated temperature. Often, this crosslinking is accomplished by additive atoms or molecules that are covalently bonded to the chains. Many of the rubber elastic materials are crosslinked; in rubbers, this is called vulcanization, a process described in Section 16.14.

NETWORK POLYMERS

Trifunctional mer units, having three active covalent bonds, form three-dimensional networks (Figure 15.7d) instead of the linear chain framework assumed by bifunctional mers. Polymers composed of trifunctional units are termed **network polymers.** Actually, a polymer that is highly crosslinked may be classified as a network polymer. These materials have distinctive mechanical and thermal properties; the epoxies and phenol-formaldehyde belong to this group.

It should be pointed out that polymers are not usually of only one distinctive structural type. For example, a predominantly linear polymer might have some limited branching and crosslinking.

15.8 MOLECULAR CONFIGURATIONS

For polymers having more than one side atom or group of atoms bonded to the main chain, the regularity and symmetry of the side group arrangement can significantly influence the properties. Consider the mer unit

$$
\begin{array}{c}
\text{H} \quad \text{H} \\
| \quad\quad | \\
-\text{C}-\text{C}- \\
| \quad\quad | \\
\text{H} \quad Ⓡ
\end{array}
$$

in which R represents an atom or side group other than hydrogen (e.g., Cl, CH_3). One arrangement is possible when the R side groups of successive mer units bond to alternate carbon atoms as follows:

$$
\begin{array}{c}
\text{H} \quad \text{H} \quad \text{H} \quad \text{H} \\
| \quad\; | \quad\; | \quad\; | \\
-\text{C}-\text{C}-\text{C}-\text{C}- \\
| \quad\; | \quad\; | \quad\; | \\
\text{H} \quad Ⓡ \quad \text{H} \quad Ⓡ
\end{array}
$$

(15.6a)

This is designated as a head-to-tail configuration.[3] Its complement, the head-to-head configuration, occurs when R groups bond to adjacent chain atoms:

$$
\begin{array}{c}
\text{H} \quad \text{H} \quad \text{H} \quad \text{H} \\
| \quad\; | \quad\; | \quad\; | \\
-\text{C}-\text{C}-\text{C}-\text{C}- \\
| \quad\; | \quad\; | \quad\; | \\
\text{H} \quad Ⓡ \quad Ⓡ \quad \text{H}
\end{array}
$$

(15.6b)

In most polymers, the head-to-tail configuration predominates; there is often a polar repulsion that occurs between R groups for the head-to-head configuration.

Isomerism (Section 15.2) is also found in polymer molecules, wherein different atomic configurations are possible for the same composition. Two isomeric subclasses, stereoisomerism and geometrical isomerism, are topics of discussion in the succeeding sections.

STEREOISOMERISM

Stereoisomerism denotes the situation in which atoms are linked together in the same order (head-to-tail) but differ in their spatial arrangement. For one stereoisomer, all the R groups are situated on the same side of the chain as follows:

$$
\begin{array}{c}
\text{H} \quad \text{H} \quad \text{H} \quad \text{H} \quad \text{H} \quad \text{H} \quad \text{H} \quad \text{H} \\
| \quad\; | \quad\; | \quad\; | \quad\; | \quad\; | \quad\; | \quad\; | \\
-\text{C}-\text{C}-\text{C}-\text{C}-\text{C}-\text{C}-\text{C}-\text{C}- \\
| \quad\; | \quad\; | \quad\; | \quad\; | \quad\; | \quad\; | \quad\; | \\
\text{H} \quad Ⓡ \quad \text{H} \quad Ⓡ \quad \text{H} \quad Ⓡ \quad \text{H} \quad Ⓡ
\end{array}
$$

(15.7)

This is called an **isotactic configuration.**

---

[3] The term *configuration* is used in reference to arrangements of units along the axis of the chain, or atom positions that are not alterable except by the breaking and then reforming of primary bonds.

In a **syndiotactic configuration,** the R groups alternate sides of the chain:

$$
\begin{array}{cccccccc}
H & H & H & \text{\textcircled{R}} & H & H & H & \text{\textcircled{R}} \\
| & | & | & | & | & | & | & | \\
-C & -C & -C & -C & -C & -C & -C & -C- \\
| & | & | & | & | & | & | & | \\
H & \text{\textcircled{R}} & H & H & H & \text{\textcircled{R}} & H & H
\end{array}
$$

(15.8)

And for random positioning,

$$
\begin{array}{cccccccc}
H & H & H & H & H & \text{\textcircled{R}} & H & H \\
| & | & | & | & | & | & | & | \\
-C & -C & -C & -C & -C & -C & -C & -C- \\
| & | & | & | & | & | & | & | \\
H & \text{\textcircled{R}} & H & \text{\textcircled{R}} & H & H & H & \text{\textcircled{R}}
\end{array}
$$

(15.9)

the term **atactic configuration** is used.

Conversion from one stereoisomer to another (e.g., isotactic to syndiotactic) is not possible by a simple rotation about single chain bonds; these bonds must first be severed, and then, after the appropriate rotation, they are reformed.

In reality, a specific polymer does not exhibit just one of these configurations; the predominant form depends on the method of synthesis.

GEOMETRICAL ISOMERISM

Other important chain configurations, or geometrical isomers, are possible within mer units having a double bond between chain carbon atoms. Bonded to each of the carbon atoms participating in the double bond is a single side-bonded atom or radical, which may be situated on one side of the chain or its opposite. Consider the isoprene mer having the structure

$$
\begin{array}{cccc}
H & \text{\textcircled{CH}}_3 & \text{\textcircled{H}} & H \\
| & | & & | \\
-C & -C & =C & -C- \\
| & & & | \\
H & & & H
\end{array}
$$

in which the CH$_3$ group and the H atom are positioned on the same side of the chain. This is termed a **cis** structure, and the resulting polymer, *cis*-isoprene, is natural rubber. For the alternative

$$
\begin{array}{cccc}
H & \text{\textcircled{CH}}_3 & & H \\
| & | & & | \\
-C & -C & =C & -C- \\
| & & | & | \\
H & & \text{\textcircled{H}} & H
\end{array}
$$

the **trans** structure, the CH$_3$ and H reside on opposite chain sides. *Trans*-isoprene, sometimes called gutta percha, has properties that are distinctly different from natural rubber as a result of this configurational alteration. Conversion of trans to cis, or vice versa, is not possible by a simple chain bond rotation because the chain double bond is extremely rigid.

By way of summary of the preceding sections, polymer molecules may be characterized in terms of their size, shape, and structure. Molecular size is specified in terms of molecular weight (or degree of polymerization). Molecular shape relates

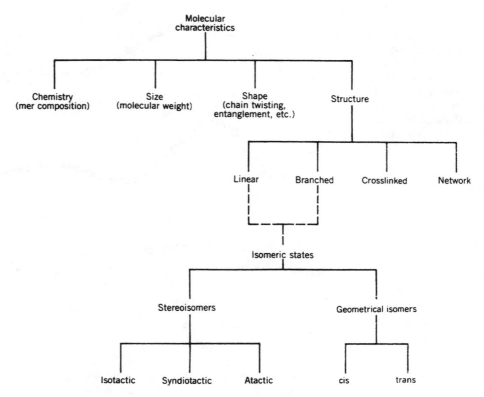

FIGURE 15.8
Classification scheme
for the characteristics
of polymer molecules.

to the degree of chain twisting, coiling, and bending. Molecular structure depends on the manner in which structural units are joined together. Linear, branched, crosslinked, and network structures are all possible, in addition to several isomeric configurations (isotactic, syndiotactic, atactic, cis, and trans). These molecular characteristics are presented in the taxonomic chart, Figure 15.8. It should be noted that some of the structural elements are not mutually exclusive of one another, and, in fact, it may be necessary to specify molecular structure in terms of more than one. For example, a linear polymer may also be isotactic.

15.9 COPOLYMERS

Polymer chemists and scientists are continually searching for new materials that can be easily and economically synthesized and fabricated, with improved properties or better property combinations than are offered by the homopolymers heretofore discussed. One group of these materials are the copolymers.

Consider a copolymer that is composed of two mer units as represented by ● and ● in Figure 15.9. Depending on the polymerization process and the relative fractions of these mer types, different sequencing arrangements along the polymer chains are possible. For one, as depicted in Figure 15.9a, the two different units are randomly dispersed along the chain in what is termed a **random copolymer.** For an **alternating copolymer,** as the name suggests, the two mer units alternate chain positions, as illustrated in Figure 15.9b. A **block copolymer** is one in which identical mers are clustered in blocks along the chain (Figure 15.9c). And, finally, homopolymer side branches of one type may be grafted to homopolymer main

FIGURE 15.9 Schematic representations of (a) random, (b) alternating, (c) block, and (d) graft copolymers. The two different mer types are designated by black and colored circles.

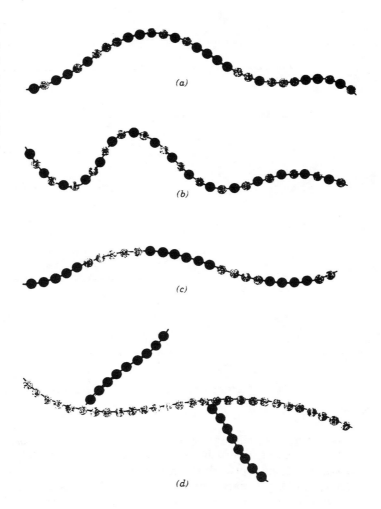

chains that are composed of a different mer; such a material is termed a **graft copolymer** (Figure 15.9d).

Synthetic rubbers, discussed in Section 16.14, are often copolymers; mer structures that are employed in some of these rubbers are contained in Table 15.5. Styrene–butadiene rubber (SBR) is a common random copolymer from which automobile tires are made. Nitrile rubber (NBR) is another random copolymer composed of acrylonitrile and butadiene. It is also highly elastic and, in addition, resistant to swelling in organic solvents; gasoline hoses are made of NBR.

15.10 POLYMER CRYSTALLINITY

The crystalline state may exist in polymeric materials. However, since it involves molecules instead of just atoms or ions, as with metals and ceramics, the atomic arrangements will be more complex for polymers. We think of **polymer crystallinity** as the packing of molecular chains so as to produce an ordered atomic array. Crystal structures may be specified in terms of unit cells, which are often quite complex. For example, Figure 15.10 shows the unit cell for polyethylene and its relationship to the molecular chain structure; this unit cell has orthorhombic geometry (Table

Table 15.5   Mers that Are Employed in Copolymer Rubbers

Mer Name	Mer Structure
Acrylonitrile	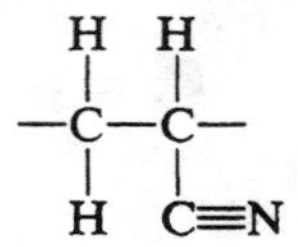 (structure: two carbons with H, H top; bottom H and C≡N)
Styrene	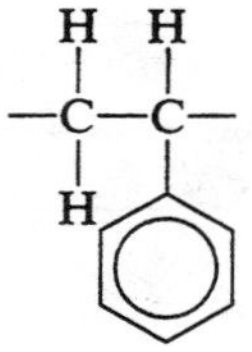 (structure: two carbons with H, H top; bottom H and phenyl ring)
Butadiene	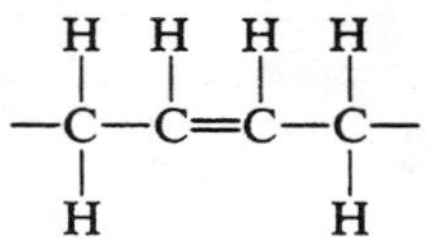 (structure: four-carbon chain with C=C double bond, H's)
Chloroprene	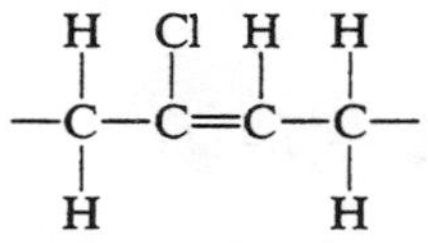 (structure: four-carbon chain with Cl substituent, C=C double bond, H's)
cis-Isoprene	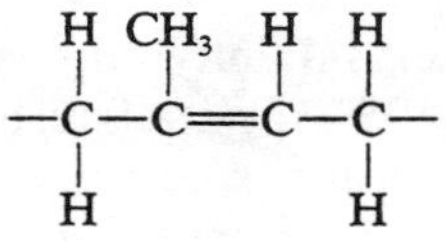 (structure: four-carbon chain with CH₃ substituent, C=C double bond, H's)
Isobutylene	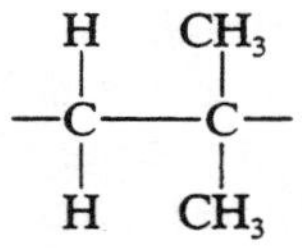 (structure: two carbons with H, CH₃ top; bottom H, CH₃)
Dimethylsiloxane	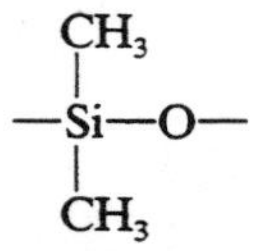 (structure: Si—O with CH₃ above and CH₃ below)

3.2). Of course, the chain molecules also extend beyond the unit cell shown in the figure.

Molecular substances having small molecules (e.g., water and methane) are normally either totally crystalline (as solids) or totally amorphous (as liquids). As a consequence of their size and often complexity, polymer molecules are often only partially crystalline (or semicrystalline), having crystalline regions dispersed within the remaining amorphous material. Any chain disorder or misalignment will result in an amorphous region, a condition that is fairly common, since twisting, kinking, and coiling of the chains prevent the strict ordering of every segment of every chain. Other structural effects are also influential in determining the extent of crystallinity, as discussed below.

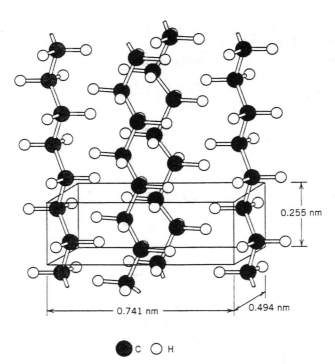

Figure 15.10
Arrangement of molecular chains in a unit cell for polyethylene. (Adapted from C. W. Bunn, *Chemical Crystallography*, Oxford University Press, Oxford, 1945, p. 233.)

0.255 nm

0.741 nm

0.494 nm

● C ○ H

The degree of crystallinity may range from completely amorphous to almost entirely (up to about 95%) crystalline; by way of contrast, metal specimens are almost always entirely crystalline, whereas many ceramics are either totally crystalline or totally noncrystalline. Semicrystalline polymers are, in a sense, analogous to two-phase metal alloys, discussed previously.

The density of a crystalline polymer will be greater than an amorphous one of the same material and molecular weight, since the chains are more closely packed together for the crystalline structure. The degree of crystallinity by weight may be determined from accurate density measurements, according to

$$\% \text{ crystallinity} = \frac{\rho_c(\rho_s - \rho_a)}{\rho_s(\rho_c - \rho_a)} \times 100 \tag{15.10}$$

where ρ_s is the density of a specimen for which the percent crystallinity is to be determined, ρ_a is the density of the totally amorphous polymer, and ρ_c is the density of the perfectly crystalline polymer. The values of ρ_a and ρ_c must be measured by other experimental means.

The degree of crystallinity of a polymer depends on the rate of cooling during solidification as well as on the chain configuration. During crystallization upon cooling through the melting temperature, the chains, which are highly random and entangled in the viscous liquid, must assume an ordered configuration. For this to occur, sufficient time must be allowed for the chains to move and align themselves.

The molecular chemistry as well as chain configuration also influence the ability of a polymer to crystallize. Crystallization is not favored in polymers that are composed of chemically complex mer structures (e.g., polyisoprene). On the other hand, crystallization is not easily prevented in chemically simple polymers such as polyethylene and polytetrafluoroethylene, even for very rapid cooling rates.

For linear polymers, crystallization is easily accomplished because there are virtually no restrictions to prevent chain alignment. Any side branches interfere with crystallization, such that branched polymers never are highly crystalline; in fact, excessive branching may prevent any crystallization whatsoever. Network polymers are almost totally amorphous, whereas various degrees of crystallinity are possible for those that are crosslinked. With regard to the stereoisomers, atactic polymers are difficult to crystallize; however, isotactic and syndiotactic polymers crystallize much more easily because the regularity of the geometry of the side groups facilitates the process of fitting together adjacent chains. Also, the bulkier or larger the side-bonded groups of atoms, the less tendency there is for crystallization.

For copolymers, as a general rule, the more irregular and random the mer arrangements, the greater is the tendency for the development of noncrystallinity. For alternating and block copolymers there is some likelihood of crystallization. On the other hand, random and graft copolymers are normally amorphous.

To some extent, the physical properties of polymeric materials are influenced by the degree of crystallinity. Crystalline polymers are usually stronger and more resistant to dissolution and softening by heat. Some of these properties are discussed in subsequent chapters.

15.11 POLYMER CRYSTALS

We shall now briefly discuss some of the models that have been proposed to describe the spatial arrangement of molecular chains in polymer crystals. One early model, accepted for many years, is the *fringed-micelle* model (Figure 15.11). It was proposed that a semicrystalline polymer consists of small crystalline regions (**crystallites,** or micelles), each having a precise alignment, which are embedded within the amorphous matrix composed of randomly oriented molecules. Thus a single chain molecule might pass through several crystallites as well as the intervening amorphous regions.

More recently, investigations centered on polymer single crystals grown from dilute solutions. These crystals are regularly shaped, thin platelets (or lamellae), approximately 10 to 20 nm thick, and on the order of 10 μm long. Frequently, these platelets will form a multilayered structure, like that shown in the electron

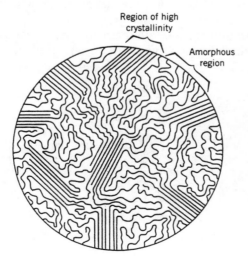

Region of high
crystallinity

Amorphous
region

FIGURE 15.11 Fringed-micelle model of a semicrystalline polymer, showing both crystalline and amorphous regions. (From H. W. Hayden, W. G. Moffatt, and J. Wulff, *The Structure and Properties of Materials,* Vol. III, *Mechanical Behavior.* Copyright © 1965 by John Wiley & Sons, New York. Reprinted by permission of John Wiley & Sons, Inc.)

micrograph of a single crystal of polyethylene, Figure 15.12. It is theorized that the molecular chains within each platelet fold back and forth on themselves, with folds occurring at the faces; this structure, aptly termed the **chain-folded model,** is illustrated schematically in Figure 15.13. Each platelet will consist of a number of molecules; however, the average chain length will be much greater than the thickness of the platelet. An actual chain fold for polyethylene that was imaged using a scanning probe microscope is shown in Color Plate J.

Many bulk polymers that are crystallized from a melt form **spherulites.** As implied by the name, each spherulite may grow to be spherical in shape; one of them, as found in natural rubber, is shown in the transmission electron micrograph on page 437. The spherulite consists of an aggregate of ribbonlike chain-folded crystallites (lamellae) approximately 10 nm thick that radiate from the center outward. In this electron micrograph, these lamellae appear as thin white lines. The detailed structure of a spherulite is illustrated schematically in Figure 15.14; shown here are the individual chain-folded lamellar crystals that are separated by amorphous material. Tie-chain molecules that act as connecting links between adjacent lamellae pass through these amorphous regions.

As the crystallization of a spherulitic structure nears completion, the extremities of adjacent spherulites begin to impinge on one another, forming more or less

FIGURE 15.13
The chain-folded
structure for a plate-
shaped polymer
crystallite.

~ 10 nm

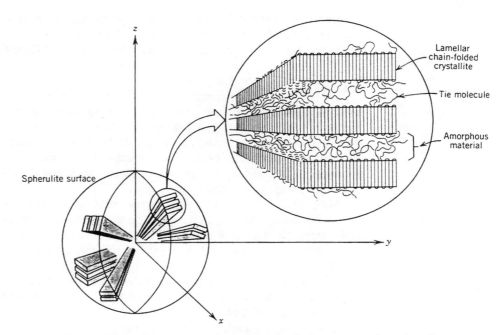

FIGURE 15.14 Schematic representation of the detailed structure of a spherulite. (From R. H. Boyd and J. Coburn.)

planar boundaries; prior to this time, they maintain their spherical shape. These boundaries are evident in Figure 15.15, which is a photomicrograph of polyethylene using cross-polarized light. A characteristic Maltese cross pattern appears within each spherulite.

Spherulites are considered to be the polymer analogue of grains in polycrystalline metals and ceramics. However, as discussed above, each spherulite is really

FIGURE 15.15 A transmission photomicrograph (using cross-polarized light) showing the spherulite structure of polyethylene. Linear boundaries form between adjacent spherulites, and within each spherulite appears a Maltese cross. 525×. (Courtesy F. P. Price, General Electric Company.)

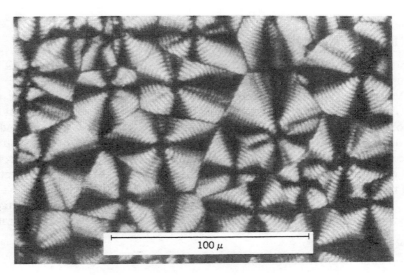

100 μ

composed of many different lamellar crystals and, in addition, some amorphous material. Polyethylene, polypropylene, polyvinyl chloride, polytetrafluoroethylene, and nylon form a spherulitic structure when they crystallize from a melt.

SUMMARY

Most polymeric materials are composed of very large molecules—chains of carbon atoms, to which are side-bonded various atoms or radicals. These macromolecules may be thought of as being composed of mers, smaller structural entities, which are repeated along the chain. Mer structures of some of the chemically simple polymers (e.g., polyethylene, polytetrafluoroethylene, polyvinyl chloride, and polypropylene) were presented.

Molecular weights for high polymers may be in excess of a million. Since all molecules are not of the same size, there is a distribution of molecular weights. Molecular weight is often expressed in terms of number and weight averages. Chain length may also be specified by degree of polymerization, the number of mer units per average molecule.

Several molecular characteristics that have an influence on the properties of polymers were discussed. Molecular entanglements occur when the chains assume twisted, coiled, and kinked shapes or contours. With regard to molecular structure, linear, branched, crosslinked, and network structures are possible, in addition to isotactic, syndiotactic, and atactic stereoisomers, and the cis and trans geometrical isomers. The copolymers include random, alternating, block, and graft types.

When the packing of molecular chains is such as to produce an ordered atomic arrangement, the condition of crystallinity is said to exist. In addition to being entirely amorphous, polymers may also exhibit virtually total and also partial crystallinity; for the latter case, crystalline regions are interdispersed within amorphous areas. Crystallinity is facilitated for polymers that are chemically simple and that have regular and symmetrical chain structures.

Polymer single crystals as thin platelets and having chain-folded structures may be grown from dilute solutions. Many semicrystalline polymers form spherulites; each spherulite consists of a collection of ribbonlike chain-folded lamellar crystallites that radiate outward from its center.

IMPORTANT TERMS AND CONCEPTS

Alternating copolymer	Graft copolymer	Network polymer
Atactic configuration	Homopolymer	Polymer
Bifunctional mer	Isomerism	Polymer crystallinity
Block copolymer	Isotactic configuration	Random copolymer
Branched polymer	Linear polymer	Saturated
Chain-folded model	Macromolecule	Spherulite
Cis (structure)	Mer	Stereoisomerism
Copolymer	Molecular chemistry	Syndiotactic configuration
Crosslinked polymer	Molecular structure	Trans (structure)
Crystallite	Molecular weight	Trifunctional mer
Degree of polymerization	Monomer	Unsaturated

REFERENCES

Baer, E., "Advanced Polymers," *Scientific American,* Vol. 255, No. 4, October 1986, pp. 178–190.

Bovey, F. A. and F. H. Winslow (Editors), *Macromolecules: An Introduction to Polymer Science,* Academic Press, New York, 1979.

Cowie, J. M. G., *Polymers: Chemistry and Physics of Modern Materials,* 2nd edition, Chapman and Hall (USA), New York, 1991.

Engineered Materials Handbook, Vol. 2, *Engineering Plastics,* ASM International, Materials Park, OH, 1988.

Rodriguez, F., *Principles of Polymer Systems,* 3rd edition, Hemisphere Publishing Company (Taylor & Francis), New York, 1989.

Rosen, S. L., *Fundamental Principles of Polymeric Materials,* 2nd edition, John Wiley & Sons, New York, 1993.

Rudin, A., *The Elements of Polymer Science and Engineering: An Introductory Text for Engineers and Chemists,* Academic Press, New York, 1982.

Schultz, J., *Polymer Materials Science,* Prentice-Hall, Englewood Cliffs, NJ, 1974.

Seymour, R. B. and C. E. Carraher, Jr., *Polymer Chemistry, An Introduction,* 3rd edition, Marcel Dekker, Inc., New York, 1992.

Sperling, L. H., *Introduction to Physical Polymer Science,* 2nd edition, John Wiley & Sons, New York, 1992.

Young, R. J. and P. Lovell, *Introduction to Polymers,* 2nd edition, Chapman and Hall, London, 1991.

Williams, D. J., *Polymer Science and Engineering,* Prentice-Hall, Inc., Englewood Cliffs, NJ, 1971.

QUESTIONS AND PROBLEMS

15.1 Differentiate between polymorphism and isomerism.

15.2 On the basis of the structures presented in this chapter, sketch mer structures for the following polymers: **(a)** polyvinyl fluoride, **(b)** polychlorotrifluoroethylene, and **(c)** polyvinyl alcohol.

15.3 Compute mer molecular weights for the following: **(a)** polyvinyl chloride, **(b)** polyethylene terephthalate, **(c)** polycarbonate, and **(d)** polydimethylsiloxane.

15.4 The number-average molecular weight of a polystyrene is 500,000 g/mol. Compute the number-average degree of polymerization.

15.5 **(a)** Compute the mer molecular weight of polypropylene.

(b) Compute the weight-average molecular weight for a polypropylene for which the weight-average degree of polymerization is 15,000.

15.6 Below, molecular weight data for a polytetrafluoroethylene material are tabulated. Compute **(a)** the number-average molecular weight, **(b)** the weight-average molecular weight, **(c)** the number-average degree of polymerization, and **(d)** the weight-average degree of polymerization.

Molecular Weight Range (g/mol)	x_i	w_i
10,000–20,000	0.03	0.01
20,000–30,000	0.09	0.04
30,000–40,000	0.15	0.11
40,000–50,000	0.25	0.23
50,000–60,000	0.22	0.24
60,000–70,000	0.14	0.18
70,000–80,000	0.08	0.12
80,000–90,000	0.04	0.07

15.7 Below, molecular weight data for some polymer are tabulated. Compute **(a)** the number-average molecular weight, and **(b)** the weight-average molecular weight. (c) If it is known that this material's weight-average degree of polymerization is 780, which one of the polymers listed in Table 15.3 is this polymer? Why? (d) What is this material's number-average degree of polymerization?

Molecular Weight Range (g/mol)	x_i	w_i
15,000–30,000	0.04	0.01
30,000–45,000	0.07	0.04
45,000–60,000	0.16	0.11
60,000–75,000	0.26	0.24
75,000–90,000	0.24	0.27
90,000–105,000	0.12	0.16
105,000–120,000	0.08	0.12
120,000–135,000	0.03	0.05

15.8 Is it possible to have a polymethyl methacrylate homopolymer with the following molecular weight data and a weight-average degree of polymerization of 585? Why or why not?

Molecular Weight Range (g/mol)	x_i	w_i
8,000–20,000	0.04	0.01
20,000–32,000	0.10	0.05
32,000–44,000	0.16	0.12
44,000–56,000	0.26	0.25
56,000–68,000	0.23	0.27
68,000–80,000	0.15	0.21
80,000–92,000	0.06	0.09

15.9 High-density polyethylene may be chlorinated by inducing the random substitution of chlorine atoms for hydrogen.

(a) Determine the concentration of Cl (in wt%) that must be added if this substitution occurs for 8% of all the original hydrogen atoms.

(b) In what ways does this chlorinated polyethylene differ from polyvinyl chloride?

15.10 What is the difference between *configuration* and *conformation* in relation to polymer chains?

15.11 For a linear polymer molecule, the total chain length L depends on the bond length between chain atoms d, the total number of bonds in the molecule N, and the angle between adjacent backbone chain atoms θ, as follows:

$$L = Nd \sin\left(\frac{\theta}{2}\right) \qquad (15.11)$$

Furthermore, the average end-to-end distance for a series of polymer molecules r in Figure 15.6 is equal to

$$r = d\sqrt{N} \qquad (15.12)$$

A linear polytetrafluoroethylene has a number-average molecular weight of 500,000 g/mol; compute average values of L and r for this material.

15.12 Using the definitions for total chain molecule length L (Equation 15.11) and average chain end-to-end distance r (Equation 15.12), for a linear polyethylene determine (a) the number-average molecular weight for $L = 2500$ nm; and (b) the number-average molecular weight for $r = 20$ nm.

15.13 Sketch portions of a linear polystyrene molecule that are (a) syndiotactic, (b) atactic, and (c) isotactic.

15.14 Sketch cis and trans mer structures for (a) butadiene, and (b) chloroprene.

15.15 Sketch the mer structure for each of the following alternating copolymers: (a) poly (butadiene-chloroprene), (b) poly(styrene-methyl methacrylate), and (c) poly(acrylonitrile-vinyl chloride).

15.16 The number-average molecular weight of a poly(acrylonitrile–butadiene) alternating copolymer is 1,000,000 g/mol; determine the average number of acrylonitrile and butadiene mer units per molecule.

15.17 Calculate the number-average molecular weight of a random poly(isobutylene–isoprene) copolymer in which the fraction of isobutylene mers is 0.25; assume that this concentration corresponds to a number-average degree of polymerization of 1500.

15.18 An alternating copolymer is known to have a number-average molecular weight of 250,000 g/mol and a number-average degree of polymerization of 3420. If one of the mers is styrene, which of ethylene, propylene, tetrafluoroethylene, and vinyl chloride is the other mer? Why?

15.19 **(a)** Determine the ratio of butadiene to styrene mers in a copolymer having a weight-average molecular weight of 350,000 g/mol and weight-average degree of polymerization of 4425.

(b) Which type(s) of copolymer(s) will this copolymer be, considering the following possibilities: random, alternating, graft, and block? Why?

15.20 Crosslinked copolymers consisting of 35 wt% ethylene and 65 wt% propylene may have elastic properties similar to those for natural rubber. For a copolymer of this composition, determine the fraction of both mer types.

15.21 A random poly(styrene–butadiene) copolymer has a weight-average molecular weight of 350,000 g/mol and a weight-average degree of polymerization of 5000. Compute the fraction of styrene and butadiene mers in this copolymer.

15.22 **(a)** Compare the crystalline state in metals and polymers.

(b) Compare the noncrystalline state as it applies to polymers and ceramic glasses.

15.23 Explain briefly why the tendency of a polymer to crystallize decreases with increasing molecular weight.

15.24 For each of the following pairs of polymers, do the following: (1) state whether or not it is possible to determine if one polymer is more likely to crystallize than the other; (2) if it is possible, note which is the more likely and then cite reason(s) for your choice; and

(3) if it is not possible to decide, then state why.

(a) Linear and syndiotactic polyvinyl chloride; linear and isotactic polystyrene.

(b) Network phenol-formaldehyde; linear and heavily crosslinked *cis*-isoprene.

(c) Linear polyethylene; lightly branched isotactic polypropylene.

(d) Alternating poly(styrene-ethylene) copolymer; random poly(vinyl chloride-tetrafluoroethylene) copolymer.

15.25 Compute the density of totally crystalline polyethylene. The orthorhombic unit cell for polyethylene is shown in Figure 15.10; also, the equivalent of two ethylene mer units is contained within each unit cell.

15.26 The density of totally crystalline polypropylene at room temperature is 0.946 g/cm³. Also, at room temperature the unit cell for this material is monoclinic with lattice parameters

$a = 0.666$ nm $\quad \alpha = 90°$
$b = 2.078$ nm $\quad \beta = 99.62°$
$c = 0.650$ nm $\quad \gamma = 90°$

If the volume of a monoclinic unit cell, V_{mono} is a function of these lattice parameters as

$$V_{mono} = abc \sin \beta$$

determine the number of mer units per unit cell.

15.27 The density and associated percent crystallinity for two polytetrafluoroethylene materials are as follows:

ρ (g/cm³)	Crystallinity (%)
2.144	51.3
2.215	74.2

(a) Compute the densities of totally crystalline and totally amorphous polytetrafluoroethylene.

(b) Determine the percent crystallinity of a specimen having a density of 2.26 g/cm³.

15.28 The density and associated percent crystallinity for two nylon 6,6 materials are as follows:

ρ (g/cm^3)	Crystallinity (%)
1.188	67.3
1.152	43.7

(a) Compute the densities of totally crystalline and totally amorphous nylon 6,6.

(b) Determine the density of a specimen having 55.4% crystallinity.

Characteristics, Applications, and Processing of Polymers

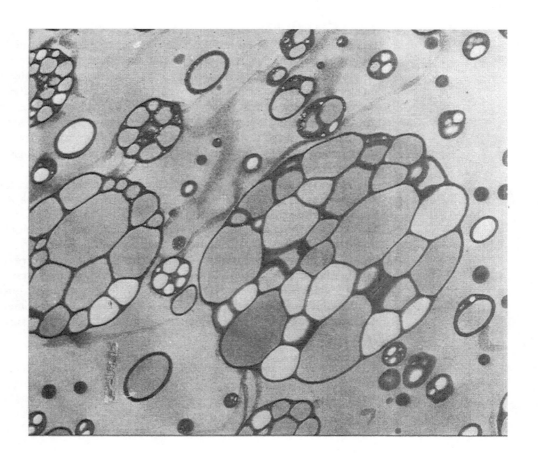

_____Scanning electron micrograph of a polystyrene which has been made more impact resistant by the addition of a rubber phase. The continuous matrix phase (gray) is polystyrene; the fine dispersed structure consists of particles of both polystyrene and rubber (white). 15,000×. (From E. R. Wagner and L. M. Robeson, _Rubber Chemistry and Technology,_ 43, 1129, 1970. Reprinted with permission.)

16.1 INTRODUCTION

This chapter discusses some of the characteristics important to polymeric materials and, in addition, the various types and processing techniques.

MECHANICAL AND THERMOMECHANICAL CHARACTERISTICS

16.2 STRESS–STRAIN BEHAVIOR

The mechanical properties of polymers are specified with many of the same parameters that are used for metals, that is, modulus of elasticity, and tensile, impact, and fatigue strengths. For many polymeric materials, the simple stress–strain test is employed for the characterization of some of these mechanical parameters.[1] The mechanical characteristics of polymers, for the most part, are highly sensitive to the rate of deformation (strain rate), the temperature, and the chemical nature of the environment (the presence of water, oxygen, organic solvents, etc.). Some modifications of the testing techniques and specimen configurations used for metals (Chapter 6) are necessary with polymers, especially for the highly elastic materials, such as rubbers.

Three typically different types of stress–strain behavior are found for polymeric materials, as represented in Figure 16.1. Curve A illustrates the stress–strain character for a brittle polymer, inasmuch as it fractures while deforming elastically. The behavior for the plastic material, curve B, is similar to that found for many metallic materials; the initial deformation is elastic, which is followed by yielding and a region of plastic deformation. Finally, the deformation displayed by curve C is totally elastic; this rubberlike elasticity (large recoverable strains produced at low stress levels) is displayed by a class of polymers termed the **elastomers.**

Modulus of elasticity (termed *tensile modulus* or sometimes just *modulus* for polymers) and ductility, in percent elongation are determined for polymers in the

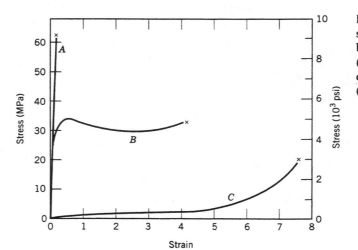

FIGURE 16.1 The stress–strain behavior for brittle (curve A), plastic (curve B), and highly elastic (elastomeric) (curve C) polymers.

---

[1] ASTM Standard D 638, "Standard Test Method for Tensile Properties of Plastics."

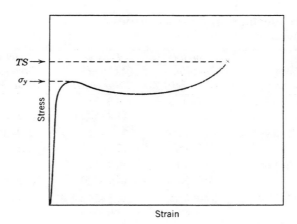

FIGURE 16.2 Schematic stress–strain curve for a plastic polymer showing how yield and tensile strengths are determined.

same manner as for metals (Section 6.6). For plastic polymers (curve B, Figure 16.1), the yield point is taken as a maximum on the curve, which occurs just beyond the termination of the linear-elastic region (Figure 16.2); the stress at this maximum is the yield strength (σ_y). Furthermore, tensile strength (TS) corresponds to the stress at which fracture occurs (Figure 16.2); TS may be greater than or less than σ_y. Strength, for these plastic polymers, is normally taken as tensile strength. Table 16.1 gives these mechanical properties for several polymeric materials; more comprehensive lists are provided in Appendices C.2, C.3, and C.4.

Polymers are, in many respects, mechanically dissimilar to metals. For example, the modulus for highly elastic polymeric materials may be as low as 7 MPa (10^3 psi), but may run as high as 4 GPa (0.6×10^6 psi) for some of the very stiff polymers; modulus values for metals are much larger and range between 48 and 410 GPa

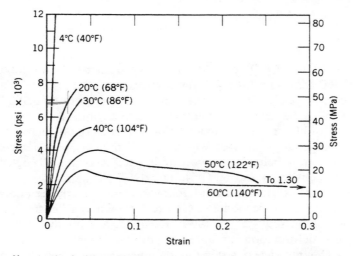

FIGURE 16.3 The influence of temperature on the stress–strain characteristics of polymethyl methacrylate. (From T. S. Carswell and H. K. Nason, "Effect of Environmental Conditions on the Mechanical Properties of Organic Plastics," *Symposium on Plastics,* American Society for Testing and Materials, Philadelphia, 1944. Copyright, ASTM, 1916 Race Street, Philadelphia, PA 19103. Reprinted with permission.)

Table 16.1 **Room-Temperature Mechanical Characteristics of Some of the More Common Polymers**

Material	Specific Gravity	Tensile Modulus [GPa (ksi)]	Tensile Strength [MPa (ksi)]	Yield Strength [MPa (ksi)]	Elongation at Break (%)
Polyethylene (low density)	0.917–0.932	0.17–0.28 (25–41)	8.3–31.4 (1.2–4.55)	9.0–14.5 (1.3–2.1)	100–650
Polyethylene (high density)	0.952–0.965	1.06–1.09 (155–158)	22.1–31.0 (3.2–4.5)	26.2–33.1 (3.8–4.8)	10–1200
Polyvinyl chloride	1.30–1.58	2.4–4.1 (350–600)	40.7–51.7 (5.9–7.5)	40.7–44.8 (5.9–6.5)	40–80
Polytetrafluoroethylene	2.14–2.20	0.40–0.55 (58–80)	20.7–34.5 (3.0–5.0)	—	200–400
Polypropylene	0.90–0.91	1.14–1.55 (165–225)	31–41.4 (4.5–6.0)	31.0–37.2 (4.5–5.4)	100–600
Polystyrene	1.04–1.05	2.28–3.28 (330–475)	35.9–51.7 (5.2–7.5)	—	1.2–2.5
Polymethyl methacrylate	1.17–1.20	2.24–3.24 (325–470)	48.3–72.4 (7.0–10.5)	53.8–73.1 (7.8–10.6)	2.0–5.5
Phenol-formaldehyde	1.24–1.32	2.76–4.83 (400–700)	34.5–62.1 (5.0–9.0)	—	1.5–2.0
Nylon 6,6	1.13–1.15	1.58–3.80 (230–550)	75.9–94.5 (11.0–13.7)	44.8–82.8 (6.5–12)	15–300
Polyester (PET)	1.29–1.40	2.8–4.1 (400–600)	48.3–72.4 (7.0–10.5)	59.3 (8.6)	30–300
Polycarbonate	1.20	2.38 (345)	62.8–72.4 (9.1–10.5)	62.1 (9.0)	110–150

Source: *Modern Plastics Encyclopedia '96.* Copyright 1995, The McGraw-Hill Companies. Reprinted with permission.

$(7 \times 10^6$ to 60×10^6 psi). Maximum tensile strengths for polymers are on the order of 100 MPa (15,000 psi)—for some metal alloys 4100 MPa (600,000 psi). And, whereas metals rarely elongate plastically to more than 100%, some highly elastic polymers may experience elongations to as much as 1000%.

In addition, the mechanical characteristics of polymers are much more sensitive to temperature changes within the vicinity of room temperature. Consider the stress–strain behavior for polymethyl methacrylate (Plexiglas) at several temperatures between 4 and 60°C (40 and 140°F) (Figure 16.3). Several features of this figure are worth noting, as follows: increasing the temperature produces (1) a decrease in elastic modulus, (2) a reduction in tensile strength, and (3) an enhancement of ductility—at 4°C (40°F) the material is totally brittle, whereas considerable plastic deformation is realized at both 50 and 60°C (122 and 140°F).

The influence of strain rate on the mechanical behavior may also be important. In general, decreasing the rate of deformation has the same influence on the stress–strain characteristics as increasing the temperature; that is, the material becomes softer and more ductile.

An understanding of deformation mechanisms of polymers is important in order for us to be able to manage the mechanical characteristics of these materials.

In this regard, two different deformation models deserve our attention. One of these involves plastic deformation that occurs in semicrystalline polymers, which is the topic of the succeeding section. The strength of these materials is often an important consideration. On the other hand, elastomers are utilized on the basis of their unusual elastic properties. The deformation mechanism of these polymers is treated in Section 16.7.

16.3 DEFORMATION OF SEMICRYSTALLINE POLYMERS

MECHANISM

Many semicrystalline polymers in bulk form will have the spherulitic structure described in Section 15.11. By way of review, let us repeat here that each spherulite consists of numerous chain-folded ribbons, or lamellae, that radiate outward from the center. Separating these lamellae are areas of amorphous material (Figure 15.14); adjacent lamellae are connected by tie chains that pass through these amorphous regions.

The mechanism of plastic deformation is best described by the interactions between lamellar and intervening amorphous regions in response to an applied tensile load. This process occurs in several stages, which are schematically diagrammed in Figure 16.4. Two adjacent chain-folded lamellae and the interlamellar amorphous material, prior to deformation, are shown in Figure 16.4a. During the initial stage of deformation (Figure 16.4b), the lamellar ribbons simply slide past one another as the tie chains within the amorphous regions become extended. Continued deformation in the second stage occurs by the tilting of the lamellae so that the chain folds become aligned with the tensile axis (Figure 16.4c). Next, crystalline block segments separate from the lamellae, which segments remain attached to one another by tie chains (Figure 16.4d). In the final stage (Figure 16.4e), the blocks and tie chains become oriented in the direction of the tensile axis. Thus appreciable tensile deformation of semicrystalline polymers produces a highly oriented structure. Of course, during this process the spherulites also experience changes in shape.

The mechanical characteristics of semicrystalline polymers are subject to modification. An increase in strength results whenever any restraint is imposed on the process illustrated in Figure 16.4. For example, increasing the degree of crosslinking will inhibit relative chain motion and thus strengthen the polymer and make it more brittle. Crosslinking may be promoted by irradiation; when a polymer specimen is exposed to certain types of radiation, side chain bonds are broken and become sites for crosslinkages to form.

Even though secondary intermolecular (e.g., van der Waals) bonds are much weaker than the primary covalent ones, they are, nevertheless, effective in inhibiting relative chain motion. In fact, the mechanical properties of polymers are highly dependent on the magnitude of these weak intermolecular forces. For a specific polymer, the degree of crystallinity can have a rather significant influence on the mechanical properties, since it affects the extent of this intermolecular secondary bonding. For crystalline regions in which molecular chains are closely packed in an ordered and parallel arrangement, extensive secondary bonding ordinarily exists between adjacent chain segments. This secondary bonding is much less prevalent in amorphous regions, by virtue of the chain misalignment. Thus increasing the crystallinity of a particular polymer generally enhances its mechanical properties. The influence of chain chemistry and structure (branching, stereoisomerism, etc.) on degree of crystallinity was discussed in Chapter 15.

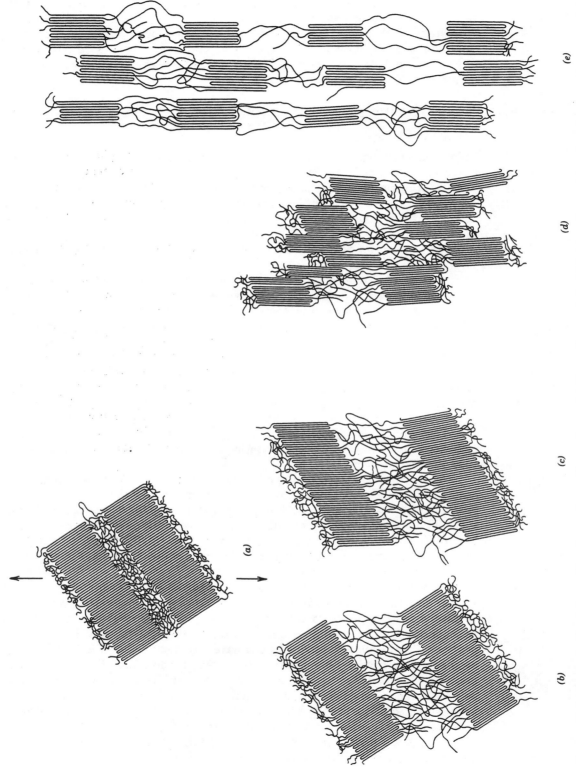

FIGURE 16.4 Stages in the deformation of a semicrystalline polymer. (*a*) Two adjacent chain-folded lamellae and interlamellar amorphous material before deformation. (*b*) Elongation of amorphous tie chains during the first stage of deformation. (*c*) Tilting of lamellar chain folds during the second stage. (*d*) Separation of crystalline block segments during the third stage. (*e*) Orientation of block segments and tie chains with the tensile axis in the final deformation stage. (From Jerold M. Schultz, *Polymer Materials Science*, copyright © 1974, pp. 500–501. Reprinted by permission of Prentice-Hall, Inc., Englewood Cliffs, NJ.)

FIGURE 16.5 The influence of degree of crystallinity and molecular weight on the physical characteristics of polyethylene. (From R. B. Richards, "Polyethylene—Structure, Crystallinity and Properties," *J. Appl. Chem.*, **1**, 370, 1951.)

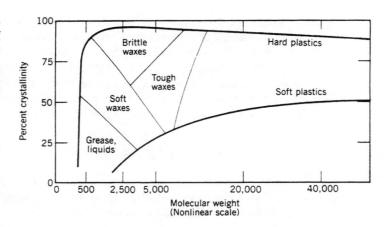

Other molecular chain characteristics, including molecular weight, influence the mechanical behavior. For relatively low molecular weight polymers, the mechanical strength increases with molecular weight. The physical state of polyethylene as a function of percent crystallinity and molecular weight is illustrated in Figure 16.5.

On a commercial basis, one of the most important techniques used to improve mechanical strength is by predeforming the polymer, so that it becomes oriented, having the structure depicted in Figure 16.4e. This process might be thought analogous to the strain hardening of metals. Predeformation by drawing is commonly used to strengthen fiber materials.

Techniques used to strengthen polymers, as discussed in this section, are included in the strengthening classification scheme for the various material types, Appendix E.1.

 MACROSCOPIC DEFORMATION

Some aspects of the macroscopic deformation of semicrystalline polymers deserve our attention. The tensile stress–strain curve for a semicrystalline material, which was initially unoriented, is shown in Figure 16.6; also included in the figure are schematic representations of specimen profile at various stages of deformation. Both upper and lower yield points are evident on the curve, which are followed by a near horizontal region. At the upper yield point, a small neck forms within

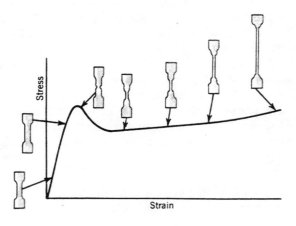

FIGURE 16.6 Schematic tensile stress–strain curve for a semicrystalline polymer. Specimen contours at several stages of deformation are included. (From Jerold M. Schultz, *Polymer Materials Science,* copyright © 1974, p. 488. Reprinted by permission of Prentice-Hall, Inc., Englewood Cliffs, NJ.)

the gauge section of the specimen. Within this neck, the chains become oriented, which leads to localized strengthening. Consequently, there is a resistance to continued deformation at this point, and specimen elongation proceeds by the propagation of this neck region along the gauge length; the chain orientation phenomenon accompanies this neck extension. This tensile behavior may be contrasted to that found for ductile metals (Section 6.6), wherein once a neck has formed, all subsequent deformation is confined to within the neck region.

16.4 CRYSTALLIZATION, MELTING, AND GLASS TRANSITION PHENOMENA

Inasmuch as the mechanical properties of polymers are highly sensitive to temperature changes, the several succeeding sections are devoted to discussions of thermal and thermomechanical characteristics of these materials. We begin with treatments of crystallization, melting, and glass-transition phenomena. Crystallization is the process by which, upon cooling, an ordered (i.e., crystalline) solid phase is produced from a liquid melt having a highly random molecular structure. The melting transformation is the reverse process that occurs when a polymer is heated. The glass-transition phenomenon occurs with amorphous or noncrystallizable polymers which, when cooled from a liquid melt, become rigid solids yet retain their disordered molecular structure that is characteristic of the liquid state; consequently, they may be considered frozen liquids (or amorphous solids). Of course, alterations of physical and mechanical properties attend crystallization, melting, and the glass transition. Furthermore, for semicrystalline polymers, crystalline regions will experience melting (and crystallization), while noncrystalline areas pass through the glass transition.

CRYSTALLIZATION

An understanding of the mechanism and kinetics of polymer crystallization is important inasmuch as the degree of crystallinity influences the mechanical and thermal properties of these materials. The crystallization of a molten polymer occurs by nucleation and growth processes, topics discussed in the context of phase transformations for metals in Section 10.3. For polymers, upon cooling through the melting temperature, nuclei form wherein small regions of the tangled and random molecules become ordered and aligned in the manner of chain-folded layers, Figure 15.13. At temperatures in excess of the melting temperature, these nuclei are unstable due to the thermal atomic vibrations that tend to disrupt the ordered molecular arrangements. Subsequent to nucleation and during the crystallization growth stage, nuclei grow by the continued ordering and alignment of additional molecular chain segments; that is, the chain-folded layers increase in lateral dimensions, or, for spherulitic structures (Figure 15.14) there is an increase in spherulite radius.

The time dependence of crystallization is the same as for many solid-state transformations—Figure 10.1; that is, a sigmoidal-shaped curve results when fraction transformation (i.e., fraction crystallized) is plotted versus the logarithm of time (at constant temperature). Such a plot is presented in Figure 16.7 for the crystallization of polypropylene at three temperatures. Mathematically, fraction crystallized y is a function of time t according to the Avrami equation, Equation 10.1, as

$$y = 1 - \exp(-kt^n) \qquad (10.1)$$

where k and n are time-independent constants, which values depend on the crystallizing system. Normally, the extent of crystallization is measured by specimen

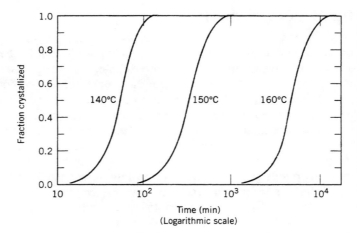

FIGURE 16.7 Plot of fraction crystallized versus the logarithm of time for polypropylene at constant temperatures of 140°C, 150°C, and 160°C. (Adapted from P. Parrini and G. Corrieri, *Makromol. Chem.*, **62**, 83, 1963. Reprinted by permission of Hüthig & Wepf Publishers, Zug, Switzerland.)

volume changes since there will be a difference in volume for liquid and crystallized phases. Rate of crystallization may be specified in the same manner as for the transformations discussed in Section 10.3, and according to Equation 10.2; that is, rate is equal to the reciprocal of time required for crystallization to proceed to 50% completion. This rate is dependent on crystallization temperature (Figure 16.7) and also on the molecular weight of the polymer; rate decreases with increasing molecular weight.

In Figure 16.7, it may be noted that crystallization was taken to completion for all three temperatures; the attainment of 100% crystallinity for this polymer is not possible. However, a fraction crystallized of 1.0 in Figure 16.7 is taken as the highest level of crystallization achieved during the tests, which, in reality, will be less than complete crystallization.

MELTING

The melting of a polymer crystal corresponds to the transformation of a solid material, having an ordered structure of aligned molecular chains, to a viscous liquid in which the structure is highly random; this phenomenon occurs, upon heating, at the **melting temperature,** T_m. There are several features distinctive to the melting of polymers that are not normally observed with metals and ceramics; these are consequences of the polymer molecular structures and lamellar crystalline morphology. First of all, melting of polymers takes place over a range of temperatures; this phenomenon is discussed in more detail below. In addition, the melting behavior depends on the history of the specimen, in particular the temperature at which it crystallized. The thickness of chain-folded lamellae will depend on crystallization temperature; the thicker the lamellae, the higher the melting temperature. And finally, melting behavior is a function of the rate of heating; increasing this rate results in an elevation of the melting temperature.

Polymeric materials are also responsive to heat treatments which produce structural and property alterations. An increase in lamellar thickness may be induced by an annealing treatment in which the material is heated at just below its melting temperature. [Annealing is also used to designate heat treatments for metals and ceramics (Sections 11.2, 11.4, and 14.4)]. Annealing also raises the melting temperature of the polymer.

THE GLASS TRANSITION

The glass transition occurs in amorphous or glassy polymers, when, upon cooling from the liquid, crystallization does not take place—that is, the polymer chains are not able to rearrange into a three-dimensional, long-range ordered structure. Upon cooling, the glass transition corresponds to an increase in viscosity, and the gradual transformation from a liquid, to a rubbery material, and, finally, to a rigid solid. The temperature at which the polymer experiences the transition from rubbery to rigid states is termed the **glass transition temperature**, T_g. Of course, this sequence of events occurs in the reverse order when a rigid glass at a temperature below T_g is heated. Furthermore, even normally crystallizable polymers may be made to form amorphous glasses if they are rapidly quenched from the melt. In addition, abrupt changes in other physical properties accompany this glass transition; e.g., stiffness (Figure 16.12), heat capacity, and coefficient of thermal expansion.

MELTING AND GLASS TRANSITION TEMPERATURES

Melting and glass transition temperatures are important parameters relative to in-service applications of polymers. They define, respectively, the upper and lower temperature limits for numerous applications, especially for semicrystalline polymers. Furthermore, they also influence the fabrication and processing procedures for polymers and polymer-matrix composites. These issues are discussed in succeeding sections of this chapter.

The temperatures at which melting and/or the glass transition occur for a polymer are determined in the same manner as for ceramic materials—from a plot of specific volume (the reciprocal of density) versus temperature. Figure 16.8 is such a plot, wherein curves A and C, for amorphous and crystalline polymers, respectively, have the same configurations as their ceramic counterparts (Figure 14.3). For the crystalline material, there is a discontinuous change in specific volume at the melting temperature T_m. The curve for the totally amorphous material is continuous but it experiences a slight decrease in slope at the glass transition temperature, T_g. The behavior is intermediate between these extremes for a semicrystalline polymer (curve B), in that both melting and glass transition phenomena are observed; T_m and T_g are properties of the respective crystalline and amorphous phases in this semicrystalline material. As discussed above, the behaviors represented in Figure 16.8 will depend on the rate of cooling or heating. Representative melting and glass transition temperatures of a number of polymers are contained in Table 16.2 and Appendix C.11.

FACTORS THAT INFLUENCE MELTING AND GLASS TRANSITION TEMPERATURES

Melting Temperature

During melting of a polymer there will necessarily occur a rearrangement of the molecules in the transformation from ordered to disordered molecular states. Molecular chemistry and structure will influence the ability of the polymer chain molecules to make these rearrangements, and, therefore, will also affect the melting temperature.

Chain stiffness, which is controlled by the ease of rotation about the chemical bonds along the chain, has a pronounced effect. The presence of double-chain bonds and aromatic groups lowers chain flexibility and causes an increase in T_m. Furthermore, the size and type of side groups influence chain rotational freedom and flexibility; bulky or large side groups tend to restrict molecular rotation, and

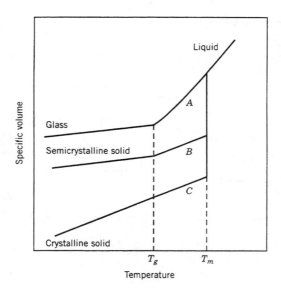

FIGURE 16.8 Specific volume versus temperature, upon cooling from the liquid melt, for totally amorphous (curve A), semicrystalline (curve B), and crystalline (curve C) polymers.

raise T_m. For example, polypropylene has a higher melting temperature than polyethylene (175°C versus 115°C, Table 16.2); the CH_3 methyl side group for polypropylene is larger than the H atom found on polyethylene. The presence of polar side groups (viz. Cl, OH, and CN), even though not excessively large, leads to significant intermolecular bonding forces, and relatively high T_ms. This may be verified by comparing the melting temperatures of polypropylene (175°C) and polyvinyl chloride (212°C).

For a specific polymer, melting temperature will also depend on molecular weight. At relatively low molecular weights, increasing $\overline{M}$ (or chain length) raises T_m (Figure 16.9). Furthermore, the melting of a polymer takes place over a range of temperatures, and, thus, there will exist a range of T_ms, rather than a single melting temperature. This is because, every polymer will be composed of molecules having a variety of molecular weights (Section 15.5), and because T_m depends on molecular weight. For most polymers, this melting temperature range will normally be on the order of several degrees Celsius. Those melting temperatures cited in Table 16.2 and Appendix C.11 are near the high ends of these ranges.

Table 16.2   Melting and Glass Transition Temperatures for Some of the More Common Polymeric Materials

Material	Glass Transition Temperature [°C (°F)]	Melting Temperature [°C (°F)]
Polyethylene (low density)	−110 (−165)	115 (240)
Polytetrafluoroethylene	−97 (−140)	327 (620)
Polyethylene (high density)	−90 (−130)	137 (279)
Polypropylene	−18 (0)	175 (347)
Nylon 6,6	57 (135)	265 (510)
Polyester (PET)	69 (155)	265 (510)
Polyvinyl chloride	87 (190)	212 (415)
Polystyrene	100 (212)	240 (465)
Polycarbonate	150 (300)	265 (510)

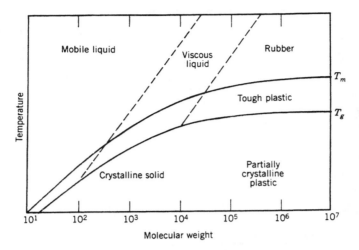

FIGURE 16.9
Dependence of polymer properties as well as melting and glass transition temperatures on molecular weight. (From F. W. Billmeyer, Jr., *Textbook of Polymer Science*, 3rd edition. Copyright © 1984 by John Wiley & Sons, New York. Reprinted by permission of John Wiley & Sons, Inc.)

Degree of branching will also affect the melting temperature of a polymer. The introduction of side branches introduces defects into the crystalline material and lowers the melting temperature. High-density polyethylene, being a predominately linear polymer, has a higher melting temperature (137°C, Table 16.2) than low-density polyethylene (115°C) which has some branching.

Glass Transition Temperature

Upon heating through the glass transition temperature, the amorphous solid polymer transforms from a rigid to a rubbery state. Correspondingly, the molecules which are virtually frozen in position below T_g begin to experience rotational and translational motions above T_g. Thus, the value of the glass transition temperature will depend on molecular characteristics that affect chain stiffness; most of these factors and their influences are the same as for the melting temperature, as discussed above. Again, chain flexibility is diminished and T_g is increased by the following:

1. The presence of bulky side groups; from Table 16.2, the respective values for polypropylene and polystyrene are −18°C and 100°C.
2. Polar side atoms or groups of atoms; this may be confirmed by comparing T_g values for polyvinyl chloride and polypropylene (87°C versus −18°C).
3. Double-chain bonds and aromatic chain groups which tend to stiffen the molecular backbone.

Increasing the molecular weight also tends to raise the glass transition temperature, as noted in Figure 16.9. A small amount of branching will tend to lower T_g; on the other hand, a high density of branches reduces chain mobility, and elevates the glass transition temperature. Some amorphous polymers are crosslinked, which has been observed to elevate T_g; crosslinks restrict molecular motion. With a high density of crosslinks, molecular motion is virtually disallowed; long-range molecular motion is prevented, to the degree that these polymers do not experience a glass transition or its accompanying softening.

From the preceding discussion it is evident that essentially the same molecular characteristics raise and lower both melting and glass transition temperatures; normally the value of T_g lies somewhere between 0.5 and $0.8T_m$. Consequently, for a homopolymer, it is not possible to independently vary both T_m and T_g. A greater degree of control over these two parameters is possible by the synthesis and utilization of copolymeric materials.

16.5 THERMOPLASTIC AND THERMOSETTING POLYMERS

One classification scheme of polymeric materials is according to the mechanical response at elevated temperatures. *Thermoplasts* (or **thermoplastic polymers**) and *thermosets* (or **thermosetting polymers**) are the two subdivisions. Thermoplasts soften when heated (and eventually liquefy) and harden when cooled—processes that are totally reversible and may be repeated. These materials are normally fabricated by the simultaneous application of heat and pressure. On a molecular level, as the temperature is raised, secondary bonding forces are diminished (by increased molecular motion) so that the relative movement of adjacent chains is facilitated when a stress is applied. Irreversible degradation results when the temperature of a molten thermoplastic polymer is raised to the point at which molecular vibrations become violent enough to break the primary covalent bonds. In addition, thermoplasts are relatively soft and ductile. Most linear polymers and those having some branched structures with flexible chains are thermoplastic.

Thermosetting polymers become permanently hard when heat is applied and do not soften upon subsequent heating. During the initial heat treatment, covalent crosslinks are formed between adjacent molecular chains; these bonds anchor the chains together to resist the vibrational and rotational chain motions at high temperatures. Crosslinking is usually extensive, in that 10 to 50% of the chain mer units are crosslinked. Only heating to excessive temperatures will cause severance of these crosslink bonds and polymer degradation. Thermoset polymers are generally harder, stronger, and more brittle, than thermoplastics, and have better dimensional stability. Most of the crosslinked and network polymers, which include vulcanized rubbers, epoxies, and phenolic and polyester resins, are thermosetting.

16.6 VISCOELASTICITY

We know that an amorphous polymer may behave like a glass at low temperatures, a rubbery solid at intermediate temperatures (above the glass transition temperature), and a viscous liquid as the temperature is further raised. For relatively small deformations, the mechanical behavior at low temperatures may be elastic; that is, in conformity to Hooke's law, $\sigma = E\epsilon$. At the highest temperatures, viscous, or liquidlike behavior, prevails. For intermediate temperatures is found a rubbery solid that exhibits the combined mechanical characteristics of these two extremes; the condition is termed **viscoelasticity.**

Elastic deformation is instantaneous, which means that total deformation (or strain) occurs the instant the stress is applied or released (i.e., the strain is independent of time). In addition, upon release of the external stress, the deformation is totally recovered—the specimen assumes its original dimensions. This behavior is represented in Figure 16.10b as strain versus time for the instantaneous load–time curve, shown in Figure 16.10a.

By way of contrast, for totally viscous behavior, deformation or strain is not instantaneous; that is, in response to an applied stress, deformation is delayed or dependent on time. Also, this deformation is not reversible or completely recovered after the stress is released. This phenomenon is demonstrated in Figure 16.10d.

FIGURE 16.10 (a)
Load versus time,
where load is applied
instantaneously at time
t_a and released at t_r.
For the load–time cycle
in (a), the strain-versus-
time responses are for
totally elastic (b),
viscoelastic (c), and
viscous (d) behavior.

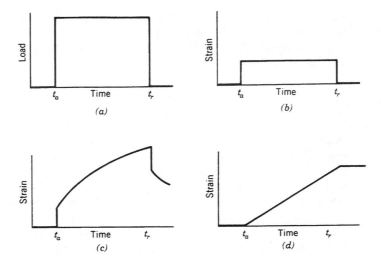

For the intermediate viscoelastic behavior, the imposition of a stress in the manner of Figure 16.10a results in an instantaneous elastic strain, which is followed by a viscous, time-dependent strain, a form of anelasticity (Section 6.4); this behavior is illustrated in Figure 16.10c.

A familiar example of these viscoelastic extremes is found in a silicone polymer that is sold as a novelty and known by some as "silly putty." When rolled into a ball and dropped onto a horizontal surface, it bounces elastically—the rate of deformation during the bounce is very rapid. On the other hand, if pulled in tension with a gradually increasing applied stress, the material elongates or flows like a highly viscous liquid. For this and other viscoelastic materials, the rate of strain determines whether the deformation is elastic or viscous.

VISCOELASTIC RELAXATION MODULUS

The viscoelastic behavior of polymeric materials is dependent on both time and temperature; several experimental techniques may be used to measure and quantify this behavior. *Stress relaxation* measurements represent one possibility. With these tests, a specimen is initially strained rapidly in tension to a predetermined and relatively low strain level. The stress necessary to maintain this strain is measured as a function of time, while temperature is held constant. Stress is found to decrease with time due to molecular relaxation processes that take place within the polymer. We may define a **relaxation modulus** $E_r(t)$, a time-dependent elastic modulus for viscoelastic polymers, as

$$E_r(t) = \frac{\sigma(t)}{\epsilon_0} \tag{16.1}$$

where $\sigma(t)$ is the measured time-dependent stress and ϵ_0 is the strain level, which is maintained constant.

Furthermore, the magnitude of the relaxation modulus is a function of temperature; and to more fully characterize the viscoelastic behavior of a polymer, isothermal stress relaxation measurements must be conducted over a range of temperatures. Figure 16.11 is a schematic log $E_r(t)$-versus-log time plot for a polymer that exhibits viscoelastic behavior; included are several curves generated at a variety of tempera-

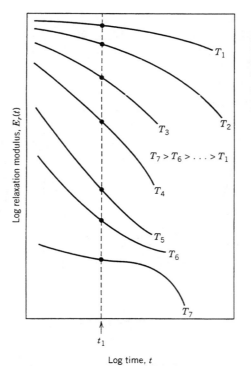

FIGURE 16.11 Schematic plot of logarithm of relaxation modulus versus logarithm of time for a viscoelastic polymer; isothermal curves are generated at temperatures T_1 through T_7. The temperature dependence of the relaxation modulus is represented as log $E_r(t_1)$ versus temperature.

tures. Worth noting from this figure are (1) the decrease of $E_r(t)$ with time (corresponding to the decay of stress, Equation 16.1), and (2) the displacement of the curves to lower $E_r(t)$ levels with increasing temperature.

To represent the influence of temperature, data points are taken at a specific time from the log $E_r(t)$-versus-log time plot—for example, t_1 in Figure 16.11—and then cross-plotted as log $E_r(t_1)$ versus temperature. Figure 16.12 is such a plot for an amorphous (atactic) polystyrene; in this case, t_1 was arbitrarily taken 10 s after the load application. Several distinct regions may be noted on the curve shown in this figure. For the first, at the lowest temperatures, in the glassy region, the material is rigid and brittle, and the value of $E_r(10)$ is that of the elastic modulus, which initially is virtually independent of temperature. Over this temperature range, the strain–time characteristics are as represented in Figure 16.10b. On a molecular level, the long molecular chains are essentially frozen in position at these temperatures.

As the temperature is increased, $E_r(10)$ drops abruptly by about a factor of 10^3 within a 20°C (35°F) temperature span; this is sometimes called the leathery, or glass transition, region, and T_g lies near the upper temperature extremity; for polystyrene (Figure 16.12), $T_g = 100$°C (212°F). Within this temperature region, a polymer specimen will be leathery; that is, deformation will be time dependent and not totally recoverable on release of an applied load, characteristics depicted in Figure 16.10c.

Within the rubbery plateau temperature region (Figure 16.12), the material deforms in a rubbery manner; here, both elastic and viscous components are present, and deformation is easy to produce because the relaxation modulus is relatively low.

The final two high-temperature regions are rubbery flow and viscous flow. Upon heating through these temperatures, the material experiences a gradual transition to a soft rubbery state, and finally to a viscous liquid. Within the viscous flow region,

FIGURE 16.12 Logarithm of the relaxation modulus versus temperature for amorphous polystyrene, showing the five different regions of viscoelastic behavior. (From A. V. Tobolsky, *Properties and Structures of Polymers.* Copyright © 1960 by John Wiley & Sons, New York. Reprinted by permission of John Wiley & Sons, Inc.)

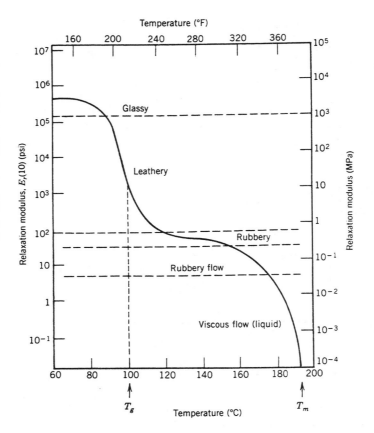

the modulus decreases dramatically with increasing temperature; and, again, the strain–time behavior is as represented in Figure 16.10d. From a molecular standpoint, chain motion intensifies so greatly that for viscous flow, the chain segments experience vibration and rotational motion quite independently of one another. At these temperatures, any deformation is entirely viscous.

Normally, the deformation behavior of a viscous polymer is specified in terms of viscosity, a measure of a material's resistance to flow by shear forces. Viscosity is discussed for the inorganic glasses in Section 13.9.

The rate of stress application also influences the viscoelastic characteristics. Increasing the loading rate has the same influence as lowering temperature.

The log $E_r(10)$-versus-temperature behavior for polystyrene materials having several molecular configurations is plotted in Figure 16.13. The curve for the amorphous material (curve C) is the same as in Figure 16.12. For a lightly crosslinked atactic polystyrene (curve B), the rubbery region forms a plateau that extends to the temperature at which the polymer decomposes; this material will not experience melting. For increased crosslinking, the magnitude of the plateau $E_r(10)$ value will also increase. Rubber or elastomeric materials display this type of behavior and are ordinarily utilized at temperatures within this plateau range.

Also shown in Figure 16.13 is the temperature dependence for an almost totally crystalline isotactic polystyrene (curve A). The decrease in $E_r(10)$ at T_g is much less pronounced than the other polystyrene materials since only a small volume fraction of this material is amorphous and experiences the glass transition. Furthermore, the relaxation modulus is maintained at a relatively high value with increasing

FIGURE 16.13 Logarithm of the relaxation modulus versus temperature for crystalline isotactic (curve A), lightly crosslinked atactic (curve B), and amorphous (curve C) polystyrene. (From A. V. Tobolsky, *Properties and Structures of Polymers.* Copyright © 1960 by John Wiley & Sons, New York. Reprinted by permission of John Wiley & Sons, Inc.)

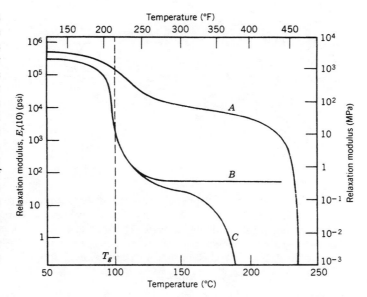

temperature until its melting temperature T_m is approached. From Figure 16.13, the melting temperature of this isotactic polystyrene is about 240°C (460°F).

VISCOELASTIC CREEP

Many polymeric materials are susceptible to time-dependent deformation when the stress level is maintained constant; such deformation is termed *viscoelastic creep.* This type of deformation may be significant even at room temperature and under modest stresses which lie below the yield strength of the material. For example, automobile tires may develop flat spots on their contact surfaces when the automobile is parked for prolonged time periods. Creep tests on polymers are conducted in the same manner as for metals (Chapter 8); that is, a stress (normally tensile) is applied instantaneously, which is maintained at a constant level while strain is measured as a function of time. Furthermore, the tests are performed under isothermal conditions. Creep results are represented as a time-dependent *creep modulus* $E_c(t)$, defined by

$$E_c(t) = \frac{\sigma_0}{\epsilon(t)} \tag{16.2}$$

wherein σ_0 is the constant applied stress and $\epsilon(t)$ is the time-dependent strain. The creep modulus is also temperature sensitive and diminishes with increasing temperature.

With regard to the influence of molecular structure on the creep characteristics, as a general rule the susceptibility to creep decreases [i.e., $E_c(t)$ increases] as the degree of crystallinity increases.

16.7 DEFORMATION OF ELASTOMERS

One of the fascinating properties of the elastomeric materials is their rubberlike elasticity. That is, they have the ability to be deformed to quite large deformations, and then elastically spring back to their original form. This behavior was probably first observed in natural rubber; however, the past few years have brought about

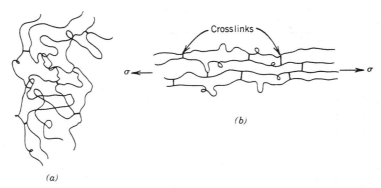

FIGURE 16.14 Schematic representation of crosslinked polymer chain molecules (a) in an unstressed state and (b) during elastic deformation in response to an applied tensile stress. (Adapted from Z. D. Jastrzebski, *The Nature and Properties of Engineering Materials,* 3rd edition. Copyright © 1987 by John Wiley & Sons, New York. Reprinted by permission of John Wiley & Sons, Inc.)

the synthesis of a large number of elastomers with a wide variety of properties. Typical stress–strain characteristics of elastomeric materials are displayed in Figure 16.1, curve C. Their moduli of elasticity are quite small and, furthermore, vary with strain since the stress–strain curve is nonlinear.

In an unstressed state, an elastomer will be amorphous and composed of molecular chains that are highly twisted, kinked, and coiled. Elastic deformation, upon application of a tensile load, is simply the partial uncoiling, untwisting, and straightening, and the resultant elongation of the chains in the stress direction, a phenomenon represented in Figure 16.14. Upon release of the stress, the chains spring back to their prestressed conformations, and the macroscopic piece returns to its original shape.

The driving force for elastic deformation is a thermodynamic parameter called *entropy,* which is a measure of the degree of disorder within a system; entropy increases with increasing disorder. As an elastomer is stretched and the chains straighten and become more aligned, the system becomes more ordered. From this state, the entropy increases if the chains return to their original kinked and coiled contours. Two intriguing phenomena result from this entropic effect. First, when stretched, an elastomer experiences a rise in temperature; second, the modulus of elasticity increases with increasing temperature, which is opposite to the behavior found in other materials (see Figure 6.7).

Several criteria must be met in order for a polymer to be elastomeric: (1) It must not easily crystallize; elastomeric materials are amorphous, having molecular chains that are naturally coiled and kinked in the unstressed state. (2) Chain bond rotations must be relatively free in order for the coiled chains to readily respond to an applied force. (3) For elastomers to experience relatively large elastic deformations, the onset of plastic deformation must be delayed. Restricting the motions of chains past one another by crosslinking accomplishes this objective. The crosslinks act as anchor points between the chains and prevent chain slippage from occurring; the role of crosslinks in the deformation process is illustrated in Figure 16.14. Crosslinking in many elastomers is carried out in a process called vulcanization, to be discussed in Section 16.14. (4) Finally, the elastomer must be above its glass transition temperature. The lowest temperature at which rubberlike behavior persists is T_g (Figure 16.12), which for many of the common elastomers is between -50 and $-90°C$ (-60 and $-130°F$). Below its glass transition temperature, an elastomer becomes brittle such that its stress–strain behavior resembles curve A in Figure 16.1.

16.8 FRACTURE OF POLYMERS

The fracture strengths of polymeric materials are low relative to those of metals and ceramics. As a general rule, the mode of fracture in thermosetting polymers is brittle. In simple terms, associated with the fracture process is the formation of cracks at regions where there is a localized stress concentration (i.e., scratches, notches, and sharp flaws). Covalent bonds in the network or crosslinked structure are severed during fracture.

For thermoplastic polymers, both ductile and brittle modes are possible, and many of these materials are capable of experiencing a ductile-to-brittle transition. Factors that favor brittle fracture are a reduction in temperature, an increase in strain rate, the presence of a sharp notch, increased specimen thickness, and, in addition, a modification of the polymer structure (chemical, molecular, and/or microstructural). Glassy thermoplastics are brittle at relatively low temperatures; as the temperature is raised, they become ductile in the vicinity of their glass transition temperatures and experience plastic yielding prior to fracture. This behavior is demonstrated by the stress–strain characteristics of polymethyl methacrylate in Figure 16.3. At 4°C, PMMA is totally brittle, whereas at 60°C it becomes extremely ductile.

One phenomenon that frequently precedes fracture in some glassy thermoplastic polymers is *crazing*. Associated with crazes are regions of very localized yielding, which lead to the formation of small and interconnected microvoids (Figure 16.15a). Fibrillar bridges form between these microvoids wherein molecular chains become oriented. If the applied tensile load is sufficient, these bridges elongate and break, causing the microvoids to grow and coalesce; as the microvoids coalesce, cracks begin to form, as demonstrated in Figure 16.15b. A craze is different from a crack in that it can support a load across its face. Furthermore, this process of craze growth prior to cracking absorbs fracture energy and effectively increases the fracture toughness of the polymer. Crazes form at highly stressed regions associated

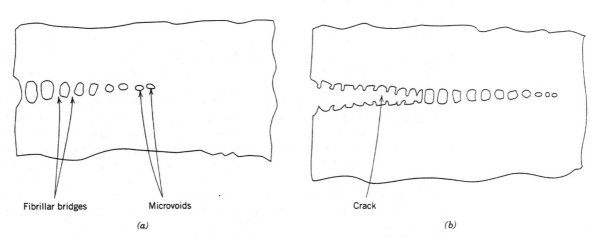

Fibrillar bridges   Microvoids   Crack

(a)   (b)

FIGURE 16.15   Schematic drawings of (a) a craze showing microvoids and fibrillar bridges, and (b) a craze followed by a crack. (From J. W. S. Hearle, *Polymers and Their Properties*, Vol. 1, *Fundamentals of Structure and Mechanics*, Ellis Horwood, Ltd., Chichester, West Sussex, England, 1982.)

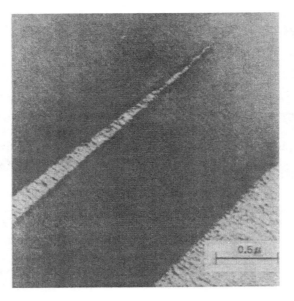

FIGURE 16.16 Photomicrograph of a craze in polyphenylene oxide. (From R. P. Kambour and R. E. Robertson, "The Mechanical Properties of Plastics," in *Polymer Science, A Materials Science Handbook*, A. D. Jenkins, Editor. Reprinted with permission of Elsevier Science Publishers.)

with scratches, flaws, and molecular inhomogeneities; in addition, they propagate perpendicular to the applied tensile stress, and typically are 5 μm or less thick. Figure 16.16 is a photomicrograph in which a craze is shown.

Principles of fracture mechanics developed in Section 8.5 also apply to brittle and quasi-brittle polymers; the susceptibility of these materials to fracture when a crack is present may be expressed in terms of the plane strain fracture toughness. The magnitude of K_{Ic} will depend on characteristics of the polymer (i.e., molecular weight, percent crystallinity, etc.) as well as temperature, strain rate, and the external environment. Representative values of K_{Ic} for several polymers are included in Table 8.1 and Appendix C.5.

16.9 MISCELLANEOUS CHARACTERISTICS

IMPACT STRENGTH

The degree of resistance of a polymeric material to impact loading of a notched piece may be of concern in some applications. Izod or Charpy tests are ordinarily conducted to assess impact strength. As with metals, polymers may exhibit ductile or brittle fracture under impact loading conditions, depending on the temperature, specimen size, strain rate, and mode of loading, as discussed in the preceding section. Both crystalline and amorphous polymers are brittle at low temperatures, and both have relatively low impact strengths. However, they experience a ductile-to-brittle transition over a relatively narrow temperature range, similar to that shown for a steel in Figure 8.17. Of course, impact strength undergoes a gradual decrease at still higher temperatures as the polymer begins to soften. Ordinarily, the two impact characteristics most sought after are a high impact strength at the ambient temperature and a ductile-to-brittle transition temperature that lies below room temperature.

FATIGUE

Polymers may experience fatigue failure under conditions of cyclic loading. As with metals, fatigue occurs at stress levels that are low relative to the yield strength.

FIGURE 16.17 Fatigue curves (stress amplitude versus the number of cycles to failure) for polyethylene terephthalate (PET), nylon, polystyrene (PS), polymethyl methacrylate (PMMA), polypropylene (PP), polyethylene (PE), and polytetrafluoroethylene (PTFE). The testing frequency was 30 Hz. (From M. N. Riddell, "A Guide to Better Testing of Plastics," *Plast. Eng.,* Vol. 30, No. 4, p. 78, 1974.)

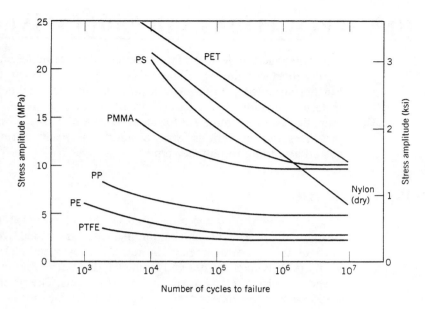

Fatigue testing in polymers has not been nearly as extensive as with metals; however, fatigue data are plotted in the same manner for both types of material, and the resulting curves have the same general shape. Fatigue curves for several common polymers are shown in Figure 16.17, as stress versus the number of cycles to failure (on a logarithmic scale). Some polymers have a fatigue limit (a stress level at which the stress at failure becomes independent of the number of cycles); others do not appear to have such a limit. As would be expected, fatigue strengths and fatigue limits for polymeric materials are much lower than for metals.

The fatigue behavior of polymers is much more sensitive to loading frequency than for metals. Cycling polymers at high frequencies and/or relatively large stresses can cause localized heating; consequently, failure may be due to a softening of the material rather than as a result of typical fatigue processes.

TEAR STRENGTH AND HARDNESS

Other mechanical properties that are sometimes influential in the suitability of a polymer for some particular application include tear resistance and hardness. The ability to resist tearing is an important property of some plastics, especially those used for thin films in packaging. *Tear strength,* the mechanical parameter that is measured, is the energy required to tear apart a cut specimen that has a standard geometry. The magnitude of tensile and tear strengths are related.

As with metals, hardness represents a material's resistance to scratching, penetration, marring, and so on. Polymers are softer than metals and ceramics, and most hardness tests are conducted by penetration techniques similar to those described for metals in Section 6.10. Rockwell tests are frequently used for polymers.[2] Other indentation techniques employed are the Durometer and Barcol.[3]

---

[2] ASTM Standard D 785, "Rockwell Hardness of Plastics and Electrical Insulating Materials."

[3] ASTM Standard D 2240, "Standard Test Method for Rubber Property—Durometer Hardness;" and ASTM Standard D 2583, "Standard Test Method for Indentation of Rigid Plastics by Means of a Barcol Impressor."

POLYMER APPLICATIONS AND PROCESSING

The large macromolecules of the commercially useful polymers must be synthesized from substances having smaller molecules in a process termed polymerization. Furthermore, the properties of a polymer may be modified and enhanced by the inclusion of additive materials. Finally, a finished piece having a desired shape must be fashioned during a forming operation. This section treats polymerization processes and the various forms of additives; specific forming procedures are discussed according to polymer type.

16.10 POLYMERIZATION

The synthesis of the large molecular weight polymers is termed *polymerization;* it is simply the process by which monomer units are joined over and over, to generate each of the constituent giant molecules. Most generally, the raw materials for synthetic polymers are derived from coal and petroleum products, which are composed of molecules having low molecular weights. The reactions by which polymerization occurs are grouped into two general classifications—addition and condensation—according to the reaction mechanism, as discussed below.

ADDITION POLYMERIZATION

Addition polymerization (sometimes called chain reaction polymerization) is a process by which bifunctional monomer units are attached one at a time in chainlike fashion to form a linear macromolecule; the composition of the resultant product molecule is an exact multiple for that of the original reactant monomer.

Three distinct stages—initiation, propagation, and termination—are involved in addition polymerization. During the initiation step, an active center capable of propagation is formed by a reaction between an initiator (or catalyst) species and the monomer unit. This process has already been demonstrated for polyethylene (Equation 15.1), which is repeated as follows:

$$
\text{R}\cdot + \begin{array}{c} \text{H} \ \ \text{H} \\ | \ \ \ | \\ \text{C}=\text{C} \\ | \ \ \ | \\ \text{H} \ \ \text{H} \end{array} \longrightarrow \text{R}-\begin{array}{c} \text{H} \ \ \text{H} \\ | \ \ \ | \\ \text{C}-\text{C} \\ | \ \ \ | \\ \text{H} \ \ \text{H} \end{array}\cdot \tag{16.3}
$$

Again, R· represents the active initiator, and · is an unpaired electron.

Propagation involves the linear growth of the molecule as monomer units become attached to one another in succession to produce the chain molecule, which is represented, again for polyethylene, as follows:

$$
\text{R}-\begin{array}{c} \text{H} \ \ \text{H} \\ | \ \ \ | \\ \text{C}-\text{C} \\ | \ \ \ | \\ \text{H} \ \ \text{H} \end{array}\cdot + \begin{array}{c} \text{H} \ \ \text{H} \\ | \ \ \ | \\ \text{C}=\text{C} \\ | \ \ \ | \\ \text{H} \ \ \text{H} \end{array} \longrightarrow \text{R}-\begin{array}{c} \text{H} \ \ \text{H} \ \ \text{H} \ \ \text{H} \\ | \ \ \ | \ \ \ | \ \ \ | \\ \text{C}-\text{C}-\text{C}-\text{C} \\ | \ \ \ | \ \ \ | \ \ \ | \\ \text{H} \ \ \text{H} \ \ \text{H} \ \ \text{H} \end{array}\cdot \tag{16.4}
$$

Chain growth is relatively rapid; the period required to grow a molecule consisting of, say, 1000 mer units is on the order of 10^{-2} to 10^{-3} s.

Propagation may end or terminate in different ways. First, the active ends of two propagating chains may react or link together to form a nonreactive molecule, as follows:

$$
R----\underset{\overset{|}{H}}{\overset{\overset{|}{H}}{C}}-\underset{\overset{|}{H}}{\overset{\overset{|}{H}}{C}}-\underset{\overset{|}{H}}{\overset{\overset{|}{H}}{C}}-\underset{\overset{|}{H}}{\overset{\overset{|}{H}}{C}}\cdot \;+\; \cdot\underset{\overset{|}{H}}{\overset{\overset{|}{H}}{C}}-\underset{\overset{|}{H}}{\overset{\overset{|}{H}}{C}}-\underset{\overset{|}{H}}{\overset{\overset{|}{H}}{C}}-\underset{\overset{|}{H}}{\overset{\overset{|}{H}}{C}}----R \longrightarrow
$$

$$
R----\underset{\overset{|}{H}}{\overset{\overset{|}{H}}{C}}-\underset{\overset{|}{H}}{\overset{\overset{|}{H}}{C}}-\underset{\overset{|}{H}}{\overset{\overset{|}{H}}{C}}-\underset{\overset{|}{H}}{\overset{\overset{|}{H}}{C}}-\underset{\overset{|}{H}}{\overset{\overset{|}{H}}{C}}-\underset{\overset{|}{H}}{\overset{\overset{|}{H}}{C}}-\underset{\overset{|}{H}}{\overset{\overset{|}{H}}{C}}-\underset{\overset{|}{H}}{\overset{\overset{|}{H}}{C}}----R \quad (16.5)
$$

thus terminating the growth of each chain. Or, an active chain end may react with an initiator or other chemical species having a single active bond, as follows:

$$
-\underset{\overset{|}{H}}{\overset{\overset{|}{H}}{C}}-\underset{\overset{|}{H}}{\overset{\overset{|}{H}}{C}}-\underset{\overset{|}{H}}{\overset{\overset{|}{H}}{C}}-\underset{\overset{|}{H}}{\overset{\overset{|}{H}}{C}}\cdot \;+\; \cdot R \longrightarrow -\underset{\overset{|}{H}}{\overset{\overset{|}{H}}{C}}-\underset{\overset{|}{H}}{\overset{\overset{|}{H}}{C}}-\underset{\overset{|}{H}}{\overset{\overset{|}{H}}{C}}-\underset{\overset{|}{H}}{\overset{\overset{|}{H}}{C}}-R \quad (16.6)
$$

with the resultant cessation of chain growth.

Molecular weight is governed by the relative rates of initiation, propagation, and termination. Ordinarily, they are controlled to ensure the production of a polymer having the desired degree of polymerization. Since termination is a somewhat random process and does not occur at the same point for each molecule, a variety of chain lengths is achieved, which accounts for a distribution of molecular weights.

Addition polymerization is used in the synthesis of polyethylene, polypropylene, polyvinyl chloride, and polystyrene, as well as many of the copolymers.

CONDENSATION POLYMERIZATION

Condensation (or step reaction) **polymerization** is the formation of polymers by stepwise intermolecular chemical reactions that normally involve more than one monomer species; there is usually a small molecular weight by-product such as water, which is eliminated. No reactant species has the chemical formula of the mer repeat unit, and the intermolecular reaction occurs every time a mer repeat unit is formed. For example, consider the formation of a polyester from the reaction between ethylene glycol and adipic acid; the intermolecular reaction is as follows:

$$
+ H_2O \quad (16.7)
$$

This stepwise process is successively repeated, producing, in this case, a linear molecule. The chemistry of the specific reaction is not important, but rather, the condensation polymerization mechanism.

Reaction times for condensation are generally longer than for addition polymerization. To produce large molecular weight materials, it is essential that the reaction times be sufficiently long and the conversion of the monomer reactants complete. As with addition polymerization, various chain lengths are produced, yielding a molecular weight distribution.

Condensation reactions often produce trifunctional monomers capable of forming crosslinked and network polymers. The thermosetting polyesters and phenolformaldehyde, the nylons, and the polycarbonates are produced by condensation polymerization. Some polymers, such as nylon, may be polymerized by either technique.

16.11 POLYMER ADDITIVES

Most of the properties of polymers discussed earlier in this chapter are intrinsic ones—that is, characteristic of or fundamental to the specific polymer. Some of these properties are related to and controlled by the molecular structure. Many times, however, it is necessary to modify the mechanical, chemical, and physical properties to a much greater degree than is possible by the simple alteration of this fundamental molecular structure. Foreign substances called *additives* are intentionally introduced to enhance or modify many of these properties, and thus render a polymer more serviceable. Typical additives include filler materials, plasticizers, stabilizers, colorants, and flame retardants.

FILLERS

Filler materials are most often added to polymers to improve tensile and compressive strengths, abrasion resistance, toughness, dimensional and thermal stability, and other properties. Materials used as particulate fillers include wood flour (finely powdered sawdust), silica flour and sand, glass, clay, talc, limestone, and even some synthetic polymers. Particle sizes range all the way from 10 nm to macroscopic dimensions. Because these inexpensive materials replace some volume of the more expensive polymer, the cost of the final product is reduced.

PLASTICIZERS

The flexibility, ductility, and toughness of polymers may be improved with the aid of additives called **plasticizers.** Their presence also produces reductions in hardness and stiffness. Plasticizers are generally liquids having low vapor pressures and low molecular weights. The small plasticizer molecules occupy positions between the large polymer chains, effectively increasing the interchain distance with a reduction in the secondary intermolecular bonding. Plasticizers are commonly used in polymers that are intrinsically brittle at room temperature, such as polyvinyl chloride and some of the acetate copolymers. In effect, the plasticizer lowers the glass transition temperature, so that at ambient conditions the polymers may be used in applications requiring some degree of pliability and ductility. These applications include thin sheets or films, tubing, raincoats, and curtains.

STABILIZERS

Some polymeric materials, under normal environmental conditions, are subject to rapid deterioration, generally in terms of mechanical integrity. Most often, this deterioration is a result of exposure to light, in particular ultraviolet radiation, and also oxidation (Section 18.12). Ultraviolet radiation interacts with, and causes a severance of some of the covalent bonds along the molecular chain which may also result in some crosslinking. Oxidation deterioration is a consequence of the chemical interaction between oxygen atoms and the polymer molecules. Additives that counteract these deteriorative processes are called **stabilizers.**

COLORANTS

Colorants impart a specific color to a polymer; they may be added in the form of dyes or pigments. The molecules in a dye actually dissolve and become part of the molecular structure of the polymer. Pigments are filler materials that do not dissolve, but remain as a separate phase; normally they have a small particle size, are transparent, and have a refractive index near to that of the parent polymer. Others may impart opacity as well as color to the polymer.

FLAME RETARDANTS

The flammability of polymeric materials is a major concern, especially in the manufacture of textiles and children's toys. Most polymers are flammable in their pure form; exceptions include those containing significant contents of chlorine and/or fluorine, such as polyvinyl chloride and polytetrafluoroethylene. The flammability resistance of the remaining combustible polymers may be enhanced by additives called **flame retardants.** These retardants may function by interfering with the combustion process through the gas phase, or by initiating a chemical reaction that causes a cooling of the combustion region and a cessation of burning.

16.12 POLYMER TYPES

There are many different polymeric materials that are familiar to us and find a wide variety of applications. These include plastics, elastomers (or rubbers), fibers, coatings, adhesives, foams, and films. Depending on its properties, a particular polymer may be used in two or more of these application categories. For example, a plastic, if crosslinked and utilized above its glass transition temperature, may make a satisfactory elastomer. Or, a fiber material may be used as a plastic if it is not drawn into filaments. This portion of the chapter includes a brief discussion of each of these types of polymer. In addition, for each, some of the common fabrication methods are noted.

16.13 PLASTICS

CHARACTERISTICS AND APPLICATIONS

Possibly the largest number of different polymeric materials come under the plastic classification. Polyethylene, polypropylene, polyvinyl chloride, polystyrene, and the fluorocarbons, epoxies, phenolics, and polyesters may all be classified as **plastics.** They have a wide variety of combinations of properties. Some plastics are very rigid and brittle; others are flexible, exhibiting both elastic and plastic deformations when stressed, and sometimes experiencing considerable deformation before fracture.

Polymers falling within this classification may have any degree of crystallinity, and all molecular structures and configurations (linear, branched, isotactic, etc.) are possible. Plastic materials may be either thermoplastic or thermosetting; in fact, this is the manner in which they are usually subclassified. The trade names,

Table 16.3 Trade Names, Characteristics, and Typical Applications for a Number of Plastic Materials

Material Type	Trade Names	Major Application Characteristics	Typical Applications
		Thermoplastics	
Acrylonitrile-butadiene-styrene (ABS)	Abson Cycolac Kralastic Lustran Novodur Tybrene	Outstanding strength and toughness, resistant to heat distortion; good electrical properties; flammable and soluble in some organic solvents	Refrigerator linings, lawn and garden equipment, toys, highway safety devices
Acrylics (poly-methyl methac-rylate)	Acrylite Diakon Lucite Plexiglas	Outstanding light transmission and resistance to weathering; only fair mechanical properties	Lenses, transparent aircraft enclosures, drafting equipment, outdoor signs
Fluorocarbons (PTFE or TFE)	Teflon Fluon Halar Halon Hostaflon TF	Chemically inert in almost all environments, excellent electrical properties; low coefficient of friction; may be used to 260°C (500°F); relatively weak and poor cold-flow properties	Anticorrosive seals, chemical pipes and valves, bearings, antiadhesive coatings, high-temperature electronic parts
Polyamides (nylons)	Nylon Durethan Herox Nomex Ultramid Zytel	Good mechanical strength, abrasion resistance, and toughness; low coefficient of friction; absorbs water and some other liquids	Bearings, gears, cams, bushings, handles, and jacketing for wires and cables
Polycarbonates	Baylon Iupilon Lexan Makrolon Merlon Nuclon	Dimensionally stable; low water absorption; transparent; very good impact resistance and ductility; chemical resistance not outstanding	Safety helmets, lenses, light globes, base for photographic film
Polyethylene	Alathon Alkathene Ethron Fortiflex Hi-fax Petrothene Rigidex Zendel	Chemically resistant, and electrically insulating; tough and relatively low coefficient of friction; low strength and poor resistance to weathering	Flexible bottles, toys, tumblers, battery parts, ice trays, film wrapping materials
Polypropylene	Bexphane Herculon Meraklon Moplen Poly-pro Pro-fax Propathene	Resistant to heat distortion; excellent electrical properties and fatigue strength; chemically inert; relatively inexpensive; poor resistance to UV light	Sterilizable bottles, packaging film, TV cabinets, luggage
Polystyrene	Carinex Celatron Hostyren Lustrex Styron Vestyron	Excellent electrical properties and optical clarity; good thermal and dimensional stability; relatively inexpensive	Wall tile, battery cases, toys, indoor lighting panels, appliance housings

Table 16.3 (Continued)

Material Type	Trade Names	Major Application Characteristics	Typical Applications
Vinyls	Darvic Exon Geon Pee Vee Cee Pliovic Saran Tygon	Good low-cost, general-purpose materials; ordinarily rigid, but may be made flexible with plasticizers; often copolymerized; susceptible to heat distortion	Floor coverings, pipe, electrical wire insulation, garden hose, phonograph records
Polyester (PET or PETE)	Celanar Crastin Dacron Hylar Melinex Mylar Terylem	One of the toughest of plastic films; excellent fatigue and tear strength, and resistance to humidity, acids, greases, oils, and solvents	Magnetic recording tapes, clothing, automotive tire cords, beverage containers
Thermosetting Polymers			
Epoxies	Araldite Epikote Epon Epi-rez Lekutherm Nepoxide	Excellent combination of mechanical properties and corrosion resistance; dimensionally stable; good adhesion; relatively inexpensive; good electrical properties	Electrical moldings, sinks, adhesives, protective coatings, used with fiberglass laminates
Phenolics	Bakelite Amberol Arofene Durite Resinox	Excellent thermal stability to over 150°C (300°F); may be compounded with a large number of resins, fillers, etc.; inexpensive	Motor housings, telephones, auto distributors, electrical fixtures
Polyesters	Aropol Baygal Derakane Laguval Laminac Selectron	Excellent electrical properties and low cost; can be formulated for room- or high-temperature use; often fiber reinforced	Helmets, fiberglass boats, auto body components, chairs, fans

Source: Adapted from C. A. Harper, Editor, *Handbook of Plastics and Elastomers.* Copyright © 1975 by McGraw-Hill Book Company. Reproduced with permission.

characteristics, and typical applications for a number of plastics are given in Table 16.3.

Several plastics exhibit especially outstanding properties. For applications in which optical transparency is critical, polystyrene and polymethyl methacrylate are especially well suited; however, it is imperative that the material be highly amorphous. The fluorocarbons have a low coefficient of friction and are extremely resistant to attack by a host of chemicals, even at relatively high temperatures. They are utilized as coatings on nonstick cookware, in bearings and bushings, and for high-temperature electronic components.

FORMING TECHNIQUES

Quite a variety of different techniques are employed in the forming of polymeric materials. The method used for a specific polymer depends on several factors: (1) whether the material is thermoplastic or thermosetting; (2) if thermoplastic, the temperature at which it softens; (3) the atmospheric stability of the material being formed; and (4) the geometry and size of the finished product. There are numerous similarities between some of these techniques and those utilized for fabricating metals and ceramics.

Fabrication of polymeric materials normally occurs at elevated temperatures and often by the application of pressure. Thermoplastics are formed above their glass transition temperatures, and an applied pressure must be maintained as the piece is cooled so that the formed article will retain its shape. One significant economic benefit of using thermoplastics is that they may be recycled; scrap thermoplastic pieces may be remelted and reformed into new shapes.

Fabrication of thermosetting polymers is ordinarily accomplished in two stages. First comes the preparation of a linear polymer (sometimes called a prepolymer) as a liquid, having a low molecular weight. This material is converted into the final hard and stiff product during the second stage, which is normally carried out in a mold having the desired shape. This second stage, termed "curing," may occur during heating and/or by the addition of catalysts, and often under pressure. During curing, chemical and structural changes occur on a molecular level: a crosslinked or a network structure forms. After curing, thermoset polymers may be removed from a mold while still hot, since they are now dimensionally stable. Thermosets cannot be recycled, do not melt, are usable at higher temperatures than thermoplastics, and are more chemically inert.

Molding is the most common method for forming plastic polymers. The several molding techniques used include compression, transfer, blow, injection, and extrusion molding. For each, a finely pelletized or granulized plastic is forced, at an elevated temperature and by pressure, to flow into, fill, and assume the shape of a mold cavity.

Compression and Transfer Molding

For compression molding, the appropriate amounts of thoroughly mixed polymer and necessary additives are placed between male and female mold members, as illustrated in Figure 16.18. Both mold pieces are heated; however, only one is movable. The mold is closed, and heat and pressure are applied, causing the plastic material to become viscous and conform to the mold shape. Before molding, raw materials may be mixed and cold pressed into a disc, which is called a preform. Preheating of the preform reduces molding time and pressure, extends the die

Figure 16.18 Schematic diagram of a compression molding apparatus. (From F. W. Billmeyer, Jr., *Textbook of Polymer Science,* 3rd edition. Copyright © 1984 by John Wiley & Sons, New York. Reprinted by permission of John Wiley & Sons, Inc.)

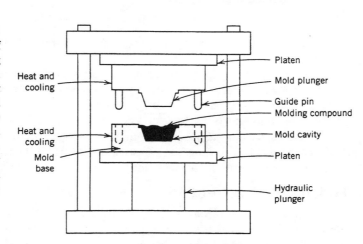

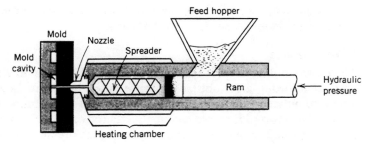

FIGURE 16.19 Schematic diagram of an injection molding apparatus. (Adapted from F. W. Billmeyer, Jr., *Textbook of Polymer Science,* 2nd edition. Copyright © 1971 by John Wiley & Sons, New York. Reprinted by permission of John Wiley & Sons, Inc.)

lifetime, and produces a more uniform finished piece. This molding technique lends itself to the fabrication of both thermoplastic and thermosetting polymers; however, its use with thermoplastics is more time consuming and expensive.

In transfer molding, a variation of compression molding, the solid ingredients are first melted in a heated transfer chamber. As the molten material is injected into the mold chamber, the pressure is distributed more uniformly over all surfaces. This process is used with thermosetting polymers and for pieces having complex geometries.

Injection Molding

Injection molding, the polymer analogue of die casting for metals, is the most widely used technique for fabricating thermoplastic materials. A schematic cross section of the apparatus used is illustrated in Figure 16.19. The correct amount of pelletized material is fed from a loading hopper into a cylinder by the motion of a plunger or ram. This charge is pushed forward into a heating chamber, at which point the thermoplastic material melts to form a viscous liquid. Next, the molten plastic is impelled, again by ram motion, through a nozzle into the enclosed mold cavity; pressure is maintained until the molding has solidified. Finally, the mold is opened, the piece is ejected, the mold is closed, and the entire cycle is repeated. Probably the most outstanding feature of this technique is the speed with which pieces may be produced. For thermoplastics, solidification of the injected charge is almost immediate; consequently, cycle times for this process are short (commonly within the range of 10 to 30 s). Thermosetting polymers may also be injection molded; curing takes place while the material is under pressure in a heated mold, which results in longer cycle times than for thermoplastics. This process is sometimes termed reaction injection molding (RIM).

Extrusion

The extrusion process is simply injection molding of a viscous thermoplastic through an open-ended die, similar to the extrusion of metals (Figure 12.2c). A mechanical screw or auger propels through a chamber the pelletized material, which is successively compacted, melted, and formed into a continuous charge of viscous fluid. Extrusion takes place as this molten mass is forced through a die orifice. Solidification of the extruded length is expedited by blowers or a water spray just before passing onto a moving conveyor. The technique is especially adapted to producing continuous lengths having constant cross-sectional geometries, for example, rods, tubes, hose channels, sheets, and filaments.

Blow Molding

The blow molding process for the fabrication of plastic containers is similar to that used for blowing glass bottles, as represented in Figure 14.5. First, a parison, or length of polymer tubing is extruded. While still in a semimolten state, the parison is placed in a two-piece mold having the desired container configuration. The hollow piece is formed by blowing air or steam under pressure into the parison, forcing the tube walls to conform to the contours of the mold. Of course the temperature and viscosity of the parison must be carefully regulated.

Casting

Like metals and ceramics, polymeric materials may be cast, as when a molten plastic material is poured into a mold and allowed to solidify. Both thermoplastic and thermosetting plastics may be cast. For thermoplastics, solidification occurs upon cooling from the molten state; however, for thermosets, hardening is a consequence of the actual polymerization or curing process, which is usually carried out at an elevated temperature.

16.14 ELASTOMERS

The characteristics of and deformation mechanism for elastomers were treated previously (Section 16.7). The present discussion, therefore, focuses on the processing and types of elastomeric materials.

VULCANIZATION

One requisite characteristic for elastomeric behavior is that the molecular structure be lightly crosslinked. The crosslinking process in elastomers is called **vulcanization,** which is achieved by a nonreversible chemical reaction, ordinarily carried out at an elevated temperature. In most vulcanizing reactions, sulfur compounds are added to the heated elastomer; sulfur atoms bond with adjacent chains and crosslink them. Sulfur bridge crosslinks are formed in polyisoprene according to the following reaction:

$$
\begin{array}{ll}
\begin{array}{c}
\text{H CH}_3\ \text{H}\ \ \text{H}\\
\,|\ \ \ |\ \ \ |\ \ \ \ |\\
-\text{C}-\text{C}=\text{C}-\text{C}-\\
\,|\ \ \ \ \ \ \ \ \ \ \ |\\
\text{H}\ \ \ \ \ \ \ \ \ \ \text{H}
\end{array}
&
\begin{array}{c}
\text{H CH}_3\ \text{H}\ \ \text{H}\\
\,|\ \ \ |\ \ \ |\ \ \ \ |\\
-\text{C}-\text{C}-\text{C}-\text{C}-\\
\,|\ \ \ \ |\ \ \ \ |\\
\text{H}\ \ \ \ \text{S}\ \ \ \text{S}\ \ \text{H}
\end{array}
\end{array}
$$

$$+\ 2\text{S}\ \longrightarrow \tag{16.8}$$

Unvulcanized rubber is soft and tacky, and has poor resistance to abrasion. Modulus of elasticity, tensile strength, and resistance to degradation by oxidation are all enhanced by vulcanization. The magnitude of the modulus of elasticity is directly proportional to the density of the crosslinks. Stress–strain curves for vulcanized and unvulcanized natural rubber are presented in Figure 16.20. To produce a

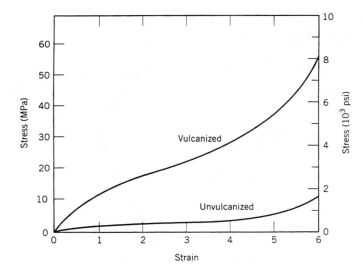

FIGURE 16.20
FIGURE 16.20
Stress–strain curves to
600% elongation for
unvulcanized and
vulcanized natural
rubber.

rubber that is capable of large extensions without rupture of the primary chain bonds, there must be relatively few crosslinks, and these must be widely separated. Useful rubbers result when about 1 to 5 parts (by weight) of sulfur is added to 100 parts of rubber. Increasing the sulfur content further hardens the rubber and also reduces its extensibility. Also, since they are crosslinked, elastomeric materials are thermosetting in nature.

ELASTOMERIC TYPES

Table 16.4 lists properties and applications of common elastomers; these properties are typical and, of course, depend on the degree of vulcanization and on whether any reinforcement is used. Natural rubber is still utilized to a large degree because it has an outstanding combination of desirable properties. However, the most important synthetic elastomer is SBR, which is used predominantly in automobile tires, reinforced with carbon black. NBR, which is highly resistant to degradation and swelling, is another common synthetic elastomer.

For many applications (e.g., automobile tires), the mechanical properties of even vulcanized rubbers are not satisfactory in terms of tensile strength, abrasion and tear resistance, and stiffness. These characteristics may be further improved by additives such as carbon black (Section 17.2). Furthermore, the techniques used in the actual fabrication of rubber parts are essentially the same as those discussed for plastics as described above, that is, compression molding, extrusion, and so on.

Finally, some mention should be made of the silicone rubbers. For these materials, the backbone carbon chain is replaced by a chain that alternates silicon and oxygen atoms:

$$
\begin{array}{c}
R \\
| \\
-Si-O- \\
| \\
R'
\end{array}
$$

where R and R' represent side-bonded atoms such as hydrogen or groups of atoms such as CH_3. For example, polydimethylsiloxane has the mer structure

Table 16.4 Tabulation of Important Characteristics and Typical Applications for Five Commercial Elastomers

Chemical Type	Trade (Common) Name	Elongation (%)	Useful Temperature Range [°C (°F)]	Major Application Characteristics	Typical Applications
Natural poly-isoprene	Natural Rubber (NR)	500–760	−60 to 120 (−75 to 250)	Excellent physical properties; good resistance to cutting, gouging, and abrasion; low heat, ozone, and oil resistance; good electrical properties	Pneumatic tires and tubes; heels and soles; gaskets
Styrene–butadiene copolymer	GRS, Buna S (SBR)	450–500	−60 to 120 (−75 to 250)	Good physical properties; excellent abrasion resistance; not oil, ozone, or weather resistant; electrical properties good, but not outstanding	Same as natural rubber
Acrylonitrile–butadiene copolymer	Buna A, Nitrile (NBR)	400–600	−50 to 150 (−60 to 300)	Excellent resistance to vegetable, animal, and petroleum oils; poor low-temperature properties; electrical properties not outstanding	Gasoline, chemical, and oil hose; seals and O-rings; heels and soles
Chloroprene	Neoprene (CR)	100–800	−50 to 105 (−60 to 225)	Excellent ozone, heat, and weathering resistance; good oil resistance; excellent flame resistance; not as good in electrical applications as natural rubber	Wire and cable; chem. tank linings; belts, hoses, seals, and gaskets
Polysiloxane	Silicone (VMQ)	100–800	−115 to 315 (−175 to 600)	Excellent resistance to high and low temperatures; low strength; excellent electrical properties	High- and low-temperature insulation; seals, diaphragms; tubing for food and medical uses

Sources: Adapted from: C. A. Harper, Editor, *Handbook of Plastics and Elastomers.* Copyright © 1975 by McGraw-Hill Book Company, reproduced with permission; and Materials Engineering's *Materials Selector,* copyright Penton/IPC.

$$
\begin{array}{c}
CH_3 \\
| \\
-Si-O- \\
| \\
CH_3
\end{array}
$$

Of course, as elastomers, these materials are crosslinked.

The silicone elastomers possess a high degree of flexibility at low temperatures [to −90°C (−130°F)] and yet are stable to temperatures as high as 250°C (480°F). In addition, they are resistant to weathering and lubricating oils. A further attractive characteristic is that some silicone rubbers vulcanize at room temperature (RTV rubbers).

16.15 FIBERS

CHARACTERISTICS AND APPLICATIONS

The **fiber** polymers are capable of being drawn into long filaments having at least a 100:1 length-to-diameter ratio. Most commercial fiber polymers are utilized in the textile industry, being woven or knit into cloth or fabric. In addition, the aramid fibers are employed in composite materials, Section 17.8. To be useful as a textile material, a fiber polymer must meet a host of rather restrictive physical and chemical properties. While in use, fibers may be subjected to a variety of mechanical deformations—stretching, twisting, shearing, and abrasion. Consequently, they must have a high tensile strength (over a relatively wide temperature range) and a high modulus of elasticity, as well as abrasion resistance. These properties are governed by the chemistry of the polymer chains and also by the fiber drawing process.

The molecular weight of fiber materials should be relatively high. Also, since the tensile strength increases with degree of crystallinity, the structure and configuration of the chains should allow the production of a highly crystalline polymer; that translates into a requirement for linear and unbranched chains that are symmetrical and have regularly repeating mer units.

Convenience in washing and maintaining clothing depends primarily on the thermal properties of the fiber polymer, that is, its melting and glass transition temperatures. Furthermore, fiber polymers must exhibit chemical stability to a rather extensive variety of environments, including acids, bases, bleaches, dry cleaning solvents, and sunlight. In addition, they must be relatively nonflammable and amenable to drying.

FORMING TECHNIQUES

The process by which fibers are formed from bulk polymer material is termed **spinning.** Most often, fibers are spun from the molten state in a process called melt spinning. The material to be spun is first heated until it forms a relatively viscous liquid. Next, it is pumped down through a plate called a spinnerette, which contains numerous small, round holes. As the molten material passes through each of these orifices, a single fiber is formed, which solidifies almost immediately upon passing into the air.

The crystallinity of a spun fiber will depend on its rate of cooling during spinning. The strength of fibers is improved by a postforming process called **drawing.** Drawing is simply the mechanical elongation of a fiber in the direction of its axis. During this process the molecular chains become oriented in the direction of drawing (Section 16.3), such that the tensile strength, modulus of elasticity, and toughness are improved. Although the mechanical strength of a drawn fiber is improved in this axial direction, strength is reduced in a transverse or radial direction. However, since fibers are normally stressed only along the axis, this strength differential is not critical. The cross section of drawn fibers is nearly circular, and the properties are uniform throughout the cross section.

16.16 MISCELLANEOUS APPLICATIONS

COATINGS

Coatings are frequently applied to the surface of materials to serve one or more of the following functions: (1) to protect the item from the environment that may produce corrosive or deteriorative reactions; (2) to improve the item's appearance; and (3) to provide electrical insulation. Many of the ingredients in coating materials are polymers, the majority of which are organic in origin. These organic coatings fall into several different classifications, as follows: paint, varnish, enamel, lacquer, and shellac.

ADHESIVES

An **adhesive** is a substance used to join together the surfaces of two solid materials (termed "adherends") to produce a joint with a high shear strength. The bonding forces between the adhesive and adherend surfaces are thought to be electrostatic, similar to the secondary bonding forces between the molecular chains in thermoplastic polymers. Even though the inherent strength of the adhesive may be much less than that of the adherend materials, nevertheless, a strong joint may be produced if the adhesive layer is thin and continuous. If a good joint is formed, the adherend material may fracture or rupture before the adhesive.

Polymeric materials that fall within the classifications of thermoplastics, thermosetting resins, elastomeric compounds, and natural adhesives (animal glue, casein, starch, and rosin) may serve adhesive functions. Polymer adhesives may be used to join a large variety of material combinations: metal–metal, metal–plastic, metal–ceramic, and so on. The primary drawback is the service temperature limitation. Organic polymers maintain their mechanical integrity only at relatively low temperatures, and strength decreases rapidly with increasing temperature.

FILMS

Within relatively recent times, polymeric materials have found widespread use in the form of thin *films*. Films having thicknesses between 0.001 and 0.005 in. (0.025 and 0.125 mm) are fabricated and used extensively as bags for packaging food products and other merchandise, as textile products, and a host of other uses. Important characteristics of the materials produced and used as films include low density, a high degree of flexibility, high tensile and tear strengths, resistance to attack by moisture and other chemicals, and low permeability to some gases, especially water vapor. Some of the polymers that meet these criteria and are manufactured in film form are polyethylene, polypropylene, cellophane, and cellulose acetate.

There are several forming methods. Many films are simply extruded through a thin die slit; this may be followed by a rolling operation that serves to reduce thickness and improve strength. Alternatively, film may be blown: continuous tubing is extruded through an annular die; then, by maintaining a carefully controlled positive gas pressure inside the tube, wall thickness may be continuously reduced to produce a thin cylindrical film, which may be cut and laid flat. Some of the newer films are produced by coextrusion; that is, multilayers of more than one polymer type are extruded simultaneously.

FOAMS

Very porous plastic materials are produced in a process called foaming. Both thermoplastic and thermosetting materials may be foamed by including in the batch a blowing agent that upon heating, decomposes with the liberation of a gas. Gas bubbles are generated throughout the now-fluid mass, which remain as pores upon cooling and give rise to a spongelike structure. The same effect is produced by bubbling an inert gas through a material while it is in a molten state. Some of the commonly foamed polymers are polyurethane, rubber, polystyrene, and polyvinyl chloride. **Foams** are commonly used as cushions in automobiles and furniture as well as in packaging and thermal insulation.

16.17 ADVANCED POLYMERIC MATERIALS

A number of new polymers having unique and desirable combinations of properties have been developed over the past several years; many have found niches in new technologies and/or have satisfactorily replaced other materials. Some of these include ultrahigh molecular weight polyethylene, liquid crystal polymers, and thermoplastic elastomers. Each of these will now be discussed.

ULTRAHIGH MOLECULAR WEIGHT POLYETHYLENE

Ultrahigh molecular weight polyethylene (*UHMWPE*) is a linear polyethylene that has an extremely high molecular weight. Its typical $\overline{M}_w$ is approximately 4×10^6 g/mol, which is an order of magnitude (i.e., factor of ten) greater than that of high-density polyethylene. Some of the extraordinary characteristics of this material are as follows:

1. An extremely high impact resistance.
2. Outstanding resistance to wear and abrasion.
3. A very low coefficient of friction.
4. A self-lubricating and nonstick surface.
5. Very good chemical resistance.
6. Excellent low-temperature properties.
7. Outstanding sound damping and energy absorption characteristics.
8. Electrically insulating and excellent dielectric properties.

However, since this material has a relatively low melting temperature, its mechanical properties diminish rapidly with increasing temperature.

This unusual combination of properties leads to numerous and diverse applications for this material, including: bullet-proof vests, composite military helmets, fishing line, ski bottom surfaces, golf ball cores, bowling alley and ice skating rink surfaces, biomedical prostheses (Section 23.8), blood filters, marking pen nibs, bulk material handling equipment (for coal, grain, cement, gravel, etc.), bushings, pump impellers, and valve gaskets.

LIQUID CRYSTAL POLYMERS

The **liquid crystal polymers** (*LCP*s) are a group of chemically complex and structurally distinct materials that have unique properties and are utilized in diverse applications. Discussion of the chemistry of these materials is beyond the scope of this book. Suffice it to say that LCPs are composed of extended, rod-shaped, and rigid molecules. In terms of molecular arrangement, these materials do not fall within any of conventional liquid, amorphous, crystalline, semicrystalline classifications, but may be considered as a new state of matter—the liquid crystalline state, being neither crystalline nor liquid. In the melt (or liquid) condition, whereas other polymer molecules are randomly oriented, LCP molecules can become aligned in highly ordered configurations. As solids, this molecular alignment remains, and, in addition, the molecules form in domain structures having characteristic intermolecular spacings. A schematic comparison of liquid crystals, amorphous polymers, and semicrystalline polymers in both melt and solid states is illustrated in Figure 16.21. Furthermore, there are three types of liquid crystals, based on orientation and

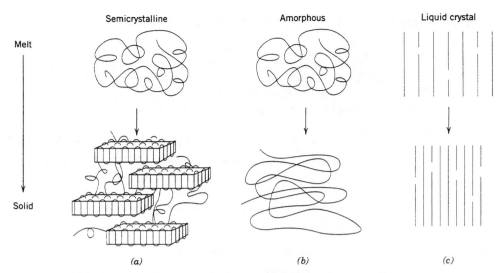

FIGURE 16.21 Schematic representations of the molecular structures in both melt and solid states for (*a*) semicrystalline, (*b*) amorphous, and (*c*) liquid crystal polymers. (Adapted from G. W. Calundann and M. Jaffe, "Anisotropic Polymers, Their Synthesis and Properties," Chapter VII in *Proceedings of the Robert A. Welch Foundation Conferences on Polymer Research*, 26th Conference, Synthetic Polymers, Nov. 1982.)

positional ordering—smectic, nematic, and cholesteric; distinctions between these types is also beyond the scope of this discussion.

The principal use of liquid crystal polymers is in *liquid crystal displays* (*LCD*s), on digital watches, laptop computers, and for other digital displays. Here cholesteric types of LCPs are employed which, at room temperature, are fluid liquids, transparent, and optically anisotropic. The displays are composed of two sheets of glass between which is sandwiched the liquid crystal material. The outer face of each glass sheet is coated with a transparent and electrically conductive film; in addition, into this film on the side that is to be viewed is etched the character-forming number/letter elements. A voltage applied through the conductive films (and thus between these two glass sheets) over one of these character-forming regions causes a disruption of the orientation of the LCP molecules in this region, a darkening of this LCP material, and, in turn, the formation of a visible character.

Some of the nematic type of liquid crystal polymers are rigid solids at room temperature and, on the basis of an outstanding combination of properties and processing characteristics, have found widespread use in a variety of commercial applications. For example, these materials exhibit the following behaviors:

1. Excellent thermal stability; they may be used to temperatures as high as 230°C (450°F).

2. Stiff and strong; their tensile moduli range between 10 and 24 GPa (1.4×10^6 and 3.5×10^6 psi), while tensile strengths are from 125 to 255 MPa (18,000 to 37,000 psi).

3. High impact strengths, which are retained upon cooling to relatively low temperatures.

4. Chemical inertness to a wide variety of acids, solvents, bleaches, etc.

5. Inherent flame resistance and combustion products that are relatively nontoxic.

The following may be said about their processing and fabrication characteristics:

1. All conventional processing techniques available for thermoplastic materials may be used.

2. Extremely low shrinkage and warpage during molding.

3. Exceptional dimensional repeatability from part to part.

4. Low melt viscosity, which permits molding of thin sections and/or complex shapes.

5. Low heats of fusion; this results in rapid melting and subsequent cooling, which shortens molding cycle times.

6. Anisotropic finished-part properties; molecular orientation effects are produced from melt flow during molding.

These materials are used extensively by the electronics industry (interconnect devices, relay and capacitor housings, brackets, etc.), by the medical equipment industry (in components to be repeatedly sterilized), and in photocopiers and fiber-optic components.

THERMOPLASTIC ELASTOMERS

The **thermoplastic elastomers** (*TPEs* or *TEs*) are a type of polymeric material that, at ambient conditions, exhibits elastomeric (or rubbery) behavior, yet is thermoplastic in nature (Section 16.5). By way of contrast, most elastomers heretofore discussed are thermosets, since they become crosslinked during vulcanization. Of the several varieties of TPEs, one of the best known and widely used is a block copolymer consisting of block segments of a hard and rigid thermoplastic mer (commonly styrene [S]), and a soft and flexible elastic mer (often butadiene [B] or isoprene [I]). These two block types alternate positions—for a common molecule, hard polymerized segments are located at chain ends, whereas the soft central region consists of polymerized butadiene or isoprene units. These TPEs are frequently termed *styrenic block copolymers,* and chain chemistries for the two (S-B-S and S-I-S) types are shown in Figure 16.22.

At ambient temperatures, the soft, amorphous, central (butadiene or isoprene) segments impart the rubbery, elastomeric behavior to the material. Furthermore, for temperatures below the T_m of the hard (styrene) component, hard chain-end

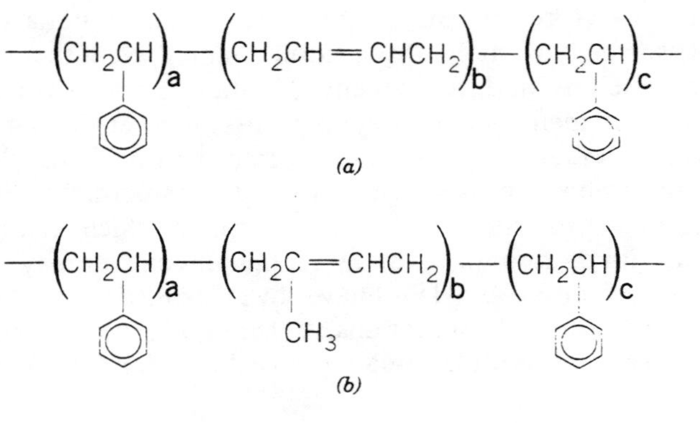

FIGURE 16.22
Representations of the chain chemistries for (*a*) styrene-butadiene-styrene (S-B-S), and (*b*) styrene-isoprene-styrene (S-I-S) thermoplastic elastomers.

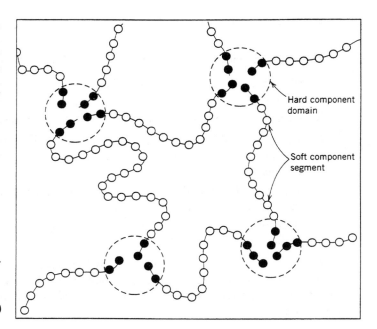

Hard component domain

Soft component segment

segments from numerous adjacent chains aggregate together to form rigid domain regions. These domains are "physical crosslinks" that act as anchor points so as to restrict soft-chain segment motions; they function in much the same way as "chemical crosslinks" for the thermoset elastomers. In Figure 16.23 is presented a schematic illustration for the structure of this TPE type.

The tensile modulus of this TPE material is subject to alteration; increasing the number of soft-component blocks per chain will lead to a decrease in modulus and, therefore, a diminishment of stiffness. Furthermore, the useful temperature range lies between T_g of the soft and flexible component and T_m of the hard, rigid one; for the styrenic block copolymers this range is between about $-70°C$ ($-95°F$) and $100°C$ ($212°F$).

In addition to the styrenic block copolymers, there are other types of TPEs, including thermoplastic olefins, copolyesters, thermoplastic polyurethanes, and elastomeric polyamides.

The chief advantage of the TPEs over the thermoset elastomers is that upon heating above T_m of the hard phase, they melt (i.e., the physical crosslinks disappear), and, therefore, they may be processed by conventional thermoplastic forming techniques (e.g., blow molding, injection molding, etc.); thermoset polymers do not experience melting, and, consequently, forming is normally more difficult. Furthermore, since the melting-solidification process is reversible and repeatable for thermoplastic elastomers, TPE parts may be reformed into other shapes. In other words, they are recyclable; thermoset elastomers are nonrecyclable. Scrap that is generated during forming procedures may also be recycled, which results in lower production costs than with thermosets. In addition, tighter controls may be maintained on part dimensions for TPEs, and TPEs have lower densities.

In quite a variety of applications, the thermoplastic elastomers have replaced the conventional thermoset elastomers. Typical uses for the TPEs include automotive exterior trim (bumpers, fascia, etc.), automotive underhood components (electrical insulation and connectors, and gaskets), shoe soles and heels, sporting goods, appliance parts, medical devices, and as components in sealants, caulking, and adhesives.

SUMMARY

On the basis of stress–strain behavior, polymers fall within three general classifications: brittle, plastic, and highly elastic. These materials are neither as strong nor as stiff as metals, and their mechanical properties are sensitive to changes in temperature.

The mechanism of plastic deformation for semicrystalline polymers having the spherulitic structure was presented. Tensile deformation is thought to occur in several stages as both amorphous tie chains and chain-folded block segments (which separate from the ribbonlike lamellae) become oriented with the tensile axis. The strength of these materials may be enhanced by radiation-induced crosslinking, and by both increased crystallinity and average molecular weight.

The molecular mechanics of crystallization, melting, and the glass transition were discussed. The manner in which melting and glass transition temperatures are determined was outlined; these parameters are important relative to the temperature range over which a particular polymer may be utilized and processed. The magnitudes of T_m and T_g increase with increasing chain stiffness; stiffness is enhanced by the presence of chain double bonds and side groups that are either bulky or polar. Molecular weight and degree of branching also affect T_m and T_g.

With regard to mechanical behavior at elevated temperatures, polymers are classified as either thermoplastic or thermosetting. The former soften when heated and harden when cooled; this cycle is reversible and repeatable. In contrast, thermosets, once having hardened, will not soften upon heating.

Viscoelastic mechanical behavior, being intermediate between totally elastic and totally viscous, is displayed by a number of polymeric materials. It is characterized by the relaxation modulus, a time-dependent modulus of elasticity. The magnitude of the relaxation modulus is very sensitive to temperature; critical to the in-service temperature range for elastomers is this temperature dependence.

Large elastic extensions are possible for the elastomeric materials that are amorphous and lightly crosslinked. Deformation corresponds to the unkinking and uncoiling of chains in response to an applied tensile stress. Crosslinking is often achieved during a vulcanization process. Many of the elastomers are copolymers, whereas the silicone elastomers are really inorganic materials.

Fracture strengths of polymeric materials are low relative to metals and ceramics. Both brittle and ductile fracture modes are possible, and some thermoplastic materials experience a ductile-to-brittle transition with a lowering of temperature, an increase in strain rate, and/or an alteration of specimen thickness or geometry. In some glassy thermoplastics, the crack formation process may be preceded by crazing; crazing can lead to an increase in ductility and toughness of the material.

Synthesis of large molecular weight polymers is attained by polymerization, of which there are two types: addition and condensation. The various properties of polymers may be further modified by using additives; these include fillers, plasticizers, stabilizers, colorants, and flame retardants.

The plastic materials are perhaps the most widely used group of polymers. Fabrication is usually accomplished by plastic deformation at an elevated temperature, using at least one of several different molding techniques; casting is also possible.

Many polymeric materials may be spun into fibers, which are used primarily in textiles. Mechanical, thermal, and chemical characteristics of these materials are especially critical. Some fibers are spun from a viscous melt, after which they are plastically elongated during a drawing operation, which improves the mechanical strength.

Other miscellaneous applications that employ polymers include coatings, adhesives, films, and foams.

This chapter concluded with discussions of three advanced polymeric materials—ultrahigh molecular weight polyethylene, liquid crystal polymers, and thermoplastic elastomers. These materials have unusual properties and are used in a host of high-technology applications.

IMPORTANT TERMS AND CONCEPTS

Addition polymerization	Foam	Stabilizer
Adhesive	Glass transition temperature	Thermoplastic polymer
Colorant	Liquid crystal polymer	Thermoplastic elastomer
Condensation polymerization	Molding	Thermosetting polymer
Drawing	Plasticizer	Ultrahigh molecular weight
Elastomer	Plastic	polyethylene
Fiber	Relaxation modulus	Viscoelasticity
Filler	Spinning	Vulcanization
Flame retardant		

REFERENCES

Billmeyer, F. W., Jr., *Textbook of Polymer Science,* 3rd edition, Wiley-Interscience, New York, 1984.

Engineered Materials Handbook, Vol. 2, *Engineering Plastics,* ASM International, Metals Park, OH, 1988.

Harper, C. A. (Editor), *Handbook of Plastics, Elastomers and Composites,* 2nd edition, McGraw-Hill Book Company, New York, 1992.

McClintock, F. A. and A. S. Argon, *Mechanical Behavior of Materials,* Addison-Wesley Publishing Company, Reading, MA, 1966.

Modern Plastics Encyclopedia, McGraw-Hill Book Company, New York. Revised and published annually.

Moore, G. R. and D. E. Kline, *Properties and Processing of Polymers for Engineers,* Prentice-Hall, Inc., Englewood Cliffs, NJ, 1984.

Muccio, E. A., *Plastic Part Technology,* ASM International, Materials Park, OH, 1991.

Muccio, E. A., *Plastics Processing Technology,* ASM International, Materials Park, OH, 1994.

Nielsen, L. E., *Mechanical Properties of Polymers and Composites,* 2nd edition, Marcel Dekker, New York, 1994.

Rosen, S. L., *Fundamental Principles of Polymeric Materials,* 2nd edition, John Wiley & Sons, New York, 1993.

Rudin, A., *The Elements of Polymer Science and Engineering: An Introductory Text for Engineers and Chemists,* Academic Press, New York, 1982.

Seymour, R. B. and C. E. Carraher, Jr., *Polymer Chemistry, An Introduction,* 3rd edition, Marcel Dekker, Inc., New York, 1992.

Tobolsky, A. V., *Properties and Structures of Polymers,* John Wiley & Sons, New York, 1960. Advanced treatment.

Williams, D. J., *Polymer Science and Engineering,* Prentice-Hall, Englewood Cliffs, NJ, 1971.

QUESTIONS AND PROBLEMS

16.1 From the stress–strain data for polymethyl methacrylate shown in Figure 16.3, determine the modulus of elasticity and tensile strength at room temperature [20°C (68°F)], and compare these values with those given in Table 16.1.

16.2 In your own words, describe the mechanisms by which **(a)** semicrystalline polymers plastically deform and **(b)** elastomers elastically deform.

16.3 Briefly explain how each of the following influences the mechanical strength of a semicrystalline polymer and why:

(a) molecular weight;

(b) degree of crystallinity; and

(c) extent of crosslinking.

16.4 Normal butane and isobutane have boiling temperatures of −0.5 and −12.3°C (31.1 and 9.9°F), respectively. Briefly explain this behavior on the basis of their molecular structures, as presented in Section 15.2.

16.5 For each of the following pairs of polymers, do the following: (1) state whether or not it is possible to decide if one polymer has a higher tensile strength than the other; (2) if this is possible, note which has the higher tensile strength and then cite the reason(s) for your choice; and (3) if it is not possible to decide, then state why.

(a) Syndiotactic polystyrene having a number-average molecular weight of 600,000 g/mol; atactic polystyrene having a number-average molecular weight of 500,000 g/mol.

(b) Random acrylonitrile-butadiene copolymer with 10% of possible sites crosslinked; block acrylonitrile-butadiene copolymer with 5% of possible sites crosslinked.

(c) Network polyester; lightly branched polypropylene.

16.6 Would you expect the tensile strength of polychlorotrifluoroethylene to be greater than, the same as, or less than that of a polytetrafluoroethylene specimen having the same molecular weight and degree of crystallinity? Why?

16.7 For each of the following pairs of polymers, plot and label schematic stress–strain curves on the same graph (i.e., make separate plots for parts a, b, c, and d).

(a) Isotactic and linear polypropylene having a weight-average molecular weight of 120,000 g/mol; atactic and linear polypropylene having a weight-average molecular weight of 100,000 g/mol.

(b) Branched polyvinyl chloride having a number-average degree of polymerization of 2000; heavily crosslinked polyvinyl chloride having a number-average degree of polymerization of 2000.

(c) Poly(styrene-butadiene) random copolymer having a number-average molecular weight of 100,000 g/mol and 10% of the available sites crosslinked and tested at 20°C; poly(styrene-butadiene) random copolymer having a number-average molecular weight of 120,000 g/mol and 15% of the available sites crosslinked and tested at −85°C. Hint: poly(styrene-butadiene) copolymers may exhibit elastomeric behavior.

(d) Polyisoprene, molecular weight of 100,000 g/mol having 10% of available sites crosslinked; polyisoprene, molecular weight of 100,000 g/mol having 20% of available sites crosslinked. Hint: polyisoprene is a natural rubber that may display elastomeric behavior.

16.8 When citing the ductility as percent elongation for semicrystalline polymers, it is not necessary to specify the specimen gauge length, as is the case with metals. Why is this so?

16.9 For each of the following pairs of polymers, plot and label schematic specific volume-versus-temperature curves on the same graph (i.e., make separate plots for parts a, b, and c):

(a) Spherulitic polypropylene, of 25% crystallinity, and having a weight-average molecular weight of 75,000 g/mol; spherulitic polystyrene, of 25% crystallinity, and having a weight-average molecular weight of 100,000 g/mol.

(b) Graft poly(styrene-butadiene) copolymer with 10% of available sites crosslinked;

random poly(styrene-butadiene) copolymer with 15% of available sites crosslinked.

(c) Polyethylene having a density of 0.985 g/cm^3 and a number-average degree of polymerization of 2500; polyethylene having a density of 0.915 g/cm^3 and a degree of polymerization of 2000.

16.10 For each of the following pairs of polymers, do the following: (1) state whether or not it is possible to determine whether one polymer has a higher melting temperature than the other; (2) if it is possible, note which has the higher melting temperature and then cite reason(s) for your choice; and (3) if it is not possible to decide, then state why.

(a) Isotactic polystyrene that has a density of 1.12 g/cm^3 and a weight-average molecular weight of 150,000 g/mol; syndiotactic polystyrene that has a density of 1.10 g/cm^3 and a weight-average molecular weight of 125,000 g/mol.

(b) Linear polyethylene that has a number-average degree of polymerization of 5,000; linear and isotactic polypropylene that has a number-average degree of polymerization of 6,500.

(c) Branched and isotactic polystyrene that has a weight-average degree of polymerization of 4,000; linear and isotactic polypropylene that has a weight-average degree of polymerization of 7,500.

16.11 Make a schematic plot showing how the modulus of elasticity of an amorphous polymer depends on the glass transition temperature. Assume that molecular weight is held constant.

16.12 Name the following polymer(s) that would be suitable for the fabrication of cups to contain hot coffee: polyethylene, polypropylene, polyvinyl chloride, PET polyester, and polycarbonate. Why?

16.13 Of those polymers listed in Table 16.2, which polymer(s) would be best suited for use as ice cube trays? Why?

16.14 Make comparisons of thermoplastic and thermosetting polymers (a) on the basis of mechanical characteristics upon heating, and (b) according to possible molecular structures.

16.15 Some of the polyesters may be either thermoplastic or thermosetting. Suggest one reason for this.

16.16 (a) Is it possible to grind up and reuse phenol-formaldehyde? Why or why not?

(b) Is it possible to grind up and reuse polypropylene? Why or why not?

16.17 In your own words, briefly describe the phenomenon of viscoelasticity.

16.18 For some viscoelastic polymers that are subjected to stress relaxation tests, the stress decays with time according to

$$\sigma(t) = \sigma(0) \exp\left(-\frac{t}{\tau}\right) \quad (16.9)$$

where $\sigma(t)$ and $\sigma(0)$ represent the time-dependent and initial (i.e., time = 0) stresses, respectively, and t and τ denote elapsed time and the relaxation time; τ is a time-independent constant characteristic of the material. A specimen of some viscoelastic polymer the stress relaxation of which obeys Equation 16.9 was suddenly pulled in tension to a measured strain of 0.6; the stress necessary to maintain this constant strain was measured as a function of time. Determine $E_r(10)$ for this material if the initial stress level was 2.76 MPa (400 psi) which dropped to 1.72 MPa (250 psi) after 60 s.

16.19 In Figure 16.24, the logarithm of $E_r(t)$ versus the logarithm of time is plotted for polyisobutylene at a variety of temperatures. Make a plot of $E_r(10)$ versus temperature and then estimate T_g.

16.20 On the basis of the curves in Figure 16.10, sketch schematic strain-time plots for the following polystyrene materials at the specified temperatures:

(a) Amorphous at 120°C.

(b) Crosslinked at 150°C.

(c) Crystalline at 230°C.

(d) Crosslinked at 50°C.

16.21 (a) Contrast the manner in which stress relaxation and viscoelastic creep tests are conducted.

(b) For each of these tests, cite the experimental parameter of interest and how it is determined.

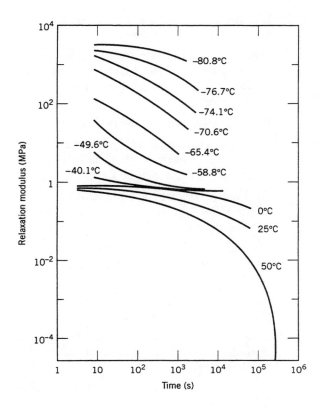

FIGURE 16.24 Logarithm of relaxation modulus versus logarithm of time for polyisobutylene between −80 and 50°C. (Adapted from E. Catsiff and A. V. Tobolsky, "Stress-Relaxation of Polyisobutylene in the Transition Region [1,2]," *J. Colloid Sci.,* **10,** 377 [1955]. Reprinted by permission of Academic Press, Inc.)

16.22 Make two schematic plots of the logarithm of relaxation modulus versus temperature for an amorphous polymer (curve *C* in Figure 16.13).

(a) On one of these plots demonstrate how the behavior changes with increasing molecular weight.

(b) On the other plot, indicate the change in behavior with increasing crosslinking.

16.23 For thermoplastic polymers, cite five factors that favor brittle fracture.

16.24 (a) Compare the fatigue limits for polystyrene (Figure 16.17) and the cast iron for which fatigue data are given in Problem 8.31.

(b) Compare the fatigue strengths at 10^6 cycles for polyethylene terephthalate (PET, Figure 16.17) and red brass (Figure 8.42).

16.25 Cite the primary differences between addition and condensation polymerization techniques.

16.26 Cite whether the molecular weight of a polymer that is synthesized by addition polymer-

ization is relatively high, medium, or relatively low for the following situations:

(a) Rapid initiation, slow propagation, and rapid termination.

(b) Slow initiation, rapid propagation, and slow termination.

(c) Rapid initiation, rapid propagation, and slow termination.

(d) Slow initiation, slow propagation, and rapid termination.

16.27 (a) How much adipic acid must be added to 50 kg of ethylene glycol to produce a linear chain structure of polyester according to Equation 16.7?

(b) What is the mass of the resulting polymer?

16.28 Nylon 6,6 may be formed by means of a condensation polymerization reaction in which hexamethylene diamine $[NH_2-(CH_2)_6-NH_2]$ and adipic acid react with one another with the formation of water as a by-product. Write out this reaction in the manner of Equation 16.7.

16.29 It is desired to produce nylon 6,6 by condensation polymerization using hexamethylene diamine and adipic acid as described in Problem 16.28. What masses of these two components are necessary to yield 37.5 kg of completely linear nylon 6,6?

16.30 (a) Why must the vapor pressure of a plasticizer be relatively low?

(b) How will the crystallinity of a polymer be affected by the addition of a plasticizer? Why?

(c) Is it possible for a crosslinked polymer to be plasticized? Why or why not?

(d) How does the addition of a plasticizer influence the tensile strength of a polymer? Why?

16.31 What is the distinction between dye and pigment colorants?

16.32 Cite four factors that determine what fabrication technique is used to form polymeric materials.

16.33 Contrast compression, injection, and transfer molding techniques that are used to form plastic materials.

16.34 Ten kg polybutadiene is vulcanized with 0.90 kg sulfur. What fraction of the possible crosslink sites is bonded to sulfur, assuming a single sulfur atom participates in each bond?

16.35 Compute the weight percent sulfur that must be added to completely crosslink an alternating chloroprene-acrylonitrile copolymer.

16.36 The vulcanization of polyisoprene is accomplished with sulfur atoms according to Equation 16.8. If 19 wt% sulfur is combined with polyisoprene, how many crosslinks will there be per isoprene mer?

16.37 (a) For the vulcanization of polyisoprene, how much sulfur (wt%) must be combined to ensure that 10% of possible sites will be crosslinked?

(b) Is it possible to have more combined sulfur atoms than there are crosslink sites for polyisoprene? Explain.

16.38 It is desired that some rubber component in its final form be vulcanized. Should vulcanization be carried out prior or subsequent to the forming operation? Why?

16.39 List the two molecular characteristics that are essential for elastomers.

16.40 Which of the following would you expect to be elastomers and which thermosetting polymers at room temperature? Justify each choice.

(a) Epoxy having a network structure.

(b) Lightly crosslinked poly(styrene-butadiene) random copolymer that has a glass-transition temperature of −50°C.

(c) Lightly branched and semicrystalline polytetrafluoroethylene that has a glass-transition temperature of −100°C.

(d) Heavily crosslinked poly(ethylene-propylene) random copolymer that has a glass-transition temperature of 0°C.

(e) Thermoplastic elastomer that has a glass-transition temperature of 75°C.

16.41 In terms of molecular structure, explain why phenol-formaldehyde (Bakelite) will not be an elastomer.

16.42 Demonstrate, in a manner similar to Equation 16.8, how vulcanization may occur in a chloroprene rubber.

16.43 During the winter months, the temperature in some parts of Alaska may go as low as −55°C (−65°F). Of the elastomers natural isoprene, styrene-butadiene, acrylonitrile-butadiene, chloroprene, and polysiloxane, which would be suitable for automobile tires under these conditions? Why?

16.44 Briefly explain the difference in molecular chemistry between silicone polymers and other polymeric materials.

16.45 Silicone polymers may be prepared to exist as liquids at room temperature. Cite differences in molecular structure between them and the silicone elastomers.

16.46 Why must fiber materials that are melt spun and then drawn be thermoplastic? Cite two reasons.

16.47 List two important characteristics for polymers that are to be used in fiber applications.

16.48 Cite five important characteristics for polymers that are to be used in thin-film applications.

16.49 Which of the following polyethylene thin films would have the better mechanical characteristics: (1) formed by blowing, or (2) formed by extrusion and then rolled? Why?

Design Questions

16.D1 **(a)** List several advantages and disadvantages of using transparent polymeric materials for eyeglass lenses.

(b) Cite four properties (in addition to being transparent) that are important for this application.

(c) Note three polymers that may be candidates for eyeglass lenses, and then tabulate values of the properties noted in part b for these three materials.

16.D2 Write an essay on polymeric materials that are used in the packaging of food products and drinks. Include a list of the general requisite characteristics of materials that are used for these applications. Now cite a specific material that is utilized for each of three different container types and the rationale for each choice.

19

Electrical Properties

It was noted in Section 4.9 that an image is generated on a scanning electron micrograph as a beam of electrons scans the surface of the specimen being examined. The electrons in this beam cause some of the specimen surface atoms to emit x-rays; the energy of an x-ray photon depends on the particular atom from which it radiates. It is possible to selectively filter out all but the x-rays emitted from one kind of atom. When projected on a cathode ray tube, small white dots are produced indicating the locations of the particular atom type; thus, a "dot map" of the image is generated.

Top: Scanning electron micrograph of an integrated circuit.

Center: A silicon dot map for the integrated circuit above, showing regions where silicon atoms are concentrated. Doped silicon is the semiconducting material from which integrated circuit elements are made.

Bottom: An aluminum dot map. Metallic aluminum is an electrical conductor and, as such, wires the circuit elements together. Approximately 200×.

19.1 INTRODUCTION

The prime objective of this chapter is to explore the electrical properties of materials, that is, their responses to an applied electric field. We begin with the phenomenon of electrical conduction: the parameters by which it is expressed, the mechanism of conduction by electrons, and how the electron energy band structure of a material influences its ability to conduct. These principles are extended to metals, semiconductors, and insulators. Particular attention is given to the characteristics of semiconductors, and then to semiconducting devices. Also treated are the dielectric characteristics of insulating materials. The final sections are devoted to the peculiar phenomena of ferroelectricity and piezoelectricity.

ELECTRICAL CONDUCTION

19.2 OHM'S LAW

One of the most important electrical characteristics of a solid material is the ease with which it transmits an electric current. **Ohm's law** relates the current I—or time rate of charge passage—to the applied voltage V as follows:

$$V = IR \tag{19.1}$$

where R is the resistance of the material through which the current is passing. The units for V, I, and R are, respectively, volts (J/C), amperes (C/s), and ohms (V/A). The value of R is influenced by specimen configuration, and for many materials is independent of current. The **resistivity** ρ is independent of specimen geometry but related to R through the expression

$$\rho = \frac{RA}{l} \tag{19.2}$$

where l is the distance between the two points at which the voltage is measured, and A is the cross-sectional area perpendicular to the direction of the current. The units for ρ are ohm-meters (Ω-m). From the expression for Ohm's law and Equation 19.2,

$$\rho = \frac{VA}{Il} \tag{19.3}$$

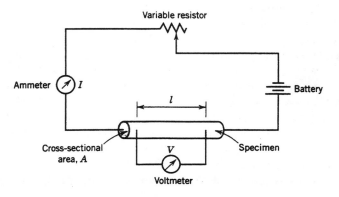

FIGURE 19.1 Schematic representation of the apparatus used to measure electrical resistivity.

Figure 19.1 is a schematic diagram of an experimental arrangement for measuring electrical resistivity.

19.3 ELECTRICAL CONDUCTIVITY

Sometimes, **electrical conductivity** σ is used to specify the electrical character of a material. It is simply the reciprocal of the resistivity, or

$$\sigma = \frac{1}{\rho} \tag{19.4}$$

and is indicative of the ease with which a material is capable of conducting an electric current. The units for σ are reciprocal ohm-meters [$(\Omega\text{-m})^{-1}$, or mho/m]. The following discussions on electrical properties use both resistivity and conductivity.

In addition to Equation 19.1, Ohm's law may be expressed as

$$J = \sigma \mathscr{E} \tag{19.5}$$

in which J is the current density, the current per unit of specimen area I/A, and $\mathscr{E}$ is the electric field intensity, or the voltage difference between two points divided by the distance separating them, that is,

$$\mathscr{E} = \frac{V}{l} \tag{19.6}$$

The demonstration of the equivalence of the two Ohm's law expressions (Equations 19.1 and 19.5) is left as a homework exercise.

Solid materials exhibit an amazing range of electrical conductivities, extending over 27 orders of magnitude; probably no other physical property experiences this breadth of variation. In fact, one way of classifying solid materials is according to the ease with which they conduct an electric current; within this classification scheme there are three groupings: *conductors, semiconductors,* and *insulators.* **Metals** are good conductors, typically having conductivities on the order of 10^7 $(\Omega\text{-m})^{-1}$. At the other extreme are materials with very low conductivities, ranging between 10^{-10} and 10^{-20} $(\Omega\text{-m})^{-1}$; these are electrical **insulators.** Materials with intermediate conductivities, generally from 10^{-6} to 10^4 $(\Omega\text{-m})^{-1}$, are termed **semiconductors.**

19.4 ELECTRONIC AND IONIC CONDUCTION

An electric current results from the motion of electrically charged particles in response to forces that act on them from an externally applied electric field. Positively charged particles are accelerated in the field direction, negatively charged particles in the direction opposite. Within most solid materials a current arises from the flow of electrons, which is termed *electronic conduction.* In addition, for ionic materials a net motion of charged ions is possible that produces a current; such is termed **ionic conduction.** The present discussion deals with electronic conduction; ionic conduction is treated briefly in Section 19.15.

19.5 ENERGY BAND STRUCTURES IN SOLIDS

In all conductors, semiconductors, and many insulating materials, only electronic conduction exists, and the magnitude of the electrical conductivity is strongly dependent on the number of electrons available to participate in the conduction process. However, not all electrons in every atom will accelerate in the presence of an electric field. The number of electrons available for electrical conduction in a particular material is related to the arrangement of electron states or levels with respect to energy, and then the manner in which these states are occupied by electrons. A thorough exploration of these topics is complicated and involves principles of quantum mechanics that are beyond the scope of this book; the ensuing development omits some concepts and simplifies others.

Concepts relating to electron energy states, their occupancy, and the resulting electron configuration for isolated atoms were discussed in Section 2.3. By way of review, for each individual atom there exist discrete energy levels that may be occupied by electrons, arranged into shells and subshells. Shells are designated by integers (1, 2, 3, etc.), and subshells by letters (s, p, d, and f). For each of s, p, d, and f subshells, there exist, respectively, one, three, five, and seven states. The electrons in most atoms fill just the states having the lowest energies, two electrons of opposite spin per state, in accordance with the Pauli exclusion principle. The electron configuration of an isolated atom represents the arrangement of the electrons within the allowed states.

Let us now make an extrapolation of some of these concepts to solid materials. A solid may be thought of as consisting of a large number, say, N, of atoms initially separated from one another, which are subsequently brought together and bonded to form the ordered atomic arrangement found in the crystalline material. At relatively large separation distances, each atom is independent of all the others and will have the atomic energy levels and electron configuration as if isolated. However, as the atoms come within close proximity of one another, electrons are acted upon, or perturbed, by the electrons and nuclei of adjacent atoms. This influence is such that each distinct atomic state may split into a series of closely spaced electron states in the solid, to form what is termed an **electron energy band.** The extent of splitting depends on interatomic separation (Figure 19.2) and begins with the

FIGURE 19.2
Schematic plot of electron energy versus interatomic separation for an aggregate of 12 atoms ($N = 12$). Upon close approach, each of the 1s and 2s atomic states splits to form an electron energy band consisting of 12 states.

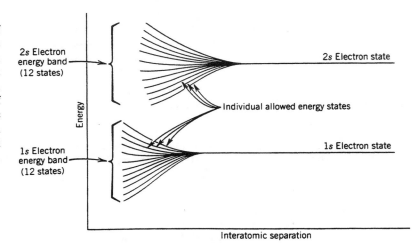

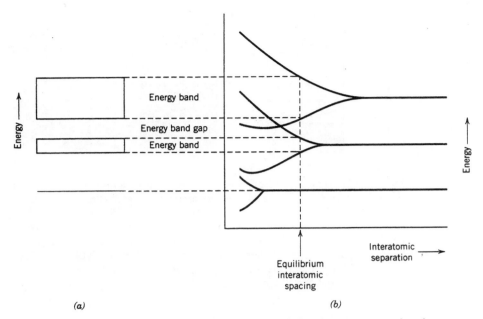

Figure 19.3 (a) The conventional representation of the electron energy band structure for a solid material at the equilibrium interatomic separation.
(b) Electron energy versus interatomic separation for an aggregate of atoms, illustrating how the energy band structure at the equilibrium separation in (a) is generated. (From Z. D. Jastrzebski, *The Nature and Properties of Engineering Materials*, 3rd edition. Copyright © 1987 by John Wiley & Sons, Inc. Reprinted by permission of John Wiley & Sons, Inc.)

outermost electron shells, since they are the first to be perturbed as the atoms coalesce. Within each band, the energy states are discrete, yet the difference between adjacent states is exceedingly small. At the equilibrium spacing, band formation may not occur for the electron subshells nearest the nucleus, as illustrated in Figure 19.3*b*. Furthermore, gaps may exist between adjacent bands, as also indicated in the figure; normally, energies lying within these band gaps are not available for electron occupancy. The conventional way of representing electron band structures in solids is shown in Figure 19.3*a*.

The number of states within each band will equal the total of all states contributed by the N atoms. For example, an s band will consist of N states, and a p band of $3N$ states. With regard to occupancy, each energy state may accommodate two electrons, which must have oppositely directed spins. Furthermore, bands will contain the electrons that resided in the corresponding levels of the isolated atoms; for example, a $4s$ energy band in the solid will contain those isolated atom's $4s$ electrons. Of course, there will be empty bands and, possibly, bands that are only partially filled.

The electrical properties of a solid material are a consequence of its electron band structure, that is, the arrangement of the outermost electron bands and the way in which they are filled with electrons. In this regard, the band that contains the highest-energy or valence electrons is termed the **valence band;** the **conduction band** is the next higher energy band, which is, under most circumstances, virtually unoccupied by electrons.

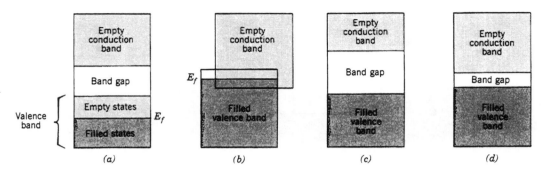

FIGURE 19.4 The various possible electron band structures in solids at 0 K. (a) The electron band structure found in metals such as copper, in which there are available electron states above and adjacent to filled states, in the same band. (b) The electron band structure of metals such as magnesium, wherein there is an overlap of the filled valence band with an empty conduction band. (c) The electron band structure characteristic of insulators; the filled valence band is separated from the empty conduction band by a relatively large band gap (>2 eV). (d) The electron band structure found in the semiconductors, which is the same as for insulators except that the band gap is relatively narrow (<2 eV).

Four different types of band structures are possible at 0 K. In the first (Figure 19.4a), the valence band is only partially filled with electrons. The energy corresponding to the highest filled state at 0 K is called the **Fermi energy** E_f, as indicated. This energy band structure is typified by some metals, in particular those that have a single s valence electron (e.g., copper). Each copper atom has one 4s electron; however, for a solid comprised of N atoms, the 4s band is capable of accommodating $2N$ electrons. Thus only half the available electron positions within this 4s valence band are filled.

For the second band structure, also found in metals (Figure 19.4b), the valence band is full, but it overlaps the conduction band, which, in the absence of any overlapping, would be completely empty. Magnesium has this band structure. Each isolated Mg atom has two 3s valence electrons. However, when a solid is formed, the 3s and 3p bands overlap. In this instance and at 0 K, the Fermi energy is taken as that energy below which, for N atoms, N states are filled, two electrons per state.

The final two band structures are similar; for each, all states in the valence band are completely filled with electrons. However, there is no overlap between this and the empty conduction band; this gives rise to an **energy band gap** in between. For very pure materials, electrons may not have energies within this gap. The difference between the two band structures lies in the magnitude of the energy gap; for materials that are insulators, the band gap is relatively wide (Figure 19.4c), whereas for semiconductors it is narrow (Figure 19.4d). The Fermi energy for these two band structures lies within the band gap—near its center.

19.6 CONDUCTION IN TERMS OF BAND AND ATOMIC BONDING MODELS

At this point in the discussion, it is vital that another concept be understood, namely, that only electrons with energies greater than the Fermi energy may be acted on and accelerated in the presence of an electric field. These are the electrons that participate in the conduction process, which are termed **free electrons.** Another

FIGURE 19.5 For a metal, occupancy of electron states (a) before and (b) after an electron excitation.

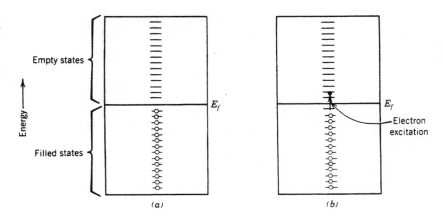

charged electronic entity called a **hole** is found in semiconductors and insulators. Holes have energies less than E_f and also participate in electronic conduction. As the ensuing discussion reveals, the electrical conductivity is a direct function of the numbers of free electrons and holes. In addition, the distinction between conductors and nonconductors (insulators and semiconductors) lies in the numbers of these free electron and hole charge carriers.

METALS

For an electron to become free, it must be excited or promoted into one of the empty and available energy states above E_f. For metals having either of the band structures shown in Figures 19.4a and 19.4b, there are vacant energy states adjacent to the highest filled state at E_f. Thus, very little energy is required to promote electrons into the low-lying empty states, as shown in Figure 19.5. Generally, the energy provided by an electric field is sufficient to excite large numbers of conduction electrons into these conducting states.

For the metallic bonding model discussed in Section 2.6, it was assumed that all the valence electrons have freedom of motion and form an "electron gas," which is uniformly distributed throughout the lattice of ion cores. Even though these electrons are not locally bound to any particular atom, they, nevertheless, must experience some excitation to become conducting electrons that are truly free. Thus, although only a fraction are excited, this still gives rise to a relatively large number of free electrons and, consequently, a high conductivity.

INSULATORS AND SEMICONDUCTORS

For insulators and semiconductors, empty states adjacent to the top of the filled valence band are not available. To become free, therefore, electrons must be promoted across the energy band gap and into empty states at the bottom of the conduction band. This is possible only by supplying to an electron the difference in energy between these two states, which is approximately equal to the band gap energy E_g. This excitation process is demonstrated in Figure 19.6. For many materials this band gap is several electron volts wide. Most often the excitation energy is from a nonelectrical source such as heat or light, usually the former.

The number of electrons excited thermally (by heat energy) into the conduction band depends on the energy band gap width as well as temperature. At a given temperature, the larger the E_g, the lower the probability that a valence electron will be promoted into an energy state within the conduction band; this results in

FIGURE 19.6
For an insulator or semiconductor, occupancy of electron states (a) before and (b) after an electron excitation from the valence band into the conduction band, in which both a free electron and a hole are generated.

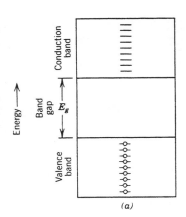 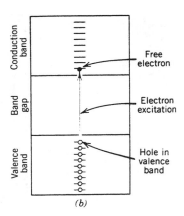

fewer conduction electrons. In other words, the larger the band gap, the lower the electrical conductivity at a given temperature. Thus, the distinction between semiconductors and insulators lies in the width of the band gap; for semiconductors it is narrow, whereas for insulating materials it is relatively wide.

Increasing the temperature of either a semiconductor or an insulator results in an increase in the thermal energy that is available for electron excitation. Thus, more electrons are promoted into the conduction band, which gives rise to an enhanced conductivity.

The conductivity of insulators and semiconductors may also be viewed from the perspective of atomic bonding models discussed in Section 2.6. For electrically insulating materials, interatomic bonding is ionic or strongly covalent. Thus, the valence electrons are tightly bound to or shared with the individual atoms. In other words, these electrons are highly localized and are not in any sense free to wander throughout the crystal. The bonding in semiconductors is covalent (or predominantly covalent) and relatively weak, which means that the valence electrons are not as strongly bound to the atoms. Consequently, these electrons are more easily removed by thermal excitation than they are for insulators.

19.7 ELECTRON MOBILITY

When an electric field is applied, a force is brought to bear on the free electrons; as a consequence, they all experience an acceleration in a direction opposite to that of the field, by virtue of their negative charge. According to quantum mechanics, there is no interaction between an accelerating electron and atoms in a perfect crystal lattice. Under such circumstances all the free electrons should accelerate as long as the electric field is applied, which would give rise to a continuously increasing electric current with time. However, we know that a current reaches a constant value the instant that a field is applied, indicating that there exists what might be termed "frictional forces," which counter this acceleration from the external field. These frictional forces result from the scattering of electrons by imperfections in the crystal lattice, including impurity atoms, vacancies, interstitial atoms, dislocations, and even the thermal vibrations of the atoms themselves. Each scattering event causes an electron to lose kinetic energy and to change its direction of motion, as represented schematically in Figure 19.7. There is, however, some net electron motion in the direction opposite to the field, and this flow of charge is the electric current.

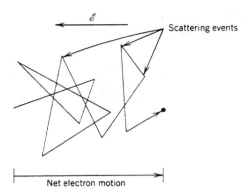

FIGURE 19.7 Schematic diagram showing the path of an electron that is deflected by scattering events.

The scattering phenomenon is manifested as a resistance to the passage of an electric current. Several parameters are used to describe the extent of this scattering, these include the *drift velocity* and the **mobility** of an electron. The drift velocity v_d represents the average electron velocity in the direction of the force imposed by the applied field. It is directly proportional to the electric field as follows:

$$v_d = \mu_e \mathscr{E} \tag{19.7}$$

The constant of proportionality μ_e is called the electron mobility, which is an indication of the frequency of scattering events; its units are square meters per volt-second (m^2/V-s).

The conductivity σ of most materials may be expressed as

$$\sigma = n|e|\mu_e \tag{19.8}$$

where n is the number of free or conducting electrons per unit volume (e.g., per cubic meter), and $|e|$ is the absolute magnitude of the electrical charge on an electron (1.6×10^{-19} C). Thus, the electrical conductivity is proportional to both the number of free electrons and the electron mobility.

19.8 ELECTRICAL RESISTIVITY OF METALS

As mentioned previously, most metals are extremely good conductors of electricity; room-temperature conductivities for several of the more common metals are contained in Table 19.1. (Appendix C.9 lists the electrical resistivities of a large number of metals and alloys.) Again, metals have high conductivities because of the large numbers of free electrons that have been excited into empty states above the Fermi energy. Thus n has a large value in the conductivity expression, Equation 19.8.

At this point it is convenient to discuss conduction in metals in terms of the resistivity, the reciprocal of conductivity; the reason for this switch should become apparent in the ensuing discussion.

Since crystalline defects serve as scattering centers for conduction electrons in metals, increasing their number raises the resistivity (or lowers the conductivity). The concentration of these imperfections depends on temperature, composition, and the degree of cold work of a metal specimen. In fact, it has been observed experimentally that the total resistivity of a metal is the sum of the contributions from thermal vibrations, impurities, and plastic deformation; that is, the scattering

Table 19.1 Room-Temperature Electrical Conductivities for Nine Common Metals and Alloys

Metal	Electrical Conductivity $[(\Omega\text{-}m)^{-1}]$
Silver	6.8×10^7
Copper	6.0×10^7
Gold	4.3×10^7
Aluminum	3.8×10^7
Iron	1.0×10^7
Brass (70 Cu–30 Zn)	1.6×10^7
Platinum	0.94×10^7
Plain carbon steel	0.6×10^7
Stainless steel	0.2×10^7

mechanisms act independently of one another. This may be represented in mathematical form as follows:

$$\rho_{\text{total}} = \rho_t + \rho_i + \rho_d \tag{19.9}$$

in which ρ_t, ρ_i, and ρ_d represent the individual thermal, impurity, and deformation resistivity contributions, respectively. Equation 19.9 is sometimes known as **Matthiessen's rule.** The influence of each ρ variable on the total resistivity is demonstrated in Figure 19.8, as a plot of resistivity versus temperature for copper and several copper–nickel alloys in annealed and deformed states. The additive nature of the individual resistivity contributions is demonstrated at −100°C.

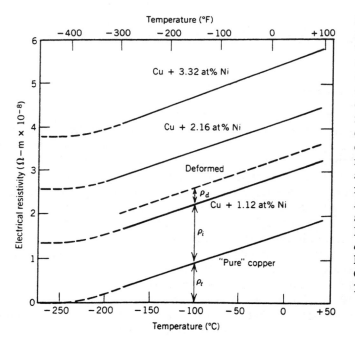

FIGURE 19.8 The electrical resistivity versus temperature for copper and three copper–nickel alloys, one of which has been deformed. Thermal, impurity, and deformation contributions to the resistivity are indicated at −100°C. [Adapted from J. O. Linde, *Ann. Physik,* **5,** 219 (1932); and C. A. Wert and R. M. Thomson, *Physics of Solids,* 2nd edition, McGraw-Hill Book Company, New York, 1970.]

INFLUENCE OF TEMPERATURE

For the pure metal and all the copper–nickel alloys shown in Figure 19.8, the resistivity rises linearly with temperature above about −200°C. Thus,

$$\rho_t = \rho_0 + aT \tag{19.10}$$

where ρ_0 and a are constants for each particular metal. This dependence of the thermal resistivity component on temperature is due to the increase with temperature in thermal vibrations and other lattice irregularities (e.g., vacancies), which serve as electron-scattering centers.

INFLUENCE OF IMPURITIES

For additions of a single impurity that forms a solid solution, the impurity resistivity ρ_i is related to the impurity concentration c_i in terms of the atom fraction (at%/100) as follows:

$$\rho_i = Ac_i(1 - c_i) \tag{19.11}$$

where A is a composition-independent constant that is a function of both the impurity and host metals. The influence of nickel impurity additions on the room-temperature resistivity of copper is demonstrated in Figure 19.9, up to 50 wt% Ni; over this composition range nickel is completely soluble in copper (Figure 9.2). Again, nickel atoms in copper act as scattering centers, and increasing the concentration of nickel in copper results in an enhancement of resistivity.

For a two-phase alloy consisting of α and β phases, a rule-of-mixtures expression may be utilized to approximate the resistivity as follows:

$$\rho_i = \rho_\alpha V_\alpha + \rho_\beta V_\beta \tag{19.12}$$

where the V's and ρ's represent volume fractions and individual resistivities for the respective phases.

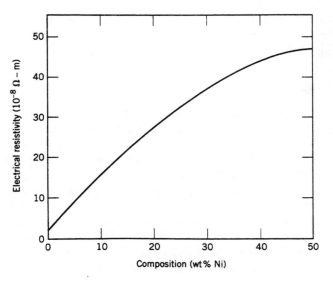

FIGURE 19.9 Room-temperature electrical resistivity versus composition for copper–nickel alloys.

INFLUENCE OF PLASTIC DEFORMATION

Plastic deformation also raises the electrical resistivity as a result of increased numbers of electron-scattering dislocations. The effect of deformation on resistivity is also represented in Figure 19.8.

19.9 ELECTRICAL CHARACTERISTICS OF COMMERCIAL ALLOYS

Electrical and other properties of copper render it the most widely used metallic conductor. Oxygen-free high-conductivity (OFHC) copper, having extremely low oxygen and other impurity contents, is produced for many electrical applications. Aluminum, having a conductivity only about one half that of copper, is also frequently used as an electrical conductor. Silver has a higher conductivity than either copper or aluminum; however, its use is restricted on the basis of cost.

On occasion, it is necessary to improve the mechanical strength of a metal alloy without impairing significantly its electrical conductivity. Both solid solution alloying and cold working improve strength at the expense of conductivity, and thus, a tradeoff must be made for these two properties. Most often, strength is enhanced by introducing a second phase that does not have so adverse an effect on conductivity. For example, copper–beryllium alloys are precipitation hardened; but even so, the conductivity is reduced by about a factor of 5 over high-purity copper.

For some applications, such as furnace heating elements, a high electrical resistivity is desirable. The energy loss by electrons that are scattered is dissipated as heat energy. Such materials must have not only a high resistivity, but also a resistance to oxidation at elevated temperatures and, of course, a high melting temperature. Nichrome, a nickel–chromium alloy, is commonly employed in heating elements.

SEMICONDUCTIVITY

The electrical conductivity of the semiconducting materials is not as high as that of the metals; nevertheless, they have some unique electrical characteristics that render them especially useful. The electrical properties of these materials are extremely sensitive to the presence of even minute concentrations of impurities. **Intrinsic semiconductors** are those in which the electrical behavior is based on the electronic structure inherent to the pure material. When the electrical characteristics are dictated by impurity atoms, the semiconductor is said to be **extrinsic.**

19.10 INTRINSIC SEMICONDUCTION

Intrinsic semiconductors are characterized by the electron band structure shown in Figure 19.4d: at 0 K, a completely filled valence band, separated from an empty conduction band by a relatively narrow forbidden band gap, generally less than 2 eV. The two elemental semiconductors are silicon (Si) and germanium (Ge), having band gap energies of approximately 1.1 and 0.7 eV, respectively. Both are found in Group IVA of the periodic table (Figure 2.6) and are covalently bonded.[1] In addition, a host of compound semiconducting materials also display intrinsic behavior. One such group is formed between elements of Groups IIIA and VA,

---

[1] The valence bands in silicon and germanium correspond to sp^3 hybrid energy levels for the isolated atom; these hybridized valence bands are completely filled at 0 K.

Table 19.2 Band Gap Energies, Electron and Hole Mobilities, and Intrinsic Electrical Conductivities at Room Temperature for Semiconducting Materials

Material	Band Gap (eV)	Electrical Conductivity [$(\Omega\text{-}m)^{-1}$]	Electron Mobility (m^2/V-s)	Hole Mobility (m^2/V-s)
Elemental				
Si	1.11	4×10^{-4}	0.14	0.05
Ge	0.67	2.2	0.38	0.18
III–V Compounds				
GaP	2.25	—	0.05	0.002
GaAs	1.42	10^{-6}	0.85	0.45
InSb	0.17	2×10^4	7.7	0.07
II–VI Compounds				
CdS	2.40	—	0.03	—
ZnTe	2.26	—	0.03	0.01

for example, gallium arsenide (GaAs) and indium antimonide (InSb); these are frequently called III–V compounds. The compounds composed of elements of Groups IIB and VIA also display semiconducting behavior; these include cadmium sulfide (CdS) and zinc telluride (ZnTe). As the two elements forming these compounds become more widely separated with respect to their relative positions in the periodic table (i.e., the electronegativities become more dissimilar, Figure 2.7), the atomic bonding becomes more ionic and the magnitude of the band gap energy increases—the materials tend to become more insulative. Table 19.2 gives the band gaps for some compound semiconductors.

CONCEPT OF A HOLE

In intrinsic semiconductors, for every electron excited into the conduction band there is left behind a missing electron in one of the covalent bonds, or in the band scheme, a vacant electron state in the valence band, as shown in Figure 19.6b. Under the influence of an electric field, the position of this missing electron within the crystalline lattice may be thought of as moving by the motion of other valence electrons that repeatedly fill in the incomplete bond (Figure 19.10). This process is expedited by treating a missing electron from the valence band as a positively charged particle called a *hole*. A hole is considered to have a charge that is of the same magnitude as that for an electron, but of opposite sign ($+1.6 \times 10^{-19}$ C). Thus, in the presence of an electric field, excited electrons and holes move in opposite directions. Furthermore, in semiconductors both electrons and holes are scattered by lattice imperfections.

INTRINSIC CONDUCTIVITY

Since there are two types of charge carrier (free electrons and holes) in an intrinsic semiconductor, the expression for electrical conduction, Equation 19.8, must be modified to include a term to account for the contribution of the hole current. Therefore, we write

$$\sigma = n|e|\mu_e + p|e|\mu_h \tag{19.13}$$

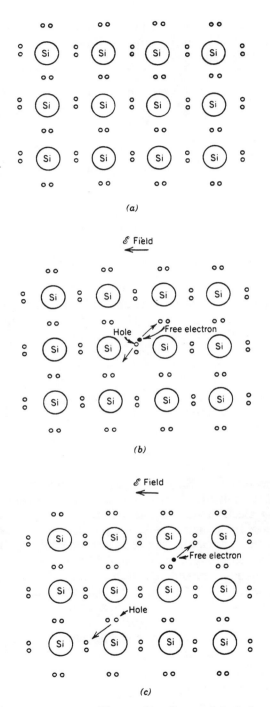

FIGURE 19.10 Electron bonding model of electrical conduction in intrinsic silicon: (a) before excitation; (b) and (c) after excitation (the subsequent free-electron and hole motions in response to an external electric field).

where p is the number of holes per cubic meter and μ_h is the hole mobility. The magnitude of μ_h is always less than μ_e for semiconductors. For intrinsic semiconductors, every electron promoted across the band gap leaves behind a hole in the valence band, thus,

$$n = p \tag{19.14}$$

and

$$\sigma = n|e|(\mu_e + \mu_h) = p|e|(\mu_e + \mu_h) \tag{19.15}$$

The room-temperature intrinsic conductivities and electron and hole mobilities for several semiconducting materials are also presented in Table 19.2.

EXAMPLE PROBLEM 19.1

For intrinsic silicon, the room-temperature electrical conductivity is 4×10^{-4} $(\Omega\text{-m})^{-1}$; the electron and hole mobilities are, respectively, 0.14 and 0.048 m²/ V-s. Compute the electron and hole concentrations at room temperature.

SOLUTION

Since the material is intrinsic, electron and hole concentrations will be the same, and therefore, from Equation 19.15,

$$n = p = \frac{\sigma}{|e|(\mu_e + \mu_h)}$$

$$= \frac{4 \times 10^{-4} \, (\Omega\text{-m})^{-1}}{(1.6 \times 10^{-19} \, \text{C})(0.14 + 0.048 \, \text{m}^2/\text{V-s})}$$

$$= 1.33 \times 10^{16} \, \text{m}^{-3}$$

19.11 EXTRINSIC SEMICONDUCTION

Virtually all commercial semiconductors are extrinsic; that is, the electrical behavior is determined by impurities, which, when present in even minute concentrations, introduce excess electrons or holes. For example, an impurity concentration of one atom in 10^{12} is sufficient to render silicon extrinsic at room temperature.

n-TYPE EXTRINSIC SEMICONDUCTION

To illustrate how extrinsic semiconduction is accomplished, consider again the elemental semiconductor silicon. An Si atom has four electrons, each of which is covalently bonded with one of four adjacent Si atoms. Now, suppose that an impurity atom with a valence of 5 is added as a substitutional impurity; possibilities would include atoms from the Group VA column of the periodic table (e.g., P, As, and Sb). Only four of five valence electrons of these impurity atoms can participate in the bonding because there are only four possible bonds with neighboring atoms. The extra nonbonding electron is loosely bound to the region around the impurity atom by a weak electrostatic attraction, as illustrated in Figure 19.11a. The binding energy of this electron is relatively small (on the order of 0.01 eV); thus, it is easily

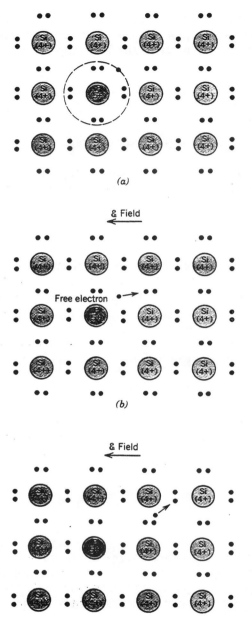

FIGURE 19.11 Extrinsic *n*-type semiconduction model (electron bonding). (*a*) An impurity atom such as phosphorus, having five valence electrons, may substitute for a silicon atom. This results in an extra bonding electron, which is bound to the impurity atom and orbits it. (*b*) Excitation to form a free electron. (*c*) The motion of this free electron in response to an electric field.

removed from the impurity atom, in which case it becomes a free or conducting electron (Figures 19.11*b* and 19.11*c*).

The energy state of such an electron may be viewed from the perspective of the electron band model scheme. For each of the loosely bound electrons, there exists a single energy level, or energy state, which is located within the forbidden band gap just below the bottom of the conduction band (Figure 19.12*a*). The electron binding energy corresponds to the energy required to excite the electron from one of these impurity states to a state within the conduction band. Each excitation event

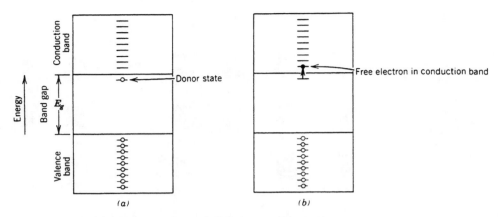

FIGURE 19.12 (a) Electron energy band scheme for a donor impurity level located within the band gap and just below the bottom of the conduction band. (b) Excitation from a donor state in which a free electron is generated in the conduction band.

(Figure 19.12b), supplies or donates a single electron to the conduction band; an impurity of this type is aptly termed a *donor*. Since each donor electron is excited from an impurity level, no corresponding hole is created within the valence band.

At room temperature, the thermal energy available is sufficient to excite large numbers of electrons from **donor states;** in addition, some intrinsic valence–conduction band transitions occur, as in Figure 19.6b, but to a negligible degree. Thus, the number of electrons in the conduction band far exceeds the number of holes in the valence band (or $n \gg p$), and the first term on the right-hand side of Equation 19.13 overwhelms the second; that is,

$$\sigma \cong n|e|\mu_e \qquad (19.16)$$

A material of this type is said to be an *n-type* extrinsic semiconductor. The electrons are *majority carriers* by virtue of their density or concentration; holes, on the other hand, are the *minority charge carriers*. For *n*-type semiconductors, the Fermi level is shifted upward in the band gap, to within the vicinity of the donor state; its exact position is a function of both temperature and donor concentration.

p-TYPE EXTRINSIC SEMICONDUCTION

An opposite effect is produced by the addition to silicon or germanium of trivalent substitutional impurities such as aluminum, boron, and gallium from Group IIIA of the periodic table. One of the covalent bonds around each of these atoms is deficient in an electron; such a deficiency may be viewed as a hole that is weakly bound to the impurity atom. This hole may be liberated from the impurity atom by the transfer of an electron from an adjacent bond as illustrated in Figure 19.13. In essence, the electron and the hole exchange positions. A moving hole is considered to be in an excited state and participates in the conduction process, in a manner analogous to an excited donor electron, as described above.

Extrinsic excitations, in which holes are generated, may also be represented using the band model. Each impurity atom of this type introduces an energy level within the band gap, above yet very close to the top of the valence band (Figure

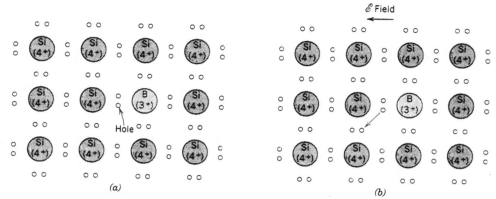

FIGURE 19.13 Extrinsic *p*-type semiconduction model (electron bonding).
(*a*) An impurity atom such as boron, having three valence electrons, may
substitute for a silicon atom. This results in a deficiency of one valence electron,
or a hole associated with the impurity atom. (*b*) The motion of this hole in
response to an electric field.

19.14*a*). A hole is imagined to be created in the valence band by the thermal
excitation of an electron from the valence band into this impurity electron state,
as demonstrated in Figure 19.14*b*. With such a transition, only one carrier is produced—a hole in the valence band; a free electron is *not* created in either the
impurity level or the conduction band. An impurity of this type is called an *acceptor,*
because it is capable of accepting an electron from the valence band, leaving behind
a hole. It follows that the energy level within the band gap introduced by this type
of impurity is called an **acceptor state.**

For this type of extrinsic conduction, holes are present in much higher concentrations than electrons (i.e., $p \gg n$), and under these circumstances a material is
termed *p-type* because positively charged particles are primarily responsible for
electrical conduction. Of course, holes are the majority carriers, and electrons are
present in minority concentrations. This gives rise to a predominance of the second
term on the right-hand side of Equation 19.13, or

$$\sigma \cong p|e|\mu_h \qquad (19.17)$$

FIGURE 19.14
(*a*) Energy band
scheme for an acceptor
impurity level located
within the band gap
and just above the top
of the valence band.
(*b*) Excitation of an
electron into the
acceptor level, leaving
behind a hole in the
valence band.

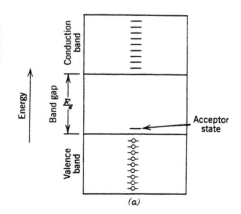

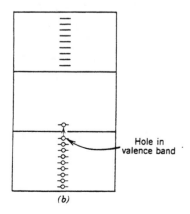

For p-type semiconductors, the Fermi level is positioned within the band gap and near to the acceptor level.

Extrinsic semiconductors (both n- and p-type) are produced from materials that are initially of extremely high purity, commonly having total impurity contents on the order of 10^{-7} at%. Controlled concentrations of specific donors or acceptors are then intentionally added, using various techniques. Such an alloying process in semiconducting materials is termed **doping.**

In extrinsic semiconductors, large numbers of charge carriers (either electrons or holes, depending on the impurity type) are created at room temperature, by the available thermal energy. As a consequence, relatively high room-temperature electrical conductivities are obtained in extrinsic semiconductors. Most of these materials are designed for use in electronic devices to be operated at ambient conditions.

EXAMPLE PROBLEM 19.2

Phosphorus is added to high-purity silicon to give a concentration of 10^{23} m^{-3} of charge carriers at room temperature.

(a) Is this material n-type or p-type?

(b) Calculate the room-temperature conductivity of this material, assuming that electron and hole mobilities are the same as for the intrinsic material.

SOLUTION

(a) Phosphorus is a Group VA element (Figure 2.6) and, therefore, will act as a donor in silicon. Thus, the 10^{23} m^{-3} charge carriers will be virtually all electrons. This electron concentration is greater than that for the intrinsic case (1.33×10^{16} m^{-3}, Example Problem 19.1); hence, this material is extrinsically n-type.

(b) In this case the conductivity may be determined using Equation 19.16, as follows:

$$\sigma = n|e|\mu_e = (10^{23} \text{ m}^{-3})(1.6 \times 10^{-19} \text{ C})(0.14 \text{ m}^2/\text{V-s})$$
$$= 2240 \ (\Omega\text{-m})^{-1}$$

19.12 THE TEMPERATURE VARIATION OF CONDUCTIVITY AND CARRIER CONCENTRATION

Figure 19.15 plots the logarithm of the electrical conductivity as a function of the logarithm of absolute temperature for intrinsic silicon, and also for silicon that has been doped with 0.0013 and 0.0052 at% boron; again, boron acts as an acceptor in silicon. Worth noting from this figure is that the electrical conductivity in the intrinsic specimen increases dramatically with rising temperature. The numbers of both electrons and holes increase with temperature because more thermal energy is available to excite electrons from the valence to the conduction band. Thus, both the values of n and p in the intrinsic conductivity expression, Equation 19.15, are enhanced. The magnitudes of electron and hole mobilities decrease slightly with temperature as a result of more effective electron and hole scattering by the thermal vibrations. However, these reductions in μ_e and μ_h by no means offset the increase

FIGURE 19.15
The temperature
dependence of the
electrical conductivity
(log–log scales) for
intrinsic silicon and
boron-doped silicon at
two doping levels.
[Adapted from G. L.
Pearson and
J. Bardeen, *Phys. Rev.*,
75, 865 (1949).]

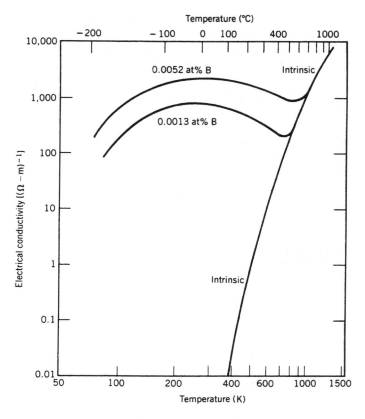

FIGURE 19.15 The temperature dependence of the electrical conductivity (log–log scales) for intrinsic silicon and boron-doped silicon at two doping levels. [Adapted from G. L. Pearson and J. Bardeen, *Phys. Rev.*, **75,** 865 (1949).]

in n and p, and the net effect of a rise in temperature is to produce a conductivity increase.

Mathematically, the dependence of intrinsic conductivity σ on the absolute temperature T is approximately

$$\ln \sigma \cong C - \frac{E_g}{2kT} \tag{19.18}$$

where C represents a temperature-independent constant and E_g and k are the band gap energy and Boltzmann's constant, respectively. Since the increase of n and p with rising temperature is so much greater than the decrease in μ_e and μ_h, the dependence of carrier concentration on temperature for intrinsic behavior is virtually the same as for the conductivity, or

$$\ln n = \ln p \cong C' - \frac{E_g}{2kT} \tag{19.19}$$

The parameter C' is a constant that is independent of temperature, yet is different from C in Equation 19.18.

In light of Equation 19.19, another method of representing the temperature dependence of the electrical behavior of semiconductors is as the natural logarithm of electron and hole concentrations versus the reciprocal of the absolute tempera-

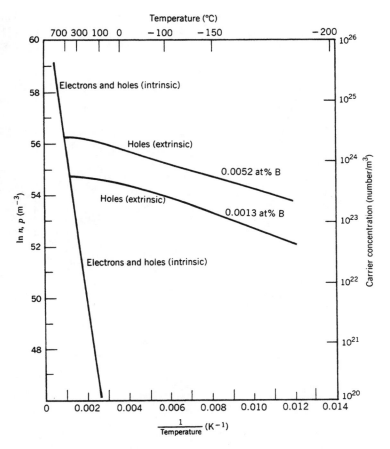

FIGURE 19.16
The logarithm of carrier (electron and hole) concentration as a function of the reciprocal of the absolute temperature for intrinsic silicon and two boron-doped silicon materials. (Adapted from G. L. Pearson and J. Bardeen, *Phys. Rev.,* **75,** 865, 1949.)

ture. Figure 19.16 is such a plot using data taken from Figure 19.15; and, as may be noted (Figure 19.16), a straight line segment results for the intrinsic material; such a plot expedites the determination of the band gap energy. According to Equation 19.19, the slope of this line segment is equal to $-E_g/2k$, or E_g may be determined as follows:

$$E_g = -2k\left(\frac{\Delta \ln p}{\Delta(1/T)}\right)$$

$$= -2k\left(\frac{\Delta \ln n}{\Delta(1/T)}\right)$$

(19.20)

This is indicated in the schematic plot of Figure 19.17.

Another important feature of the behavior shown in Figures 19.15 and 19.16 is that at temperatures below about 800 K (527°C), the boron-doped materials are extrinsically *p*-type; that is, virtually all the carrier holes result from extrinsic excitations—electron transitions from the valence band into the boron acceptor level, which leave behind valence band holes (Figure 19.14). The available thermal energies at these temperatures are sufficient to promote significant numbers of these excitations, yet insufficient to stimulate many electrons from the valence band across the band gap. Thus, the extrinsic conductivity far exceeds that of the intrinsic

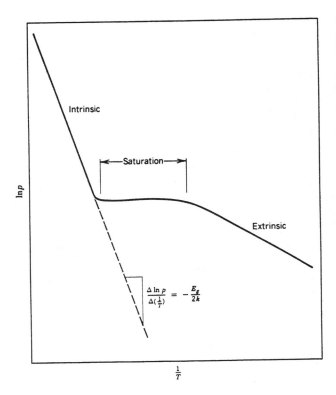

FIGURE 19.17 Schematic plot of the natural logarithm of hole concentration as a function of the reciprocal of absolute temperature for a p-type semiconductor that exhibits extrinsic, saturation, and intrinsic behavior.

material. For example, at 400 K (127°C) the conductivities for intrinsic silicon and extrinsic 0.0013 at% boron-doped material are approximately 10^{-2} and 600 $(\Omega\text{-m})^{-1}$, respectively (Figure 19.15). This comparison indicates the sensitivity of conductivity to even extremely small concentrations of some impurity elements.

Furthermore, the extrinsic conductivity is also sensitive to temperature, as indicated in Figure 19.15, for both boron-doped materials. Beginning at about 75 K (−200°C), the conductivity first increases with temperature, reaches a maximum, and then decreases slightly prior to becoming intrinsic. Or, in terms of carrier (i.e., hole) concentration, Figure 19.16, ln p first increases linearly with decreasing $1/T$ (or increasing temperature). Large numbers of extrinsic excitations are possible even at these relatively low temperatures inasmuch as the acceptor level lies just above the top of the valence band. With further temperature increase ($1/T$ decrease), the hole concentration eventually becomes independent of temperature, Figure 19.16. At this point virtually all of the boron atoms have accepted electrons from the valence band, or are said to be *saturated;* this is appropriately termed the *saturation region* (Figure 19.17). (Donor impurities become *exhausted* instead of saturated.) The number of holes in this region is approximately equal to the number of dopant impurity (i.e., boron) atoms.

The decrease of conductivity with increasing temperature within the saturation region for the two extrinsic curves in Figure 19.15 may be explained by the reduction in hole mobility with rising temperature. From the extrinsic conductivity expression, Equation 19.17, both e and p are independent of temperature in this region, and the only temperature dependence comes from the mobility.

Also worth noting from Figures 19.15 and 19.16 is that at about 800 K (527°C), the conductivity of both boron-doped materials becomes intrinsic. At the outset of intrinsic behavior, the number of intrinsic valence band-to-conduction band transitions becomes greater than the number of holes that are extrinsically generated.

A couple of final comments relate to the influence of boron acceptor content on the electrical behavior of silicon. First, the extrinsic and saturation conductivities and hole concentrations are greater for the material with the higher boron content (Figures 19.15 and 19.16), a result not unexpected, since more B atoms are present from which holes may be produced. Also, the intrinsic outset temperature becomes elevated as the dopant content increases.

EXAMPLE PROBLEM 19.3

If the room-temperature [25°C (298 K)] electrical conductivity of intrinsic germanium is 2.2 $(\Omega\text{-m})^{-1}$, estimate its conductivity at 150°C (423 K).

SOLUTION

This problem is solved by employment of Equation 19.18. First, we determine the value of the constant C using the room-temperature data, after which the value at 150°C may be computed. From Table 19.2, the value of E_g for germanium is 0.67 eV, and, therefore,

$$C = \ln \sigma + \frac{E_g}{2kT}$$

$$= \ln(2.2) + \frac{0.67 \text{ eV}}{(2)(8.62 \times 10^{-5} \text{ eV/K})(298 \text{ K})} = 13.83$$

Now, at 150°C (423 K),

$$\ln \sigma = C - \frac{E_g}{2kT}$$

$$= 13.83 - \frac{0.67 \text{ eV}}{(2)(8.62 \times 10^{-5} \text{ eV/K})(423 \text{ K})} = 4.64$$

or

$$\sigma = 103.8 \ (\Omega\text{-m})^{-1}$$

DESIGN EXAMPLE 19.1

The room-temperature electrical conductivity of intrinsic silicon is 4×10^{-4} $(\Omega\text{-m})^{-1}$ (Table 19.2). An extrinsic n-type silicon material is desired having a room-temperature conductivity of 150 $(\Omega\text{-m})^{-1}$. Specify a donor impurity type that may be used as well as its concentration in atom percent to yield these electrical characteristics. Assume that the electron and hole mobilities are the same as for the intrinsic material, and that at room temperature the donor impurities are exhausted.

S O L U T I O N

First of all, those elements which, when added to silicon render it *n*-type, lie one group to the right of silicon in the periodic table; these include the group VA elements (Figure 2.6)—i.e., nitrogen, phosphorus, arsenic, and antimony.

Since this material is extrinsic and *n*-type, $n \gg p$, the electrical conductivity is a function of the free electron concentration according to Equation 19.16. Furthermore, the design stipulates that the donor impurity atoms are exhausted; therefore, the number of free electrons is about equal to the number of donor impurities, N_d. That is

$$n \sim N_d$$

We now solve Equation 19.16 for *n* using the stipulated conductivity [150 $(\Omega\text{-m})^{-1}$] and the electron mobility value provided in Table 19.2 (0.14 m^2/V-s). Thus

$$n = N_d = \frac{\sigma}{|e|\mu_e}$$

$$= \frac{150\,(\Omega\text{-m})^{-1}}{(1.6 \times 10^{-19}\,\text{C})(0.14\,m^2/\text{V-s})}$$

$$= 6.7 \times 10^{21}\,m^{-3}$$

It next becomes necessary to calculate the concentration of donor impurities in atom percent. This computation first requires the determination of the number of silicon atoms per cubic meter, N_{Si}, using Equation 4.2, which is as follows

$$N_{Si} = \frac{N_A \rho_{Si}}{A_{Si}}$$

$$= \frac{(6.023 \times 10^{23}\,\text{atoms/mol})(2.33\,\text{g/cm}^3)(10^6\,\text{cm}^3/m^3)}{28.09\,\text{g/mol}}$$

$$= 5 \times 10^{28}\,m^{-3}$$

The concentration of donor impurities in atom percent (C_d') is just the ratio of N_d and $N_d + N_{Si}$ multiplied by 100 as

$$C_d' = \frac{N_d}{N_d + N_{Si}} \times 100$$

$$= \frac{6.7 \times 10^{21}\,m^{-3}}{(6.7 \times 10^{21}\,m^{-3}) + (5 \times 10^{28}\,m^{-3})} \times 100 = 1.34 \times 10^{-5}$$

Thus, a silicon material having a room-temperature *n*-type electrical conductivity of 150 $(\Omega\text{-m})^{-1}$ must contain 1.34×10^{-5} at% nitrogen, phosphorus, arsenic, or antimony.

19.13 THE HALL EFFECT

For some material, it is on occasion desired to determine its majority charge carrier type, concentration, and mobility. Such determinations are not possible from a simple electrical conductivity measurement; a **Hall effect** experiment must also be conducted. This Hall effect is a result of the phenomenon whereby a magnetic field applied perpendicular to the direction of motion of a charged particle exerts a

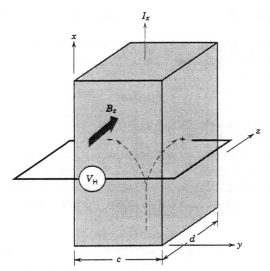

FIGURE 19.18 Schematic demonstration of the Hall effect. Positive and/or negative charge carriers that are part of the I_x current are deflected by the magnetic field B_z give rise to the Hall voltage, V_H.

force on the particle perpendicular to both the magnetic field and the particle motion directions.

In demonstrating the Hall effect, consider the specimen geometry shown in Figure 19.18, a parallelepiped specimen having one corner situated at the origin of a Cartesian coordinate system. In response to an externally applied electric field, the electrons and/or holes move in the x direction and give rise to a current I_x. When a magnetic field is imposed in the positive z direction (denoted as B_z), the resulting force brought to bear on the charge carriers will cause them to be deflected in the y direction—holes (positively charged carriers) to the right specimen face and electrons (negatively charged carriers) to the left face, as indicated in the figure. Thus, a voltage, termed the *Hall voltage* V_H, will be established in the y direction. The magnitude of V_H will depend on I_x, B_z, and the specimen thickness d as follows:

$$V_H = \frac{R_H I_x B_z}{d} \qquad (19.21)$$

In this expression R_H is termed the *Hall coefficient,* which is a constant for a given material. For metals, wherein conduction is by electrons, R_H is negative and equal to

$$R_H = \frac{1}{n|e|} \qquad (19.22)$$

Thus, n may be determined, inasmuch as R_H may be measured using Equation 19.21 and the magnitude of e, the charge on an electron, is known.

Furthermore, from Equation 19.8, the electron mobility μ_e is just

$$\mu_e = \frac{\sigma}{n|e|} \qquad (19.23a)$$

Or, using Equation 19.22,

$$\mu_e = |R_H|\sigma \qquad (19.23b)$$

Thus, the magnitude of μ_e may also be determined if the conductivity σ has also been measured.

For semiconducting materials, the determination of majority carrier type and computation of carrier concentration and mobility are more complicated and will not be discussed here.

EXAMPLE PROBLEM 19.4

The electrical conductivity and electron mobility for aluminum are 3.8×10^7 $(\Omega\text{-m})^{-1}$ and 0.0012 m^2/V-s, respectively. Calculate the Hall voltage for an aluminum specimen that is 15 mm thick for a current of 25 A and a magnetic field of 0.6 tesla (imposed in a direction perpendicular to the current).

SOLUTION

The Hall voltage V_H may be determined using Equation 19.21. However, it first becomes necessary to compute the Hall coefficient (R_H) from Equation 19.23b as

$$R_H = -\frac{\mu_e}{\sigma}$$

$$= -\frac{0.0012 \text{ m}^2/\text{V-s}}{3.8 \times 10^7 \, (\Omega\text{-m})^{-1}} = -3.16 \times 10^{-11} \text{ V-m/A-tesla}$$

Now, employment of Equation 19.21 leads to

$$V_H = \frac{R_H I_x B_z}{d}$$

$$= \frac{(-3.16 \times 10^{-11} \text{ V-m/A-tesla})(25 \text{ A})(0.6 \text{ tesla})}{15 \times 10^{-3} \text{ m}}$$

$$= -3.16 \times 10^{-8} \text{ V}$$

19.14 SEMICONDUCTOR DEVICES

The unique electrical properties of semiconductors permit their use in devices to perform specific electronic functions. Diodes and transistors, which have replaced old-fashioned vacuum tubes, are two familiar examples. Advantages of semiconductor devices (sometimes termed solid-state devices) include small size, low power consumption, and no warmup time. Vast numbers of extremely small circuits, each consisting of numerous electronic devices, may be incorporated onto a small silicon "chip." The invention of semiconductor devices, which has given rise to miniaturized circuitry, is responsible for the advent and extremely rapid growth of a host of new industries in the past few years.

THE p–n RECTIFYING JUNCTION

A rectifier, or **diode**, is an electronic device that allows the current to flow in one direction only; for example, a rectifier transforms an alternating current into direct current. Before the advent of the p–n junction semiconductor rectifier, this operation was carried out using the vacuum tube diode. The p–n **rectifying junction** is con-

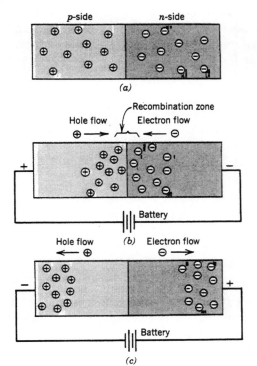

FIGURE 19.19 For a p–n rectifying junction, representations of electron and hole distributions for (a) no electrical potential, (b) forward bias, and (c) reverse bias.

structed from a single piece of semiconductor which is doped so as to be n-type on one side and p-type on the other (Figure 19.19a). If pieces of n- and p-type materials are joined together, a poor rectifier results, since the presence of a surface between the two sections renders the device very inefficient. Also, single crystals of semiconducting materials must be used in all devices because electronic phenomena that are deleterious to operation occur at grain boundaries.

Before the application of any potential across the p–n specimen, holes will be the dominant carriers on the p-side, and electrons will predominate in the n-region, as illustrated in Figure 19.19a. An external electric potential may be established across a p–n junction with two different polarities. When a battery is used, the positive terminal may be connected to the p-side, and the negative terminal to the n-side; this is referred to as a **forward bias.** The opposite polarity (minus to p and plus to n) is termed **reverse bias.**

The response of the charge carriers to the application of a forward-biased potential is demonstrated in Figure 19.19b. The holes on the p-side and the electrons on the n-side are attracted to the junction. As electrons and holes encounter one another near the junction, they continuously recombine and annihilate one another, according to

$$\text{electron} + \text{hole} \longrightarrow \text{energy} \tag{19.24}$$

Thus for this bias, large numbers of charge carriers flow across the semiconductor and to the junction, as evidenced by an appreciable current and a low resistivity. The current–voltage characteristics for forward bias are shown on the right-hand half of Figure 19.20.

For reverse bias (Figure 19.19c), both holes and electrons, as majority carriers,

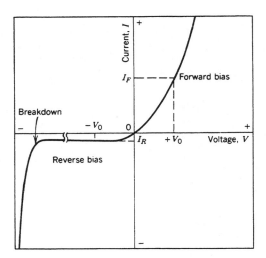

FIGURE 19.20   The current–voltage characteristics of a *p–n* junction for forward and reverse biases. The phenomenon of breakdown is also shown.

are rapidly drawn away from the junction; this separation of positive and negative charges (or polarization) leaves the junction region relatively free of mobile charge carriers. Recombination will not occur to any appreciable extent, so that the junction is now highly insulative. Figure 19.20 also illustrates the current–voltage behavior for reverse bias.

The rectification process in terms of input voltage and output current is demonstrated in Figure 19.21. Whereas voltage varies sinusoidally with time (Figure 19.21*a*), maximum current flow for reverse bias voltage I_R is extremely small in comparison to that for forward bias I_F (Figure 19.21*b*). Furthermore, correspondence between I_F and I_R and the imposed maximum voltage ($\pm V_0$) is noted in Figure 19.20.

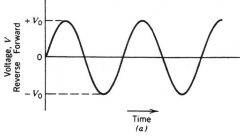

FIGURE 19.21   (*a*) Voltage versus time for the input to a *p–n* rectifying junction. (*b*) Current versus time, showing rectification of voltage in (*a*) by a *p–n* rectifying junction having the voltage–current characteristics shown in Figure 19.20.

At high reverse bias voltages, sometimes on the order of several hundred volts, large numbers of charge carriers (electrons and holes) are generated. This gives rise to a very abrupt increase in current, a phenomenon known as *breakdown*, also shown in Figure 19.20, and discussed in more detail in Section 19.21.

THE TRANSISTOR

Transistors, which are extremely important semiconducting devices in today's micro-electronic circuitry, are capable of two primary types of function. First, they can perform the same operation as their vacuum tube precursor, the triode; that is, they can amplify an electrical signal. In addition, they serve as switching devices in computers for the processing and storage of information. The two major types are the **junction** (or bimodal) **transistor** and the *metal-oxide-semiconductor field-effect transistor* (abbreviated as **MOSFET**).

Junction Transistors

The junction transistor is composed of two *p–n* junctions arranged back to back in either the *n–p–n* or the *p–n–p* configuration; the latter variety is discussed here. Figure 19.22 is a schematic representation of a *p–n–p* junction transistor along with its attendant circuitry. A very thin *n*-type *base* region is sandwiched in between *p*-type *emitter* and *collector* regions. The circuit that includes the emitter–base junction (junction 1) is forward biased, whereas a reverse bias voltage is applied across the base–collector junction (junction 2).

Figure 19.23 illustrates the mechanics of operation in terms of the motion of charge carriers. Since the emitter is *p*-type and junction 1 is forward biased, large numbers of holes enter the base region. These injected holes are minority carriers in the *n*-type base, and some will combine with the majority electrons. However, if the base is extremely narrow and the semiconducting materials have been properly prepared, most of these holes will be swept through the base without recombination, then across junction 2 and into the *p*-type collector. The holes now become a part of the emitter–collector circuit. A small increase in input voltage within the emitter–base circuit produces a large increase in current across junction 2. This large increase in collector current is also reflected by a large increase in voltage across the load resistor, which is also shown in the circuit (Figure 19.22). Thus, a

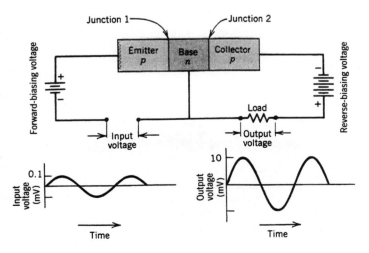

FIGURE 19.22 Schematic diagram of a *p–n–p* junction transistor and its associated circuitry, including input and output voltage–time characteristics showing voltage amplification. (Adapted from A. G. Guy, *Essentials of Materials Science*, McGraw-Hill Book Company, New York, 1976.)

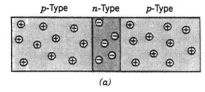

p-Type   *n*-Type   *p*-Type

(a)

Junction 1   Junction 2
Emitter   Base   Collector

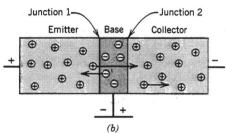

(b)

FIGURE 19.23 For a junction transistor (*p–n–p* type), the distributions and directions of electron and hole motion (*a*) when no potential is applied and (*b*) with appropriate bias for voltage amplification.

voltage signal that passes through a junction transistor experiences amplification; this effect is also illustrated in Figure 19.22 by the two voltage–time plots.

Similar reasoning applies to the operation of an *n–p–n* transistor, except that electrons instead of holes are injected across the base and into the collector.

The MOSFET

One variety of MOSFET consists of two small islands of *p*-type semiconductor that are created within a substrate of *n*-type silicon, as shown in cross section in Figure 19.24; the islands are joined by a narrow *p*-type channel. Appropriate metal connections (source and drain) are made to these islands; an insulating layer of silicon dioxide is formed by the surface oxidation of the silicon. A final connector (gate) is then fashioned onto the surface of this insulating layer.

The operation of a MOSFET differs from that of the junction transistor in that a single type of charge carrier (either electron or hole) is active. The conductivity of the channel is varied by the presence of an electric field imposed on the gate. For example, imposition of a positive field on the gate will drive charge carriers (in this case holes) out of the channel, thereby reducing the electrical conductivity. Thus, a small alteration in the field at the gate will produce a relatively large variation in current between the source and the drain. In some respects, then, the operation of a MOSFET is very similar to that described for the junction transistor. The primary difference is that the gate current is exceedingly small in comparison

FIGURE 19.24 Schematic cross-sectional view of a MOSFET transistor.

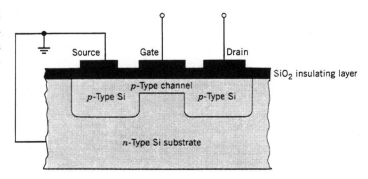

Source   Gate   Drain

SiO$_2$ insulating layer

p-Type channel
p-Type Si   *p*-Type Si

n-Type Si substrate

to the base current of a junction transistor. MOSFETs are, therefore, used where the signal sources to be amplified cannot sustain an appreciable current.

Semiconductors in Computers

In addition to their ability to amplify an imposed electrical signal, transistors and diodes may also act as switching devices, a feature utilized for arithmetic and logical operations, and also for information storage in computers. Computer numbers and functions are expressed in terms of a binary code (i.e., numbers written to the base 2). Within this framework, numbers are represented by a series of two states (sometimes designated 0 and 1). Now, transistors and diodes within a digital circuit operate as switches that also have two states—on and off, or conducting and nonconducting; "off" corresponds to one binary number state, and "on" to the other. Thus, a single number may be represented by a collection of circuit elements containing transistors that are appropriately switched.

MICROELECTRONIC CIRCUITRY

During the past few years, the advent of microelectronic circuitry, where thousands of electronic components and circuits are incorporated into a very small space, has revolutionized the field of electronics. This revolution was precipitated, in part, by aerospace technology, which necessitated computers and electronic devices that were small and had low power requirements. As a result of refinement in processing and fabrication techniques, there has been an astonishing depreciation in the cost of integrated circuitry. Consequently, at the time of this writing, personal computers are affordable to a large segment of the population in the United States. Also, the use of **integrated circuits** has become infused into many other facets of our lives—calculators, communications, watches, industrial production and control, and all phases of the electronics industry.

Inexpensive microelectronic circuits are mass produced by using some very ingenious fabrication techniques. The process begins with the growth of relatively large cylindrical single crystals of high-purity silicon from which thin circular wafers are cut. Many microelectronic or integrated circuits, sometimes called "chips," are prepared on a single wafer; a photograph of one such wafer containing numerous chips is shown in Figure 23.20. A chip is rectangular, typically on the order of 6 mm ($\frac{1}{4}$ in.) on a side and contains thousands of circuit elements: diodes, transistors, resistors, and capacitors. One such microprocessor chip is shown in its entirety in Figure 23.22b; also shown are the numerous electrical leads that are used to connect this chip to its leadframe, which in turn is bonded to a printed circuit board. Enlarged photographs of microprocessor chips at different magnifications are presented in Figures 19.25a and 19.25b; these micrographs reveal the intricacy of integrated circuits. At this time, 16,000,000 component chips are being produced, and memory capabilities currently double about every 18 months.

Microelectronic circuits consist of many layers that lie within or are stacked on top of the silicon wafer in a precisely detailed pattern. Using photolithographic techniques, for each layer, very small elements are masked in accordance with a microscopic pattern. Circuit elements are constructed by the selective introduction of specific materials (by diffusion or ion implantation) into unmasked regions to create localized n-type, p-type, high-resistivity, or conductive areas. This procedure is repeated layer by layer until the total integrated circuit has been fabricated, as illustrated in the MOSFET schematic (Figure 19.24). Elements of integrated circuits are shown in Figure 19.25 and on page 591.

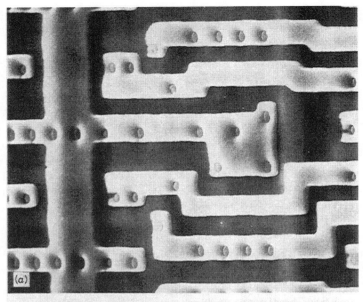

FIGURE 19.25 (a) Scanning electron micrograph showing a small region of a microprocessing chip (a 0.5 MB selected address device). The narrow, white regions are an aluminum top layer that serves as the wiring for this device. The gray regions are diffusion-layer doped silicon that have been coated with an interlayer dielectric. Approximately 2000×. (b) An optical photomicrograph showing a portion of a circuit that is used to test microprocessing chips. The narrow, light regions are aluminum connectors, while the white, square areas are test pads (semiconductor devices); test circuits (also composed of semiconductor devices) appear in the upper left-hand corner of the photograph. Approximately 50×. (Both photographs courtesy of Nick Gonzales of National Semiconductor Corporation, West Jordan, Utah.)

ELECTRICAL CONDUCTION IN IONIC CERAMICS AND IN POLYMERS

Most polymers and ionic ceramics are insulating materials at room temperature and, therefore, have electron energy band structures similar to that represented in Figure 19.4c; a filled valence band is separated from an empty conduction band by a relatively large band gap, usually greater than 2 eV. Thus, at normal temperatures only very few electrons may be excited across the band gap by the available thermal energy, which accounts for the very small values of conductivity; Table 19.3 gives the room-temperature electrical conductivity of several of these materials. (The electrical resistivities of a large number of ceramic and polymeric materials are provided in Appendix C.9.) Of course, many materials are utilized on the basis of their ability to insulate, and thus a high electrical resistivity is desirable. With rising temperature insulating materials experience an increase in electrical conductivity, which may ultimately be greater than that for semiconductors.

19.15 CONDUCTION IN IONIC MATERIALS

Both cations and anions in ionic materials possess an electric charge and, as a consequence, are capable of migration or diffusion when a electric field is present. Thus an electric current will result from the net movement of these charged ions, which will be present in addition to that due to any electron motion. Of course, anion and cation migrations will be in opposite directions. The total conductivity of an ionic material σ_{total} is thus equal to the sum of both electronic and ionic contributions, as follows:

$$\sigma_{total} = \sigma_{electronic} + \sigma_{ionic} \qquad (19.25)$$

Table 19.3 Typical Room-Temperature Electrical Conductivities for 13 Nonmetallic Materials

Material	Electrical Conductivity $[(\Omega\text{-}m)^{-1}]$
Graphite	3×10^4–2×10^5
Ceramics	
Concrete (dry)	10^{-9}
Soda-lime glass	10^{-10}–10^{-11}
Porcelain	10^{-10}–10^{-12}
Borosilicate glass	$\sim 10^{-13}$
Aluminum oxide	$< 10^{-13}$
Fused silica	$< 10^{-18}$
Polymers	
Phenol-formaldehyde	10^{-9}–10^{-10}
Polymethyl methacrylate	$< 10^{-12}$
Nylon 6,6	10^{-12}–10^{-13}
Polystyrene	$< 10^{-14}$
Polyethylene	10^{-15}–10^{-17}
Polytetrafluoroethylene	$< 10^{-17}$

Either contribution may predominate depending on the material, its purity, and, of course, temperature.

A mobility μ_i may be associated with each of the ionic species as follows:

$$\mu_i = \frac{n_i e D_i}{kT} \tag{19.26}$$

where n_i and D_i represent, respectively, the valence and diffusion coefficient of a particular ion; e, k, and T denote the same parameters as explained earlier in the chapter. Thus, the ionic contribution to the total conductivity increases with increasing temperature, as does the electronic component. However, in spite of the two conductivity contributions, most ionic materials remain insulative, even at elevated temperatures.

19.16 ELECTRICAL PROPERTIES OF POLYMERS

Most polymeric materials are poor conductors of electricity (Table 19.3) because of the unavailability of large numbers of free electrons to participate in the conduction process. The mechanism of electrical conduction in these materials is not well understood, but it is felt that conduction in polymers of high purity is electronic.

CONDUCTING POLYMERS

Within the past several years, polymeric materials have been synthesized that have electrical conductivities on par with metallic conductors; they are appropriately termed *conducting polymers*. Conductivities as high as 1.5×10^7 $(\Omega\text{-m})^{-1}$ have been achieved in these materials; on a volume basis, this value corresponds to one fourth of the conductivity of copper, or twice its conductivity on the basis of weight.

This phenomenon is observed in a dozen or so polymers, including polyacetylene, polyparaphenylene, polypyrrole, and polyaniline that have been doped with appropriate impurities. As is the case with semiconductors, these polymers may be made either *n*-type (i.e., free-electron dominant) or *p*-type (i.e., hole dominant) depending on the dopant. However, unlike semiconductors, the dopant atoms or molecules do not substitute for or replace any of the polymer atoms.

High-purity polymers have electron band structures characteristic of electrical insulators (Figure 19.4c). The mechanism by which large numbers of free electrons and holes are generated in these conducting polymers is complex and not well understood. In very simple terms, it appears that the dopant atoms lead to the formation of new energy bands that overlap the valence and conduction bands of the intrinsic polymer, giving rise to a partially filled conduction or valence band, and the production at room temperature of a high concentration of free electrons or holes. Orienting the polymer chains, either mechanically (Section 16.3) or magnetically, during synthesis results in a highly anisotropic material having a maximum conductivity along the direction of orientation.

These conducting polymers have the potential to be used in a host of applications inasmuch as they have low densities, are highly flexible, and are easy to produce. Rechargeable batteries are currently being manufactured that employ polymer electrodes; in many respects these are superior to their metallic counterpart batteries. Other possible applications include wiring in aircraft and aerospace components, antistatic coatings for clothing, electromagnetic screening materials, and electronic devices (e.g., transistors and diodes).

DIELECTRIC BEHAVIOR

A **dielectric** material is one that is electrically insulating (nonmetallic) and exhibits or may be made to exhibit an electric dipole structure; that is, there is a separation of positive and negative electrically charged entities on a molecular or atomic level. This concept of an electric dipole was introduced in Section 2.7. As a result of dipole interactions with electric fields, dielectric materials are utilized in capacitors.

19.17 CAPACITANCE

When a voltage is applied across a capacitor, one plate becomes positively charged, the other negatively charged, with the corresponding electric field directed from the positive to the negative. The **capacitance** C is related to the quantity of charge stored on either plate Q by[2]

$$C = \frac{Q}{V} \tag{19.27}$$

where V is the voltage applied across the capacitor. The units of capacitance are coulombs per volt, or farads (F).

Now, consider a parallel-plate capacitor with a vacuum in the region between the plates (Figure 19.26a). The capacitance may be computed from the relationship

$$C = \epsilon_0 \frac{A}{l} \tag{19.28}$$

where A represents the area of the plates and l is the distance between them. The parameter ϵ_0, called the **permittivity** of a vacuum, is a universal constant having the value of 8.85×10^{-12} F/m.

If a dielectric material is inserted into the region within the plates (Figure 19.26b), then

$$C = \epsilon \frac{A}{l} \tag{19.29}$$

where ϵ is the permittivity of this dielectric medium, which will be greater in magnitude than ϵ_0. The relative permittivity ϵ_r, often called the **dielectric constant,** is equal to the ratio

$$\epsilon_r = \frac{\epsilon}{\epsilon_0} \tag{19.30}$$

which is greater than unity and represents the increase in charge storing capacity by insertion of the dielectric medium between the plates. The dielectric constant is one material property that is of prime consideration for capacitor design. The ϵ_r values of a number of dielectric materials are contained in Table 19.4.

---

[2] By convention, the uppercase "C" is used to represent both capacitance and the unit of charge, coulomb. To minimize confusion in this discussion, the capacitance designation will be italicized, as C.

FIGURE 19.26
A parallel-plate
capacitor (a) when a
vacuum is present and
(b) when a dielectric
material is present.
(From K. M. Ralls,
T. H. Courtney, and
J. Wulff, *Introduction to
Materials Science and
Engineering*. Copyright
© 1976 by John
Wiley & Sons, Inc.
Reprinted by
permission of John
Wiley & Sons, Inc.)

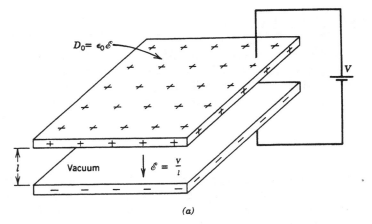

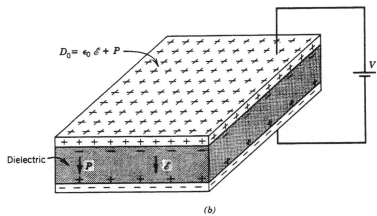

Table 19.4   Dielectric Constants and Strengths for Some Dielectric Materials

Material	Dielectric Constant		Dielectric Strength (V/mil)[a]
	60 Hz	1 MHz	
Ceramics			
Titanate ceramics	—	15–10,000	50–300
Mica	—	5.4–8.7	1000–2000
Steatite (MgO–SiO_2)	—	5.5–7.5	200–350
Soda–lime glass	6.9	6.9	250
Porcelain	6.0	6.0	40–400
Fused silica	4.0	3.8	250
Polymers			
Phenol-formaldehyde	5.3	4.8	300–400
Nylon 6,6	4.0	3.6	400
Polystyrene	2.6	2.6	500–700
Polyethylene	2.3	2.3	450–500
Polytetrafluoroethylene	2.1	2.1	400–500

[a] One mil = 0.001 in. These values of dielectric strength are average ones, the magnitude being dependent on specimen thickness and geometry, as well as the rate of application and duration of the applied electric field.

FIGURE 19.27   Schematic representation of an electric dipole generated by two electric charges (of magnitude q) separated by the distance d; the associated polarization vector p is also shown.

19.18 FIELD VECTORS AND POLARIZATION

Perhaps the best approach to an explanation of the phenomenon of capacitance is with the aid of field vectors. To begin, for every electric dipole, there is a separation between a positive and a negative electric charge as demonstrated in Figure 19.27. An electric dipole moment p is associated with each dipole as follows:

$$p = qd \tag{19.31}$$

where q is the magnitude of each dipole charge and d is the distance of separation between them. In reality, a dipole moment is a vector that is directed from the negative to the positive charge, as indicated in Figure 19.27. In the presence of an electric field $\mathscr{E}$, which is also a vector quantity, a force (or torque) will come to bear on an electric dipole to orient it with the applied field; this phenomenon is illustrated in Figure 19.28. The process of dipole alignment is termed **polarization.**

Again, returning to the capacitor, the surface charge density D, or quantity of charge per unit area of capacitor plate (C/m^2), is proportional to the electric field. When a vacuum is present, then

$$D_0 = \epsilon_0 \mathscr{E} \tag{19.32}$$

the constant of proportionality being ϵ_0. Furthermore, an analogous expression exists for the dielectric case, that is,

$$D = \epsilon \mathscr{E} \tag{19.33}$$

Sometimes, D is also called the **dielectric displacement.**

The increase in capacitance, or dielectric constant, can be explained using a simplified model of polarization within a dielectric material. Consider the capacitor in Figure 19.29a, the vacuum situation, wherein a charge of $+Q_0$ is stored on the top plate, and $-Q_0$ on the bottom one. When a dielectric is introduced and an

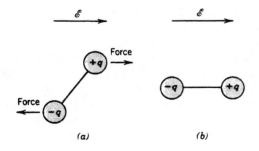

FIGURE 19.28   (a) Imposed forces (torque) acting on a dipole by an electric field. (b) Final dipole alignment with the field.

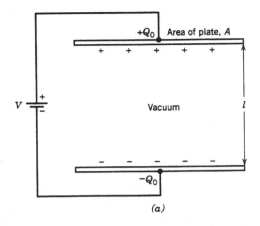

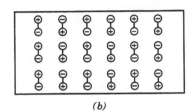

FIGURE 19.29 Schematic representations of (a) the charge stored on capacitor plates for a vacuum, (b) the dipole arrangement in an unpolarized dielectric, and (c) the increased charge storing capacity resulting from the polarization of a dielectric material. (Adapted from A. G. Guy, *Essentials of Materials Science,* McGraw-Hill Book Company, New York, 1976.)

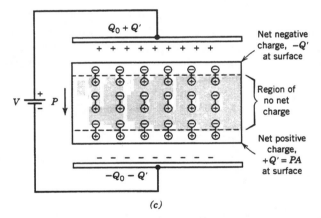

electric field is applied, the entire solid within the plates becomes polarized (Figure 19.29c). As a result of this polarization, there is a net accumulation of negative charge of magnitude $-Q'$ at the dielectric surface near the positively charged plate and, in a similar manner, a surplus of $+Q'$ charge at the surface adjacent to the negative plate. For the region of dielectric removed from these surfaces, polarization effects are not important. Thus, if each plate and its adjacent dielectric surface are considered to be a single entity, the induced charge from the dielectric ($+Q'$ or $-Q'$) may be thought of as nullifying some of the charge that originally existed on the plate for a vacuum ($-Q_0$ or $+Q_0$). The voltage imposed across the plates is maintained at the vacuum value by increasing the charge at the negative (or bottom) plate by an amount $-Q'$, and the top plate by $+Q'$. Electrons are caused to flow from the positive to the negative plate by the external voltage source such that the proper voltage is reestablished. And so the charge on each plate is now $Q_0 + Q'$, having been increased by an amount Q'.

Table 19.5 **Primary and Derived Units for Various Electrical Parameters and Field Vectors**

| Quantity | Symbol | SI Units | |
		Derived	Primary
Electric potential	V	volt	kg-m^2/s^2-C
Electric current	I	ampere	C/s
Electric field strength	$\mathscr{E}$	volt/meter	kg-m/s^2-C
Resistance	R	ohm	kg-m^2/s-C^2
Resistivity	ρ	ohm-meter	kg-m^3/s-C^2
Conductivity	σ	(ohm-meter)$^{-1}$	s-C^2/kg-m^3
Electric charge	Q	coulomb	C
Capacitance	C	farad	s^2-C^2/kg-m^2
Permittivity	ϵ	farad/meter	s^{2}C^2/kg-m^3
Dielectric constant	ϵ_r	ratio	ratio
Dielectric displacement	D	farad-volt/m^2	C/m^2
Electric polarization	P	farad-volt/m^2	C/m^2

In the presence of a dielectric, the surface charge density on the plates of a capacitor may also be represented by

$$D = \epsilon_0 \mathscr{E} + P \qquad (19.34)$$

where P is the *polarization*, or the increase in charge density above that for a vacuum because of the presence of the dielectric; or, from Figure 19.29c, $P = Q'/A$, where A is the area of each plate. The units of P are the same as for D (C/m^2).

The polarization P may also be thought of as the total dipole moment per unit volume of the dielectric material, or as a polarization electric field within the dielectric that results from the mutual alignment of the many atomic or molecular dipoles with the externally applied field $\mathscr{E}$. For many dielectric materials, P is proportional to $\mathscr{E}$ through the relationship

$$P = \epsilon_0(\epsilon_r - 1)\mathscr{E} \qquad (19.35)$$

in which case ϵ_r is independent of the magnitude of the electric field.

Table 19.5 lists the several dielectric parameters along with their units.

EXAMPLE PROBLEM 19.5

Consider a parallel-plate capacitor having an area of 6.45×10^{-4} m^2 (1 in.^{2}) and a plate separation of 2×10^{-3} m (0.08 in.) across which a potential of 10 V is applied. If a material having a dielectric constant of 6.0 is positioned within the region between the plates, compute

(a) The capacitance.

(b) The magnitude of the charge stored on each plate.

(c) The dielectric displacement D.

(d) The polarization.

SOLUTION

(a) Capacitance is calculated using Equation 19.29; however, the permittivity ϵ of the dielectric medium must first be determined from Equation 19.30 as follows:

$$\epsilon = \epsilon_r \epsilon_0 = (6.0)(8.85 \times 10^{-12} \text{ F/m})$$

$$= 5.31 \times 10^{-11} \text{ F/m}$$

Thus, the capacitance is

$$C = \epsilon \frac{A}{l} = (5.31 \times 10^{-11} \text{ F/m})\left(\frac{6.45 \times 10^{-4} \text{ m}^2}{2 \times 10^{-3} \text{ m}}\right)$$

$$= 1.71 \times 10^{-11} \text{ F}$$

(b) Since the capacitance has been determined, the charge stored may be computed using Equation 19.27, according to

$$Q = CV = (1.71 \times 10^{-11} \text{ F})(10 \text{ V}) = 1.71 \times 10^{-10} \text{ C}$$

(c) The dielectric displacement is calculated from Equation 19.33, which yields

$$D = \epsilon \mathscr{E} = \epsilon \frac{V}{l} = \frac{(5.31 \times 10^{-11} \text{ F/m})(10 \text{ V})}{2 \times 10^{-3} \text{ m}}$$

$$= 2.66 \times 10^{-7} \text{ C/m}^2$$

(d) Using Equation 19.34, the polarization may be determined as follows:

$$P = D - \epsilon_0 \mathscr{E} = D - \epsilon_0 \frac{V}{l}$$

$$= 2.66 \times 10^{-7} \text{ C/m}^2 - \frac{(8.85 \times 10^{-12} \text{ F/m})(10 \text{ V})}{2 \times 10^{-3} \text{ m}}$$

$$= 2.22 \times 10^{-7} \text{ C/m}^2$$

19.19 TYPES OF POLARIZATION

Again, polarization is the alignment of permanent or induced atomic or molecular dipole moments with an externally applied electric field. There are three types or sources of polarization: electronic, ionic, and orientation. Dielectric materials ordinarily exhibit at least one of these polarization types depending on the material and also the manner of the external field application.

ELECTRONIC POLARIZATION

Electronic polarization may be induced to one degree or another in all atoms. It results from a displacement of the center of the negatively charged electron cloud relative to the positive nucleus of an atom by the electric field (Figure 19.30a). This polarization type is found in all dielectric materials, and, of course, exists only while an electric field is present.

IONIC POLARIZATION

Ionic polarization occurs only in materials that are ionic. An applied field acts to displace cations in one direction and anions in the opposite direction, which gives

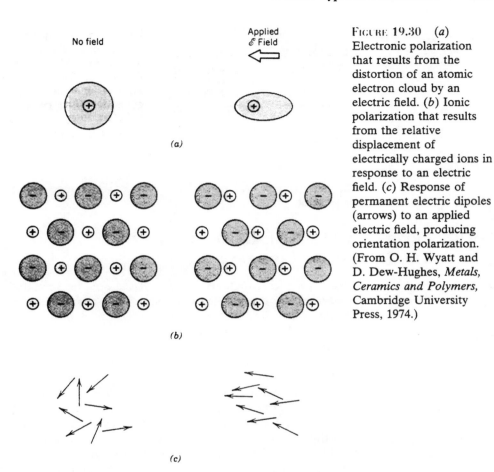

No field

Applied
$\mathscr{E}$ Field

(a)

(b)

(c)

FIGURE 19.30 (a) Electronic polarization that results from the distortion of an atomic electron cloud by an electric field. (b) Ionic polarization that results from the relative displacement of electrically charged ions in response to an electric field. (c) Response of permanent electric dipoles (arrows) to an applied electric field, producing orientation polarization. (From O. H. Wyatt and D. Dew-Hughes, *Metals, Ceramics and Polymers*, Cambridge University Press, 1974.)

rise to a net dipole moment. This phenomenon is illustrated in Figure 19.30b. The magnitude of the dipole moment for each ion pair p_i is equal to the product of the relative displacement d_i and the charge on each ion, or

$$p_i = qd_i \tag{19.36}$$

ORIENTATION POLARIZATION

The third type, **orientation polarization,** is found only in substances that possess permanent dipole moments. Polarization results from a rotation of the permanent moments into the direction of the applied field, as represented in Figure 19.30c. This alignment tendency is counteracted by the thermal vibrations of the atoms, such that polarization decreases with increasing temperature.

The total polarization P of a substance is equal to the sum of the electronic, ionic, and orientation polarizations (P_e, P_i, and P_o, respectively), or

$$P = P_e + P_i + P_o \tag{19.37}$$

It is possible for one or more of these contributions to the total polarization to be either absent or negligible in magnitude relative to the others. For example,

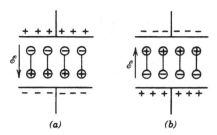

FIGURE 19.31 Dipole orientations for (a) one polarity of an alternating electric field and (b) for the reversed polarity. (Adapted from Richard A. Flinn and Paul K. Trojan, *Engineering Materials and Their Applications*, 4th edition. Copyright © 1990 by John Wiley & Sons, Inc. Reprinted by permission of John Wiley & Sons, Inc.)

ionic polarization will not exist in covalently bonded materials in which no ions are present.

19.20 FREQUENCY DEPENDENCE OF THE DIELECTRIC CONSTANT

In many practical situations the current is alternating (ac); that is, an applied voltage or electric field changes direction with time, as indicated in Figure 19.21a. Now, consider a dielectric material that is subject to polarization by an ac electric field. With each direction reversal, the dipoles attempt to reorient with the field, as illustrated in Figure 19.31, a process requiring some finite time. For each polarization type, some minimum reorientation time exists, which depends on the ease with which the particular dipoles are capable of realignment. A **relaxation frequency** is taken as the reciprocal of this minimum reorientation time.

A dipole cannot keep shifting orientation direction when the frequency of the applied electric field exceeds its relaxation frequency, and therefore, will not make a contribution to the dielectric constant. The dependence of ϵ_r on the field frequency is represented schematically in Figure 19.32 for a dielectric medium that exhibits all three types of polarization; note that the frequency axis is scaled logarithmically. As indicated in Figure 19.32, when a polarization mechanism ceases to function, there is an abrupt drop in the dielectric constant; otherwise, ϵ_r is virtually frequency independent. Table 19.4 gave values of the dielectric constant at 60 Hz and 1 MHz;

FIGURE 19.32 Variation of dielectric constant with frequency of an alternating electric field. Electronic, ionic, and orientation polarization contributions to the dielectric constant are indicated.

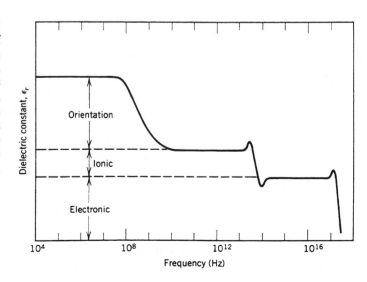

these provide an indication of this frequency dependence at the low end of the frequency spectrum.

The absorption of electrical energy by a dielectric material that is subjected to an alternating electric field is termed *dielectric loss.* This loss may be important at electric field frequencies in the vicinity of the relaxation frequency for each of the operative dipole types for a specific material. A low dielectric loss is desired at the frequency of utilization.

19.21 DIELECTRIC STRENGTH

When very high electric fields are applied across dielectric materials, large numbers of electrons may suddenly be excited to energies within the conduction band. As a result, the current through the dielectric by the motion of these electrons increases dramatically; sometimes localized melting, burning, or vaporization produces irreversible degradation and perhaps even failure of the material. This phenomenon is known as dielectric breakdown. The **dielectric strength,** sometimes called the breakdown strength, represents the magnitude of an electric field necessary to produce breakdown. Table 19.4 presented dielectric strengths for several materials.

19.22 DIELECTRIC MATERIALS

A number of ceramics and polymers are utilized as insulators and/or in capacitors. Many of the ceramics, including glass, porcelain, steatite, and mica, have dielectric constants within the range of 6 to 10 (Table 19.4). These materials also exhibit a high degree of dimensional stability and mechanical strength. Typical applications include powerline and electrical insulation, switch bases, and light receptacles. The titania (TiO_2) and titanate ceramics, such as barium titanate ($BaTiO_3$), can be made to have extremely high dielectric constants, which render them especially useful for some capacitor applications.

The magnitude of the dielectric constant for most polymers is less than for ceramics, since the latter may exhibit greater dipole moments; ϵ_r values for polymers generally lie between 2 and 5. These materials are commonly utilized for insulation of wires, cables, motors, generators, and so on, and, in addition, for some capacitors.

OTHER ELECTRICAL CHARACTERISTICS OF MATERIALS

Two other relatively important and novel electrical characteristics that are found in some materials deserve brief mention, namely, ferroelectricity and piezoelectricity.

19.23 FERROELECTRICITY

The group of dielectric materials called **ferroelectrics** exhibit spontaneous polarization, that is, polarization in the absence of an electric field. They are the dielectric analogue of ferromagnetic materials, which may display permanent magnetic behavior. There must exist in ferroelectric materials permanent electric dipoles, the origin of which is explained for barium titanate, one of the most common ferroelectrics. The spontaneous polarization is a consequence of the positioning of the Ba^{2+}, Ti^{4+}, and O^{2-} ions within the unit cell, as represented in Figure 19.33. The Ba^{2+} ions are located at the corners of the unit cell, which is of tetragonal symmetry (a cube that

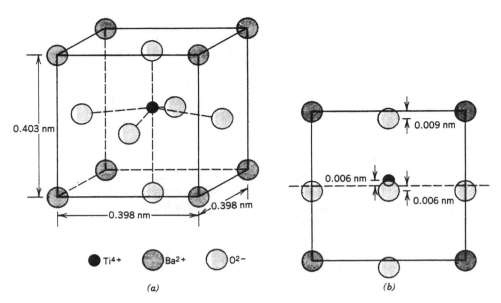

FIGURE 19.33   A barium titanate (BaTiO$_3$) unit cell (*a*) in an isometric projection, and (*b*) looking at one face, which shows the displacements of Ti^{4+} and O^{2-} ions from the center of the face.

has been elongated slightly in one direction). The dipole moment results from the relative displacements of the O^{2-} and Ti^{4+} ions from their symmetrical positions as shown in the side view of the unit cell. The O^{2-} ions are located near, but slightly below, the centers of each of the six faces, whereas the Ti^{4+} ion is displaced upward from the unit cell center. Thus, a permanent ionic dipole moment is associated with each unit cell. However, when barium titanate is heated above its *ferroelectric Curie temperature* [120°C (250°F)], the unit cell becomes cubic, and all ions assume symmetric positions within the cubic unit cell; the material now has a perovskite crystal structure (Section 13.2), and the ferroelectric behavior ceases.

Spontaneous polarization of this group of materials results as a consequence of interactions between adjacent permanent dipoles wherein they mutually align, all in the same direction. For example, with barium titanate, the relative displacements of O^{2-} and Ti^{4+} ions are in the same direction for all the unit cells within some volume region of the specimen. Other materials display ferroelectricity; these include Rochelle salt (NaKC$_4$H$_4$O$_6 \cdot$4H$_2$O), potassium dihydrogen phosphate (KH$_2$PO$_4$), potassium niobate (KNbO$_3$), and lead zirconate–titanate (Pb[ZrO$_3$, TiO$_3$]). Ferroelectrics have extremely high dielectric constants at relatively low applied field frequencies; for example, at room temperature, ϵ_r for barium titanate may be as high as 5000. Consequently, capacitors made from these materials can be significantly smaller than capacitors made from other dielectric materials.

19.24 PIEZOELECTRICITY

An unusual property exhibited for a few ceramic materials is piezoelectricity, or, literally, pressure electricity: polarization is induced and an electric field is established across a specimen by the application of external forces. Reversing the sign of an external force (i.e., from tension to compression) reverses the direction of the field. The piezoelectric effect is demonstrated in Figure 19.34.

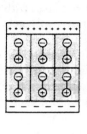 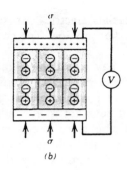

FIGURE 19.34 (a) Dipoles within a piezoelectric material. (b) A voltage is generated when the material is subjected to a compressive stress. (Adapted from L. Van Vlack, *Elements of Materials Science and Engineering*, © 1989 by Addison-Wesley Publishing Company, Inc. Reprinted by permission of Addison-Wesley Publishing Company, Inc.)

(a)   (b)

Piezoelectric materials are utilized in transducers, devices that convert electrical energy into mechanical strains, or vice versa. Familiar applications that employ piezoelectrics include phonograph pickups, microphones, ultrasonic generators, strain gages, and sonar detectors. In a phonograph cartridge, as the stylus traverses the grooves on a record, a pressure variation is imposed on a piezoelectric material located in the cartridge, which is then transformed into an electric signal, and amplified before going to the speaker.

Piezoelectric materials include titanates of barium and lead, lead zirconate $(PbZrO_3)$, ammonium dihydrogen phosphate $(NH_4H_2PO_4)$, and quartz. This property is characteristic of materials having complicated crystal structures with a low degree of symmetry. The piezoelectric behavior of a polycrystalline specimen may be improved by heating above its Curie temperature and then cooling to room temperature in a strong electric field.

SUMMARY

The ease with which a material is capable of transmitting an electric current is expressed in terms of electrical conductivity or its reciprocal, resistivity. On the basis of its conductivity, a solid material may be classified as a metal, a semiconductor, or an insulator.

For most materials, an electric current results from the motion of free electrons, which are accelerated in response to an applied electric field. The number of these free electrons depends on the electron energy band structure of the material. An electron band is just a series of electron states that are closely spaced with respect to energy, and one such band may exist for each electron subshell found in the isolated atom. By "electron energy band structure" is meant the manner in which the outermost bands are arranged relative to one another and then filled with electrons. A distinctive band structure type exists for metals, for semiconductors, and for insulators. An electron becomes free by being excited from a filled state in one band, to an available empty state above the Fermi energy. Relatively small energies are required for electron excitations in metals, giving rise to large numbers of free electrons. Larger energies are required for electron excitations in semiconductors and insulators, which accounts for their lower free electron concentrations and smaller conductivity values.

Free electrons being acted on by an electric field are scattered by imperfections in the crystal lattice. The magnitude of electron mobility is indicative of the frequency of these scattering events. In many materials, the electrical conductivity is proportional to the product of the electron concentration and the mobility.

636 • Chapter 19 / Electrical Properties

For metallic materials, electrical resistivity increases with temperature, impurity content, and plastic deformation. The contribution of each to the total resistivity is additive.

Semiconductors may be either elements (Si and Ge) or covalently bonded compounds. With these materials, in addition to free electrons, holes (missing electrons in the valence band), may also participate in the conduction process. On the basis of electrical behavior, semiconductors are classified as either intrinsic or extrinsic. For intrinsic behavior, the electrical properties are inherent to the pure material, and electron and hole concentrations are equal; electrical behavior is dictated by impurities for extrinsic semiconductors. Extrinsic semiconductors may be either n- or p-type depending on whether electrons or holes, respectively, are the predominant charge carriers. Donor impurities introduce excess electrons; acceptor impurities, excess holes.

The electrical conductivity of semiconducting materials is particularly sensitive to impurity type and content, as well as to temperature. The addition of even minute concentrations of some impurities enhances the conductivity drastically. Furthermore, with rising temperature, intrinsic conductivity experiences an exponential increase. Extrinsic conductivity may also increase with temperature.

A number of semiconducting devices employ the unique electrical characteristics of these materials to perform specific electronic functions. Included are the p–n rectifying junction, and junction and MOSFET transistors. Transistors are used for amplification of electrical signals, as well as for switching devices in computer circuitries.

Dielectric materials are electrically insulative, yet susceptible to polarization in the presence of an electric field. This polarization phenomenon accounts for the ability of the dielectrics to increase the charge storing capability of capacitors, the efficiency of which is expressed in terms of a dielectric constant. Polarization results from the inducement by, or orientation with the electric field, of atomic or molecular dipoles; a dipole is said to exist when there is a net spatial separation of positively and negatively charged entities. Possible polarization types include electronic, ionic, and orientation; not all types need be present in a particular dielectric. For alternating electric fields, whether a specific polarization type contributes to the total polarization and dielectric constant depends on frequency; each polarization mechanism ceases to function when the applied field frequency exceeds its relaxation frequency.

This chapter concluded with brief discussions of two other electrical phenomena. Ferroelectric materials are those that may exhibit polarization spontaneously, that is, in the absence of any external electric field. Finally, piezoelectricity is the phenomenon whereby polarization is induced in a material by the imposition of external forces.

IMPORTANT TERMS AND CONCEPTS

Acceptor state	Dielectric strength	Energy band gap
Capacitance	Diode	Extrinsic semiconductor
Conduction band	Dipole, electric	Fermi energy
Conductivity, electrical	Donor state	Ferroelectric
Dielectric	Doping	Forward bias
Dielectric constant	Electrical resistance	Free electron
Dielectric displacement	Electron energy band	Hall effect

Hole
Insulator
Integrated circuit
Intrinsic semiconductor
Ionic conduction
Junction transistor
Matthiessen's rule
Metal

Mobility
MOSFET
Ohm's law
Permittivity
Piezoelectric
Polarization
Polarization, electronic
Polarization, ionic

Polarization, orientation
Rectifying junction
Relaxation frequency
Resistivity, electrical
Reverse bias
Semiconductor
Valence band

REFERENCES

Azaroff, L. V. and J. J. Brophy, *Electronic Processes in Materials,* McGraw-Hill Book Company, New York, 1963. Reprinted by TechBooks, Fairfax, VA. Chapters 6–12.

Bube, R. H., *Electrons in Solids,* 3rd edition, Academic Press, San Diego, 1992.

Bylander, E. G., *Materials for Semiconductor Functions,* Hayden Book Company, New York, 1971. Good fundamental treatment of the physics of semiconductors and various semiconducting devices.

Chaudhari, P., "Electronic and Magnetic Materials," *Scientific American,* Vol. 255, No. 4, October 1986, pp. 136–144.

Ehrenreich, H., "The Electrical Properties of Materials," *Scientific American,* Vol. 217, No. 3, September 1967, pp. 194–204.

Hummel, R. E., *Electronic Properties of Materials,* 2nd edition, Springer-Verlag New York, Inc., New York, 1992.

Kingery, W. D., H. K. Bowen, and D. R. Uhlmann, *Introduction to Ceramics,* 2nd edition, John Wiley & Sons, New York, 1976. Chapters 17 and 18.

Kittel, C., *Introduction to Solid State Physics,* 6th edition, John Wiley & Sons, Inc., New York, 1986. An advanced treatment.

Meindl, J. D., "Microelectronic Circuit Elements," *Scientific American,* Vol. 237, No. 3, September 1977, pp. 70–81.

Navon, D. H., *Semiconductor Microdevices and Materials,* Saunders College Publishing, Philadelphia, PA, 1986.

Noyce, R. N., "Microelectronics," *Scientific American,* Vol. 237, No. 3, September 1977, pp. 62–69.

Oldham, W. G., "The Fabrication of Microelectronic Circuits," *Scientific American,* Vol. 237, No. 3, September 1977, pp. 110–128.

Rose, R. M., L. A. Shepard, and J. Wulff, *The Structure and Properties of Materials,* Vol. IV, *Electronic Properties,* John Wiley & Sons, New York, 1966. Chapters 1, 2, 4–8, and 12.

Warnes, L. A. A., *Electronic Materials,* Van Nostrand Reinhold, New York, 1990.

Wert, C. A. and R. M. Thomson, *Physics of Solids,* 2nd edition, McGraw-Hill Book Company, New York, 1970. Chapters 9 and 11–19.

QUESTIONS AND PROBLEMS

19.1 (a) Compute the electrical conductivity of a 7.0-mm (0.28-in.) diameter cylindrical silicon specimen 57 mm (2.25 in.) long in which a current of 0.25 A passes in an axial direction. A voltage of 24 V is measured across two probes that are separated by 45 mm (1.75 in.). **(b)** Compute the resistance over the entire 57 mm (2.25 in.) of the specimen.

19.2 A copper wire 100 m long must experience a voltage drop of less than 1.5 V when a current of 2.5 A passes through it. Using the data in Table 19.1, compute the minimum diameter of the wire.

19.3 An aluminum wire 4 mm in diameter is to offer a resistance of no more than 2.5 Ω. Using the data in Table 19.1, compute the maximum wire length.

19.4 Demonstrate that the two Ohm's law expressions, Equations 19.1 and 19.5, are equivalent.

19.5 (a) Using the data in Table 19.1, compute the resistance of an aluminum wire 5 mm (0.20 in.) in diameter and 5 m (200 in.) long. **(b)** What would be the current flow if the potential drop across the ends of the wire is 0.04 V? **(c)** What is the current density? **(d)** What is the magnitude of the electric field across the ends of the wire?

19.6 What is the distinction between electronic and ionic conduction?

19.7 How does the electron structure of an isolated atom differ from that of a solid material?

19.8 In terms of electron energy band structure, discuss reasons for the difference in electrical conductivity between metals, semiconductors, and insulators.

19.9 If a metallic material is cooled through its melting temperature at an extremely rapid rate, it will form a noncrystalline solid (i.e., a metallic glass). Will the electrical conductivity of the noncrystalline metal be greater or less than its crystalline counterpart? Why?

19.10 Briefly tell what is meant by the drift velocity and mobility of a free electron.

19.11 (a) Calculate the drift velocity of electrons in silicon at room temperature and when the magnitude of the electric field is 500 V/m. **(b)** Under these circumstances, how long does it take an electron to traverse a 25 mm (1 in.) length of crystal?

19.12 An n-type semiconductor is known to have an electron concentration of 5×10^{17} m^{-3}. If the electron drift velocity is 350 m/s in an electric field of 1000 V/m, calculate the conductivity of this material.

19.13 At room temperature the electrical conductivity and the electron mobility for aluminum are 3.8×10^7 (Ω-m)$^{-1}$ and 0.0012 m^2/V-s, respectively. **(a)** Compute the number of free electrons per cubic meter for aluminum at room temperature. **(b)** What is the number of free electrons per aluminum atom? Assume a density of 2.7 g/cm^3.

19.14 (a) Calculate the number of free electrons per cubic meter for gold assuming that there are 1.5 free electrons per gold atom. The electrical conductivity and density for Au are

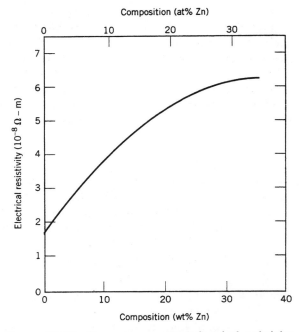

FIGURE 19.35 Room-temperature electrical resistivity versus composition for copper–zinc alloys. (Adapted from *Metals Handbook: Properties and Selection: Nonferrous Alloys and Pure Metals,* Vol. 2, 9th edition, H. Baker, Managing Editor, American Society for Metals, 1979, p. 315.)

4.3×10^7 (Ω-m)$^{-1}$ and 19.32 g/cm^3, respectively. **(b)** Now compute the electron mobility for Au.

19.15 From Figure 19.35, estimate the value of A in Equation 19.11 for zinc as an impurity in copper–zinc alloys.

19.16 (a) Using the data in Figure 19.8, determine the values of ρ_0 and a from Equation 19.10 for pure copper. Take the temperature T to be in degrees Celsius. **(b)** Determine the value of A in Equation 19.11 for nickel as an impurity in copper, using the data in Figure 19.8. **(c)** Using the results of parts a and b, estimate the electrical resistivity of copper containing 2.50 at% Ni at 120°C.

19.17 Determine the electrical conductivity of a Cu-Ni alloy that has a yield strength of 125 MPa (18,000 psi). You will find Figure 7.16b helpful.

19.18 Tin bronze has a composition of 92 wt% Cu and 8 wt% Sn, and consists of two phases at room temperature: an α phase, which is copper containing a very small amount of tin in solid solution, and an ϵ phase, which consists of approximately 37 wt% Sn. Compute the room temperature conductivity of this alloy given the following data:

Phase	Electrical Resistivity (Ω-m)	Density (g/cm^3)
α	1.88×10^{-8}	8.94
ϵ	5.32×10^{-7}	8.25

19.19 A cylindrical metal wire 3 mm (0.12 in.) in diameter is required to carry a current of 12 A with a minimum of 0.01 V drop per foot (300 mm) of wire. Which of the metals and alloys listed in Table 19.1 are possible candidates?

19.20 (a) Compute the number of free electrons and holes that exist in intrinsic germanium at room temperature, using the data in Table 19.2. (b) Now calculate the number of free electrons per atom for germanium and silicon (Example Problem 19.1). (c) Explain the difference. You will need the densities for Ge and Si, which are 5.32 and 2.33 g/cm³, respectively.

19.21 For intrinsic semiconductors, both electron and hole concentrations depend on temperature as follows:

$$n, p \propto \exp\left(-\frac{E_g}{2kT}\right) \quad (19.38)$$

or, taking natural logarithms,

$$\ln n, \ln p \propto -\frac{E_g}{2kT}$$

Thus, a plot of the intrinsic $\ln n$ (or $\ln p$) versus $1/T$ $(K)^{-1}$ should be linear and yield a slope of $-E_g/2k$. Using this information and Figure 19.16, determine the band gap energy for silicon. Compare this value with the one given in Table 19.2.

19.22 Define the following terms as they pertain to semiconducting materials: intrinsic, extrinsic, compound, elemental. Now provide an example of each.

19.23 Is it possible for compound semiconductors to exhibit intrinsic behavior? Explain your answer.

19.24 For each of the following pairs of semiconductors, decide which will have the smaller band gap energy E_g and then cite the reason for your choice: (a) ZnS and CdSe, (b) Si and C (diamond), (c) Al_2O_3 and ZnTe, (d) InSb and ZnSe, and (e) GaAs and AlP.

19.25 (a) In your own words, explain how donor impurities in semiconductors give rise to free electrons in numbers in excess of those generated by valence band–conduction band excitations. (b) Also explain how acceptor impurities give rise to holes in numbers in excess of those generated by valence band–conduction band excitations.

19.26 (a) Explain why no hole is generated by the electron excitation involving a donor impurity atom. (b) Explain why no free electron is generated by the electron excitation involving an acceptor impurity atom.

19.27 Will each of the following elements act as a donor or an acceptor when added to the indicated semiconducting material? Assume that the impurity elements are substitutional.

Impurity	Semiconductor
Al	Si
P	Ge
Cd	GaAs
S	AlP
Sb	ZnSe
In	CdTe

19.28 (a) At approximately what position is the Fermi energy for an intrinsic semiconductor? (b) At approximately what position is the Fermi energy for an n-type semiconductor? (c) Make a schematic plot of Fermi energy versus temperature for an n-type semiconductor up to a temperature at which it becomes intrinsic. Also note on this plot energy positions corresponding to the top of the valence band and the bottom of the conduction band.

19.29 (a) The room-temperature electrical conductivity of a silicon specimen is 500 $(\Omega$-m$)^{-1}$. The electron concentration is known to be 2.0×10^{22} m^{-3}. Using the electron and hole mobilities for silicon in Table 19.2, compute the hole concentration. **(b)** On the basis of the result in part a, is the specimen intrinsic, *n*-type extrinsic, or *p*-type extrinsic? Why?

19.30 Using the data in Table 19.2, compute the electron and hole concentrations for intrinsic InSb at room temperature.

19.31 Germanium to which 5×10^{22} m^{-3} Sb atoms have been added is an extrinsic semiconductor at room temperature, and virtually all the Sb atoms may be thought of as being ionized (i.e., one charge carrier exists for each Sb atom). **(a)** Is this material *n*-type or *p*-type? **(b)** Calculate the electrical conductivity of this material, assuming electron and hole mobilities of 0.1 and 0.05 m^2/V-s, respectively.

19.32 The following electrical characteristics have been determined for both intrinsic and *p*-type extrinsic gallium antimonide (GaSb) at room temperature:

	$\sigma(\Omega\text{-}m)^{-1}$	$n\ (m^{-3})$	$p\ (m^{-3})$
Intrinsic	8.9×10^4	8.7×10^{23}	8.7×10^{23}
Extrinsic (*p*-type)	2.3×10^5	7.6×10^{22}	1.0×10^{25}

Calculate electron and hole mobilities.

19.33 Compare the temperature dependence of the conductivity for metals and intrinsic semiconductors. Briefly explain the difference in behavior.

19.34 Using the data in Table 19.2, estimate the electrical conductivity of intrinsic GaAs at 150°C (423 K).

19.35 Briefly explain the presence of the factor 2 in the denominator of the second term on the right-hand side of Equation 19.19.

19.36 Using the data in Table 19.2, estimate the temperature at which the electrical conductivity of intrinsic GaAs is 4×10^{-4} $(\Omega\text{-}m)^{-1}$.

19.37 The intrinsic electrical conductivities of a semiconductor at 20 and 200°C (293 and 473 K) are 3×10^{-4} and 160 $(\Omega\text{-}m)^{-1}$, respectively. Determine the approximate band gap energy for this material.

19.38 Below, the intrinsic electrical conductivity of a semiconductor at two temperatures is tabulated:

T (K)	$\sigma\ (\Omega\text{-}m)^{-1}$
450	0.12
550	2.25

(a) Determine the band gap energy (in eV) for this material.

(b) Estimate the electrical conductivity at 300 K (27°C).

19.39 The slope of the extrinsic portions of the curves in Figure 19.16 is related to the position of the acceptor level in the band gap (Figure 19.14). Write an expression for the dependence of *p* on the position of this level.

19.40 Some hypothetical metal is known to have an electrical resistivity of 4×10^{-8} (Ω-m). Through a specimen of this metal that is 25 mm thick is passed a current of 30 A; when a magnetic field of 0.75 tesla is simultaneously imposed in a direction perpendicular to that of the current, a Hall voltage of -1.26×10^{-7} V is measured. Compute **(a)** the electron mobility for this metal, and **(b)** the number of free electrons per cubic meter.

19.41 Some metal alloy is known to have electrical conductivity and electron mobility values of 1.5×10^7 $(\Omega\text{-}m)^{-1}$ and 0.0020 m^2/V-s, respectively. Through a specimen of this alloy that is 35 mm thick is passed a current of 45 A. What magnetic field would need to be imposed to yield a Hall voltage of -1.0×10^{-7} V?

19.42 Briefly describe electron and hole motions in a *p–n* junction for forward and reverse biases; then explain how these lead to rectification.

19.43 How is the energy in the reaction described by Equation 19.24 dissipated?

19.44 What are the two functions that a transistor may perform in an electronic circuit?

19.45 Would you expect increasing temperature to influence the operation of *p–n* junction rectifiers and transistors? Explain.

19.46 Cite the differences in operation and application for junction transistors and MOSFETs.

19.47 At temperatures between 775°C (1048 K) and 1100°C (1373 K), the activation energy and preexponential for the diffusion coefficient of Fe^{2+} in FeO are 102,000 J/mol and 7.3×10^{-8} m²/s, respectively. Compute the mobility for an Fe^{2+} ion at 1000°C (1273 K).

19.48 A parallel-plate capacitor using a dielectric material having an ϵ_r of 2.2 has a plate spacing of 2 mm (0.08 in.). If another material having a dielectric constant of 3.7 is used and the capacitance is to be unchanged, what must be the new spacing between the plates?

19.49 A parallel-plate capacitor with dimensions of 100 mm by 25 mm and a plate separation of 3 mm must have a minimum capacitance of 38 pF (3.8×10^{-11} F) when an ac potential of 500 V is applied at a frequency of 1 MHz. Which of those materials listed in Table 19.4 are possible candidates? Why?

19.50 Consider a parallel-plate capacitor having an area of 2500 mm² and a plate separation of 2 mm, and with a material of dielectric constant 4.0 positioned between the plates. **(a)** What is the capacitance of this capacitor? **(b)** Compute the electric field that must be applied for a charge of 8.0×10^{-9} C to be stored on each plate.

19.51 In your own words, explain the mechanism by which charge storing capacity is increased by the insertion of a dielectric material within the plates of a capacitor.

19.52 For CaO, the ionic radii for Ca^{2+} and O^{2-} ions are 0.100 and 0.140 nm, respectively. If an externally applied electric field produces a 5% expansion of the lattice, compute the dipole moment for each Ca^{2+}–O^{2-} pair. Assume that this material is completely unpolarized in the absence of an electric field.

19.53 The polarization P of a dielectric material positioned within a parallel-plate capacitor is to be 4.0×10^{-6} C/m².

(a) What must be the dielectric constant if an electric field of 10^5 V/m is applied?

(b) What will be the dielectric displacement D?

19.54 A charge of 2.0×10^{-10} C is to be stored on each plate of a parallel-plate capacitor having an area of 650 mm² (1.0 in.²) and a plate separation of 4.0 mm (0.16 in.).

(a) What voltage is required if a material having a dielectric constant of 3.5 is positioned within the plates?

(b) What voltage would be required if a vacuum is used?

(c) What are the capacitances for parts a and b?

(d) Compute the dielectric displacement for part a.

(e) Compute the polarization for part a.

19.55 (a) For each of the three types of polarization, briefly describe the mechanism by which dipoles are induced and/or oriented by the action of an applied electric field. (b) For solid lead titanate ($PbTiO_3$), gaseous neon, diamond, solid KCl, and liquid NH_3 what kind(s) of polarization is (are) possible? Why?

19.56 The dielectric constant for a soda–lime glass measured at very high frequencies (on the order of 10^{15} Hz) is approximately 2.3. What fraction of the dielectric constant at relatively low frequencies (1 MHz) is attributed to ionic polarization? Neglect any orientation polarization contributions.

19.57 Compute the magnitude of the dipole moment associated with each unit cell of $BaTiO_3$, as illustrated in Figure 19.33.

19.58 Briefly explain why the ferroelectric behavior of $BaTiO_3$ ceases above its ferroelectric Curie temperature.

19.59 Would you expect the physical dimensions of a piezoelectric material such as $BaTiO_3$ to change when it is subjected to an electric field? Why or why not?

Design Problems

19.D1 A 95 wt% Pt-5 wt% Ni alloy is known to have an electrical resistivity of 2.35×10^{-7} Ω-m at room temperature (25°C). Calculate the composition of a platinum-nickel alloy that gives a room-temperature resistivity of 1.75×10^{-7} Ω-m. The room-temperature resistivity of pure platinum may be determined from the data in Table 19.1; assume that platinum and nickel form a solid solution.

19.D2 Using information contained in Figures 19.8

and 19.35, determine the electrical conductivity of an 80 wt% Cu-20 wt% Zn alloy at $-150°C$ ($-240°F$).

19.D3 Is it possible to alloy copper with nickel to achieve a minimum tensile strength of 375 MPa (54,400 psi) and yet maintain an electrical conductivity of 2.5×10^6 $(\Omega\text{-m})^{-1}$? If not, why? If so, what concentration of nickel is required? You may want to consult Figure 7.16a.

19.D4 Specify an acceptor impurity type and concentration (in weight percent) that will produce a *p*-type silicon material having a room temperature electrical conductivity of 50 $(\Omega\text{-m})^{-1}$. Use intrinsic electron and hole mobilities, and assume that the acceptor impurities are saturated.

19.D5 The base semiconducting material used in virtually all of our modern integrated circuits is silicon. However, silicon has some limitations and restrictions. Write an essay comparing the properties and applications (and/or potential applications) of silicon and gallium arsenide.

20

Thermal Properties

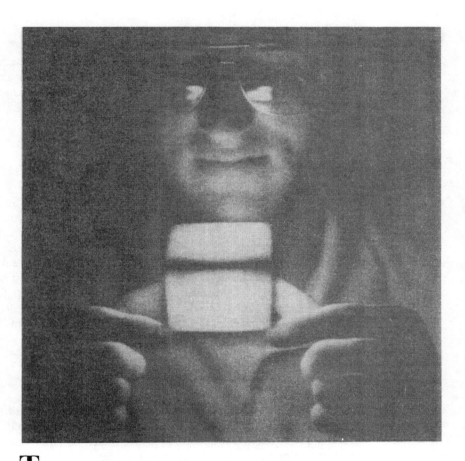

This photograph shows a white-hot cube of a silica fiber insulation material, which, only seconds after having been removed from a hot furnace, can be held by its edges with the bare hands. Initially, the heat transfer from the surface is relatively rapid; however, the thermal conductivity of this material is so small that heat conduction from the interior [maximum temperature approximately 1250°C (2300°F)] is extremely slow.

This material was developed especially for the tiles that cover the Space Shuttle Orbiters and protect and insulate them during their fiery reentry into the atmosphere. Other attractive features of this *high-temperature reusable surface insulation* (*HRSI*) include low density and a low coefficient of thermal expansion. (Photograph courtesy of Lockheed Missiles & Space Company, Inc.)

20.1 INTRODUCTION

By "thermal property" is meant the response of a material to the application of heat. As a solid absorbs energy in the form of heat, its temperature rises and its dimensions increase. The energy may be transported to cooler regions of the specimen if temperature gradients exist, and ultimately, the specimen may melt. Heat capacity, thermal expansion, and thermal conductivity are properties that are often critical in the practical utilization of solids.

20.2 HEAT CAPACITY

A solid material, when heated, experiences an increase in temperature signifying that some energy has been absorbed. **Heat capacity** is a property that is indicative of a material's ability to absorb heat from the external surroundings; it represents the amount of energy required to produce a unit temperature rise. In mathematical terms, the heat capacity C is expressed as follows:

$$C = \frac{dQ}{dT} \tag{20.1}$$

where dQ is the energy required to produce a dT temperature change. Ordinarily, heat capacity is specified per mole of material (e.g., J/mol-K, or cal/mol-K). **Specific heat** (often denoted by a lowercase c) is sometimes used; this represents the heat capacity per unit mass and has various units (J/kg-K, cal/g-K, Btu/lb$_m$-°F).

There are really two ways in which this property may be measured, according to the environmental conditions accompanying the transfer of heat. One is the heat capacity while maintaining the specimen volume constant, C_v; the other is for constant external pressure, which is denoted C_p. The magnitude of C_p is always greater than C_v; however, this difference is very slight for most solid materials at room temperature and below.

VIBRATIONAL HEAT CAPACITY

In most solids the principal mode of thermal energy assimilation is by the increase in vibrational energy of the atoms. Again, atoms in solid materials are constantly vibrating at very high frequencies and with relatively small amplitudes. Rather than being independent of one another, the vibrations of adjacent atoms are coupled by virtue of the atomic bonding. These vibrations are coordinated in such a way that traveling lattice waves are produced, a phenomenon represented in Figure 20.1. These may be thought of as elastic waves or simply sound waves, having short wavelengths and very high frequencies, which propagate through the crystal at the velocity of sound. The vibrational thermal energy for a material consists of a series of these elastic waves, which have a range of distributions and frequencies. Only certain energy values are allowed (the energy is said to be quantized), and a single quantum of vibrational energy is called a **phonon.** (A phonon is analogous to the quantum of electromagnetic radiation, the **photon.**) On occasion, the vibrational waves themselves are termed phonons.

The thermal scattering of free electrons during electronic conduction (Section 19.7) is by these vibrational waves, and these elastic waves also participate in the transport of energy during thermal conduction (see Section 20.4).

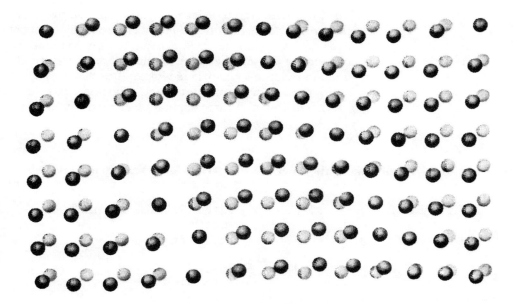

  ○ Normal lattice positions for atoms

  ● Positions displaced because of vibrations

FIGURE 20.1 Schematic representation of the generation of lattice waves in a crystal by means of atomic vibrations. (Adapted from "The Thermal Properties of Materials" by J. Ziman. Copyright © 1967 by Scientific American, Inc. All rights reserved.)

TEMPERATURE DEPENDENCE OF THE HEAT CAPACITY

The variation with temperature of the vibrational contribution to the heat capacity at constant volume for many relatively simple crystalline solids is shown in Figure 20.2. The C_v is zero at 0 K, but it rises rapidly with temperature; this corresponds to an increased ability of the lattice waves to enhance their average energy with ascending temperature. At low temperatures the relationship between C_v and the absolute temperature T is

$$C_v = AT^3 \tag{20.2}$$

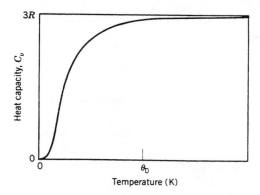

FIGURE 20.2 The temperature dependence of the heat capacity at constant volume; θ_D is the Debye temperature.

where A is a temperature-independent constant. Above what is called the *Debye temperature* θ_D, C_v levels off and becomes essentially independent of temperature at a value of approximately $3R$, R being the gas constant. Thus even though the total energy of the material is increasing with temperature, the quantity of energy required to produce a one-degree temperature change is constant. The value of θ_D is below room temperature for many solid materials, and 25 J/mol-K (6 cal/mol-K) is a reasonable room-temperature approximation for C_v. Table 20.1 presents

Table 20.1 Tabulation of the Thermal Properties for a Variety of Materials

Material	c_p $(J/kg\text{-}K)^a$	α_l $[(°C)^{-1} \times 10^{-6}]^b$	k $(W/m\text{-}K)^c$	L $[\Omega\text{-}W/(K)^2 \times 10^{-8}]$
		Metals		
Aluminum	900	23.6	247	2.20
Copper	386	17.0	398	2.25
Gold	128	14.2	315	2.50
Iron	448	11.8	80	2.71
Nickel	443	13.3	90	2.08
Silver	235	19.7	428	2.13
Tungsten	138	4.5	178	3.20
1025 Steel	486	12.0	51.9	—
316 Stainless steel	502	16.0	15.9	—
Brass (70Cu-30Zn)	375	20.0	120	—
Kovar (54Fe-29Ni-17Co)	460	5.1	17	2.80
Invar (64Fe-36Ni)	500	1.6	10	2.75
Super Invar (63Fe-32Ni-5Co)	500	0.72	10	2.68
		Ceramics		
Alumina (Al_2O_3)	775	7.6	39	—
Magnesia (MgO)	940	13.5^d	37.7	—
Spinel ($MgAl_2O_4$)	790	7.6^d	15.0^e	—
Fused silica (SiO_2)	740	0.4	1.4	—
Soda-lime glass	840	9.0	1.7	—
Borosilicate (Pyrex) glass	850	3.3	1.4	—
		Polymers		
Polyethylene (high density)	1850	106–198	0.46–0.50	—
Polypropylene	1925	145–180	0.12	—
Polystyrene	1170	90–150	0.13	—
Polytetrafluoroethylene (Teflon)	1050	126–216	0.25	—
Phenol-formaldehyde, phenolic (Bakelite)	1590–1760	122	0.15	—
Nylon 6,6	1670	144	0.24	—
Polyisoprene	—	220	0.14	—

^{a} To convert to cal/g-K, multiply by 2.39×10^{-4}; to convert to Btu/lb$_m$-°F, multiply by 2.39×10^{-4}.

^{b} To convert to (°F)$^{-1}$, multiply by 0.56.

^{c} To convert to cal/s-cm-K, multiply by 2.39×10^{-3}; to convert to Btu/ft-h-°F, multiply by 0.578.

^{d} Value measured at 100°C.

^{e} Mean value taken over the temperature range 0–1000°C.

experimental specific heats for a number of materials; c_p values for still more materials are tabulated in Appendix C.8.

OTHER HEAT CAPACITY CONTRIBUTIONS

Other energy-absorptive mechanisms also exist that can add to the total heat capacity of a solid. In most instances, however, these are minor relative to the magnitude of the vibrational contribution. There is an electronic contribution in that electrons absorb energy by increasing their kinetic energy. However, this is possible only for free electrons—those that have been excited from filled states to empty states above the Fermi energy (Section 19.6). In metals, only electrons at states near the Fermi energy are capable of such transitions, and these represent only a very small fraction of the total number. An even smaller proportion of electrons experiences excitations in insulating and semiconducting materials. Hence, this electronic contribution is ordinarily insignificant, except at temperatures near 0 K.

Furthermore, in some materials other energy-absorptive processes occur at specific temperatures, for example, the randomization of electron spins in a ferromagnetic material as it is heated through its Curie temperature. A large spike is produced on the heat capacity-versus-temperature curve at the temperature of this transformation.

20.3 THERMAL EXPANSION

Most solid materials expand upon heating and contract when cooled. The change in length with temperature for a solid material may be expressed as follows:

$$\frac{l_f - l_0}{l_0} = \alpha_l(T_f - T_0) \tag{20.3a}$$

or

$$\frac{\Delta l}{l_0} = \alpha_l \Delta T \tag{20.3b}$$

where l_0 and l_f represent, respectively, initial and final lengths with the temperature change from T_0 to T_f. The parameter α_l is called the **linear coefficient of thermal expansion;** it is a material property that is indicative of the extent to which a material expands upon heating, and has units of reciprocal temperature [$(°C)^{-1}$ or $(°F)^{-1}$]. Of course, heating or cooling affects all the dimensions of a body, with a resultant change in volume. Volume changes with temperature may be computed from

$$\frac{\Delta V}{V_0} = \alpha_v \Delta T \tag{20.4}$$

where ΔV and V_0 are the volume change and the original volume, respectively, and α_v symbolizes the volume coefficient of thermal expansion. In many materials, the value of α_v is anisotropic; that is, it depends on the crystallographic direction along which it is measured. For materials in which the thermal expansion is isotropic, α_v is approximately $3\alpha_l$.

From an atomic perspective, thermal expansion is reflected by an increase in the average distance between the atoms. This phenomenon can best be understood

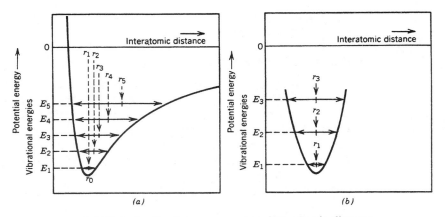

FIGURE 20.3   (a) Plot of potential energy versus interatomic distance, demonstrating the increase in interatomic separation with rising temperature. With heating, the interatomic separation increases from r_0 to r_1 to r_2, and so on. (b) For a symmetric potential energy-versus-interatomic distance curve, there is no increase in interatomic separation with rising temperature (i.e., $r_1 = r_2 = r_3$). (Adapted from R. M. Rose, L. A. Shepard, and J. Wulff, *The Structure and Properties of Materials*, Vol. 4, *Electronic Properties*. Copyright © 1966 by John Wiley & Sons, New York. Reprinted by permission of John Wiley & Sons, Inc.)

by consultation of the potential energy versus interatomic spacing curve for a solid material introduced previously (Figure 2.8b), and reproduced in Figure 20.3a. The curve is in the form of a potential energy trough, and the equilibrium interatomic spacing at 0 K, r_0, corresponds to the trough minimum. Heating to successively higher temperatures (T_1, T_2, T_3, etc.) raises the vibrational energy from E_1 to E_2 to E_3, and so on. The average vibrational amplitude of an atom corresponds to the trough width at each temperature, and the average interatomic distance is represented by the mean position, which increases with temperature from r_0 to r_1 to r_2, and so on.

Thermal expansion is really due to the asymmetric curvature of this potential energy trough, rather than the increased atomic vibrational amplitudes with rising temperature. If the potential energy curve were symmetric (Figure 20.3b), there would be no net change in interatomic separation and, consequently, no thermal expansion.

For each class of materials (metals, ceramics, and polymers), the greater the atomic bonding energy, the deeper and more narrow this potential energy trough. As a result, the increase in interatomic separation with a given rise in temperature will be lower, yielding a smaller value of α_l. Table 20.1 lists the linear coefficients of thermal expansion for several materials. With regard to temperature dependence, the magnitude of the coefficient of expansion increases with rising temperature. The values in Table 20.1 are taken at room temperature unless indicated otherwise. A more comprehensive list of coefficients of thermal expansion is provided in Appendix C.6.

METALS

As noted in Table 20.1, linear coefficients of thermal expansion for some of the common metals range between about 5×10^{-6} and 25×10^{-6} $(°C)^{-1}$. For some applications, a high degree of dimensional stability with temperature fluctuations is essential. This has resulted in the development of a family of iron-nickel and iron-nickel-cobalt alloys that have α_l values on the order of 1×10^{-6} $(°C)^{-1}$. One such alloy, tradename of Kovar (Table 20.1), has been designed to have expansion characteristics close to those of borosilicate (or Pyrex) glass; when joined to Pyrex and subjected to temperature variations, thermal stresses and possible fracture at the junction are avoided. Kovar and two other low-expansion alloys (Invar and Super-Invar) which have small α_l values are also included in Table 20.1.

CERAMICS

Relatively strong interatomic bonding forces are found in many ceramic materials as reflected in comparatively low coefficients of thermal expansion; values typically range between about 0.5×10^{-6} and 15×10^{-6} $(°C)^{-1}$. For noncrystalline ceramics and also those having cubic crystal structures, α_l is isotropic. Otherwise, it is anisotropic; and, in fact, some ceramic materials, upon heating, contract in some crystallographic directions while expanding in others. For inorganic glasses, the coefficient of expansion is dependent on composition. Fused silica (high-purity SiO_2 glass) has a small expansion coefficient, 0.5×10^{-6} $(°C)^{-1}$. This is explained by a low atomic packing density such that interatomic expansion produces relatively small macroscopic dimensional changes.

Ceramic materials that are to be subjected to temperature changes must have coefficients of thermal expansion that are relatively low, and in addition, isotropic. Otherwise, these brittle materials may experience fracture as a consequence of nonuniform dimensional changes in what is termed **thermal shock,** as discussed later in the chapter.

POLYMERS

Some polymeric materials experience very large thermal expansions upon heating as indicated by coefficients that range from approximately 50×10^{-6} to 400×10^{-6} $(°C)^{-1}$. The highest α_l values are found in linear and branched polymers because the secondary intermolecular bonds are weak, and there is a minimum of crosslinking. With increased crosslinking, the magnitude of the expansion coefficient diminishes; the lowest coefficients are found in the thermosetting network polymers such as Bakelite, in which the bonding is almost entirely covalent.

20.4 THERMAL CONDUCTIVITY

Thermal conduction is the phenomenon by which heat is transported from high- to low-temperature regions of a substance. The property that characterizes the ability of a material to transfer heat is the **thermal conductivity.** It is best defined in terms of the expression

$$q = -k\frac{dT}{dx} \tag{20.5}$$

where q denotes the *heat flux,* or heat flow, per unit time per unit area (area being taken as that perpendicular to the flow direction), k is the thermal conductivity, and dT/dx is the *temperature gradient* through the conducting medium.

The units of q and k are W/m^2 $(Btu/ft^2\text{-}h)$ and W/m-K $(Btu/ft\text{-}h\text{-}°F)$, respectively. Equation 20.5 is valid only for steady-state heat flow, that is, for situations in which the heat flux does not change with time. Also, the minus sign in the expression indicates that the direction of heat flow is from hot to cold, or down the temperature gradient.

Equation 20.5 is similar in form to Fick's first law (Equation 5.3) for atomic diffusion. For these expressions, k is analogous to the diffusion coefficient D, and the temperature gradient parallels the concentration gradient, dC/dx.

MECHANISMS OF HEAT CONDUCTION

Heat is transported in solid materials by both lattice vibration waves (phonons) and free electrons. A thermal conductivity is associated with each of these mechanisms, and the total conductivity is the sum of the two contributions, or

$$k = k_l + k_e \tag{20.6}$$

where k_l and k_e represent the lattice vibration and electron thermal conductivities, respectively; usually one or the other predominates. The thermal energy associated with phonons or lattice waves is transported in the direction of their motion. The k_l contribution results from a net movement of phonons from high- to low-temperature regions of a body across which a temperature gradient exists.

Free or conducting electrons participate in electronic thermal conduction. To the free electrons in a hot region of the specimen is imparted a gain in kinetic energy. They then migrate to colder areas, where some of this kinetic energy is transferred to the atoms themselves (as vibrational energy) as a consequence of collisions with phonons or other imperfections in the crystal. The relative contribution of k_e to the total thermal conductivity increases with increasing free electron concentrations, since more electrons are available to participate in this heat transference process.

METALS

In high-purity metals, the electron mechanism of heat transport is much more efficient than the phonon contribution because electrons are not as easily scattered as phonons and have higher velocities. Furthermore, metals are extremely good conductors of heat because relatively large numbers of free electrons exist that participate in thermal conduction. The thermal conductivities of several of the common metals are given in Table 20.1; values generally range between about 20 and 400 W/m-K.

Since free electrons are responsible for both electrical and thermal conduction in pure metals, theoretical treatments suggest that the two conductivities should be related according to the *Wiedemann–Franz law:*

$$L = \frac{k}{\sigma T} \tag{20.7}$$

where σ is the electrical conductivity, T is the absolute temperature, and L is a constant. The theoretical value of L, 2.44×10^{-8} Ω-W/(K)^2, should be independent of temperature and the same for all metals if the heat energy is transported entirely by free electrons. Included in Table 20.1 are the experimental L values for these several metals; note that the agreement between these and the theoretical value is quite reasonable (well within a factor of 2).

Alloying metals with impurities results in a reduction in the thermal conductivity, for the same reason that the electrical conductivity is diminished (Section 19.8); namely, the impurity atoms, especially if in solid solution, act as scattering centers, lowering the efficiency of electron motion. A plot of thermal conductivity versus

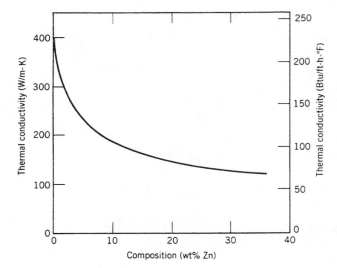

Figure 20.4 Thermal conductivity versus composition for copper–zinc alloys. (Adapted from *Metals Handbook: Properties and Selection: Nonferrous Alloys and Pure Metals*, Vol. 2, 9th edition, H. Baker, Managing Editor, American Society for Metals, 1979, p. 315.)

composition for copper–zinc alloys (Figure 20.4) displays this effect. Also, stainless steels, which are highly alloyed, become relatively resistive to heat transport.

CERAMICS

Nonmetallic materials are thermal insulators inasmuch as they lack large numbers of free electrons. Thus the phonons are primarily responsible for thermal conduction: k_e is much smaller than k_l. Again, the phonons are not as effective as free electrons in the transport of heat energy as a result of the very efficient phonon scattering by lattice imperfections.

Thermal conductivity values for a number of ceramic materials are contained in Table 20.1; room-temperature thermal conductivities range between approximately 2 and 50 W/m-K. Glass and other amorphous ceramics have lower conductivities than crystalline ceramics, since the phonon scattering is much more effective when the atomic structure is highly disordered and irregular.

The scattering of lattice vibrations becomes more pronounced with rising temperature; hence, the thermal conductivity of most ceramic materials normally diminishes with increasing temperature, at least at relatively low temperatures (Figure 20.5). As Figure 20.5 indicates, the conductivity begins to increase at higher temperatures, which is due to radiant heat transfer: significant quantities of infrared radiant heat may be transported through a transparent ceramic material. The efficiency of this process increases with temperature.

Porosity in ceramic materials may have a dramatic influence on thermal conductivity; increasing the pore volume will, under most circumstances, result in a reduction of the thermal conductivity. In fact, many ceramics that are used for thermal insulation are porous. Heat transfer across pores is ordinarily slow and inefficient. Internal pores normally contain still air, which has an extremely low thermal conductivity—approximately 0.02 W/m-K. Furthermore, gaseous convection within the pores is also comparatively ineffective.

POLYMERS

As noted in Table 20.1, thermal conductivities for most polymers are on the order of 0.3 W/m-K. For these materials, energy transfer is accomplished by the vibration

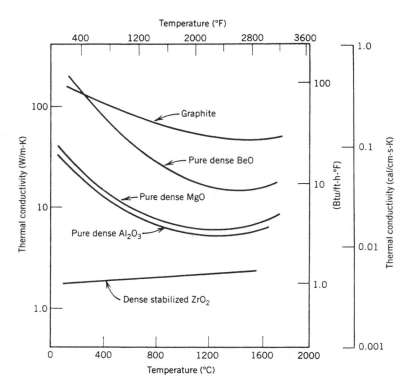

FIGURE 20.5
Dependence of thermal conductivity on temperature for several ceramic materials. (Adapted from W. D. Kingery, H. K. Bowen, and D. R. Uhlmann, *Introduction to Ceramics*, 2nd edition. Copyright © 1976 by John Wiley & Sons, New York. Reprinted by permission of John Wiley & Sons, Inc.)

and rotation of the chain molecules. The magnitude of the thermal conductivity depends on the degree of crystallinity; a polymer with a highly crystalline and ordered structure will have a greater conductivity than the equivalent amorphous material. This is due to the more effective coordinated vibration of the molecular chains for the crystalline state.

Polymers are often utilized as thermal insulators because of their low thermal conductivities. As with ceramics, their insulative properties may be further enhanced by the introduction of small pores, which are ordinarily introduced by foaming during polymerization (Section 16.16). Foamed polystyrene (Styrofoam) is commonly used for drinking cups and insulating chests.

20.5 THERMAL STRESSES

Thermal stresses are stresses induced in a body as a result of changes in temperature. An understanding of the origins and nature of thermal stresses is important because these stresses can lead to fracture or undesirable plastic deformation.

STRESSES RESULTING FROM RESTRAINED THERMAL EXPANSION AND CONTRACTION

Let us first consider a homogeneous and isotropic solid rod that is heated or cooled uniformly; that is, no temperature gradients are imposed. For free expansion or contraction, the rod will be stress free. If, however, axial motion of the rod is restrained by rigid end supports, thermal stresses will be introduced. The magnitude of the stress σ resulting from a temperature change from T_0 to T_f is

$$\sigma = E\alpha_l(T_0 - T_f) = E\alpha_l\Delta T \qquad (20.8)$$

where E is the modulus of elasticity and α_l is the linear coefficient of thermal expansion. Upon heating ($T_f > T_0$), the stress is compressive ($\sigma < 0$), since rod expansion has been constrained. Of course, if the rod specimen is cooled ($T_f < T_0$), a tensile stress will be imposed ($\sigma > 0$). Also, the stress in Equation 20.8 is the same as that which would be required to elastically compress (or elongate) the rod specimen back to its original length after it had been allowed to freely expand (or contract) with the $T_0 - T_f$ temperature change.

EXAMPLE PROBLEM 20.1

A brass rod is to be used in an application requiring its ends to be held rigid. If the rod is stress free at room temperature [20°C (68°F)], what is the maximum temperature to which the rod may be heated without exceeding a compressive stress of 172 MPa (25,000 psi)? Assume a modulus of elasticity of 100 GPa (14.6×10^6 psi) for brass.

SOLUTION

Use Equation 20.8 to solve this problem, where the stress of 172 MPa is taken to be negative. Also, the initial temperature T_0 is 20°C, and the magnitude of the linear coefficient of thermal expansion from Table 20.1 is 20.0×10^{-6} (°C)$^{-1}$. Thus, solving for the final temperature T_f yields

$$T_f = T_0 - \frac{\sigma}{E\alpha_l}$$

$$= 20° - \frac{-172 \text{ MPa}}{(100 \times 10^3 \text{ MPa})[20 \times 10^{-6} \text{ (°C)}^{-1}]}$$

$$= 20°\text{C} + 86°\text{C} = 106°\text{C} (223°\text{F})$$

STRESSES RESULTING FROM TEMPERATURE GRADIENTS

When a solid body is heated or cooled, the internal temperature distribution will depend on its size and shape, the thermal conductivity of the material, and the rate of temperature change. Thermal stresses may be established as a result of temperature gradients across a body, which are frequently caused by rapid heating or cooling, in that the outside changes temperature more rapidly than the interior; differential dimensional changes serve to restrain the free expansion or contraction of adjacent volume elements within the piece. For example, upon heating, the exterior of a specimen is hotter and, therefore, will have expanded more than the interior regions. Hence, compressive surface stresses are induced and are balanced by tensile interior stresses. The interior–exterior stress conditions are reversed for rapid cooling such that the surface is put into a state of tension.

THERMAL SHOCK OF BRITTLE MATERIALS

For ductile metals and polymers, alleviation of thermally induced stresses may be accomplished by plastic deformation. However, the nonductility of most ceramics enhances the possibility of brittle fracture from these stresses. Rapid cooling of a brittle body is more likely to inflict such thermal shock than heating, since the induced surface stresses are tensile. Crack formation and propagation from surface flaws are more probable when an imposed stress is tensile (Section 13.7).

The capacity of a material to withstand this kind of failure is termed its *thermal shock resistance*. For a ceramic body that is rapidly cooled, the resistance to thermal shock depends not only on the magnitude of the temperature change, but also on the mechanical and thermal properties of the material. The thermal shock resistance is best for ceramics that have high fracture strengths σ_f and high thermal conductivities, as well as low moduli of elasticity and low coefficients of thermal expansion. The resistance of many materials to this type of failure may be approximated by a thermal shock resistance parameter *TSR:*

$$TSR \cong \frac{\sigma_f k}{E\alpha_l} \qquad (20.9)$$

Thermal shock may be prevented by altering the external conditions to the degree that cooling or heating rates are reduced and temperature gradients across a body are minimized. Modification of the thermal and/or mechanical characteristics in Equation 20.9 may also enhance the thermal shock resistance of a material. Of these parameters, the coefficient of thermal expansion is probably most easily changed and controlled. For example, common soda–lime glasses, which have an α_l of approximately 9×10^{-6} $(°C)^{-1}$, are particularly susceptible to thermal shock, as anyone who has baked can probably attest. Reducing the CaO and Na_2O contents while at the same time adding B_2O_3 in sufficient quantities to form borosilicate (or Pyrex) glass will reduce the coefficient of expansion to about 3×10^{-6} $(°C)^{-1}$; this material is entirely suitable for kitchen oven heating and cooling cycles. The introduction of some relatively large pores or a ductile second phase may also improve the thermal shock characteristics of a material; both serve to impede the propagation of thermally induced cracks.

It is often necessary to remove thermal stresses in ceramic materials as a means of improving their mechanical strengths and optical characteristics. This may be accomplished by an annealing heat treatment, as discussed for glasses in Section 14.4.

SUMMARY

This chapter discussed heat absorption, thermal expansion, and thermal conduction—three important thermal phenomena. Heat capacity represents the quantity of heat required to produce a unit rise in temperature for one mole of a substance; on a per-unit mass basis, it is termed specific heat. Most of the energy assimilated by many solid materials is associated with increasing the vibrational energy of the atoms; contributions to the total heat capacity by other energy-absorptive mechanisms (i.e., increased free-electron kinetic energies) are normally insignificant.

For many crystalline solids and at temperatures within the vicinity of 0 K, the heat capacity measured at constant volume varies as the cube of the absolute temperature; in excess of the Debye temperature, C_v becomes temperature independent, assuming a value of approximately $3R$.

Solid materials expand when heated and contract when cooled. The fractional change in length is proportional to the temperature change, the constant of proportionality being the coefficient of thermal expansion. Thermal expansion is reflected by an increase in the average interatomic separation, which is a consequence of the asymmetric nature of the potential energy versus interatomic spacing curve trough. The larger the interatomic bonding energy, the lower the coefficient of thermal expansion.

The transport of thermal energy from high- to low-temperature regions of a material is termed thermal conduction. For steady-state heat transport, the flux is proportional to the temperature gradient along the direction of flow; the proportionality constant is the thermal conductivity.

For solid materials, heat is transported by free electrons and by vibrational lattice waves, or phonons. The high thermal conductivities for relatively pure metals are due to the large numbers of free electrons, and also the efficiency with which these electrons transport thermal energy. By way of contrast, ceramics and polymers are poor thermal conductors because free-electron concentrations are low and phonon conduction predominates.

Thermal stresses, which are introduced in a body as a consequence of temperature changes, may lead to fracture or undesirable plastic deformation. The two prime sources of thermal stresses are restrained thermal expansion (or contraction), and temperature gradients established during heating or cooling.

Thermal shock is the fracture of a body resulting from thermal stresses induced by rapid temperature changes. Because ceramic materials are brittle, they are especially susceptible to this type of failure. The thermal shock resistance of many materials is proportional to the fracture strength and thermal conductivity, and inversely proportional to both the modulus of elasticity and the coefficient of thermal expansion.

IMPORTANT TERMS AND CONCEPTS

Heat capacity	Phonon	Thermal shock
Linear coefficient of thermal expansion	Specific heat	Thermal stress
	Thermal conductivity	

REFERENCES

Kingery, W. D., H. K. Bowen, and D. R. Uhlmann, *Introduction to Ceramics,* 2nd edition, John Wiley & Sons, New York, 1976. Chapters 12 and 16.

Rose, R. M., L. A. Shepard, and J. Wulff, *The Structure and Properties of Materials,* Vol. IV,

Electronic Properties, John Wiley & Sons, New York, 1966. Chapters 3 and 8.

Ziman, J., "The Thermal Properties of Materials," *Scientific American,* Vol. 217, No. 3, September 1967, pp. 180–188.

QUESTIONS AND PROBLEMS

20.1 Estimate the energy required to raise the temperature of 5 kg (11.0 lb$_m$) of the following materials from 20 to 150°C (68 to 300°F): aluminum, brass, alumina, and polypropylene.

20.2 To what temperature would 25 lb$_m$ of a 1025 steel specimen at 25°C (77°F) be raised if 125 Btu of heat is supplied?

20.3 (a) Determine the room temperature heat capacities at constant pressure for the following materials: aluminum, silver, tungsten, and 70Cu-30Zn brass. (b) How do these val-

ues compare with one another? How do you explain this?

20.4 For copper, the heat capacity at constant volume C_v at 20 K is 0.38 J/mol-K, and the Debye temperature is 340 K. Estimate the specific heat (a) at 40 K and (b) at 400 K.

20.5 The constant A in Equation 20.2 is $12\pi^4 R/5 \theta_D^3$, where R is the gas constant and θ_D is the Debye temperature (K). Estimate θ_D for aluminum, given that the specific heat is 4.60 J/kg-K at 15 K.

20.6 (a) Briefly explain why C_v rises with increasing temperature at temperatures near 0 K. **(b)** Briefly explain why C_v becomes virtually independent of temperature at temperatures far removed from 0 K.

20.7 A bimetallic strip is constructed from strips of two different metals that are bonded along their lengths. Explain how such a device may be used in a thermostat to regulate temperature.

20.8 **(a)** Explain why a brass lid ring on a glass canning jar will loosen when heated. **(b)** Suppose the ring is made of tungsten instead of brass. What will be the effect of heating the lid and jar? Why?

20.9 A copper wire 15 m (49.2 ft) long is cooled from 40 to −9°C (104 to 15°F). How much change in length will it experience?

20.10 A 0.4 m (15.7 in.) rod of a metal elongates 0.48 mm (0.019 in.) on heating from 20 to 100°C (68 to 212°F). Determine the value of the linear coefficient of thermal expansion for this material.

20.11 Briefly explain thermal expansion using the potential energy-versus-interatomic spacing curve.

20.12 The difference between the specific heats at constant pressure and volume is described by the expression

$$c_p - c_v = \frac{\alpha_v^2 v_0 T}{\beta} \qquad (20.10)$$

where α_v is the volume coefficient of thermal expansion, v_0 is the specific volume (i.e., volume per unit mass, or the reciprocal of density), β is the compressibility, and T is the absolute temperature. Compute the values of c_v at room temperature (293 K) for copper and nickel using the data in Table 20.1, assume that $\alpha_v = 3\alpha_l$ and given that the values of β for Cu and Ni are 8.35×10^{-12} and 5.51×10^{-12} (Pa)$^{-1}$, respectively.

20.13 To what temperature must a cylindrical rod of tungsten 10.000 mm in diameter and a plate of 316 stainless steel having a circular hole 9.988 mm in diameter have to be heated for the rod to just fit into the hole? Assume that the initial temperature is 25°C.

20.14 Explain why, on a cold day, the metal door handle of an automobile feels colder to the touch than a plastic steering wheel, even though both are at the same temperature.

20.15 **(a)** Calculate the heat flux through a sheet of brass 7.5 mm (0.30 in.) thick if the temperatures at the two faces are 150 and 50°C (302 and 122°F); assume steady-state heat flow. **(b)** What is the heat loss per hour if the area of the sheet is 0.5 m² (5.4 ft²)? **(c)** What will be the heat loss per hour if soda–lime glass instead of brass is used? **(d)** Calculate the heat loss per hour if brass is used and the thickness is increased to 15 mm (0.59 in.).

20.16 **(a)** Would you expect Equation 20.7 to be valid for ceramic and polymeric materials? Why or why not? **(b)** Estimate the value for the Wiedemann-Franz constant L [in Ω-W/(K)²] at room temperature (293 K) for the following nonmetals: silicon (intrinsic), glass-ceramic (Pyroceram), fused silica, polycarbonate and polytetrafluoroethylene. Consult Tables C.7 and C.9, Appendix C.

20.17 **(a)** The thermal conductivity of a single-crystal specimen is slightly greater than a polycrystalline one of the same material. Why is this so? **(b)** The thermal conductivity of a plain carbon steel is greater than for a stainless steel. Why is this so?

20.18 Briefly explain why the thermal conductivities are higher for crystalline than noncrystalline ceramics.

20.19 Briefly explain why metals are typically better thermal conductors than ceramic materials.

20.20 **(a)** Briefly explain why porosity decreases the thermal conductivity of ceramic and polymeric materials, rendering them more thermally insulative. **(b)** Briefly explain how the degree of crystallinity affects the thermal conductivity of polymeric materials and why.

20.21 For some ceramic materials, why does the thermal conductivity first decrease and then increase with rising temperature?

20.22 For each of the following pairs of materials, decide which has the larger thermal conductivity. Justify your choices.

(a) Pure silver; sterling silver (92.5 wt% Ag–7.5 wt% Cu).

(b) Fused silica; polycrystalline silica.

(c) Linear polyethylene (M_n = 450,000 g/mol); lightly branched polyethylene (M_n = 650,000 g/mol).

(d) Atactic polypropylene (M_w = 10^6 g/mol); isotactic polypropylene (M_w = 5 × 10^5 g/mol).

20.23 We might think of a porous material as being a composite wherein one of the phases is a pore phase. Estimate upper and lower limits for the room-temperature thermal conductivity of a magnesium oxide material having a volume fraction of 0.30 of pores that are filled with still air.

20.24 Nonsteady-state heat flow may be described by the following partial differential equation:

$$\frac{\partial T}{\partial t} = D_T \frac{\partial^2 T}{\partial x^2}$$

where D_T is the thermal diffusivity; this expression is the thermal equivalent of Fick's second law of diffusion (Equation 5.4b). The thermal diffusivity is defined according to

$$D_T = \frac{k}{\rho c_p}$$

In this expression, k, ρ, and c_p represent the thermal conductivity, the mass density, and the specific heat at constant pressure, respectively.

(a) What are the SI units for D_T?

(b) Determine values of D_T for copper, brass, magnesia, fused silica, polystyrene, and polypropylene using the data in Table 20.1. Density values are included in Table C.1, Appendix C.

20.25 Beginning with Equation 20.3, show that Equation 20.8 is valid.

20.26 (a) Briefly explain why thermal stresses may be introduced into a structure by rapid heating or cooling. (b) For cooling, what is the nature of the surface stresses? (c) For heating, what is the nature of the surface stresses? (d) For a ceramic material, is thermal shock more likely to occur on rapid heating or cooling? Why?

20.27 (a) If a rod of brass 0.35 m (13.8 in.) long is heated from 15° to 85°C (60° to 185°F) while its ends are maintained rigid, determine the type and magnitude of stress that develops. Assume that at 15°C the rod is stress free. (b) What will be the stress magnitude if a rod 1 m (39.4 in.) long is used? (c) If the rod in part a is cooled from 15° to −15°C (60° to 5°F), what type and magnitude of stress will result?

20.28 A steel wire is stretched with a stress of 70 MPa (10,000 psi) at 20°C (68°F). If the length is held constant, to what temperature must the wire be heated to reduce the stress to 17 MPa (2500 psi)?

20.29 If a cylindrical rod of nickel 100.00 mm long and 8.000 mm in diameter is heated from 20°C to 200°C while its ends are maintained rigid, determine its change in diameter. You may want to consult Table 6.1.

20.30 The two ends of a cylindrical rod of 1025 steel 75.00 mm long and 10.000 mm in diameter are maintained rigid. If the rod is initially at 25°C, to what temperature must it be cooled to have a 0.008-mm reduction in diameter?

20.31 What measures may be taken to reduce the likelihood of thermal shock of a ceramic piece?

Design Problems

20.D1 Railroad tracks made of 1025 steel are to be laid during the time of year when the temperature averages 4°C (40°F). If a joint space of 5.4 mm (0.210 in.) is allowed between the standard 11.9-m (39-ft) long rails, what is the hottest possible temperature that can be tolerated without the introduction of thermal stresses?

20.D2 The ends of a cylindrical rod 6.4 mm (0.25 in.) in diameter and 250 mm (10 in.) long are mounted between rigid supports. The rod is stress free at room temperature [20°C (68°F)]; and upon cooling to −40°C (−40°F), a maximum thermally induced tensile stress of 125 MPa (18,125 psi) is possible. Of which of the following metals or alloys may the rod be fabricated: aluminum, copper, brass, 1025 steel, and tungsten? Why?

20.D3 **(a)** What are the units for the thermal shock resistance parameter (TSR)? **(b)** Rank the following ceramic materials according to their thermal shock resistance: glass-ceramic (Pyroceram), partially stabilized zirconia, mullite, and borosilicate (Pyrex) glass. Appropriate data may be found in Tables C.2, C.4, C.6, and C.7, Appendix C.

20.D4 Equation 20.9, for the thermal shock resistance of a material, is valid for relatively low rates of heat transfer. When the rate is high, then, upon cooling of a body, the maximum temperature change allowable without thermal shock, ΔT_f, is approximately

$$\Delta T_f \cong \frac{\sigma_f}{E\alpha_l}$$

where σ_f is the fracture strength. Using the data in Tables C.2, C.4, and C.6 (Appendix C), determine ΔT_f for a glass-ceramic (Pyroceram), partially stabilized zirconia, mullite, and fused silica.

Answers to Selected Problems

Chapter 2

2.3 **(a)** 1.66×10^{-24} g/amu;

(b) 2.73×10^{26} atoms/lb-mol

2.13

$$r_0 = \left(\frac{A}{nB}\right)^{1/(1-n)}$$

$$E_0 = -\frac{A}{\left(\dfrac{A}{nB}\right)^{1/(1-n)}} + \frac{B}{\left(\dfrac{A}{nB}\right)^{n/(1-n)}}$$

2.14 **(c)** $r_0 = 0.279$ nm; $E_0 = -4.57$ eV

2.18 63.2% for TiO_2; 1.0% for InSb

Chapter 3

3.3 $V_C = 1.21 \times 10^{-28}$ m^3

3.9 $R = 0.138$ nm

3.12 **(a)** $V_C = 1.40 \times 10^{-28}$ m^3;

(b) $a = 0.323$ nm, $c = 0.515$ nm

3.15 Metal B: face-centered cubic

3.17 **(a)** $n = 8.0$; **(b)** $\rho = 4.96$ g/cm^3

3.20 $V_C = 8.63 \times 10^{-2}$ nm^3

3.25 **(a)** Direction 1: $[2\bar{1}\bar{2}]$; **(b)** Plane 1: (211)

3.27 Direction A: $[0\bar{1}\bar{1}]$; Direction C: [112]

3.28 Direction B: $[2\bar{3}2]$; Direction D: $[13\bar{6}]$

3.29 **(b)** $[\bar{1}\bar{1}0]$, $[\bar{1}10]$, and $[1\bar{1}0]$

3.31 Plane B: $(\bar{1}\bar{1}2)$ or $(11\bar{2})$

3.32 Plane A: $(3\bar{2}\bar{2})$

3.33 Plane B: (221)

3.35 **(a)** $(1\bar{1}00)$

3.38 **(a)** (100) and $(0\bar{1}0)$

3.39 **(c)** [010]

3.40 [100]: LD = 0.71

3.41 [111]: LD = 1.0

3.42 (100): PD = 0.79

3.43 (110): PD = 0.83

3.49 $2\theta = 81.38°$

3.50 $d_{110} = 0.2862$ nm

3.52 **(a)** $d_{321} = 0.1523$ nm; **(b)** $R = 0.2468$ nm

3.54 $d_{110} = 0.2015$ nm; $a = 0.285$ nm

Chapter 4

4.1 $N_v/N = 4.6 \times 10^{-4}$

4.3 $Q_v = 0.75$ eV/atom

4.5 For FCC, $r = 0.41R$

4.8 $C_{Pb} = 10.0$ wt%; $C_{Sn} = 90.0$ wt%

4.10 $C'_{Sn} = 72.5$ at%; $C'_{Pb} = 27.5$ at%

4.12 $C'_{Fe} = 94.2$ at%; $C'_{Si} = 5.8$ at%

4.14 3.3×10^{28} m^{-3}

4.17 $N_{Au} = 3.36 \times 10^{21}$ atoms/cm^3

4.21 $C_{Nb} = 35.2$ wt%

4.23 **(a)** FCC: $\mathbf{b} = a/2$ [110];

(b) Al: $|\mathbf{b}| = 0.2862$ nm

4.28 $d \approx 0.07$ mm

4.30 **(a)** $N = 32$

Chapter 5

5.6 $M = 4.1 \times 10^{-3}$ kg/h

5.8 $D = 2.3 \times 10^{-11}$ m^2/s

5.11 $t = 31.3$ h

5.15 $t = 135$ h

5.18 $T = 901$ K (628°C)

5.21 **(a)** $Q_d = 316$ kJ/mol (75.5 kcal/mol);
$D_0 = 3.5 \times 10^{-4}$ m^2/s;

(b) $D = 1.1 \times 10^{-14}$ m^2/s

5.24 $T = 1044$ K (771°C)

5.29 $x = 1.6$ mm

Chapter 6

6.2 l_0 = 475 mm (18.7 in.)

6.5 **(a)** F = 89,400 N (20,000 lb_f);

(b) l_i = 115.28 mm (4.511 in.)

6.7 Δl = 0.23 mm (0.009 in.)

6.10

$$\left(\frac{dF}{dr}\right)_{r_0} = -\frac{2A}{\left(\dfrac{A}{nB}\right)^{3/(1-n)}} + \frac{nB[n+1]}{\left(\dfrac{A}{nB}\right)^{(n+2)/(1-n)}}$$

6.12 **(a)** Δl = 0.325 mm (0.013 in.);

(b) Δd = -5.9×10^{-3} mm (-2.3×10^{-4} in.); decrease

6.13 F = 7800 N (1785 lb_f)

6.14 ν = 0.280

6.16 E = 170.5 GPa (24.7 $\times 10^6$ psi)

6.19 **(a)** Δl = 0.10 mm (4×10^{-3} in.);

(b) Δd = -3.6×10^{-3} mm (-1.4×10^{-4} in.)

6.22 Steel and brass

6.25 **(a)** Both elastic and plastic;

(b) Δl = 2.5 mm (0.10 in.)

6.27 **(b)** E = 200 GPa (29 $\times 10^6$ psi);

(c) σ_y = 750 MPa (110,000 psi);

(d) TS = 1250 MPa (180,000 psi);

(e) %EL = 11.2%;

(f) U_r = 1.40×10^6 J/m^3 (210 in.-lb_f/in.^{3})

6.30 Figure 6.11: U_r = 3.2×10^5 J/m^3 (45.3 in.-lb_f/in.^{3})

6.32 σ_y = 381 MPa (55,500 psi)

6.37 ϵ_T = 0.311

6.39 σ_T = 460 MPa (66,400 psi)

6.41 Toughness = 7.33×10^8 J/m^3 (1.07×10^5 in.-lb_f/in.^{3})

6.43 n = 0.246

6.45 **(a)** ϵ (elastic) $\cong$ 0.005; ϵ (plastic) $\cong$ 0.020;

(b) l_i = 469.3 mm (18.36 in.)

6.47 **(a)** 125 HB (70 HRB)

6.52 Figure 6.11: σ_w = 125 MPa (18,000 psi)

Chapter 9

9.5 **(a)** $\epsilon + \eta$; C_ϵ = 87 wt% Zn-13 wt% Cu, C_η = 97 wt% Zn-3 wt% Cu;

(c) Liquid; C_L = 55 wt% Ag-45 wt% Cu;

(e) $\beta + \gamma$; C_β = 49 wt% Zn-51 wt% Cu, C_γ = 57 wt% Zn-43 wt% Cu;

(g) α; C_α = 63.8 wt% Ni-36.2 wt% Cu.

9.7 **(a)** W_ϵ = 0.70, W_η = 0.30;

(c) W_L = 1.0;

(e) W_β = 0.50, W_γ = 0.50;

(g) W_α = 1.0

9.9 **(a)** V_ϵ = 0.70, V_η = 0.30

9.11 **(a)** T = 280°C (535°F)

9.12 **(a)** m_s = 5022 g;

(b) C_L = 64 wt% sugar;

(c) m_s = 2355 g

9.16 Is possible

9.19 **(a)** T = 550°C (1020°F);

(b) C_α = 22 wt% Pb-78 wt% Mg;

(c) T = 465°C (870°F);

(d) C_L = 66 wt% Pb-34 wt% Mg

9.22 **(a)** $T \cong$ 230°C (445°F);

(b) C_α = 15 wt% Sn; C_L = 42 wt% Sn

9.23 C_α = 88.3 wt% A-11.7 wt% B; C_β = 5.0 wt% A-95 wt% B

9.25 Not possible

9.29 Is possible

9.32 C_0 = 82.4 wt% Sn-17.6 wt% Pb

9.35

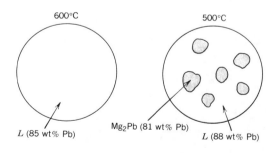

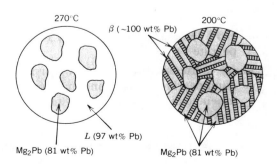

9.39 Eutectics: **(1)** 12 wt% Nd, 632°C, $L \to$ Al + $Al_{11}Nd_3$;

(2) 97 wt% Nd, 635°C, $L \to AlNd_3$ + Nd; Congruent melting point: 73 wt% Nd, 1460°C, $L \to Al_2Nd$
Peritectics: **(1)** 59 wt% Nd, 1235°C, $L + Al_2Nd \to Al_{11}Nd_3$;

(2) 84 wt% Nd, 940°C, $L + Al_2Nd \to$ AlNd;

(3) 91 wt% Nd, 795°C, $L + AlNd \to AlNd_2$;

(4) 94 wt% Nd, 675°C, $L + AlNd_2 \to AlNd_3$
No eutectoids are present.

9.42 For point B, $F = 2$

9.47 $C_0 = 0.69$ wt% C

9.50 **(a)** α-ferrite; **(b)** 5.64 kg ferrite, 0.36 kg Fe_3C;

(c) 2.52 kg proeutectoid ferrite, 3.48 kg pearlite

9.52 $C_0 = 0.63$ wt% C

9.54 $C_0 = 0.61$ wt% C

9.57 Possible

9.60 Two answers are possible: $C_0 = 1.11$ wt% C and 0.72 wt% C

9.63 HB (alloy) = 141

9.66 **(a)** T (eutectoid) = 700°C (1290°F); **(b)** ferrite;

(c) $W_{\alpha'} = 0.20$, $W_p = 0.80$

Chapter 13
13.5 **(a)** Sodium chloride; **(d)** cesium chloride
13.7 APF = 0.73
13.9 **(a)** FCC; **(b)** tetrahedral; **(c)** one half
13.11 **(a)** octahedral; **(b)** all
13.14 **(a)** $a = 0.437$ nm; **(b)** $a = 0.434$ nm
13.16 ρ (calculated) = 4.11 g/cm³; ρ (measured) = 4.10 g/cm³
13.18 **(a)** $\rho = 4.20$ g/cm³
13.20 Cesium chloride
13.22 APF = 0.84
13.24 APF = 0.68
13.28 **(a)** $C = 45.9$ wt% Al_2O_3–54.1 wt% SiO_2
13.32 **(a)** Li^+ vacancy; one Li^+ vacancy for every Ca^{2+} added; **(b)** Cl^- vacancy; one Cl^- vacancy for every O^{2-} added.

13.35 **(a)** 8.1% of Mg^{2+} vacancies
13.37 $\rho_t = 4.1$ nm
13.40 $R = 9.1$ mm (0.36 in.)
13.41 $F_f = 10,100$ N (2165 lb$_f$)
13.44 **(a)** $E_0 = 342$ GPa; **(b)** $E = 280$ GPa
13.46 **(b)** $P = 0.19$

Chapter 15
15.4 $n_n = 4800$
15.6 **(a)** $\overline{M}_n = 49{,}800$ g/mol; **(c)** $n_n = 498$
15.9 **(a)** $C_{Cl} = 29.0$ wt%
15.11 $L = 1254$ nm; $r = 15.4$ nm
15.16 9333 of both styrene and butadiene mers
15.18 propylene
15.21 f(styrene) = 0.32; f(butadiene) = 0.68
15.25 $\rho = 0.998$ g/cm³
15.27 **(a)** $\rho_a = 2.000$ g/cm³, $\rho_c = 2.301$ g/cm³; **(b)** % crystallinity = 87.9%

Chapter 16
16.18 $E_r(10) = 4.25$ MPa (616 psi)
16.27 **(a)** m(adipic acid) = 117.7 kg
(b) m(polyester) = 153.2 kg
16.34 15%
16.36 One sulfur crosslink per pair of isoprene mers

Chapter 19
19.2 $d = 1.88$ mm
19.5 **(a)** $R = 6.7 \times 10^{-3}$ Ω; **(b)** $I = 6$ A;
(c) $J = 3.1 \times 10^5$ A/m²;
(d) $\mathscr{E} = 8 \times 10^{-3}$ V/m
19.12 $\sigma = 0.028$ (Ω-m)$^{-1}$
19.13 **(a)** $n = 1.98 \times 10^{29}$ m^{-3};
(b) 3.28 free electrons/atom
19.16 **(a)** $\rho_0 = 1.55 \times 10^{-8}$ Ω-m, $a = 6.7 \times 10^{-11}$ Ω-m/°C;
(b) $A = 1.12 \times 10^{-6}$ Ω-m;
(c) $\rho = 5.1 \times 10^{-8}$ Ω-m
19.18 $\sigma = 7.3 \times 10^6$ (Ω-m)$^{-1}$
19.20 **(b)** for Si, 2.7×10^{-13}; for Ge, 5.6×10^{-10}
19.29 **(a)** $n = 6.4 \times 10^{21}$ m^{-3}; **(b)** n-type extrinsic
19.32 $\mu_e = 0.50$ m²/V-s; $\mu_h = 0.14$ m²/V-s
19.37 $E_g = 1.75$ eV
19.38 **(b)** $\sigma = 3.8 \times 10^{-5}$ (Ω-m)$^{-1}$
19.41 $B_z = 0.58$ tesla

19.48 $l = 3.4$ mm (0.135 in.)

19.52 $p_i = 1.92 \times 10^{-30}$ C-m

19.54 **(a)** $V = 40$ V; **(b)** $V = 139$ V;
   (e) $P = 2.21 \times 10^{-7}$ C/m^2

19.56 Fraction of ϵ_r due to $P_i = 0.67$

19.D2 $\rho = 4.1 \times 10^{-8}$ Ω-m

19.D3 Possible; 30 wt% $< C_{Ni} <$ 32.5 wt%

Chapter 20

20.2 $T_f = 49°C$ (120°F)

20.4 **(a)** $c_v = 47.8$ J/kg-K; **(b)** $c_v = 392$ J/kg-K

20.9 $\Delta l = -12.5$ mm (-0.49 in.)

20.13 $T_f = 129.5°C$

20.15 **(b)** $dQ/dt = 2.9 \times 10^9$ J/h

20.23 k(upper) $= 26.4$ W/m-K

20.27 **(a)** $\sigma = 136$ MPa (20,000 psi); compression

20.28 $T_f = 41°C$ (106°F)

20.29 $\Delta d = 0.0251$ mm

20.D1 $T_f = 42°C$ (107°F)

20.D4 Glass ceramic: $\Delta T_f = 335°C$; mullite;
   $\Delta T_f = 224°C$

Index

Page numbers in *italics* refer to the glossary.

TEXTBOOK OF POLYMER SCIENCE

THIRD EDITION

FRED W. BILLMEYER, JR.

Professor of Analytical Chemistry
Rensselaer Polytechnic Institute, Troy, New York

A Wiley-Interscience Publication

John Wiley & Sons

New York • Chichester • Brisbane • Toronto • Singapore

Library of Congress Cataloging in Publication Data:

Billmeyer, Fred W.
    Textbook of polymer science.

    Includes bibliographies and indexes.
    1. Polymers and polymerization. I. Title.

QD381.B52 1984   668.9   83-19870
ISBN 0-471-03196-8

Printed in the United States of America

20 19 18 17 16 15 14 13 12

CONTENTS

PART ONE

INTRODUCTION

CHAPTER ONE

THE SCIENCE OF LARGE MOLECULES

A. BASIC CONCEPTS OF POLYMER SCIENCE

Over half a century ago, Wolfgang Ostwald (1917)† coined the term *the land of neglected dimensions* to describe the range of sizes between molecular and macroscopic within which occur most colloidal particles. The term *neglected dimensions* might have been applied equally well to the world of polymer molecules, the high-molecular-weight compounds so important to man and his modern technology. It was not until the 1930's that the science of high polymers began to emerge, and the major growth of the technology of these materials came even later. Yet today polymer dimensions are neglected no more, for industries associated with polymeric materials employ more than half of all American chemists and chemical engineers.

The science of macromolecules is divided between biological and nonbiological materials. Each is of great importance. Biological polymers form the very foundation of life and intelligence and provide much of the food on which man exists. This book, however, is concerned primarily with the chemistry, physics, and technology of nonbiological polymers. These are the synthetic materials used for plastics, fibers, and elastomers, with a few naturally occurring polymers, such as rubber, wool, and cellulose, included. Today these substances are truly indispensable to mankind, being essential to clothing, shelter, transportation, and communication, as well as to the conveniences of modern living.

A *polymer* is a large molecule built up by the repetition of small, simple chemical units. In some cases the repetition is linear, much as a chain is built up from its links. In other cases the chains are *branched* or interconnected to form three-

---

†Parenthetical years or names and years refer to items in the bibliography at the end of the chapter.

3

dimensional networks. The *repeat unit* of the polymer is usually equivalent or nearly equivalent to the *monomer,* or starting material from which the polymer is formed. Thus (Table 1-1) the repeat unit of poly(vinyl chloride) is —CH_2CHCl—; its monomer is vinyl chloride, CH_2=$CHCl$.

The length of the polymer chain is specified by the number of repeat units in the chain. This is called the *degree of polymerization* (DP). The molecular weight of the polymer is the product of the molecular weight of the repeat unit and the DP. Using poly(vinyl chloride) as an example, a polymer of DP 1000 has a molecular weight of 63 × 1000 = 63,000. Most high polymers useful for plastics, rubbers, or fibers have molecular weights between 10,000 and 1,000,000.

Unlike many products whose structure and reactions were well known before their industrial application, some polymers were produced on an industrial scale long before their chemistry or physics was studied. Empiricism in recipes, processes, and control tests was usual.

Gradually the study of polymer properties began. Almost all were first called anomalous because they were so different from the properties of low-molecular-weight compounds. It was soon realized, however, that polymer molecules are many times larger than those of ordinary substances. The presumably anomalous properties of polymers were shown to be normal for such materials, as the consequences of their size were included in the theoretical treatments of their properties.

Polymerization Processes.   The processes of polymerization were divided by Flory (1953) and Carothers (Mark 1940) into two groups known as *condensation*

TABLE 1-1.   Some Linear High Polymers, Their Monomers, and Their Repeat Units

Polymer	Monomer	Repeat Unit
Polyethylene	CH_2=CH_2	—CH_2CH_2—
Poly(vinyl chloride)	CH_2=$CHCl$	—CH_2CHCl
Polyisobutylene	CH_2=$\overset{\displaystyle CH_3}{\underset{\displaystyle CH_3}{C}}$	—CH_2—$\overset{\displaystyle CH_3}{\underset{\displaystyle CH_3}{C}}$—
Polystyrene[a]	CH_2=CH	—CH_2—CH—
Polycaprolactam (6-nylon)	H—$\underset{\displaystyle H}{N}$($CH_2)_5\overset{\displaystyle O}{C}$—OH	—$\underset{\displaystyle H}{N}$($CH_2)_5\overset{\displaystyle O}{C}$—
Polyisoprene (natural rubber)	CH_2=CH—$\underset{\displaystyle CH_3}{C}$=$CH_2$	—CH_2CH=$\underset{\displaystyle CH_3}{C}$—$CH_2$—

[a]By convention, the symbol ◯ is used throughout to represent the benzene ring, double bonds being omitted.

and *addition* polymerization or, in more precise terminology (Chapter 2A), *step-reaction* and *chain-reaction* polymerization.

Condensation or *step-reaction polymerization* is entirely analogous to condensation in low-molecular-weight compounds. In polymer formation the condensation takes place between two polyfunctional molecules to produce one larger polyfunctional molecule, with the possible elimination of a small molecule such as water. The reaction continues until almost all of one of the reagents is used up; an equilibrium is established that can be shifted at will at high temperatures by controlling the amounts of the reactants and products.

Addition or *chain-reaction polymerization* involves chain reactions in which the chain carrier may be an ion or a reactive substance with one unpaired electron called a *free radical*. A free radical is usually formed by the decomposition of a relatively unstable material called an *initiator*. The free radical is capable of reacting to open the double bond of a vinyl monomer and add to it, with an electron remaining unpaired. In a very short time (usually a few seconds or less) many more monomers add successively to the growing chain. Finally two free radicals react to annihilate each other's growth activity and form one or more polymer molecules.

With some exceptions, polymers made in chain reactions often contain only carbon atoms in the main chain (*homochain polymers*), whereas polymers made in step reactions may have other atoms, originating in the monomer functional groups, as part of the chain (*heterochain polymers.*)

Molecular Weight and Its Distribution. In both chain and stepwise polymerization, the length of a chain is determined by purely random events. In step reactions, the chain length is determined by the local availability of reactive groups at the ends of the growing chains. In radical polymerization, chain length is determined by the time during which the chain grows before it diffuses into the vicinity of a second free radical and the two react. In either case, the polymeric product contains molecules having many different chain lengths. Molecular weight and molecular-weight distribution in polymers is considered further in Section *D*.

Branched and Network Polymers. In contrast to the linear-chain molecules discussed so far, some polymers have branched chains, often as a result of side reactions during polymerization (Fig. 1-1*a*). The term *branching* implies that the individual molecules are still discrete; in still other cases *crosslinked* or *network structures* are formed (Fig. 1-1*b*), as in the use of monomers containing more than two reactive groups in stepwise polymerization. If, for example, glycerol is substituted for ethylene glycol in the reaction with a dibasic acid, a three-dimensional network polymer results. In recent years, a variety of branched polymer structures, some with outstanding high-temperature properties, has been synthesized (Chapter 15).

In commercial practice crosslinking reactions may take place during the fabrication of articles made with *thermosetting* resins. The crosslinked network extending throughout the final article is stable to heat and cannot be made to flow or melt. In contrast, most linear or branched polymers can be made to soften and take on

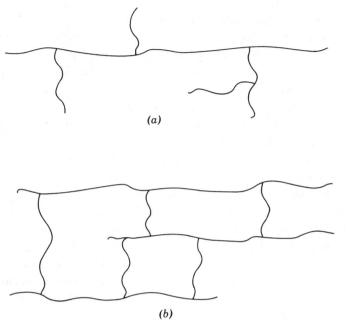

FIG. 1-1.   Schematic representation of (a) branched and (b) network polymers.

new shapes by the application of heat and pressure. They are said to be *thermo-plastic*.

The Texture of Polymers.   The geometrical arrangement of the atoms in a polymer chain can be divided conveniently into two categories:

a.   Arrangements fixed by the chemical bonding in the molecule, such as cis and trans isomers, or *d* and *l* forms. Throughout this book, such arrangements are described as *configurations*. The configuration of a polymer chain cannot be altered unless chemical bonds are broken and reformed.

b.   Arrangements arising from rotation about single bonds. These arrangements, including the manifold forms that the polymer chain may have in solution, are described as *conformations*.

In dilute solution, where the polymer chain is surrounded by small molecules, or in the melt, where it is in an environment of similar chains, the polymer molecule is in continual motion because of its thermal energy, assuming many different *conformations* in rapid succession. As a polymer melt is cooled, or as this molecular motion so characteristic of polymers is restrained through the introduction of strong interchain forces, the nature of the polymer sample changes systematically in ways that are important in determining its physical properties and end uses (Fig. 1-2).

In the molten state, polymer chains move freely, though often with enormous viscosity, past one another if a force is applied. This is the principle utilized in the

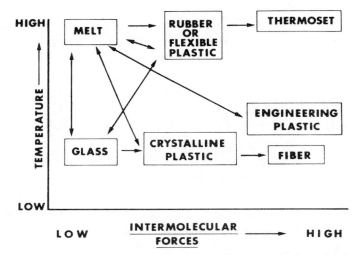

FIG. 1-2. The interrelation of the states of bulk polymers. The arrows indicate the directions in which changes from one state to another can take place (Billmeyer 1969).

fabrication of most polymeric articles and is the chief example of the plasticity from which the very name *plastics* is derived. If the irreversible flow characteristic of the molten state is inhibited by the introduction of a tenuous network of primary chemical-bond crosslinks in the process commonly called *vulcanization* (Chapter 19), but the local freedom of motion of the polymer chains is not restricted, the product shows the elastic properties we associate with typical rubbers. If, however, the interchain forces result from secondary bonds, such as the interaction of polar groups, rather than primary chemical bonds, the rubber is not one of high elasticity but has the properties of limpness and flexibility: A familiar example is the vinyl film widely used alone or in coated fabrics. Secondary-bond forces are capable of forming and breaking reversibly as the temperature is changed, as indicated by the arrows in Fig. 1-2.

Continued primary-bond crosslinking in the postpolymerization step of vulcanization converts rubber into hard rubber or ebonite, whereas crosslinking concurrent with polymerization produces a wide variety of thermosetting materials. Common examples are the phenol-formaldehyde and amine-formaldehyde families widely used as plastics.

As the temperature of a polymer melt or rubber is lowered, a point known as the *glass-transition temperature* is reached where polymeric materials undergo a marked change in properties associated with the virtual cessation of local molecular motion. Thermal energy is required for segments of a polymer chain to move with respect to one another; if the temperature is low enough, the required amounts of energy are not available. Below their glass-transition temperature, amorphous polymers have many of the properties associated with ordinary inorganic glasses, including hardness, stiffness, brittleness, and transparency.

In addition to undergoing a glass transition as the temperature is lowered, some polymers can *crystallize* at temperatures below that designated as their crystalline

melting point. Not all polymers are capable of crystallizing; to oversimplify somewhat, the requirements for crystallizability in a polymer are that it have either a
geometrically regular structure or that any substituent atoms or groups on the
backbone chain be small enough so that, if irregularly spaced, they can still fit into
an ordered structure by virtue of their small size (see Chapter 10).

The properties of crystalline polymers are highly desirable. Crystalline polymers
are strong, tough, stiff, and generally more resistant to solvents and chemicals than
their noncrystalline counterparts. Further improvements in these desirable properties
can be brought about in at least two ways.

First, by increasing intermolecular forces through the selection of highly polar
polymers, and by using inherently stiff polymer chains, crystalline melting points
can be raised so that the desirable mechanical properties associated with crystallinity
are retained to quite high temperatures. The resulting plastics are capable of com-
peting with metals and ceramics in engineering applications (Chapters 12 and 15).

Second, the properties of crystalline polymers can be improved for materials in
fiber form by the process of orientation or drawing. The result is the increased
strength, stiffness, and dimensional stability associated with synthetic fibers (Chapter 18).

GENERAL REFERENCES

Mark 1966, 1977; Billmeyer 1972, 1982; Elias 1977, Part I; Bovey 1979.

B. THE RISE OF MACROMOLECULAR SCIENCE

Early Investigations

Natural polymers have been utilized throughout the ages. Since his beginning man
has been dependent on animal and vegetable matter for sustenance, shelter, warmth,
and other requirements and desires. Natural resins and gums have been used for
thousands of years. Asphalt was utilized in prebiblical times; amber was known to
the ancient Greeks; and gum mastic was used by the Romans.

About a century ago the unique properties of natural polymers were recognized.
The term *colloid* was proposed to distinguish polymers as a class from materials
that could be obtained in crystalline form. The concept was later broadened to that
of the "colloidal state of matter," which was considered to be like the gaseous,
liquid, and solid states. Although useful for describing many colloidal substances,
such as gold sols and soap solutions, the concept of a reversibly attainable colloidal
state of matter has no validity.

The hypothesis that colloidal materials are very high in molecular weight is also
quite old, but before the work of Raoult and van't Hoff in the 1880's no suitable
methods were available for estimating molecular weights. When experimental methods did become available, molecular weights ranging from 10,000 to 40,000 were

obtained for such substances as rubber, starch, and cellulose nitrate. The existence of large molecules implied by these measurements was not accepted by the chemists of the day for two reasons.

First, true macromolecules were not distinguished from other colloidal substances that could be obtained in noncolloidal form as well. When a material of well-known structure was seen in the colloidal state, its apparent high molecular weight was considered erroneous. Thus it was assumed that Raoult's solution law did not apply to any material in the colloidal state. Second, coordination complexes and the association of molecules were often used to explain polymeric structures in terms of physical aggregates of small molecules.

In the search by the early organic chemists for pure compounds in high yields, many polymeric substances were discovered and as quickly discarded as oils, tars, or undistillable residues. A few of these materials, however, attracted interest. Poly(ethylene glycol) was prepared about 1860; the individual polymers with degrees of polymerization up to 6 were isolated and their structures correctly assigned. The concept of extending the structure to very high molecular weights by continued condensation was understood.

The Rise of Polymer Science

Acceptance of the Existence of Macromolecules. Acceptance of the macromolecular hypothesis came about in the 1920's, largely because of the efforts of Staudinger (1920), who received the Nobel Prize in 1953 for his championship of this viewpoint. He proposed long-chain formulas for polystyrene, rubber, and polyoxymethylene. His extensive investigations of the latter polymers left no doubt as to their long-chain nature. More careful molecular-weight measurements substantiated Staudinger's conclusions, as did x-ray studies showing structures for cellulose and other polymers that were compatible with chain formulas. The outstanding series of investigations by Carothers (1929, 1931) supplied quantitative evidence substantiating the macromolecular viewpoint.

The Problem of End Groups. One deterrent to the acceptance of the macromolecular theory was the problem of the ends of the long-chain molecules. Since the degree of polymerization of a typical polymer is at least several hundred, chemical methods for detecting end groups were at first not successful. Staudinger (1925) suggested that no end groups were needed to saturate terminal valences of the long chains; they were considered to be unreactive because of the size of the molecules. Large ring structures were also hypothesized (Staudinger 1928), and this concept was popular for many years. Not until Flory (1937) elucidated the mechanism for chain-reaction polymerization did it become clear that the ends of long-chain molecules consist of normal, satisfied valence structures. This was but one of many of his contributions to polymer science honored when Flory received the Nobel Prize in 1974. The presence and nature of end groups have since been investigated in detail by chemical and physical methods (Chapter 8A).

Molecular Weight and Its Distribution.   Staudinger (1928) was among the first to recognize the large size of polymer molecules and to utilize the dependence on molecular weight of a physical property, such as dilute-solution viscosity (Staudinger 1930), for determining polymer molecular weights. He also understood clearly that synthetic polymers are polydisperse (Staudinger 1928). A few years later Lansing (1935) distinguished unmistakably among the various average molecular weights obtainable experimentally.

Configurations of Polymer Chain Atoms.   Staudinger's name is also associated with the first studies (1935) of the configuration of polymer chain atoms. He showed that the phenyl groups in polystyrene are attached to alternate chain carbon atoms. This regular head-to-tail configuration has since been established for most vinyl polymers. The mechanism for producing branches in normally linear vinyl polymers was introduced by Flory (1937), but such branches were not adequately identified and characterized for another decade (see Chapter 8E). Natta (1955a,b) first recognized the presence of sterospecific regularity in vinyl polymers. He received the Nobel Prize in 1963.

Early Industrial Developments

Rubber.   The modern plastics industry began with the utilization of natural rubber for erasers and in rubberized fabrics a few years before Goodyear's discovery of vulcanization in 1839. In the next decade the rubber industry arose both in England and in the United States. In 1851 hard rubber, or ebonite, was patented and commercialized.

Derivatives of Cellulose.   Cellulose nitrate, or nitrocellulose, discovered in 1838, was successfully commercialized by Hyatt in 1870. His product, Celluloid, cellulose nitrate plasticized with camphor, could be formed into a wide variety of useful products by the application of heat and pressure. It has been superseded in almost all uses by more stable and more suitable polymers. Cellulose acetate was discovered in 1865, and partially acetylated products were commercialized as acetate rayon fibers and cellulose acetate plastics in the early 1900's. Cellulose itself, dissolved and reprecipitated by chemical treatment, was introduced still later as viscose rayon and cellophane.

Synthetic Polymers.   The oldest of the purely synthetic plastics is the family of phenol-formaldehyde resins, of which Baekeland's Bakelite was the first commercial product. Small-scale production of phenolic resins and varnishes was begun in 1907 (Baekeland 1909).

The first commercial use of styrene was in synthetic rubbers made by copolymerization with dienes in the early 1900's. Polystyrene was produced commercially in Germany about 1930 and successfully in the United States in 1937. Large-scale production of vinyl chloride-acetate resins began in the early 1920's also. Table 1-2 shows the approximate dates of introduction of some of the synthetic plastics of greatest commercial interest.

TABLE 1-2. Some Commercially Important Polymers and Their Dates of Introduction

Date	Polymer	Date	Polymer
1930	Styrene–butadiene rubber	1943	Silicones
1936	Poly(vinyl chloride)	1944	Poly(ethylene terephthalate)
1936	Polychloroprene (neoprene)	1947	Epoxies
1936	Poly(methyl methacrylate)	1948	ABS resins
1936	Poly(vinyl acetate)	1955	Polyethylene, linear
1937	Polystyrene	1956	Polyoxymethylene
1939	66-Nylon	1957	Polypropylene
1941	Polytetrafluoroethylene	1957	Polycarbonate
1942	Unsaturated polyesters	1964	Ionomer resins
1943	Polyethylene, branched	1965	Polyimides
1943	Butyl rubber	1970	Thermoplastic elastomers
1943	6-Nylon	1974	Aromatic polyamides

GENERAL REFERENCES

Flory 1953; Mark 1966, 1967, 1977, 1981; Staudinger 1970; Marvel 1981; Seymour 1982.

C. MOLECULAR FORCES AND CHEMICAL BONDING IN POLYMERS

The nature of the bonds that hold atoms together in molecules is explained by quantum mechanics in terms of an atom consisting of a small nucleus, concentrating the mass and positive charge, surrounded by clouds or shells of electrons relatively far away. It is among the outermost, more loosely bound electrons, called *valence electrons*, that chemical reactions and primary-bond formation take place.

Primary Bonds

Ionic Bond. The most stable electronic configuration for most atoms (except hydrogen) important in polymers is a complete outer shell of eight electrons, called an *octet*. In inorganic systems this structure may be obtained by the donation of an electron by one atom to another to form an *ionic* bond:

$$\text{Na}\cdot + \cdot \ddot{\underset{..}{\text{Cl}}}\colon \longrightarrow \text{Na}^+ + \colon\ddot{\underset{..}{\text{Cl}}}\colon^-$$

These bonds are not usually found in macromolecular substances except in the use of divalent ions to provide "crosslinks" between carboxyl groups in natural resins, and in *ionomers* (Chapter 13).

Covalent Bond. These bonds are formed when one or more pairs of valence electrons are shared between two atoms, again resulting in stable electronic shells:

$$
\cdot \overset{\cdot}{\underset{\cdot}{C}} \cdot + 4H \cdot \longrightarrow H : \overset{\overset{\displaystyle H}{\cdot \cdot}}{\underset{\underset{\displaystyle H}{\cdot \cdot}}{C}} : H
$$

The *covalent bond* is the predominant bond in polymers.

Coordinate Bond. This bond is similar to the covalent bond in that electrons are shared to produce stable octets; but in the coordinate bond both of the shared electrons come from one atom. Addition compounds of boron trichloride are common examples:

$$
\begin{array}{ccc}
& : \overset{\cdot \cdot}{\underset{\cdot \cdot}{Cl}} : & \\
: \overset{\cdot \cdot}{\underset{\cdot \cdot}{Cl}} : B & + : \overset{\cdot \cdot}{\underset{\cdot \cdot}{O}} : R & \\
& : \overset{\cdot \cdot}{\underset{\cdot \cdot}{Cl}} : \quad R &
\end{array}
\longrightarrow
\begin{array}{c}
: \overset{\cdot \cdot}{\underset{\cdot \cdot}{Cl}} : \\
: \overset{\cdot \cdot}{\underset{\cdot \cdot}{Cl}} : B : \overset{\cdot \cdot}{\underset{\cdot \cdot}{O}} : R \\
: \overset{\cdot \cdot}{\underset{\cdot \cdot}{Cl}} : R
\end{array}
$$

where R is an organic group. The *coordinate* or *semipolar* bond has properties between those of the ionic and covalent bonds. No polymers containing true coordinate bonds have reached commercialization.

Metallic Bond. In the *metallic bond* the number of valence electrons is far too small to provide complete outer shells for all the atoms. The resulting bonds involve the concept of positively charged atoms embedded in a permeating "gas" of electrons free to move about at will. The metallic bond is not utilized in polymeric systems.

Typical Primary-Bond Distances and Energies. From studies of the positions of atoms in molecules and the energetics of molecular formation and dissociation, it is possible to assign typical energies and lengths to primary bonds. Table 1-3 lists some of these properties of interest in polymeric systems. The angles between successive single bonds involving the atomic arrangements usual in polymers range between 105° and 113°, not far from the tetrahedral angle of 109°28′.

Secondary-Bond Forces

Even when all the primary valences within covalent molecules are saturated, there are still forces acting between the molecules. These are generally known as *secondary valence* or *intermolecular forces*, or *van der Waals forces*. The following three types are recognized, and the first and third in particular contribute greatly to the physical properties of polymers.

Dipole Forces. When different atoms in a molecule carry equal and opposite electric charges, the molecule is said to be *polar* or to have a *dipole moment*. At

TABLE 1-3. Typical Primary-Bond Lengths and Energies

Bond	Bond Length (Å)	Dissociation Energy (kJ/mole)
C—C	1.54	347
C≡C	1.34	611
C—H	1.10	414
C—N	1.47	305
C≡N	1.15	891
C—O	1.46	360
C≡O	1.21	749
C—F	1.35	473
C—Cl	1.77	339
N—H	1.01	389
O—H	0.96	464
O—O	1.32	146

large distances such a molecule acts like an electrically neutral system, but at molecular distances the charge separation becomes significant and leads to a net intermolecular force of attraction. The magnitude of the interaction energy depends on the mutual alignment of the dipoles. Molecular orientation of this sort is always opposed by thermal agitation; hence the dipole force is strongly dependent upon temperature.

Induction Forces. A polar molecule also influences surrounding molecules that do not have permanent dipoles. The electric field associated with a dipole causes slight displacements of the electrons and nuclei of surrounding molecules, which lead to induced dipoles. The intermolecular force between the permanent and induced dipoles is called the *induction force*. The ease with which the electronic and nuclear displacements are made is called the *polarizability* of the molecule. The energy of the induction force is always small and independent of temperature.

Dispersion Forces. The existence of intermolecular forces in nonpolar materials, plus the small temperature dependence of intermolecular forces even where the dipole effect is known to far outweigh the induction effect, suggests the presence of a third type of intermolecular force. All molecules have time-dependent dipole moments that average out to zero and which arise from different instantaneous configurations of the electrons and nuclei. These fluctuations lead to perturbations of the electronic clouds of neighboring atoms and give rise to attractive forces called *dispersion forces*. They are present in all molecules and make up a major portion of the intermolecular forces unless very strong dipoles are present. In nonpolar materials only the dispersion forces exist. They are independent of temperature. Occasionally the term *van der Waals' forces* is applied to the dispersion forces alone.

Interrelation of Intermolecular Forces.   The energy of the intermolecular attractive forces varies as the inverse sixth power of the intermolecular distance. As with primary-bond forces, repulsion arises when the atoms approach more closely than an equilibrium distance of 3–5 Å. The energy of typical secondary-bond attractive forces is 8–40 kJ/mole, divided among the three secondary-bond types according to the polarizability and dipole moment of the bonding molecules.

The Hydrogen Bond.   The bond in which a hydrogen atom is associated with two other atoms is particularly important in many polymers, including proteins, and is held by many to be essential to life processes. Since the classical concepts of chemical bonding allow hydrogen to form only one covalent bond, the hydrogen bond can be considered electrostatic or ionic in character. This model does not, however, account for all the properties of the hydrogen bond; it is appealing to consider the bond covalent in some cases. The hydrogen bond occurs between two functional groups in the same or different molecules. The hydrogen is usually attached to an acidic group (a proton donor), typically a hydroxyl, carboxyl, amine, or amide group. The other group must be basic, usually oxygen, as in carbonyls, ethers, or hydroxyls; nitrogen, as in amines and amides; and occasionally halogens. The association of such polar liquid molecules as water, alcohols, and hydrofluoric acid, the formation of dimers of simple organic acids, and important structural effects in polar polymers such as nylon, cellulose, and proteins are due to hydrogen bonding.

Typically, hydrogen bonds range between 2.4 and 3.2 Å in length and between 12 and 30 kJ/mole in dissociation energy. Only fluorine, nitrogen, oxygen, and (occasionally) chlorine are electronegative enough to form hydrogen bonds.

Intermolecular Forces and Physical Properties

Secondary-bond forces are not of great importance in the formation of stable chemical compounds. They lead, rather, to the aggregation of separate molecules into solid and liquid phases. As a result, many physical properties such as volatility, viscosity, surface tension and frictional properties, miscibility, and solubility are determined largely by intermolecular forces.

The *cohesive energy* is the total energy necessary to remove a molecule from a liquid or solid to a position far from its neighbors. This is approximately equal to the heat of vaporization or sublimation at constant volume and can be estimated from thermodynamic data. The cohesive energy per unit volume, usually called the *cohesive energy density,* and its variation with molecular structure illustrate the effects of intermolecular forces on the physical properties of matter.

Volatility and Molecular Weight.   The tendency of a molecule to volatilize from its liquid is a function of its total translational energy and therefore of the temperature. The boiling point depends on the relation of the translational energy to the cohesive energy and thus is a function of molecular weight in a homologous series. At high molecular weights the total cohesive energy per molecule becomes greater than primary-bond energy, and the molecules decompose before they volatilize. This point is reached at molecular weights far below those of typical polymers.

The melting point is also related to the cohesive energy, but here another important factor comes into play. This is the influence of molecular order or entropy. In thermodynamic terms, changes of state take place only when the free-energy† change in the process

$$\Delta G = \Delta H - T \Delta S$$

is favorable, and the enthalpy term ΔH may easily be outweighed by the entropy term $T \Delta S$ whenever a radical change in molecular configurations occurs in the process. Thus, in general, a high boiling point is associated with a high melting point, but the relation between melting point and molecular structure is fairly complicated. Symmetrical molecules, which have low entropies of fusion, melt at higher temperatures than do similar but less symmetrical molecules.

Effect of Polarity. A molecule containing strongly polar groups exerts correspondingly strong attractive forces on its neighbors. This is reflected in higher boiling and melting points and other manifestations of higher cohesive energy density.

Miscibility and Solubility. These properties are also determined by the intermolecular forces. The thermal effect on mixing or solution is the difference between the cohesive energy of the mixture and that of the individual pure components. Again entropy considerations are important, but in general a negative heat of mixing favors solubility and a positive heat of mixing favors immiscibility. The intermolecular forces therefore lead directly to the solubility law of "like dissolves like."

The role of the intermolecular forces and the cohesive energy density in determining the solubility of polymers is discussed further in Chapter 7A.

Intermolecular Forces and Polymer Types. Table 1-4 lists the cohesive energy densities of some typical polymers. These data corroborate the conclusions of Section A regarding the texture of polymers, for, in the absence of primary-bond crosslinks, it is the intermolecular forces that provide the restraints on molecular motion, which, as illustrated in Fig. 1-2, are a major determinant of the nature of bulk polymers.

If the intermolecular forces are small and the cohesive energy is low, and the molecules have relatively flexible chains, they comply readily to applied stresses and have properties usually associated with elastomers. Somewhat higher cohesive energy densities, accompanied in some cases by bulky side groups giving stiffer chains, are characteristic of typical plastics. If the cohesive energy is higher still, the materials exhibit the high resistance to stress, high strength, and good mechanical

---

†This book follows the convention of defining the (Gibbs) *free energy* (now sometimes called the *free enthalpy*) as $G = H - TS$, and the *work content* or Helmholtz free energy as $A = E - TS$.

TABLE 1-4. Cohesive Energy Densities of Linear Polymers[a]

Polymer	Repeat Unit	Cohesive Energy Density (J/cm^3)
Polyethylene	—CH_2CH_2—	259
Polyisobutylene	—$CH_2C(CH_3)_2$—	272
Polyisoprene	—$CH_2C(CH_3)$=$CHCH_2$—	280
Polystyrene	—$CH_2CH(C_6H_5)$—	310
Poly(methyl methacrylate)	—$CH_2C(CH_3)$ $(COOCH_3)$—	347
Poly(vinyl acetate)	—$CH_2CH(OCOCH_3)$—	368
Poly(vinyl chloride)	—CH_2CHCl—	381
Poly(ethylene terephthalate)	—$CH_2CH_2OCOC_6H_4COO$—	477
Poly(hexamethylene adipamide)	—$NH(CH_2)_6NHCO(CH_2)_4CO$—	774
Polyacrylonitrile	—CH_2CHCN—	992

[a]Walker (1952) and Small (1953).

properties typical of fibers, especially where molecular symmetry is favorable for crystallization. Chain stiffness or flexibility, referred to above, is largely determined by hindrance to free rotation about carbon–carbon single bonds in the polymer chain.

GENERAL REFERENCES

Ketelaar 1953; Cottrell 1958; Pauling 1960, 1964; Pimentel 1960; Chu 1967; Phillips 1970; Elias 1977, Part I.

D. MOLECULAR WEIGHT AND MOLECULAR-WEIGHT DISTRIBUTION

Perhaps the most important feature distinguishing polymers from low-molecular-weight species is the existence of a distribution of chain lengths and therefore degrees of polymerization and molecular weights in all known polymers (except possibly some biological macromolecules). This distribution can be illustrated by plotting the weight of polymer of a given molecular weight against the molecular weight, as in Fig. 1-3.

Because of the existence of the distribution in any finite sample of polymer, the experimental measurement of molecular weight can give only an average value. Several different averages are important. For example, some methods of molecular-weight measurement in effect count the number of molecules in a known mass of material. Through knowledge of Avogadro's number, this information leads to the

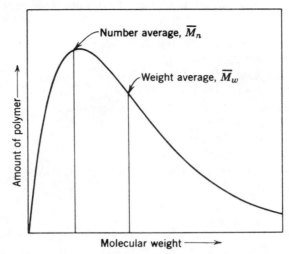

FIG. 1-3. Distribution of molecular weights in a typical polymer.

number-average molecular weight $\bar{M}_n$ of the sample. For typical polymers the number average lies near the peak of the weight-distribution curve or the most probable molecular weight.

If the sample contains N_i molecules of the *i*th kind, for a total number of molecules $\Sigma_{i=1}^{\infty} N_i$, and each of the *i*th kind of molecule has a mass m_i, then the total mass of all the molecules is $\Sigma_{i=1}^{\infty} N_i m_i$. The number-average molecular mass is

$$\bar{m}_n = \frac{\Sigma_{i=1}^{\infty} m_i N_i}{\Sigma_{i=1}^{\infty} N_i} \tag{1-1}$$

and multiplication by Avogadro's number gives the number-average molecular weight (mole weight);

$$\bar{M}_n = \frac{\Sigma_{i=1}^{\infty} M_i N_i}{\Sigma_{i=1}^{\infty} N_i} \tag{1-2}$$

Number-average molecular weights of commercial polymers usually lie in the range 10,000–100,000, although some materials have values of $\bar{M}_n$ 10-fold higher, and others 10-fold lower. In most cases, however, the physical properties associated with typical high polymers are not well developed if $\bar{M}_n$ is below about 10,000.

After $\bar{M}_n$, the next higher average molecular weight that can be measured by absolute methods is the weight-average molecular weight $\bar{M}_w$. This quantity is defined as

$$\bar{M}_w = \frac{\Sigma_{i=1}^{\infty} N_i M_i^2}{\Sigma_{i=1}^{\infty} N_i M_i} \tag{1-3}$$

TABLE 1-5.   Typical Ranges of $\bar{M}_w/\bar{M}_n$ in Synthetic Polymers[a]

Polymer	Range
Hypothetical monodisperse polymer	1.000
Actual "monodisperse" "living" polymers	1.01–1.05
Addition polymer, termination by coupling	1.5
Addition polymer, termination by disproportionation, or condensation polymer	2.0
High conversion vinyl polymers	2–5
Polymers made with autoacceleration	5–10
Addition polymers prepared by coordination polymerization	8–30
Branched polymers	20–50

[a]Billmeyer (1977).

It should be noted that each molecule contributes to $\bar{M}_w$ in proportion to the square of its mass: A quantity proportional to the first power of M measures only concentration, and not molecular weight. In terms of concentrations $c_i = N_iM_i$ and weight fractions $w_i = c_i/c$, where $c = \Sigma_{i=1}^{\infty} c_i$,

$$\bar{M}_w = \frac{\Sigma_{i=1}^{\infty} c_iM_i}{c} = \sum_{i=1}^{\infty} w_iM_i \qquad (1\text{-}4)$$

Unfortunately, there appears to be no simple analogy for $\bar{M}_w$ akin to counting molecules to obtain $\bar{M}_n$.

Because heavier molecules contribute more to $\bar{M}_w$ than light ones, $\bar{M}_w$ is always greater than $\bar{M}_n$, except for a hypothetical monodisperse polymer. The value of $\bar{M}_w$ is greatly influenced by the presence of high-molecular-weight species, just as $\bar{M}_n$ is influenced by species at the low end of the molecular-weight distribution curve.

The quantity $\bar{M}_w/\bar{M}_n$ is a useful measure of the breadth of the molecular-weight distribution curve and is the parameter most often quoted for describing this feature. The range of values of $\bar{M}_w/\bar{M}_n$ in synthetic polymers is quite large, as illustrated in Table 1-5.

For some types of polymerization, the distribution of molecular weights (more often expressed as degrees of polymerization) can be calculated statistically; this topic is discussed in Chapter 3E. Experimental methods for measuring the molecular-weight averages defined above, among others, are the subject of Chapter 8.

GENERAL REFERENCES

Peebles 1971; Slade 1975; Billingham 1977.

DISCUSSION QUESTIONS AND PROBLEMS

1. Define the following terms: polymer, monomer, repeat unit, network, degree of polymerization, homochain polymer, heterochain polymer, thermoplastic, thermosetting, configuration, conformation.

2. Discuss some of the properties that make polymers useful materials, and show how they result from unique features of polymer structure such as high molecular weight. (This topic is amplified in later chapters.)

3. Consider three hypothetical monodisperse polymers, with $M = 10,000$, $M = 100,000$, and $M = 1,000,000$. For each, calculate $\bar{M}_w$ and $\bar{M}_n$ after adding the following to 100 parts by weight c_i of the polymer with $M = 100,000$:

   a. 20 parts by weight of the polymer with $M = 10,000$.

   b. 20 parts by weight of the polymer with $M = 1,000,000$.

   Calculate $\bar{M}_w$ and $\bar{M}_n$ after adding the following to 100 parts by number (of molecules) of the polymer with $M = 100,000$:

   c. 20 parts by number of the polymer with $M = 10,000$.

   d. 20 parts by number of the polymer with $M = 1,000,000$.

   Discuss the dependence of $\bar{M}_w$ and $\bar{M}_n$ on the presence of high- and low-molecular-weight material.

BIBLIOGRAPHY

Baekeland 1909. L. H. Baekeland, "The Synthesis, Constitution, and Uses of Bakelite," *J. Ind. Eng. Chem.* **1**, 149–161 (1909); reprinted in *Chemtech* **6**, 40–53 (1976).

Billingham 1977. N. C. Billingham, *Molar Mass Measurements in Polymer Science*, Halsted Press, John Wiley & Sons, New York, 1977.

Billmeyer 1969. Fred W. Billmeyer, Jr., "Molecular Structure and Polymer Properties," *J. Paint Technol.* **41**, 3–16; erratum, 209 (1969).

Billmeyer 1972. Fred W. Billmeyer, Jr., *Synthetic Polymers: Building the Giant Molecule*, Doubleday, Garden City, New York, 1972.

Billmeyer 1977. Fred W. Billmeyer, Jr., "The Size and Weight of Polymer Molecules," Chapter 4 in Herman S. Kaufman and Joseph J. Falcetta, eds., *Introduction to Polymer Science and Technology: An SPE Textbook*, Wiley-Interscience, New York, 1977.

Billmeyer 1982. Fred W. Billmeyer, Jr., "Polymers," pp. 745–755 in Martin Grayson, ed., *Kirk–Othmer Encyclopedia of Chemical Technology*, 3rd ed., Vol. 18, Wiley-Interscience, New York, 1982.

Bovey 1979. F. A. Bovey and F. H. Winslow, "The Nature of Macromolecules," Chapter 1 in F. A. Bovey and F. H. Winslow, eds., *Macromolecules: An Introduction to Polymer Science*, Academic Press, New York, 1979.

Carothers 1929. W. H. Carothers, "An Introduction to the General Theory of Condensation Polymers," *J. Am. Chem. Soc.* **51**, 2548–2559 (1929).

Carothers 1931. Wallace H. Carothers, "Polymerization," *Chem. Rev.* **8**, 353–426 (1931).

Chu 1967. Benjamin Chu, *Molecular Forces: Based on the Baker Lectures of Peter J. W. Debye*, Wiley-Interscience, New York, 1967.

Cottrell 1958. Tom L. Cottrell, *The Strengths of Chemical Bonds*, 2nd ed., Academic Press, New York, 1958.

Elias 1977. Hans-Georg Elias, *Macromolecules · 1 · Structure and Properties*, Plenum Press, New York, 1977.

Flory 1937. Paul J. Flory, "Mechanism of Vinyl Polymerization," *J. Am. Chem. Soc.* **59**, 241–253 (1937).

Flory 1953. Paul J. Flory, *Principles of Polymer Chemistry*, Cornell University Press, Ithaca, New York, 1953.

Ketelaar 1953. J. A. A. Ketelaar, *Chemical Constitution*, Elsevier, New York, 1953.

Lansing 1935. W. D. Lansing and E. O. Kraemer, "Molecular Weight Analysis of Mixtures by Sedimentation Equilibrium in the Svedberg Ultracentrifuge," *J. Am. Chem. Soc.* **57**, 1369–1377 (1935).

Mark 1940. H. Mark and G. Stafford Whitby, eds., *Collected Papers of Wallace Hume Carothers on High Polymeric Substances*, Interscience, New York, 1940.

Mark 1966. Herman F. Mark and the Editors of *Life, Giant Molecules*, Time, New York, 1966.

Mark 1967. H. F. Mark, "Polymers—Past, Present and Future," pp. 19–55 in W. O. Milligan, ed., *Proceedings of the Robert A. Welch Foundation Conferences on Chemical Research, X. Polymers*, The Robert A. Welch Foundation, Houston, 1967.

Mark 1977. Herman F. Mark and Sheldon Atlas, "Introduction to Polymer Science," Chapter 1 in Herman S. Kaufman and Joseph J. Falcetta, eds., *Introduction to Polymer Science and Technology: An SPE Textbook*, Wiley-Interscience, New York, 1977.

Mark 1981. Herman Mark, "Polymer Chemistry in Europe and America—How it all Began," *J. Chem. Educ.* **58**, 527–534 (1981).

Marvel 1981. C. S. Marvel, "The Development of Polymer Chemistry in America—The Early Days," *J. Chem. Educ.* **58**, 535–539 (1981).

Natta 1955a. G. Natta, Piero Pino, Paolo Corradini, Ferdinando Danusso, Enrico Mantica, Giorgio Mazzanti, and Giovanni Moranglio, "Crystalline High Polymers of α-Olefins," *J. Am. Chem. Soc.* **77**, 1708–1710 (1955).

Natta 1955b. G. Natta, "A New Class of α-Olefin Polymers with Exceptional Regularity of Structure" (in French), *J. Polym. Sci.* **16**, 143–154 (1955).

Ostwald 1917. Dr. Wolfgang Ostwald, *An Introduction to Theoretical and Applied Colloid Chemistry (The World of Neglected Dimensions)* (translated by Dr. Martin H. Fischer), John Wiley & Sons, New York, 1917.

Pauling 1960. Linus Pauling, *The Nature of the Chemical Bond*, 3rd ed., Cornell University Press, Ithaca, New York, 1960.

Pauling 1964. Linus Pauling and Roger Hayward, *The Architecture of Molecules*, W. H. Freeman, San Francisco, California, 1964.

Peebles 1971. Leighton H. Peebles, Jr., *Molecular Weight Distributions in Polymers*, Wiley-Interscience, New York, 1971.

Phillips 1970. James C. Phillips, *Covalent Bonding in Crystals, Molecules and Polymers*, Chicago University Press, Chicago, Illinois, 1970.

Pimentel 1960. George C. Pimentel and Aubrey L. McClellan, *The Hydrogen Bond*, W. H. Freeman, San Francisco, California, 1960.

Seymour 1982. Raymond B. Seymour, ed., *History of Polymer Science and Technology*, Marcel Dekker, New York, 1982.

Slade 1975. Philip E. Slade, Jr., *Polymer Molecular Weights*, Vol. 4 of Philip E. Slade, Jr., and Lloyd T. Jenkins, eds., *Techniques of Polymer Evaluation*, Marcel Dekker, New York, 1975.

Small 1953. P. A. Small, "Some Factors Affecting the Solubility of Polymers," *J. Appl. Chem.* **3**, 71–80 (1953).

Staudinger 1920. H. Staudinger, "Polymerization" (in German), *Ber. Dtsch. Chem. Ges. B* **53**, 1073–1085 (1920).

Staudinger 1925. H. Staudinger, "The Constitution of Polyoxymethylenes and Other High-Molecular Compounds" (in German), *Helv. Chim. Acta* **8**, 67–70 (1925).

Staudinger 1928. H. Staudinger, "The Constitution of High Polymers. XIII" (in German), *Ber. Dtsch. Chem. Ges. B* **61**, 2427–2431 (1928).

Staudinger 1930. H. Staudinger and W. Heuer, "Highly Polymerized Compounds, XXXIII. A Relation Between the Viscosity and the Molecular Weight of Polystyrenes" (in German), *Ber. Dtsch. Chem. Ges. B* **63**, 222–234 (1930).

Staudinger 1935. H. Staudinger and A. Steinhofer, "Highly Polymerized Compounds. CVII. Polystyrenes" (in German), *Justus Liebigs Ann. Chem.* **517**, 35–53 (1935).

Staudinger 1970. Herman Staudinger, *From Organic Chemistry to Macromolecules*, Wiley-Interscience, New York, 1970.

Walker 1952. E. E. Walker, "The Solvent Action of Organic Substances on Polyacrylonitrile," *J. Appl. Chem.* **2**, 470–481 (1952).

PART FOUR

STRUCTURE AND PROPERTIES

CHAPTER ELEVEN

RHEOLOGY AND THE MECHANICAL PROPERTIES OF POLYMERS

Rheology is, by definition, the science of deformation and flow of matter. The rheological behavior of polymers involves several widely different phenomena, which can be related to some extent to different molecular mechanisms. These phenomena and their associated major mechanisms are as follows:

a. *Viscous flow*, the irreversible bulk deformation of polymeric material, associated with irreversible slippage of molecular chains past one another.

b. *Rubberlike elasticity*, where the local freedom of motion associated with small-scale movement of chain segments is retained, but large-scale movement (flow) is prevented by the restraint of a diffuse network structure.

c. *Viscoelasticity*, where the deformation of the polymer specimen is reversible but time dependent and associated (as in rubber elasticity) with the distortion of polymer chains from their equilibrium conformations through activated segment motion involving rotation about chemical bonds.

d. *Hookean elasticity*, where the motion of chain segments is drastically restricted and probably involves only bond stretching and bond angle deformation: The material behaves like a glass.

These four phenomena are discussed in Sections A–D, respectively. Together they form the basis for a description of the mechanical properties of amorphous polymers. The mechanical properties of semicrystalline polymers, however, depend intimately on the restraining nature of their crystalline regions and can be inferred only in part from the rheological behavior of amorphous polymers. The mechanical properties of crystalline polymers are therefore discussed separately in Section *E*.

A. VISCOUS FLOW

Phenomena of Viscous Flow

If a force per unit area *s* causes a layer of liquid at a distance *x* from a fixed boundary wall to move with a velocity *v*, the viscosity η is defined as the ratio between the shear stress *s* and the velocity gradient $\partial v / \partial x$ or rate of shear $\dot{\gamma}$:

$$s = \eta \frac{\partial v}{\partial x} = \eta \dot{\gamma} \qquad (11\text{-}1)$$

If η is independent of the rate of shear, the liquid is said to be *Newtonian* or to exhibit ideal flow behavior (Fig. 11-1*a*). Two types of deviation from Newtonian flow are commonly observed in polymer solutions and melts (Bauer 1967). One is *shear thinning* or *pseudoplastic* behavior, a reversible decrease in viscosity with increasing shear rate (Fig. 11-1*b*). Shear thinning results from the tendency of the applied force to disturb the long chains from their favored equilibrium conformation (Chapter 7*B*), causing elongation in the direction of shear. An opposite effect, *shear*

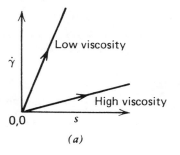

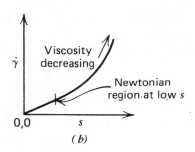

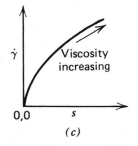

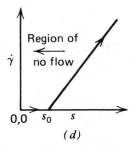

FIG. 11-1.   Dependence of shear rate $\dot{\gamma}$ on shear stress *s* for (a) Newtonian, (b) pseudoplastic, and (c) dilatant behavior, and (d) the presence of a yield stress s_0 followed by Newtonian behavior.

thickening or *dilatant* behavior (Fig. 11-1c), in which viscosity increases with increasing shear rate, is not observed in polymers.

A second deviation from Newtonian flow is the exhibition of a *yield value*, a critical stress below which no flow occurs. Above the yield value, flow may be either Newtonian (as indicated in Fig. 11-1d) or non-Newtonian. For most polymer melts, only an apparent yield value is observed.

The above effects are shear dependent but time independent. Some fluids also exhibit reversible time-dependent changes in viscosity when sheared at constant stress. Viscosity decreases with time in a *thixotropic fluid*, and increases with time in a *rheopectic* fluid, under constant shear stress.

For low-molecular-weight liquids, the temperature dependence of viscosity is found to follow the simple exponential relationship

$$\eta = A e^{E/RT} \tag{11-2}$$

where E is an *activation energy for viscous flow* and A is a constant.

These features of the flow of liquids can be explained in terms of several molecular theories. That of Eyring (Glasstone 1941) is based upon a lattice structure for the liquid, containing some unoccupied sites or holes. These sites move at random throughout the liquid as they are filled and created anew by molecules jumping from one site to another. Under an applied stress the probability of such jumps is higher in the direction that relieves the stress. If each jump is made by overcoming an energy barrier of height E, the theory leads to Eq. 11-2. The energy of activation E is expected to be related to the latent heat of vaporization of the liquid, since the removal of a molecule from the surroundings of its neighbors forms a part of both processes. Such a relation is indeed found and is taken as evidence that the particle that moves from site to site is probably a single molecule.

As molecular weight is increased in a homologous series of liquids up to the polymer range, the activation energy of flow E does not increase proportionally with the heat of vaporization but levels off at a value independent of molecular weight. This is taken to mean that in long chains the unit of flow is considerably smaller than the complete molecule. It is rather a segment of the molecule whose size is of the order of 5–50 carbon atoms. Viscous flow takes place by successive jumps of segments (with, of course, some degree of coordination) until the whole chain has shifted.

Dynamics of Polymer Melts.   It is now accepted that polymer chains are strongly intertwined and entangled in the melt; the dynamic behavior of such a system has been reviewed (Graessley 1974), but is only poorly understood. Thermodynamically, the chains are essentially ideal, as was first realized by Flory (1949). Their freedom of motion results from the presence of a *correlation hole* around each flow unit, within which the concentration of similar units from other chains is reduced. The presence of these correlation holes, and of the ideal but entangled nature of chains in the melt, has been confirmed by neutron-scattering experiments (Cotton 1974).

Flow Measurement

Methods commonly used for measuring the viscosity of polymer solutions and melts are listed in Table 11-1. The most important of these methods involve rotational and capillary devices (Van Wazer 1963, Whorlow 1979, Dealy 1981, 1983).

Rotational Viscometry. Rotational viscometers are available with several different geometries, including concentric cylinders, two cones of different angles, a cone and a plate, or combinations of these. Measurements with rotational devices become difficult to interpret at very high shear stresses, owing to the generation of heat in the specimen because of dissipation of energy, and to the tendency of the specimen to migrate out of the region of high shear. This phenomenon, the *Weissenberg effect*, arises because the stress in any material can always be analyzed into the components of a 3×3 stress tensor, in which the off-diagonal elements, called *normal stresses* because they act perpendicular to the surface of the specimen, are not negligible in viscoelastic fluids.

A simple rotational instrument used in the rubber industry is the *Mooney viscosimeter*. This empirical instrument measures the torque required to revolve a rotor at constant speed in a sample of the polymer at constant temperature. It is used to study changes in the flow characteristics of rubber during milling or mastication (Chapter 19). The *Brabender Plastograph* is a similar device.

Capillary Viscometry. Capillary rheometers, usually made of metal and operated either by dead weight or by gas pressure, or at constant displacement rate, have advantages of good precision, ruggedness, and ease of operation. They may be built to cover the range of shear stresses found in commercial fabrication operations. However, they have the disadvantage that the shear stress in the capillary varies from zero at the center to a maximum at the wall.

An elementary capillary rheometer (extrusion plastometer) is used to determine the flow rate of polyethylene in terms of *melt index*, defined as the mass rate of

TABLE 11-1. Summary of Methods for Measuring Viscosity

Method	Approximate Useful Viscosity Range (Poise)
Capillary pipette	$10^{-2}–10^3$
Falling sphere	$1–10^5$
Capillary extrusion	$1–10^8$
Parallel plate	$10^4–10^9$
Falling coaxial cylinder	$10^5–10^{11}$
Stress relaxation	$10^3–10^{10}$
Rotating cylinder	$1–10^{12}$
Tensile creep	$10^5->10^{12}$

flow of polymer through a specified capillary under controlled conditions of temperature and pressure.

Experimental Results

Molecular Weight and Shear Dependence.   As discussed further in Chapter 12, the most important structural variable determining the flow properties of polymers is molecular weight or, alternatively, chain length, Z (the number of atoms in the chain). Although early data (Flory 1940) suggested that log η was proportional to $Z^{1/2}$, it is now well established (Fox 1956) for essentially all polymers studied that, for values of Z above a critical value Z_c,

$$\log \eta = 3.4 \log \bar{Z}_w + k \tag{11-3}$$

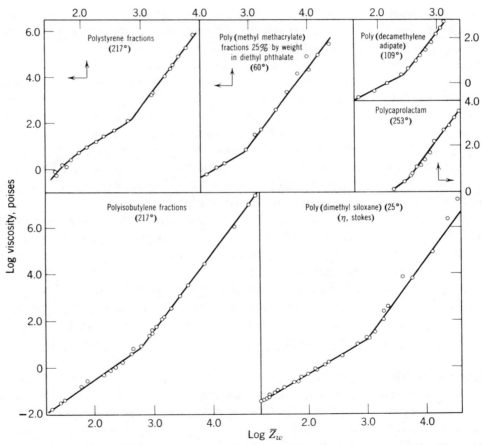

FIG. 11-2.   Dependence of melt viscosity η on chain length $\bar{Z}_w$ for low shear rate, showing the regions below $Z_c \simeq 600$, where η is approximately proportional to $\bar{Z}_w^{1.75}$, and above Z_c, where $\eta \sim \bar{Z}_w^{3.4}$ (Fox 1956).

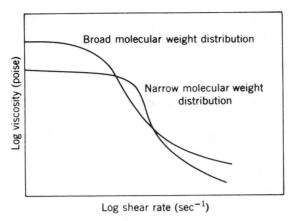

FIG. 11-3.   Generalized melt viscosity–shear rate curves for polymers with broad and narrow distributions of molecular weight.

where k is temperature dependent. This equation is valid only for shear stress sufficiently low (10^2–10^3 dynes/cm^2) that the viscosity is Newtonian. The weight-average chain length $\bar{Z}_w$ is usually assumed to be the appropriate average for the above conditions. de Gennes (1979) discusses the unusual exponent 3.4 in terms of scaling concepts, considering it a major unsolved problem. Theories to explain it, including his own *reptation* model (de Gennes 1971), based on the wriggling motion of a chain inside a ''tube'' formed by its neighbors, fail to predict the exponent closer than 3.0 with no obvious reason for the discrepancy.

For chain lengths below Z_c, which is about 600 for many polymers, the viscosity is found to depend upon a power of $\bar{Z}_w$ (and hence $\bar{M}_w$) in the range 1.75–2.0. In this range, shear rate has little effect on viscosity. Typical experimental data for the two regions described above are shown in Fig. 11-2.

While the Newtonian melt viscosity is determined by $\bar{M}_w$ as described in Eq. 11-3, the dependence of viscosity on shear rate also depends upon the molecular-weight distribution. As depicted schematically in Fig. 11-3, the drop in melt viscosity below its Newtonian value begins at a lower shear rate and continues over a broader range of shear rates for polymers with broader distributions of molecular weight. At sufficiently high shear rates, the melt viscosity appears to depend primarily on $\bar{M}_n$ rather than $\bar{M}_w$. Qualitative information, at least, about the molecular-weight distribution can be obtained from melt viscosity–shear rate studies.

Flow Instabilities.   At shear stresses in the neighborhood of 2×10^6 dynes/cm^2 for many polymers, instabilities in the flow appear, with the result that the upper Newtonian region is rarely realized in bulk polymers. These instabilities are manifested as a striking and abrupt change in the shape of the polymer stream emerging from the capillary of the rheometer. At and above a critical stress, the shape of the emerging stream changes from that of a regular cylinder to a rough or distorted one.

Temperature Dependence of Viscosity.   On close examination of polymer systems, the activation energy for viscous flow of Eq. 11-2 is found to be constant only for small ranges of temperature. For pure liquids, it was found many years ago that most of the change in viscosity with temperature is associated with the concurrent change in volume. This observation led to theories of viscosity based on the concept of free volume, whose application to polymers is discussed in Section D. A major result of these theories is the WLF equation (Eqs. 11-13 and 11-22), in which the temperature dependence of melt viscosity is expressed in terms of the glass transition temperature T_g (or another reference temperature) and universal constants. Since the terms describing the variation of melt viscosity with temperature and with molecular weight are independent, the WLF equation can be combined with Eq. 11-3 to yield the relation, for low shear rates,

$$\log \eta = 3.4 \log \bar{Z}_w - \frac{17.44(T - T_g)}{51.6 + T - T_g} + k' \tag{11-4}$$

where k' is a constant depending only on polymer type. This equation holds over the temperature range from T_g to about $T_g + 100$ K.

GENERAL REFERENCES

Eirich 1956–1969; Van Wazer 1963; Carley 1975; Walters 1975; Nielsen 1977; White 1978; Whorlow 1979; Dealy 1981; Hull 1981; Pierce 1982; Rosen 1982, Chapters 15 and 17.

B.   KINETIC THEORY OF RUBBER ELASTICITY

Rubberlike elasticity is in many respects a unique phenomenon, involving properties markedly different from those of low-molecular-weight solids, liquids, or gases. The properties of typical elastomers are defined by the following requirements:

a.   They must stretch rapidly and considerably under tension, reaching high elongations (500–1000%) with low damping, that is, little loss of energy as heat.

b.   They must exhibit high tensile strength and high modulus (stiffness) when fully stretched.

c.   They must retract rapidly, exhibiting the phenomenon of *snap* or *rebound*.

d.   They must recover their original dimensions fully on the release of stress, exhibiting the phenomena of *resilience* and *low permanent set*.

Although the thermodynamics associated with rubber elasticity was developed in the middle of the nineteenth century, the molecular requirements for the exhibition of rubbery behavior were not recognized until 1932. Theories of the mechanism relating these molecular-structure requirements to the phenomena of rubber elasticity were developed soon after.

As discussed further in Chapter 12E, the molecular requirements of elastomers may be summarized as follows:

a. The material must be a high polymer.

b. It must be above its glass transition temperature T_g to obtain high local segment mobility.

c. It must be amorphous in its stable (unstressed) state for the same reason.

d. It must contain a network of crosslinks to restrain gross mobility of its chains.

Thermodynamics of Rubber Elasticity

The Ideal Elastomer.   In discussions of the mechanical properties of a polymer, parameters related to its distortion must be included, as well as the variables defining the state of the system, such as pressure and temperature. In particular, when a sample of rubber is stretched, work is done on it and its free energy is changed. By restricting the development to stretching in one direction, for simplicity, the elastic work W_{el} equals $f \, dl$, where f is the retractive force and dl the change in length. If the change in free energy is G,

$$f = \left(\frac{\partial G}{\partial l}\right)_{T,p} = \left(\frac{\partial H}{\partial l}\right)_{T,p} - T\left(\frac{\partial S}{\partial l}\right)_{T,p} \tag{11-5}$$

In analogy with an ideal gas, where

$$\left(\frac{\partial E}{\partial V}\right)_T = 0, \qquad p = T\left(\frac{\partial S}{\partial V}\right)_T \tag{11-6}$$

an *ideal elastomer* is defined by the condition that

$$\left(\frac{\partial H}{\partial l}\right)_{T,p} = 0, \qquad f = -T\left(\frac{\partial S}{\partial l}\right)_{T,p} \tag{11-7}$$

The negative sign results since work is done on the specimen to increase its length.

Entropy Elasticity.   Equation 11-7 shows that the retractive force in an ideal elastomer is due to its decrease in entropy on extension. The molecular origin of this *entropy elasticity* is the distortion of the polymer chains from their most probable conformations in the unstretched sample. As described in Chapter 7B, the distribution of these conformations is Gaussian, the probability of finding a chain end in a unit volume of the space coordinates x, y, z at a distance r from the other end being

$$W(x, y, z) = \left(\frac{b}{\sqrt{\pi}}\right)^3 e^{-b^2 r^2} \tag{11-8}$$

where $b^2 = \frac{3}{2} xl^2$, x being the number of links, with length l. Since the entropy of the system is proportional to the logarithm of the number of configurations it can have,

$$S = \text{const.} - kb^2 r^2 \tag{11-9}$$

where k is Boltzmann's constant. It follows that for a single polymer chain the retractive force f' for an extension of magnitude dr is

$$f' = -T\frac{dS}{dr} = 2kTb^2 r \tag{11-10}$$

It is customarily assumed that the retractive force f (Eq. 11-7) for a bulk polymer sample can be identified as the sum of the forces f' for all the chains in the specimen. This assumption, which is inaccurate in detail but justified in most cases, implies that individual chains contribute additively and without interaction to the elasticity of the macroscopic sample, and that the distribution of end-to-end distances undergoes transformation identically with the sample dimensions (affine transformation).

Stress–Strain Behavior of Elastomers

The stress–strain curves of typical elastomers (Fig. 11-4) show marked deviations from the straight line required by Hooke's law. The relatively low slope of the curve (defined near the origin as the modulus) decreases to about one-third its original value over the first hundred percent elongation, and later increases, often to quite high values at high elongations. To explain this behavior, it is convenient first to examine the stress–strain properties of a simple model, and then to consider the relation of the model to actual elastomers.

A Simple Model of an Elastomeric Network (Guth 1946).   It is assumed that the actual tangled mass of polymer chains may be represented by an idealized network of flexible chains, irregular in detail but homogeneous and isotropic, extending throughout the sample. The network consists of m chains of average length $(\overline{r^2})^{1/2}$ per unit volume directed along each of three perpendicular axes. To obtain the proper space-filling properties of the model it is assumed that the space between the chains is filled with an incompressible fluid exerting a hydrostatic pressure p outward against the elastic tension of the chains. By considering the equilibration of inward and outward forces when a cube of this material is stretched

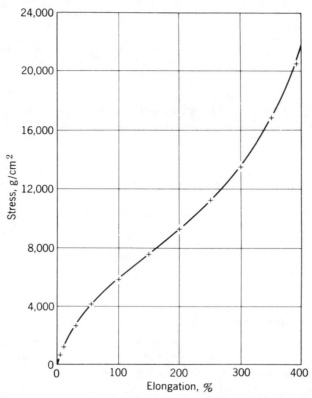

FIG. 11-4.   Stress–strain curve for a typical elastomer (Guth 1946).

into a parallelepiped, using Eq. 11-10, it can be shown that the stress s is related to the strain γ by

$$s = 2mkTb^2\left(\gamma - \frac{1}{\gamma^2}\right) \tag{11-11}$$

The modulus† is given by

$$G = \frac{ds}{d\gamma} = 2mkTb^2\left(1 + \frac{2}{\gamma^3}\right) \tag{11-12}$$

As the strain increases from zero ($\gamma = 1$) to large values of γ, the slope decreases to one-third its initial value as required by the experimental facts. Equation 11-12 predicts the stress--strain curve of actual elastomers very well up to elongations of 300% or more (Fig. 11-5).

---

†Note that the symbol G is conventionally used to represent both the Gibbs free energy (Eq. 11-5) and, throughout the remainder of this chapter, the modulus of elasticity.

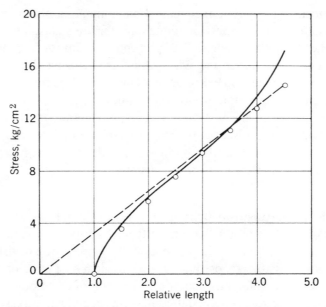

FIG. 11-5. Experimental and theoretical stress–strain curves (Guth 1946): experimental (——), computed from Eq. 11-12 (○), and asymptote of Eq. 11-12 for high elongations (- - -).

Behavior at High Extensions. Figure 11-5 suggests that at elongations greater than about 300%, the stress–strain curves of actual elastomers have a higher slope than that predicted by Eq. 11-12. This is far below the ultimate elongation of 1000% for a good elastomer. One reason for the failure of the theory is that the Gaussian distribution of chain lengths that holds at low elongations fails in the region of interest for elastomers, as the actual lengths approach those of fully extended chains. A better approximation than the Gaussian is available. With its use the theory predicts the actual stress–strain curves rather well for elastomers that do not crystallize on stretching. In the cases where crystallinity does develop, the slope still increases faster than predicted. As is true in general for the problem of the mechanical behavior of crystalline polymers (Section *E*), a quantitative theory of the effect of crystallinity on the modulus of elastomers has not been developed.

GENERAL REFERENCES

Treloar 1975; Smith 1977; Brydson 1978, Chapter 3; Gent 1978; Shen 1978.

C. VISCOELASTICITY

Sections *A* and *B* have dealt with the equilibrium response of linear and network polymer structures to external stress. In this section are considered the time-dependent mechanical properties of amorphous polymers. As in the studies of rate phenomena, theories of dynamic mechanical phenomena in polymers are less thoroughly developed than those referring to the equilibrium states. They are also more dependent on the details of models. The present problem is, first, to find suitable models or mathematical functions with which to describe the several types of molecular motion postulated earlier to be associated with the processes of elasticity, viscoelasticity, and viscous flow in polymers; and, second, to utilize these models in relating the behavior of the polymers to their molecular structure.

The description of the viscoelastic response of amorphous polymers to small stresses is greatly simplified by the application of the following two general principles that are widely applicable to these systems.

The Boltzmann Superposition Principle.

This principle states that strain is a linear function of stress, so that the total effect of applying several stresses is the sum of the effects of applying each one separately. Application of the superposition principle makes it possible to predict the mechanical response of an amorphous polymer to a wide range of loading conditions from a limited amount of experimental data. The principle applies to both static and time-dependent stresses.

Time—Temperature Equivalence.

An increase in temperature accelerates molecular and segmental motion, bringing the system more rapidly to equilibrium or apparent equilibrium and accelerating all types of viscoelastic processes. A convenient way of formulating this effect of temperature is in terms of the ratio a_T of the time constant (*relaxation time*) of a particular response τ at temperature T to its value τ_0 at a convenient reference temperature T^0. For many cases, including most nonpolar amorphous polymers, a_T does not vary with τ, so that changes in temperature shift the distribution of relaxation times, representing all possible molecular responses of the system, to smaller or greater values of τ but do not otherwise alter it. Time and temperature affect viscoelasticity only through the product of a_T and actual time, and a_T is called a *shift factor*. Its application to experimental data is described in the following section.

Despite the marked dependence on molecular structure of the relation between a_T and absolute temperature, nearly general empirical relations have been derived by expressing the temperature for each material in terms of its glass-transition temperature T_g or some nearly equivalent reference temperature. Among the most successful of these relations is the Williams–Landel–Ferry (WLF) equation (Williams 1955):

$$\log a_T = \frac{-17.44(T - T_g)}{51.6 + T - T_g} \qquad (11\text{-}13)$$

This equation holds over the temperature range from T_g to about $T_g + 100$ K. The constants are related to the free volume as described in Section D.

Experimental Methods

Stress Relaxation.   If elongation is stopped during the determination of the stress–strain curve of a polymer (Chapter 9*F*), the force or stress decreases with time as the specimen approaches equilibrium or quasi-equilibrium under the imposed strain. The direct observation and measurement of this phenomenon constitutes the *stress relaxation* experiment. Usually the sample is deformed rapidly to a specified strain, and stress at this strain is observed for periods ranging from several minutes to several days or longer.

It has been shown both experimentally and theoretically that the stress-relaxation behavior of rubbery polymers can be factored into independent functions of strain and time. At small strains, the stress–strain function is almost linear and can be represented by a time-dependent modulus of elasticity $G(t)$.

Typical stress-relaxation data for a well-studied sample of polyisobutylene are shown in Fig. 11-6, where $G(t)$ is plotted against time for experiments performed at several temperatures. By means of time–temperature equivalence these data may be shifted to produce a "master curve," as shown in Fig. 11-7. The curve indicates that any specified modulus can be observed after a period that depends, through

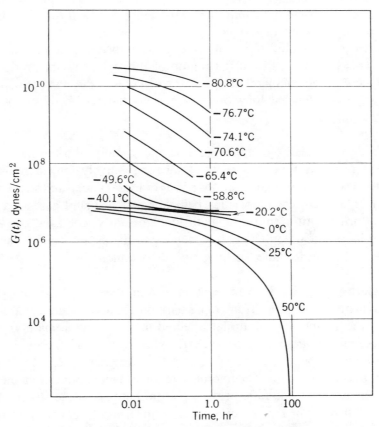

FIG. 11-6.   Stress relaxation of polyisobutylene (Tobolsky 1956).

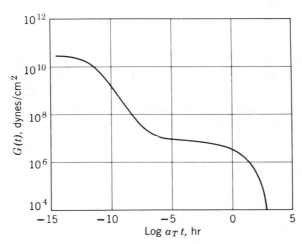

FIG. 11-7. Stress relaxation master curve for polyisobutylene (Tobolsky 1956).

the factor a_T, on temperature. As temperature is increased, a given modulus is observed at shorter times.

Master curves such as that of Fig. 11-7 show the different types of viscoelastic behavior usually observed with amorphous materials. At small times the high modulus and low slope are characteristic of glassy behavior. The following region of rapidly decreasing modulus represents the glass transition, described further in Section D. This is followed by a flat region of rubbery behavior produced either through entanglements among relatively long molecules or through permanent crosslinks. The ultimate slope at long times represents the region of viscous flow in uncrosslinked polymers.

Creep. Creep is studied by subjecting a sample rapidly to a constant stress and observing the resulting time-dependent strain for relatively long periods of time, frequently for a week or more or even for a year or more. Creep and stress relaxation are complementary aspects of plastics behavior and in many cases may provide equivalent information for studies of both fundamental viscoelastic properties and performance in practical applications. Creep experiments are usually easier, more economical, and more feasible for long periods of time.

Dynamic Methods. The delayed reaction of a polymer to stress and strain also affects its dynamic properties. If a simple harmonic stress of angular frequency ω is applied to the sample, the strain lags behind the stress by a phase angle whose tangent measures the *internal friction* $\Delta E/E$, where ΔE is the energy dissipated in taking the sample through a stress cycle and E is the energy stored in the sample when the strain is a maximum. The internal friction is a maximum when the dynamic modulus of the material (the ratio of the stress to that part of the strain which is in phase with the stress) is in a region of relaxation. In terms of frequency the relaxation behavior of the dynamic modulus and the internal friction is illustrated in Fig. 11-8.

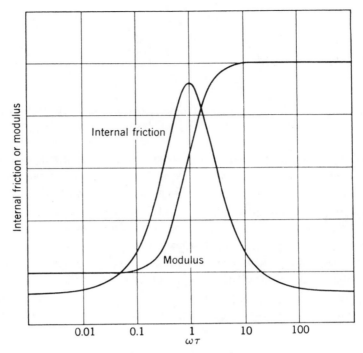

FIG. 11-8. Variation of dynamic modulus and internal friction with frequency.

At low frequencies (about 1 sec^{-1}) it is convenient to measure the internal friction of polymers by observing the free decay of torsional oscillations of a thin fiber or film loaded with a large moment of inertia (*torsion pendulum*). The internal friction is the logarithm of the ratio of the amplitudes of successive free oscillations, while the modulus is calculated from the frequency of the oscillations.

A natural extension of this technique is to force oscillation with an external driving force. In such techniques the specimen is driven in flexural, torsional, or longitudinal oscillations by an oscillating force of constant amplitude but variable frequency, and the displacement amplitude of the resulting oscillation is observed. These techniques are particularly useful in the kilocycle frequency range. At very high frequencies (above 1 megacycle), the dimensions of the sample become awkwardly small for mechanical techniques, and it is convenient to measure the attenuation of sound waves in the sample. These methods are discussed fully by Ferry (1980).

Sperling (1982) describes a simple classroom experiment illustrating the above principles.

Models of Viscoelastic Behavior

Before attempting to devise a model to duplicate the viscoelastic behavior of an actual polymer, it is well to examine the response γ of ideal systems to a stress s. An ideal elastic element is represented by a spring which obeys Hooke's law, with

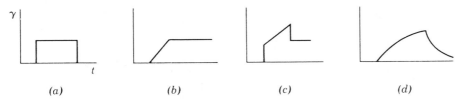

FIG. 11-9. Strain–time relationships at constant stress for simple models (Alfrey 1948): (a) ideal elastic spring, (b) Newtonian fluid (dashpot), (c) Maxwell element, (d) Voigt element.

a modulus of elasticity G. The elastic deformation is instantaneous and independent of time: $\gamma = (1/G)s$ (Fig. 11-9a). A completely viscous response is that of a Newtonian fluid, whose deformation is linear with time while the stress is applied and is completely irrecoverable: $d\gamma/dt = (1/\eta)s$, where η is the viscosity of the fluid (Fig. 11-9b). A simple mechanical analogy of a Newtonian fluid is a dashpot.

The two elements of spring and dashpot can be combined in two ways. If they are placed in series, the resulting *Maxwell element* (Fig. 11-10a) exhibits flow plus elasticity on the application of stress (Fig. 11-9c); when the stress is applied, the spring elongates while the dashpot slowly yields. On the removal of the stress the spring recovers but the dashpot does not. The strain is given by the equation

$$\frac{d\gamma}{dt} = \frac{1}{\eta}s + \frac{1}{G}\frac{ds}{dt} \qquad (11\text{-}14)$$

The relation of creep to stress relaxation may be seen by considering the experiment in which a strain is obtained and then held by fixing the ends of the system: $d\gamma/dt = 0$ in Eq. 11-14. The equation can then be solved:

$$s = s_0 e^{-(G/\eta)t} = s_0 e^{-t/\tau} \qquad (11\text{-}15)$$

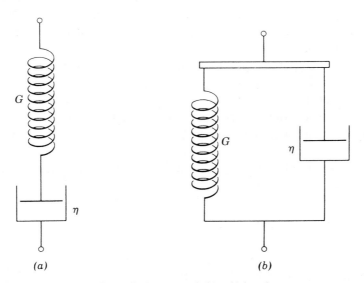

FIG. 11-10. (a) A Maxwell element and (b) a Voigt element.

where the stress s relaxes from its initial value s_0 exponentially as a function of time. The time η/G after which the stress reaches $1/e$ of its initial value is the relaxation time τ.

The response of a tangled mass of polymer chains to a stress is better represented by a parallel combination of spring and dashpot in a *Kelvin* or *Voigt element* (Fig. 11-10*b*). This element shows a *retarded elastic* or *viscoelastic* response (Fig. 11-9*d*). The dashpot acts as a damping resistance to the establishment of the equilibrium of the spring. The equation for the strain is

$$\eta \frac{d\gamma}{dt} + G\gamma = s \tag{11-16}$$

If a stress is applied and after a time removed (Fig. 11-9*d*), the deformation curve is given by

$$\gamma = \frac{s}{G}(1 - e^{-(G/\eta)t}) = \frac{s}{G}(1 - e^{-t/\tau}) \tag{11-17}$$

where τ is a *retardation time*. When the stress is removed the sample returns to its original shape along the exponential curve:

$$\gamma = \gamma_0 e^{-t/\tau} \tag{11-18}$$

General Mechanical Models for an Amorphous Polymer. The three components that make up the simplest behavior of an actual polymer sample in creep can be represented by a mechanical model which combines a Maxwell and a Voigt element in series. If a stress is suddenly applied to this model, the strain changes with time as shown in Fig. 11-11; the corresponding behavior of the model is shown in Fig. 11-12.

The model departs from the initial conditions (*a*) at time t_1 by an elastic deformation s/G_1 (*b*). A viscoelastic response approaching s/G_2 as an equilibrium value

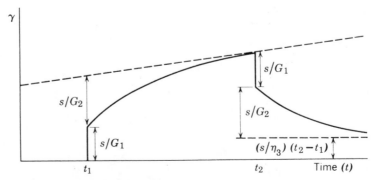

FIG. 11-11.   Strain–time relationship for a generalized mechanical model for creep combining elasticity, viscoelasticity, and flow (Alfrey 1948).

and a viscous flow at the rate s/η_3 follow (c). On the removal of the stress at time t_2, the elastic element relaxes immediately (d) and the viscoelastic one slowly (e), but the viscous flow is never recovered.

Alternatively, the creep and stress-relaxation experiments can be described with a generalized model consisting of a Maxwell and a Voigt element arranged in parallel. The two generalized models are entirely equivalent.

Although these models exhibit the chief characteristics of the viscoelastic behavior of polymers, they are nevertheless very much oversimplified. The flow of the polymer is probably not Newtonian, and its elastic response may not be Hookean. Moreover, the behavior of a real polymer cannot be characterized by a single relaxation time, but requires a spectrum of relaxation times to account for all phases of its behavior.

Treatment of Experimental Data

Distribution of Relaxation Times.   Equation 11-17 indicates that most of the relaxation associated with a single element takes place within one cycle of log time. In contrast, experiments indicate (as in Fig. 11-7) that relaxation phenomena in polymers extend over much wider ranges of time. Thus the actual behavior of polymers can be described only in terms of a distribution of model elements and an associated distribution of relaxation or retardation times:

$$\gamma(t) = s \int_{-\infty}^{\infty} \bar{J} (\log \tau)(1 - e^{-t/\tau})d \log \tau \qquad (11\text{-}19)$$

where $J = 1/G$ is the *elastic compliance* and $\bar{J}(\log \tau)$ the distribution of retardation times.

In principle, knowledge of $\gamma(t)$ over the entire range of time allows $\bar{J}(\log \tau)$ to be evaluated explicitly. This is difficult in practice, however, and it is convenient for mathematical simplicity to adopt simple empirical forms of the distribution

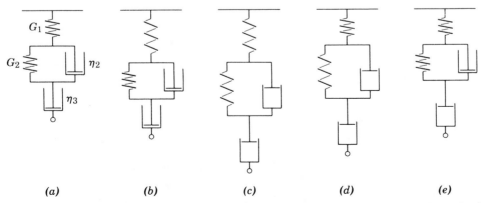

| (a) | (b) | (c) | (d) | (e) |

FIG. 11-12.   Interpretation of strain–time curve of Fig. 11-11 in terms of the generalized mechanical model for creep.

function $\bar{J}(\log \tau)$ and evaluate their parameters from the more limited experimental data at hand. Alternatively, the experimental data may be fitted graphically by summing the theoretical curves corresponding to a small number (three or four) of discrete relaxation times. The usefulness of the distribution of relaxation times arises from its identification with certain molecular parameters of the specimen, as described below.

Molecular Structure and Viscoelasticity

The phenomena of relaxation processes can be thought of in terms of the effect of thermal motion on the orientation of polymer molecules. When a mechanical stress is applied to a polymer, introducing deformations of the chains, the entropy of the system decreases as less probable conformations are taken up. The free energy correspondingly increases. If the sample is kept in the deformed state, stress relaxation takes place as a result of the thermal motions of the chains, the molecular deformations are obliterated, and the excess free energy is dissipated as heat. The details of the stress-relaxation process depend upon the multiplicity of ways in which the polymer molecules can regain their most probable conformations through thermal motion. These complex motions of a polymer molecule can be expressed as a series of characteristic modes requiring various degrees of long-range cooperation among the segments of the chain. Thus the first mode corresponds to translation of the entire molecule, requiring maximum cooperation, the second corresponds to motion of the ends of the chain in opposite directions, requiring somewhat less cooperation, and so on. With each of these modes is associated a characteristic relaxation time; there are so many modes that over most of the time scale the discrete spectrum of relaxation times can be approximated by a continuous distribution.

Theories based on the above considerations, derived for dilute solutions of polymer molecules, have been combined (Ferry 1980) with the concepts of entanglement of long molecules successful in predicting the molecular-weight dependence of viscous flow (Section A). Although exact numerical agreement is not achieved, for example, in calculating the dynamic modulus of polyisobutylene over a wide range of frequency and molecular weight, the qualitative situation seems extremely satisfactory.

In the rubbery region, the maximum relaxation time is strongly dependent on molecular weight. In this region the motions of the molecules are long range in nature, involving motions of units of the order of the length of the molecule itself. This is the region where entanglements are important.

In the region around the glass transition, however, only vibrations of the parts of the molecule between entanglements are important. So long as the molecules are long enough for entanglements to exist, this portion of the curve is expected, and found, to be essentially independent of the molecular weight and to depend primarily upon the local structure of the polymer.

GENERAL REFERENCES

Alfrey 1948, 1967; Eirich 1956–1969; Tobolsky 1960; Van Wazer 1963; McCrum 1967; Ward 1971; Nielsen 1974; Sauer 1975; Sternstein 1977; Kramer 1978; Tager 1978, Chapter 7; Ferry 1980; Young 1981, Chapter 5; Rosen 1982, Chapter 18.

D. THE GLASSY STATE AND THE GLASS TRANSITION

As anticipated in the previous sections, and in particular in Fig. 11-7, all amorphous polymers assume at sufficiently low temperatures the characteristics of glasses, including hardness, stiffness, and brittleness. Many aspects of the glassy state and the glass transition were mentioned in Section C; what remains is to discuss measurement of the transition temperature and its molecular interpretation in more detail.

One property associated with the glassy state is a low volume coefficient of expansion. This low coefficient occurs as the result of a change in slope of the curve of volume versus temperature at the point called the *glass-transition temperature* T_g. This behavior is shown for natural rubber in Fig. 11-13. In the high-temperature region, the slope of the curve (expansion coefficient) is characteristic of a rubber; below T_g at about $-70°C$, it is characteristic of a glass.

Figure 11-13 illustrates another general phenomenon: The amorphous regions in partially crystalline polymers also assume a glassy state, T_g being independent of degree of crystallinity to a first approximation. The magnitude of the phenomena associated with T_g decreases with decreasing amorphous content, however. As a result, T_g is sometimes difficult to detect in highly crystalline polymers. In terms of the lamellar model (Chapter 10C) the glass transition is considered to involve defect regions within or at the boundaries of the lamellae.

In contrast to crystalline melting at a temperature T_m (about $+10°C$ in Fig. 11-13), there is not an abrupt change in volume at T_g, but only a change in the slope

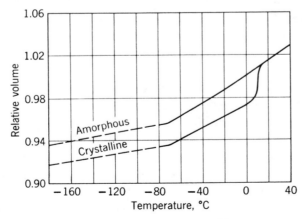

FIG. 11-13. Volume behavior of rubber near the glass-transition temperature (Bekkedahl 1934).

of the volume-temperature curve. In analogy to thermodynamic first- and second-order transitions, T_g is sometimes referred to as a second-order or apparent second-order transition. This nomenclature is considered poor, however, since it implies more thermodynamic significance than the nature of the transition warrants.

Measurement of T_g

The glass-transition temperature can be detected in a variety of experiments, which can be roughly classified into those dealing with bulk properties of the polymer, and those measuring the nature and extent of molecular motion. The classification is to some extent arbitrary, since, as indicated below, T_g is in fact the temperature of onset of extensive molecular motion.

Bulk Properties. Perhaps the most common way of estimating T_g is by means of the volume expansion coefficient, as indicated above. Other bulk properties whose temperature coefficients undergo marked changes at T_g, and which can therefore be used for its determination, include heat content (Chapter 9E), refractive index, stiffness, and hardness.

Molecular Motion. Experiments that are sensitive to the onset of molecular motion in polymer chains may be used to detect the glass transition. Such methods include the measurement of internal friction (Section C), dielectric loss in polar polymers, and NMR spectroscopy (Chapter 9B).

Phenomena Related to T_g. The onset of brittleness, as measured in impact tests, and the softening of amorphous polymers, as measured in thermal tests of various sorts, take place at temperatures near T_g (see Chapter 9F).

Time Effects Near T_g. If a polymer sample is cooled rapidly to a temperature just below T_g, its volume continues to decrease for many hours. In consequence, the value observed as T_g in a volume–temperature experiment depends on the time scale of the measurements. It is convenient to define T_g in terms of an arbitrary convenient (but not highly critical) time interval, such as 10 min to 1 hr.

For similar reasons, other tests for T_g give results somewhat dependent on the time scale of the experiments, with tests requiring shorter times yielding higher values of T_g. The brittle temperature as determined in an impact test is, for example, normally somewhat higher than T_g as otherwise measured.

Molecular Interpretation of T_g

In the glassy state, large-scale molecular motion does not take place, rather, atoms and small groups of atoms move against the local restraints of secondary bond forces, much as atoms vibrate around their equilibrium positions in a crystal lattice, except that the glassy state does not have the regularity of the crystalline state. The glass transition corresponds to the onset of liquidlike motion of much longer segments of molecules, characteristic of the rubbery state. This motion requires more free volume than the short-range excursions of atoms in the glassy state. The rise in the relative free volume with increasing temperature above T_g leads to the higher observed volume expansion coefficient in this region. Since the fully extended chain is the conformation of minimum energy (Chapter 10B), it tends to be assumed more frequently as the temperature is lowered. As the molecules thus straighten out, the free volume decreases. In consequence, flow becomes more difficult. The glass transition (observed at infinite time)—or, alternatively, the onset of crystallization where possible—is taken as the point where the number of possible conformations of the amorphous phase decreases sharply toward one.

The fraction f of "free" volume may be defined as

$$f = f_g + (T - T_g)\, \Delta\alpha, \qquad T \geq T_g$$
$$f = f_g \qquad\qquad\qquad\qquad T < T_g$$

(11-20)

Thus f is constant at the value f_g for all temperatures below T_g. Here the volume expansion coefficient α is that resulting from the increase in amplitude of molecular vibrations with temperature. Above T_g new free volume is created as the result of an increase $\Delta\alpha$ in the expansion coefficient.

Williams, Landel, and Ferry (Williams 1955) proposed that log viscosity varies linearly with $1/f$ above T_g, so that

$$\ln\left(\frac{\eta}{\eta_g}\right) = \frac{1}{f} - \frac{1}{f_g}$$

(11-21)

Substitution into Eq. 11-20 leads to

$$\log\left(\frac{\eta}{\eta_g}\right) = -\frac{a(T - T_g)}{b + T - T_g}$$

(11-22)

which is the WLF equation presented in Section C (Eq. 11-13), the numerical constants for a and b given there being determined by fitting literature data on the viscosity–temperature behavior of many glass-forming substances. The shift factor a_T is seen to be just the ratio of the viscosity at T relative to that at T_g. The latter is about 10^{13} poise for many substances.

Equation 11-22 also implies that both the viscosity of the polymer and the activation energy for viscous flow $\Delta E = 2.3R\, d(\log \eta)/d(1/T)$ should become infinite at $T = T_g - b = T_g - 51.6$. Thus by extrapolating downward from behavior well above T_g, one would predict that all molecular motion should become completely frozen at $T < T_g - 51.6$. What happens, of course, is that new mechanisms of deformation take over more or less sharply as this critical range is approached, in fact at T_g.

The above discussion embodies elements of several theories of the glass transition, based on free-volume concepts, kinetics, and statistical thermodynamics.

These theories are summarized by Ward (1971) and Ferry (1980); important contributions were made by Doolittle (1951), Bueche (1953), Gibbs (1958), DiMarzio (1958), Kovacs (1958), Cohen (1959), and Adam (1965).

Molecular Motion Below T_g

The foregoing discussion is concerned with the transition involving the motion of long segments of the polymer chain. At lower temperatures, other transitions may occur, produced by the motion of short sections of the main chain or of side chains. Although some characteristics of the glassy state, such as brittleness, may occasionally occur only below one of these lower transitions, it is proposed that the transition of highest temperature be called T_g. Alternatively, the transitions may be denoted α, β, γ, and so on, in order of descending temperature.

Transitions due to the motion of short segments of the main polymer chain occur most prominently in crystalline polymers such as polyethylene, polypropylene, and polytetrafluoroethylene. Such polymers also typically exhibit an α-transition.

Side-chain transitions occur in methacrylate polymers as a result of the relaxation of the carbomethoxy side chain at about 20°C (torsion pendulum) and the relaxation of the aliphatic ester group below −150°C.

GENERAL REFERENCES

Ward 1971; Nielsen 1974; Armeniades 1975; Tager 1978, Chapters 8 and 9; Ferry 1980; Young 1981, Chapter 5.

E. THE MECHANICAL PROPERTIES OF CRYSTALLINE POLYMERS

The models developed in the preceding sections represent well the rheological and mechanical properties of amorphous polymers. The viscoelastic properties of crystalline polymers are much more complex, however, and are not amenable to adequate theoretical explanation for three reasons.

First, an amorphous polymer is isotropic. This means that models suitable for describing shear stress, for example, are adequate to describe tensile stress or other types. Since crystalline polymers are not isotropic, this universality does not hold and the range of application of any model is severely limited.

Second, the homogeneous nature of amorphous polymers ensures that an applied stress is distributed uniformly throughout the system, at least down to very small dimensions. In crystalline polymers the relatively large crystallites are bound together in such a way that large stress concentrations inevitably develop.

Finally, a crystalline polymer is a mixture of regions of different degrees of order ranging all the way from completely ordered crystallites to completely amorphous regions. As the stress on the sample changes, the amounts of these regions change continuously as the crystallites melt or grow. This change of composition with respect to ordering is the most difficult obstacle to overcome in formulating a theory of the mechanical behavior of crystalline polymers. Even in the simplest cases the necessity of having the mechanical model change continuously with the applied stress has led to serious difficulties.

In consequence, neither the Boltzmann superposition principle nor time–temperature equivalence apply to crystalline polymers. Without these simplifying principles, attempts to explain the viscoelastic response of crystalline polymers in terms of models become complex and are only qualitative.

Typical Behavior

An orderly, if qualitative, discussion of the mechanical properties of crystalline polymers requires their classification into several categories, as indicated in Table 11-2. It is in the range of intermediate degree of crystallinity that the properties, unique to polymers, of most importance for mechanical and engineering applications are found. Further, these properties are found for the most part in the temperature range between T_g and T_m, and at temperatures not far below T_g. Well below the glass transition, molecular motion is essentially absent and the material behaves as a hard, glassy solid with the presence or absence of crystallinity making little difference: for example, the properties of atactic and isotactic polystyrene are quite similar at room temperature. Above T_m, of course, crystallinity plays no part in the properties of the amorphous viscoelastic melt.

Polymers with low crystallinity include plasticized poly(vinyl chloride) and elastic polyamides. These materials behave like lightly crosslinked amorphous polymers, their crystalline regions acting like crosslinks which are stable with respect to time but unstable with respect to temperature. The viscoelastic properties of these polymers are much like those of amorphous polymers except that the transition region between glassy and rubbery or liquid behavior is very much broadened on the temperature scale.

At very low extensions (< 1%), at temperatures well below T_m, and at not too long times, polymers with intermediate degrees of crystallinity (such as low-density polyethylene) behave much like those with very low crystallinity. Time–temperature equivalence is not applicable to such polymers. The transition regions of these polymers in modulus and the corresponding distributions of relaxation times are exceptionally broad, as indicated by the master curves of Fig. 11-14. (It should be

TABLE 11-2. Classification of Crystalline Polymers

Predominant Properties in Temperature Range	Degree of Crystallinity		
	Low (5–10%)	Intermediate (20–60%)	High (70–90%)
Above T_g	Rubbery	Leathery, tough	Stiff, hard (brittle)
Below T_g	Glassy, brittle	Hornlike, tough	Stiff, hard, brittle

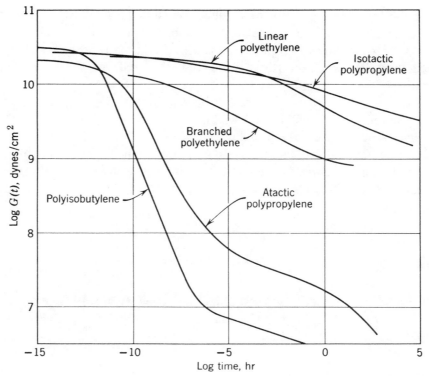

FIG. 11-14. Stress-relaxation master curves for several crystalline and amorphous polymers (Tobolsky 1960).

pointed out that these curves were themselves derived by application of time–temperature equivalence and must be considered only as idealizations.)

At higher extensions, these polymers exhibit the phenomena of a yield stress and cold drawing, with the accompanying changes in crystalline morphology described in Chapter 10E. No adequate theory relating rheological and mechanical behavior in this region to structure has yet been formulated. Polymers of intermediate degree of crystallinity are characteristically leathery or horny in texture, and exhibit good impact resistance which in many cases is retained even below T_g. The exact structural features responsible for this toughness have not been well defined.

The major effects of a further increase in crystallinity to very high values include (a) a further increase in modulus, as the high modulus characteristic of the crystalline regions is approached, and (b) the onset of a tendency toward brittleness, in the sense of failure at low strains. Such polymers, of which high-density polyethylene is typical, can be cold drawn only with difficulty. Tensile failure usually occurs at or slightly beyond the yield stress, accompanied by distortion or deformation that appears to occur at slip boundaries or dislocations, reminiscent of the viscoelastic behavior of metals.

Crystallization on Stressing. The application of a mechanical stress to a noncrystalline but crystallizable polymer can cause crystallinity to develop, either by raising T_m or by increasing the rate of crystallization. An example of the former effect is the crystallization of natural rubber on stretching described in Section B. At room temperature, unstretched natural rubber is above its crystalline melting point. As a tensile stress is applied, T_m is raised and the rubber crystallizes to an oriented structure. When the stress is released, T_m is reduced and the rubber melts as it retracts.

An example of the effect of stress on crystallization rate is seen in polymers such as poly(ethylene terephthalate) which can be quenched to a metastable amorphous state at temperatures well below T_m. Without an applied stress, the rate of nucleation and crystal growth is very low. When a tensile stress is applied, T_m is raised and the rate of crystallization is greatly increased so that crystallization takes place during stretching. These crystals do not melt when the stress is removed, of course.

GENERAL REFERENCES

Alfrey 1948, 1967; Tobolsky 1960; McCrum 1967; Ward 1971; Nielsen 1974; Schultz 1974, Chapter 11; McCullough 1977; Tager 1978, Chapter 9; Ferry 1980; Young 1981, Chapter 5.

DISCUSSION QUESTIONS AND PROBLEMS

1. Define and distinguish among the following terms: (a) shear thickening, (b) shear thinning, (c) thixotropic, (d) rheopectic, (e) Newtonian behavior.

2. State the equations relating the melt viscosity of a polymer to (a) molecular weight and (b) temperature.

3. List four physical properties characteristic of typical elastomers.

4. List four molecular-structure characteristics necessary for the development of typical elastomer physical properties.

5. Describe two quantitative aspects of the elastomeric state that are explained by the kinetic theory of rubber elasticity.

6. Why can the kinetic theory of rubber elasticity not predict the entire stress–strain curve for a typical elastomer?

7. Derive the stress–strain equation for the simple stretching of an elastomer, Eq. 11-11.

8. Derive an equation similar to Eq. 11-11 for the case of an elastomer with each dimension increased by a factor σ due to swelling with an organic solvent.

9. List three types of response of a typical polymer to stress and suggest a molecular mechanism for each type.

10. Sketch a strain–time curve for each of the mechanisms described in Question 9.

11. Describe briefly (a) creep and (b) stress relaxation.

12. Why cannot the theories of the viscoelasticity of amorphous polymers be extended to crystalline polymers?

BIBLIOGRAPHY

Adam 1965. Gerold Adam and Julian H. Gibbs, "On the Temperature Dependence of Cooperative Relaxation Properties in Glass-Forming Liquids," *J. Chem. Phys.* **43**, 139–146 (1965).

Alfrey 1948. Turner Alfrey, Jr., *Mechanical Behavior of High Polymers,* Interscience, New York, 1948.

Alfrey 1967. Turner Alfrey, Jr., and Edward F. Gurnee, *Organic Polymers,* Prentice-Hall, Englewood Cliffs, New Jersey, 1967.

Armeniades 1975. C. D. Armeniades and Eric Baer, "Transitions and Relaxations in Polymers," Chapter 6 in Herman S. Kaufman and Joseph J. Falcetta, eds., *Introduction to Polymer Science and Technology: An SPE Textbook,* Wiley-Interscience, New York, 1975.

Bauer 1967. Walter H. Bauer and Edward A. Collins, "Thixotropy and Dilatancy," Chapter 8 in Frederick R. Eirich, ed., *Rheology—Theory and Applications,* Vol. 4, Academic Press, New York, 1967.

Bekkedahl 1934. Norman Bekkedahl, "Forms of Rubber as Indicated by Temperature–Volume Relationship," *J. Res. Nat. Bur. Stand.* **13**, 411–431 (1934).

Brydson 1978. J. A. Brydson, *Rubber Chemistry,* Applied Science, London, 1978.

Bueche 1953. F. Bueche, "Segmental Mobility of Polymers Near Their Glass Temperatures," *J. Chem. Phys.* **21**, 1850–1855 (1953).

Carley 1975. James F. Carley, "Rheology," Chapter 8 in Herman S. Kaufman and Joseph J. Falcetta, eds., *Introduction to Polymer Science and Technology: An SPE Textbook,* Wiley-Interscience, New York, 1975.

Cohen 1959. Morrel H. Cohen and David Turnbull, "Molecular Transport in Liquids and Glasses," *J. Chem. Phys.* **31**, 1164–1169 (1959).

Cotton 1974. J. P. Cotton, D. Decker, H. Benoit, B. Farnoux, J. Higgins, G. Janniuk, R. Ober, C. Picot, and J. des Cloizeaux, "Conformation of Polymer Chains in the Bulk," *Macromolecules* **7**, 863–872 (1974).

Dealy 1981. John M. Dealy, *Rheometers for Molten Plastics: A Practical Guide to Testing & Property Measurement,* Van Nostrand Reinhold, New York, 1981.

Dealy 1983. J. M. Dealy, "Melt Rheometer Update," *Plastics Eng.* **34**, 57–61 (1983).

de Gennes 1971. P. G. de Gennes, "Reptation of a Polymer Chain in the Presence of Fixed Obstacles," *J. Chem. Phys.* **55**, 572–579 (1971).

de Gennes 1979. Pierre-Gilles de Gennes, *Scaling Concepts in Polymer Physics,* Cornell University Press, Ithaca, New York, 1979.

DiMarzio 1958. E. A. DiMarzio and J. H. Gibbs, "Chain Stiffness and the Lattice Theory of Polymer Phases," *J. Chem. Phys.* **28**, 807–813 (1958).

Doolittle 1951. Arthur K. Doolittle, "Studies in Newtonian Flow. II. The Dependence of the Viscosity of Liquids on Free-Space," *J. Appl. Phys.* **22**, 1471–1475 (1951).

Eirich 1956-1969. Frederick R. Eirich, ed., *Rheology—Theory and Applications,* Academic Press, New York, Vol. 1, 1956; Vol. 2, 1958; Vol. 3, 1960; Vol. 4, 1967; Vol. 5, 1969.

Ferry 1980. John D. Ferry, *Viscoelastic Properties of Polymers*, 3rd ed., John Wiley & Sons, New York, 1980.

Flory 1940. Paul J. Flory, "Viscosities of Linear Polyesters. An Exact Relationship between Viscosity and Chain Length," *J. Am. Chem. Soc.* **62**, 1057–1070 (1940).

Flory 1949. Paul J. Flory, "The Configuration of Real Polymer Chains," *J. Chem. Phys.* **17**, 303–310 (1949).

Fox 1956. T. G Fox, Serge Gratch, and S. Loshaek, "Viscosity Relationships for Polymers in Bulk and in Concentrated Solution," Chapter 12 in Frederick R. Eirich, ed., *Rheology—Theory and Applications*, Vol. 1, Academic Press, New York, 1956.

Gent 1978. A. N. Gent, "Rubber Elasticity: Basic Concepts and Behavior," Chapter 1 in Frederick R. Eirich, ed., *Science and Technology of Rubber*, Academic Press, New York, 1978.

Gibbs 1958. Julian H. Gibbs and Edmund A. DiMarzio, "Nature of the Glass Transition and the Glassy State," *J. Chem. Phys.* **28**, 373–383 (1958).

Glasstone 1941. Samuel Glasstone, Keith J. Laidler, and Henry Eyring, *The Theory of Rate Processes*, McGraw-Hill, New York, 1941.

Graessley 1974. William W. Graessley, "The Entanglement Concept in Polymer Rheology," *Adv. Polym. Sci.* **16**, 1–179 (1974).

Guth 1946. E. Guth, H. M. James, and H. Mark, "The Kinetic Theory of Rubber Elasticity," pp. 253–299 in H. Mark and G. S. Whitby, eds., *Scientific Progress in the Field of Rubber and Synthetic Elastomers (Advances in Colloid Science)*, Vol. 2, Interscience, New York, 1946.

Hull 1981. Harry H. Hull, *An Approach to Rheology Through Multi-Variable Thermodynamics: Or, Inside the Thermodynamic Black Box*, Harry A. Hull, Sun City, Florida, 1981.

Kovacs 1958. A. J. Kovacs, "The Isothermal Volume Contraction of Amorphous Polymers" (in French), *J. Polym. Sci.* **30**, 131–147 (1958).

Kramer 1978. Ole Kramer and John D. Ferry, "Dynamic Mechanical Properties," Chapter 5 in Frederick R. Eirich, ed., *Science and Technology of Rubber*, Academic Press, New York, 1978.

McCrum 1967. N. G. McCrum, B. Read, and G. Williams, *Anelastic and Dielectric Effects in Polymeric Solids*, John Wiley & Sons, New York, 1967.

McCullough 1977. R. L. McCullough, "Anisotropic Elastic Behavior of Crystalline Polymers," in J. M. Schultz, ed., *Treatise on Materials Science and Technology*, Vol. 10, Part B (Herbert Herman, series ed.), Academic Press, New York, 1977.

Nielsen 1974. Lawrence E. Nielsen, *Mechanical Properties of Polymers and Composites*, Marcel Dekker, New York, 1974.

Nielsen 1977. Lawrence E. Nielsen, *Polymer Rheology*, Marcel Dekker, New York, 1977.

Pierce 1982. Percy E. Pierce and Clifford K. Schoff, "Rheological Measurements," pp. 259–319 in Martin Grayson, ed., *Kirk–Othmer Encyclopedia of Chemical Technology*, 3rd ed., Vol. 20, Wiley-Interscience, New York, 1982.

Rosen 1982. Stephen L. Rosen, *Fundamental Principles of Polymeric Materials*, Wiley-Interscience, New York, 1982.

Sauer 1975. J. A. Sauer and K. D. Pae, "Mechanical Properties of High Polymers," Chapter 7 in Herman S. Kaufman and Joseph J. Falcetta, eds., *Introduction to Polymer Science and Technology: An SPE Textbook*, Wiley-Interscience, New York, 1975.

Schultz 1974. Jerold Schultz, *Polymer Materials Science*, Prentice-Hall, New York, 1974.

Shen 1978. Mitchel Shen, "The Molecular and Phenomenological Basis of Rubberlike Elasticity," Chapter 4 in Frederick R. Eirich, ed., *Science and Technology of Rubber*, Academic Press, New York, 1978.

Smith 1977. Thor L. Smith, "Molecular Aspects of Rubber Elasticity," in J. M. Schultz, ed., *Treatise on Materials Science and Technology*, Vol. 10, Part A (Herbert Herman, series ed.), Academic Press, New York, 1977.

Sperling 1982. L. H. Sperling, "Molecular Motion in Polymers," *J. Chem. Educ.* **59,** 942–943 (1982).

Sternstein 1977. S. S. Sternstein, "Mechanical Properties of Glassy Polymers," in J. M. Schultz, ed., *Treatise on Materials Science and Technology,* Vol. 10, Part B (Herbert Herman, series ed.), Academic Press, New York, 1977.

Tager 1978. A. Tager, *Physical Chemistry of Polymers* (translated by David Sobolev and Nicholas Bobrov), Mir, Moscow, 1978 (Imported Publications, Chicago).

Tobolsky 1956. Arthur V. Tobolsky and Ephriam Catsiff, "Elastoviscous Properties of Polyisobutylene (and Other Amorphous Polymers) from Stress-Relaxation Studies. IX. A Summary of Results," *J. Polym. Sci.* **19,** 111–121 (1956).

Tobolsky 1960. Arthur V. Tobolsky, *Properties and Structure of Polymers,* John Wiley & Sons, New York, 1960.

Treloar 1975. L. R. G. Treloar, *The Physics of Rubber Elasticity,* 3rd ed., Clarendon Press, Oxford, 1975.

Van Wazer 1963. J. R. Van Wazer, J. W. Lyons, K. Y. Kim, and R. E. Colwell, *Viscosity and Flow Measurement, A Laboratory Handbook of Rheology,* Wiley-Interscience, New York, 1963.

Walters 1975. K. Walters, *Rheometry,* John Wiley & Sons, New York, 1975.

Ward 1971. I. M. Ward, *Mechanical Properties of Solid Polymers,* Wiley-Interscience, New York, 1971.

White 1978. James Lindsay White, "Rheological Behavior of Unvulcanized Rubber," Chapter 6 in Frederick R. Eirich, ed., *Science and Technology of Rubber,* Academic Press, New York, 1978.

Whorlow 1979. R. W. Whorlow, *Rheological Techniques,* John Wiley & Sons, New York, 1979.

Williams 1955. Malcolm L. Williams, Robert F. Landel, and John D. Ferry, "The Temperature Dependence of Relaxation Mechanisms in Amorphous Polymers and Other Glass-Forming Liquids," *J. Am. Chem. Soc.* **77,** 3701–3707 (1955).

Young 1981. Robert J. Young, *Introduction to Polymers,* Chapman and Hall, New York, 1981.

SUBJECT INDEX

FIFTH EDITION

FUNDAMENTALS OF

ORGANIC CHEMISTRY

T. W. GRAHAM SOLOMONS

University of South Florida

JOHN WILEY & SONS, INC.

New York   Chichester   Brisbane   Toronto   Singapore

Section Three

Library of Congress Cataloging in Publication Data:

Solomons, T. W. Graham.
    Fundamentals of organic chemistry / T. W. Graham Solomons. — 5th ed.
        p. cm.
    Includes index.
    ISBN 0-471-14649-8 (cloth : alk. paper)
    1. Chemistry, Organic.   I. Title.
QD251.2.S657   1997   96-22583
547—dc20   CIP

Printed in the United States of America

10 9 8 7 6 5 4 3 2

CONTENTS

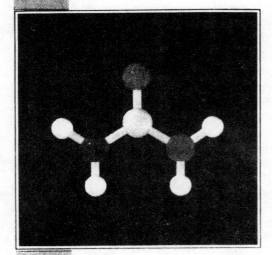

CHAPTER 1

Urea
(Section 1.2A)

CARBON COMPOUNDS AND CHEMICAL BONDS

1.1 INTRODUCTION

Organic chemistry is *the chemistry of the compounds of carbon.* The compounds of carbon constitute the central chemicals of all living things on this planet. Carbon compounds include deoxyribonucleic acids (DNAs), the giant molecules that contain the genetic information for all living species. Carbon compounds make up the proteins of our blood, muscle, and skin. They make up the enzymes that catalyze the reactions that occur in our bodies. Together with oxygen in the air we breathe, carbon compounds in our diets furnish the energy that sustains life.

Considerable evidence indicates that several billion years ago most of the carbon atoms on the earth existed in the form of the gas CH_4, called methane. This simple organic compound, along with water, ammonia, and hydrogen, were the main components of the primordial atmosphere. It has been shown experimentally that when electrical discharges and other forms of highly energetic radiation pass through this kind of atmosphere, many of these simple compounds become fragmented into highly reactive pieces. These pieces combine into more complex compounds. Compounds called amino acids, formaldehyde, hydrogen cyanide, purines, and pyrimidines can form in this way. It is thought that these, and other compounds produced in the primordial atmosphere in the same way, were carried by rain into the sea until the sea became a vast storehouse containing all of the compounds necessary for the emergence of life. Amino acids apparently reacted with each other to form the first proteins. Molecules of formaldehyde reacted with each other to become sugars, and some of these sugars, together with inorganic phosphates, combined with purines and pyrimidines to become simple molecules of ribonucleic acids (RNAs) and DNA. Molecules of RNA, because they can carry genetic information and can act as enzymes, were apparently instrumental in the emergence of the first primitive self-replicating systems. From these first systems, in a manner far from understood, through the long process of natural selection came all the living things on Earth today.

Not only are we composed largely of organic compounds, not only are we derived from and nourished by them, *we also live in an Age of Organic Chemistry.* The clothing we wear, whether a natural substance such as wool or cotton or a synthetic such as nylon or a polyester, is made up of carbon compounds. Many of the materials that go into the houses that shelter us are organic. The gasoline that propels our automobiles, the rubber of their tires, and the plastic of their interiors are all organic. Most of the medicines that help us cure diseases and relieve suffering are organic. Organic pesticides help us eliminate many of the agents that spread diseases in both plants and animals.

Organic chemicals are also factors in some of our most serious problems. Many of the organic chemicals introduced into the environment have had consequences far beyond those originally intended. A number of insecticides, widely used for many years, have now been banned because they harm many species other than insects and they pose a danger to humans. Organic compounds called polychlorobiphenyls (PCBs) are responsible for pollution of the Hudson River that may take years to reverse. Organic compounds used as propellants for aerosols have been banned because they threatened to destroy the ozone layer of the outer atmosphere, a layer that protects us from extremely harmful radiation.

Thus for good or bad, organic chemistry is associated with nearly every aspect of our lives. We would be wise to understand it as best we can.

1.2 THE DEVELOPMENT OF ORGANIC CHEMISTRY AS A SCIENCE

Humans have used organic compounds and their reactions for thousands of years. Their first deliberate experience with an organic reaction probably dates from their discovery of fire. The ancient Egyptians used organic compounds (indigo and alizarin) to dye cloth. The famous "royal purple" used by the Phoenicians was also an organic substance, obtained from mollusks. The fermentation of grapes to produce ethyl alcohol and the acidic qualities of "soured wine" are both described in the Bible and were probably known earlier.

As a science, organic chemistry is less than 200 years old. Most historians of science date its origin to the early part of the nineteenth century, a time in which an erroneous belief was dispelled.

1.2A Vitalism

During the 1780s scientists began to distinguish between **organic compounds** and **inorganic compounds.** Organic compounds were defined as compounds that could be obtained from *living organisms.* Inorganic compounds were those that came from *nonliving sources.* Along with this distinction, a belief called "vitalism" grew. According to this idea, the intervention of a "vital force" was necessary for the synthesis of an organic compound. Such synthesis, chemists held then, could take place only in living organisms. It could not take place in the flasks of a chemistry laboratory.

Between 1828 and 1850 a number of compounds that were clearly "organic" were synthesized from sources that were clearly "inorganic." The first of these syntheses was accomplished by Friedrich Wöhler in 1828. Wöhler found that the organic compound urea (a constituent of urine) could be made by evaporating an aqueous solution containing the inorganic compound ammonium cyanate.

$$\text{NH}_4{}^+\text{NCO}^- \xrightarrow{\text{heat}} \text{H}_2\text{N}-\overset{\displaystyle \overset{\text{O}}{\|}}{\text{C}}-\text{NH}_2$$

Ammonium cyanate   **Urea**

Although "vitalism" disappeared slowly from scientific circles after Wöhler's synthesis, its passing made possible the flowering of the science of organic chemistry that has occurred since 1850.

Despite the demise of vitalism in science, the word "organic" is still used today by some people to mean "coming from living organisms" as in the terms "organic vitamins" and "organic fertilizers." The commonly used term "organic food" means that the food was grown without the use of synthetic fertilizers and pesticides. An "organic vitamin" means to these people that the vitamin was isolated from a natural source and not synthesized by a chemist. While there are sound arguments to be made against using food contaminated with certain pesticides, while there may be environmental benefits to be obtained from organic farming, and while "natural" vitamins may contain beneficial substances not present in synthetic vitamins, it is impossible to argue that pure "natural" vitamin C, for example, is healthier than pure "synthetic" vitamin C, since the two substances are identical in all respects. In science today, the study of compounds from living organisms is called natural product chemistry.

1.2B Empirical and Molecular Formulas

In the eighteenth and nineteenth centuries extremely important advances were made in the development of qualitative and quantitative methods for analyzing organic substances. In 1784 Antoine Lavoisier first showed that organic compounds were composed primarily of carbon, hydrogen, and oxygen. Between 1811 and 1831, *quantitative* methods for determining the composition of organic compounds were developed by Justus Liebig, J. J. Berzelius, and J. B. A. Dumas.

A great confusion was dispelled in 1860 when Stanislao Cannizzaro showed that the earlier hypothesis of Amedeo Avogadro (1811) could be used to distinguish between **empirical** and **molecular formulas.** As a result, many molecules that had appeared earlier to have the same formula were seen to be composed of different numbers of atoms. For example, ethylene, cyclopentane, and cyclohexane all have the same empirical formula: CH_2. However, they have molecular formulas of C_2H_4, C_5H_{10}, and C_6H_{12}, respectively. Appendix A of the Study Guide that accompanies this book contains a review of how empirical and molecular formulas are determined and calculated.

1.3 THE STRUCTURAL THEORY OF ORGANIC CHEMISTRY

Between 1858 and 1861, August Kekulé, Archibald Scott Couper, and Alexander M. Butlerov, working independently, laid the basis for one of the most fundamental theories in chemistry: **the structural theory.** Two central premises are fundamental:

1. The atoms of the elements in organic compounds can form a fixed number of bonds. The measure of this ability is called **valence.** Carbon is *tetravalent;* that is, carbon atoms form four bonds. Oxygen is *divalent;* and hydrogen and (usually) the halogens are *monovalent.*

$$-\overset{|}{\underset{|}{C}}-\qquad\qquad -O-\qquad\qquad H-\quad Cl-$$

Carbon atoms	**Oxygen atoms**	**Hydrogen and halogen**
are tetravalent	**are divalent**	**atoms are monovalent**

2. A carbon atom can use one or more of its valences to form bonds to other carbon atoms.

Carbon–carbon bonds

$$-\overset{|}{\underset{|}{C}}-\overset{|}{\underset{|}{C}}-\qquad\qquad \underset{/}{\overset{\backslash}{C}}=\underset{\backslash}{\overset{/}{C}}\qquad\qquad -C\equiv C-$$

Single bond	**Double bond**	**Triple bond**

In his original publication Couper represented these bonds by lines much in the same way that most of the formulas in this book are drawn. In his textbook (published in 1861), Kekulé gave the science of organic chemistry its modern definition: *a study of the compounds of carbon.*

1.3A Isomers: The Importance of Structural Formulas

The structural theory allowed early organic chemists to begin to solve a fundamental problem that plagued them: the problem of **isomerism.** These chemists frequently found examples of **different compounds that have the same molecular formula.** Such compounds are called **isomers.**

Let us consider an example. There are two compounds with the molecular formula C_2H_6O that are clearly different because they have different properties (see Table 1.1). These compounds, therefore, are classified as being isomers of one another; they are said to be **isomeric.** Notice that these two isomers have different boiling points, and, because of this, one isomer, called *dimethyl ether,* is a gas at room temperature; the other isomer, called *ethyl alcohol,* is a liquid. The two isomers also have different melting points, and they show a striking difference in their reactivity towards sodium. Dimethyl ether *does not react* with sodium; ethyl alcohol *does react,* and the reaction produces hydrogen gas.

Because the molecular formula (C_2H_6O) for these two compounds is the same, it

TABLE 1.1   Properties of ethyl alcohol and dimethyl ether

	ETHYL ALCOHOL C_2H_6O	DIMETHYL ETHER C_2H_6O
Boiling point (°C)	78.5	− 24.9
Melting point (°C)	− 117.3	− 138
Reaction with sodium	Displaces hydrogen	No reaction

gives us no basis for understanding the differences between them. The structural theory remedies this situation, however. It does so by giving us different **structures** (Fig. 1.1), and different **structural formulas** for the two compounds.

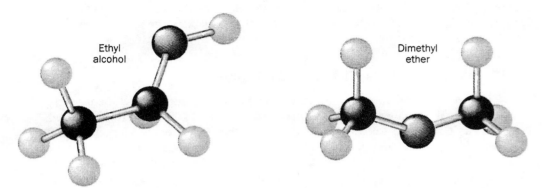

FIGURE 1.1   Ball-and-stick models show the different structures of ethyl alcohol and dimethyl ether.

$$\begin{array}{ccccc}
& \text{H} & \text{H} & & \\
& | & | & & \\
\text{H} - \text{C} - \text{C} - \text{O} - \text{H} & & \\
& | & | & & \\
& \text{H} & \text{H} & & \\
\end{array}
\qquad
\begin{array}{ccccc}
& \text{H} & & \text{H} & \\
& | & & | & \\
\text{H} - \text{C} - \text{O} - \text{C} - \text{H} \\
& | & & | & \\
& \text{H} & & \text{H} & \\
\end{array}$$

Ethyl alcohol   **Dimethyl ether**

One glance at the structural formulas for these two compounds reveals their difference. The two compounds differ in their **connectivity:** The atoms of ethyl alcohol are connected in a way that is different from those of dimethyl ether. In ethyl alcohol there is a C—C—O linkage; in dimethyl ether the linkage is C—O—C. Ethyl alcohol has a hydrogen atom attached to oxygen; in dimethyl ether all of the hydrogen atoms are attached to carbon. It is the hydrogen atom covalently bonded to oxygen in ethyl alcohol that is displaced when this alcohol reacts with sodium:

$$2\ \begin{array}{ccc}
\text{H} & \text{H} \\
| & | \\
\text{H}-\text{C}-\text{C}-\text{O}-\text{H} \\
| & | \\
\text{H} & \text{H}
\end{array} + 2\ \text{Na} \longrightarrow 2\ \begin{array}{ccc}
\text{H} & \text{H} \\
| & | \\
\text{H}-\text{C}-\text{C}-\text{O}^-\text{Na}^+ \\
| & | \\
\text{H} & \text{H}
\end{array} + \textbf{H}_2$$

This is just the way water reacts with sodium:

$$2\ \text{H}-\text{O}-\textbf{H} + 2\ \text{Na} \longrightarrow 2\ \text{H}-\text{O}^-\text{Na}^+ + \textbf{H}_2$$

Hydrogen atoms that are covalently bonded to carbon are normally unreactive toward sodium. As a result, none of the hydrogen atoms in dimethyl ether is displaced by sodium.

> The hydrogen atom attached to oxygen also accounts for the fact that ethyl alcohol is a liquid at room temperature. As we shall see in Section 2.16, this hydrogen atom allows molecules of ethyl alcohol to form hydrogen bonds to each other and gives ethyl alcohol a boiling point much higher than that of dimethyl ether.

Ethyl alcohol and dimethyl ether are examples of what are now called **constitutional isomers.** * *Constitutional isomers are different compounds that have the same molecular formula, but differ in their connectivity, that is, in the sequence in which their atoms are bonded together.* Constitutional isomers usually have different physical properties (e.g., melting point, boiling point, and density) and different chemical properties. The differences, however, may not always be as large as those between ethyl alcohol and dimethyl ether.

1.3B The Tetrahedral Shape of Methane

In 1874, the structural formulas originated by Kekulé, Couper, and Butlerov were expanded into three dimensions by the independent work of J. H. van't Hoff and J. A. Le Bel. van't Hoff and Le Bel proposed that the four bonds of the carbon atom in methane, for example, are arranged in such a way that they would point toward the corners of a regular tetrahedron, the carbon atom being placed at its center (Fig. 1.2). The necessity for knowing the arrangement of the atoms in space, taken together with an understanding of the order in which they are connected, is central to an understanding of organic chemistry, and we shall have much more to say about this later, in Chapters 4 and 5.

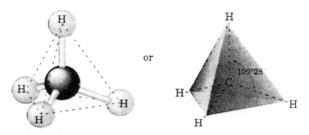

FIGURE 1.2   The tetrahedral structure of methane.

1.4   CHEMICAL BONDS: THE OCTET RULE

The first explanations of the nature of chemical bonds were advanced by G. N. Lewis (of the University of California, Berkeley) and W. Kössel (of the University of Munich) in 1916. Two major types of chemical bonds were proposed.

1.   The **ionic** (or **electrovalent**) bond, formed by the transfer of one or more electrons from one atom to another to create ions.
2.   The **covalent** bond, a bond that results when atoms share electrons.

The central idea in their work on bonding is that atoms without the electronic configuration of a noble gas generally react to produce such a configuration.

The concepts and explanations that arise from the original propositions of Lewis and Kössel are satisfactory for explanations of many of the problems we deal with in organic chemistry today. For this reason we shall review these two types of bonds in more modern terms.

---

*An older term for isomers of this type was **structural isomers.** The International Union of Pure and Applied Chemistry (IUPAC) now recommends that use of the term "structural" when applied to isomers of this type be abandoned.

1.4A Ionic Bonds

Atoms may gain or lose electrons and form charged particles called *ions*. An ionic bond is an attractive force between oppositely charged ions. One source of such ions is a reaction between atoms of widely differing electronegativities (Table 1.2). *Electronegativity measures the ability of an atom to attract electrons.* Notice in Table 1.2 that electronegativity increases as we go across a horizontal row of the periodic table from left to right:

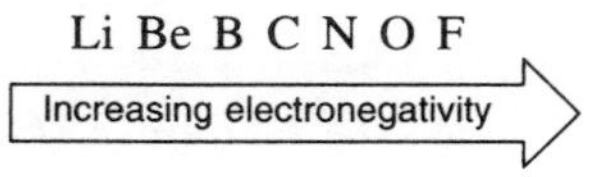

Li Be B C N O F

> Increasing electronegativity ⟩

and that it decreases as we go down a vertical column:

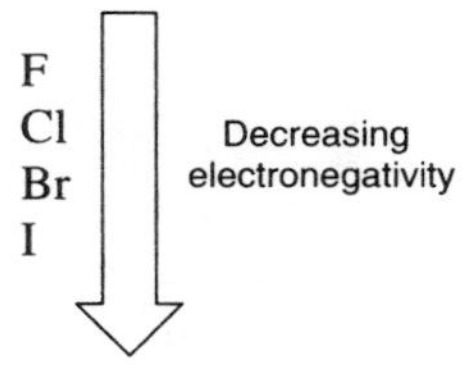

F
Cl
Br
I

Decreasing
electronegativity

⇩

An example of the formation of an ionic bond is the reaction of lithium and fluorine atoms.

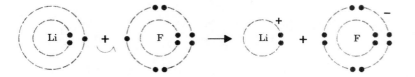

Lithium, a typical metal, has a very low electronegativity; fluorine, a nonmetal, is the most electronegative element of all. The loss of an electron (a negatively charged species) by the lithium atom leaves a lithium cation (Li^+); the gain of an electron by the fluorine atom gives a fluoride anion (F^-). Why do these ions form? In terms of the Lewis–Kössel theory both atoms achieve the electronic configuration of a noble gas by becoming ions. The lithium cation with two electrons in its valence shell is like an atom of the nobel gas helium, and the fluoride anion with eight electrons in its valence

TABLE 1.2 Electronegativities of some of the elements

			H			
			2.1			
Li	**Be**	**B**	**C**	**N**	**O**	**F**
1.0	1.5	2.0	2.5	3.0	3.5	4.0
Na	**Mg**	**Al**	**Si**	**P**	**S**	**Cl**
0.9	1.2	1.5	1.8	2.1	2.5	3.0
K						**Br**
0.8						2.8

shell is like an atom of the noble gas neon. Moreover, crystalline lithium fluoride forms from the individual lithium and fluoride ions. In this process negative fluoride ions become surrounded by positive lithium ions, and positive lithium ions by negative fluoride ions. In this crystalline state, the ions have substantially lower energies than the atoms from which they have been formed. Lithium and fluorine are thus ''stabilized'' when they react to form crystalline lithium fluoride.

We represent the formula for lithium fluoride as LiF, because this is the simplest formula for this ionic compound.

Ionic substances, because of their strong internal electrostatic forces, are usually very high melting solids, often having melting points above 1000°C. In polar solvents, such as water, the ions are solvated (see Section 2.16E), and such solutions usually conduct an electric current.

Ionic compounds form only when atoms of very different electronegativities transfer electrons to become ions.

1.4B Covalent Bonds

When two or more atoms of the same or similar electronegativities react, a complete transfer of electrons does not occur. In these instances the atoms achieve noble gas configurations by *sharing electrons. Covalent* bonds form between the atoms, and the products are called *molecules.* Molecules may be represented by electron-dot formulas or, more conveniently, by dash formulas, where each dash represents a pair of electrons shared by two atoms. Some examples are shown here. These formulas

$$H_2 \qquad H\cdot + \cdot H \longrightarrow H:H \qquad \text{or} \qquad H\!-\!H$$

$$Cl_2 \qquad :\ddot{C}l\cdot + \cdot \ddot{C}l: \longrightarrow :\ddot{C}l:\ddot{C}l: \qquad \text{or} \qquad :\ddot{C}l\!-\!\ddot{C}l:$$

$$CH_4 \qquad \cdot \dot{\underset{.}{C}}\cdot + 4\,H\cdot \longrightarrow H:\overset{H}{\underset{\ddot{H}}{\ddot{C}}}:H \qquad \text{or} \qquad H\!-\!\overset{\displaystyle H}{\underset{\displaystyle H}{\overset{|}{\underset{|}{C}}}}\!-\!H$$

are often called **Lewis structures;** in writing them we show only the electrons of the valence shell.

In certain cases, multiple covalent bonds are formed; for example,

$$N_2 \qquad :N::N: \qquad \text{or} \qquad :N\equiv N:$$

and ions themselves may contain covalent bonds.

$$\overset{+}{NH_4} \qquad H:\overset{H}{\underset{\ddot{H}}{\ddot{N}}}\!\!{}^{+}\!\!:H \qquad \text{or} \qquad H\!-\!\overset{\displaystyle H}{\underset{\displaystyle H}{\overset{|}{\underset{|}{N}}}}{}^{\pm}\!-\!H$$

1.5 WRITING LEWIS STRUCTURES

When we write Lewis structures (electron-dot formulas) we assemble the molecule or ion from the constituent atoms showing only the valence electrons (i.e., the electrons of the outermost shell). By having the atoms share or transfer electrons, we try to give each atom the electronic configuration of the noble gas in the same horizontal row of the periodic table. For example, we give hydrogen atoms two electrons because by doing so we give them the structure of helium. We give carbon, nitrogen, oxygen, and fluorine atoms eight electrons because by doing this we give them the electronic configuration of neon. The number of valence electrons of an atom can be obtained from the periodic table because it is equal to the group number of the atom. Carbon, for example, is in Group **IVA** and it has four valence electrons; fluorine, in Group **VIIA** has seven; hydrogen in Group **IA**, has one.

SAMPLE PROBLEM

Write the Lewis structure of CH_3F.

ANSWER:

1. We find the total number of valence electrons of all the atoms:

    $$4 + 3(1) + 7 = 14$$
    ↑   ↑   ↑
    C H_3 F

2. We use pairs of electrons to form bonds between all atoms that are bonded to each other. We represent these bonding pairs with lines. In our example this requires four pairs of electrons (8 of our 14 valence electrons).

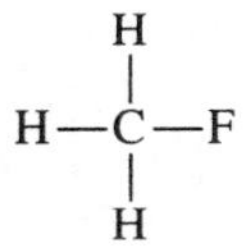

    $$\begin{array}{c} H \\ | \\ H - C - F \\ | \\ H \end{array}$$

3. We then add the remaining electrons in pairs so as to give each hydrogen 2 electrons (a duet) and every other atom 8 electrons (an octet). In our example, we assign the remaining 6 valence electrons to the fluorine atom in three nonbonding pairs.

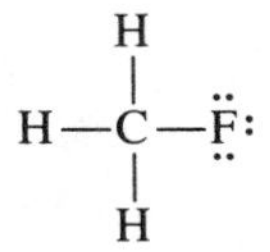

    $$\begin{array}{c} H \\ | \\ H - C - \ddot{\underset{..}{F}}: \\ | \\ H \end{array}$$

If the structure is an ion, we add or subtract electrons to give it the proper charge.

SAMPLE PROBLEM

Write the Lewis structure for the chlorate ion (ClO_3^-).

ANSWER:

1. We find the total number of valence electrons of all the atoms including the extra electron needed to give the ion a negative charge:

$$7 + 3(6) + 1 = 26$$

$$\uparrow \quad \uparrow \quad \uparrow$$

$$\text{Cl} \quad \text{O}_3 \quad e^-$$

2. We use three pairs of electrons to form bonds between the chlorine atom and the three oxygen atoms:

$$\begin{array}{c} \text{O} \\ | \\ \text{O}-\overset{\displaystyle}{\underset{\displaystyle}{\text{Cl}}}-\text{O} \end{array}$$

3. We then add the remaining 20 electrons in pairs so as to give each atom an octet.

$$\left[\begin{array}{c} :\ddot{\text{O}}: \\ | \\ :\ddot{\text{O}}-\overset{\displaystyle}{\underset{\displaystyle}{\text{Cl}}}-\ddot{\text{O}}: \end{array} \right]^-$$

If necessary, we use multiple bonds to give atoms the noble gas configuration. The carbonate ion (CO_3^{2-}) illustrates this.

$$\left[\begin{array}{c} :\ddot{\text{O}} \\ \| \\ \text{C} \\ \ddot{\text{O}} \quad \ddot{\text{O}} \end{array} \right]^{2-}$$

The organic molecules ethene (C_2H_4) and ethyne (C_2H_2) have a double and triple bond, respectively.

$$\begin{array}{cc} \text{H} & \text{H} \\ \diagdown & \diagup \\ & \text{C}=\text{C} \\ \diagup & \diagdown \\ \text{H} & \text{H} \end{array} \quad \text{and} \quad \text{H}-\text{C}\equiv\text{C}-\text{H}$$

1.6 EXCEPTIONS TO THE OCTET RULE

Atoms share electrons, not just to obtain the configuration of an inert gas, but because sharing electrons produces increased electron density between the positive nuclei. The resulting attractive forces of nuclei for electrons is the "glue" that holds the atoms together (cf. Section 1.11). Elements of the second period of the periodic table can have a maximum of four bonds (i.e., have eight electrons around them) because these elements have only $2s$ and $2p$ orbitals available for bonding and a total of eight electrons fills these orbitals (Section 1.11). The octet rule, therefore, only applies to these elements, and even here, as we shall see in compounds of beryllium and boron, fewer than eight electrons are possible. Elements of the third period, and beyond, have d orbitals that can be used for bonding. These elements can accommodate more than eight electrons in their valence shell and therefore can form more than four covalent bonds. Examples are compounds such as PCl_5 and SF_6.

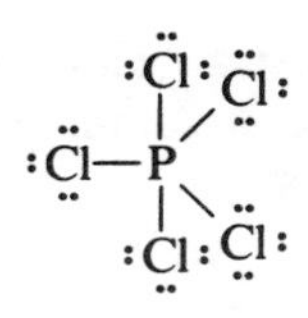

SAMPLE PROBLEM

Write a Lewis structure for the sulfate ion (SO_4^{2-}).

ANSWER:

1. We find the total number of valence electrons including the extra 2 electrons needed to give the ion a negative charge:

$$6 + 4(6) + 2 = 32$$

    S O_4 $2e^-$

2. We use pairs of electrons to form bonds between the sulfur atom and the four oxygen atoms:

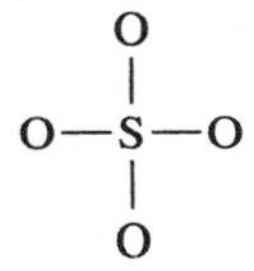

3. We add the remaining 24 electrons as unshared pairs on oxygen atoms and as double bonds between the sulfur atom and two oxygen atoms. This gives each oxygen 8 electrons and the sulfur atom 12.

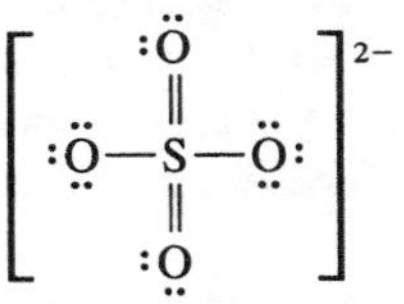

Some highly reactive molecules or ions have atoms with fewer than eight electrons in their outer shell. An example is boron trifluoride (BF_3). In the BF_3 molecule the central boron atom has only six electrons around it.

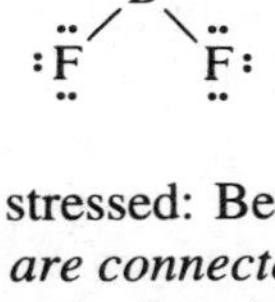

Finally, one point needs to be stressed: Before we can write some Lewis structures, *we must know how the atoms are connected to each other.* Consider nitric acid, for example. Even though the formula for nitric acid is often written HNO_3, the hydrogen is actually connected to an oxygen, not to the nitrogen. The structure is $HONO_2$ and not HNO_3. Thus the correct Lewis structure is

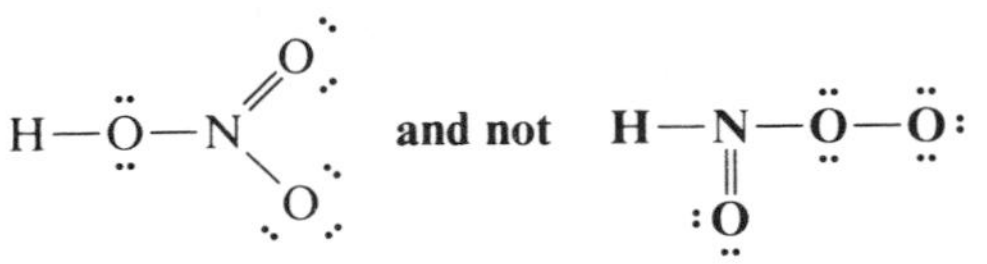

This knowledge comes ultimately from experiments. If you have forgotten the structures of some of the common inorganic molecules and ions (such as those listed in Problem 1.1), this may be a good time for a review of the relevant portions of your general chemistry text.

PROBLEM 1.1

Write Lewis structures for each of the following:

(a) HF   (d) HNO_2 (g) H_3PO_4
(b) F_2 (e) H_2SO_3 (h) H_2CO_3
(c) CH_3F (f) BH_4^- (i) HCN

1.7 FORMAL CHARGE

When we write Lewis structures, it is often convenient to assign unit positive or negative charges, called **formal charges,** to certain atoms in the molecule or ion. This is nothing more than a bookkeeping method for electrical charges, because *the arithmetic sum of all of the formal charges equals the total charge on the molecule or ion.*

We calculate formal charges on individual atoms **by subtracting the number of valence electrons assigned to an atom in its bonded state from the number of valence electrons it has as a neutral free atom.** (Recall that the number of valence electrons in a neutral free atom is equal to its **group number** on the periodic table.)

We assign valence electrons to atoms in the bonded state by apportioning them. **We divide shared electrons equally between the atoms that share them and we assign unshared pairs to the atom that possesses them.**

Consider first the ammonium ion, an ion that has no unshared pairs. We divide all of the valence electrons equally between the atoms that share them. Each hydrogen is assigned *one electron* (e^-) and we subtract this from *one* (the number of valence electrons in a neutral hydrogen atom) to give a formal charge of 0 for each hydrogen atom. The nitrogen atom is assigned *four electrons.* We subtract this from *five* (the number of valence electrons in a neutral nitrogen atom) to give a formal charge of $+1$. In effect, we say that because the nitrogen atom in the ammonium ion lacks one electron when compared to a neutral nitrogen atom (in which the number of protons and electrons are equal) it has a formal charge of +1.*

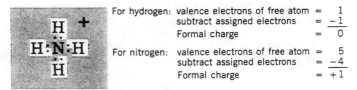

For hydrogen: valence electrons of free atom = 1
subtract assigned electrons = −1
Formal charge = 0

For nitrogen: valence electrons of free atom = 5
subtract assigned electrons = −4
Formal charge = +1

Charge on ion = (4)(0) + 1 = +1

Let us next consider the nitrate ion (NO_3^-), an ion that has oxygen atoms with unshared electron pairs. Here we find that the nitrogen atom has a formal charge of +1, that two oxygen atoms have formal charges of −1, and that one oxygen has a formal charge equal to 0.

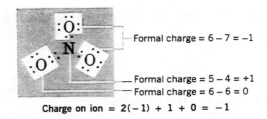

Formal charge = 6 − 7 = −1

Formal charge = 5 − 4 = +1
Formal charge = 6 − 6 = 0

Charge on ion = 2(−1) + 1 + 0 = −1

Molecules, of course, have no net electrical charge. Molecules, by definition, are neutral. Therefore, the sum of the formal charges on each atom making up a molecule must be zero. Consider the following examples:

Ammonia

H—N̈—H or H:N:H
      |
      H

Formal charge = 5 − 5 = 0
Formal charge = 1 − 1 = 0

Charge on molecule = 0 + 3(0) = 0

Water

H—Ö—H or H:Ö:H

Formal charge = 6 − 6 = 0
Formal charge = 1 − 1 = 0

Charge on molecule = 0 + 2(0) = 0

* An alternative method for calculating formal charge is to use the equation:

$$F = Z - S/2 - U$$

where F is the formal charge, Z is the group number, S equals the number of shared electrons, and U is the number of unshared electrons.

PROBLEM 1.2 _____

Write a Lewis structure for each of the following negative ions, and assign the formal negative charge to the correct atom.

(a) NO_2^- (d) HSO_4^-

(b) NH_2^- (e) HCO_3^-

(c) CN^- (f) HC_2^-

1.7A Summary of Formal Charges

With this background it should now be clear that each time an oxygen atom of the type $-\ddot{O}:$ appears in a molecule or ion it will have a formal charge of -1, and that each time an oxygen atom of the type $=\ddot{O}:$ or $-\ddot{O}-$ appears it will have a formal charge of 0. Similarly, $-\underset{|}{\overset{|}{N}}-$ will be $+1$, and $-\underset{|}{\ddot{N}}-$ will be zero. These common structures are summarized in Table 1.3.

TABLE 1.3   A summary of formal charges

GROUP	FORMAL CHARGE OF +1	FORMAL CHARGE OF 0	FORMAL CHARGE OF −1
3		$-B-$	$-\overset{|}{\underset{|}{B}}\,\bar{}$
4	$-\overset{+}{\underset{|}{C}}-$ $=\overset{+}{C}$ $\equiv\overset{+}{C}$	$-\overset{|}{\underset{|}{C}}-$ $=\overset{|}{C}-$ $\equiv C-$	$-\ddot{\underset{|}{C}}\,\bar{}$ $=\overset{|}{C}:^-$ $\equiv C:^-$
5	$-\overset{|}{\underset{|}{N}}\,\overset{+}{}$ $=\overset{+}{\underset{|}{N}}-$ $\equiv\overset{+}{N}-$	$-\ddot{\underset{|}{N}}-$ $=\ddot{N}-$ $\equiv N:$	$-\ddot{\underset{|}{N}}\,\bar{}$ $=\ddot{N}:^-$
6	$-\overset{..}{\underset{|}{O}}\,\overset{+}{}$ $=\overset{..}{O}-\underset{+}{}$	$-\overset{..}{\underset{..}{O}}-$ $=\ddot{O}:$	$-\overset{..}{\underset{..}{O}}:^-$
7	$-\overset{..}{\underset{..}{X}}\,\overset{+}{}$	$-\overset{..}{\underset{..}{X}}:$ (X = F, Cl, Br, or I) $:\overset{..}{\underset{..}{X}}:^-$	

PROBLEM 1.3 _____

Assign the proper formal charge to the colored atom in each of the following structures:

(a) 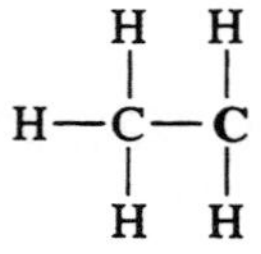
$$H-\underset{\underset{H}{|}}{\overset{\overset{H}{|}}{C}}-\underset{\underset{H}{|}}{\overset{\overset{H}{|}}{C}}$$

(d) 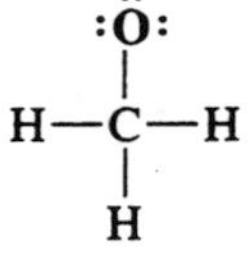
$$H-\underset{\underset{H}{|}}{\overset{\overset{:\ddot{O}:}{|}}{C}}-H$$

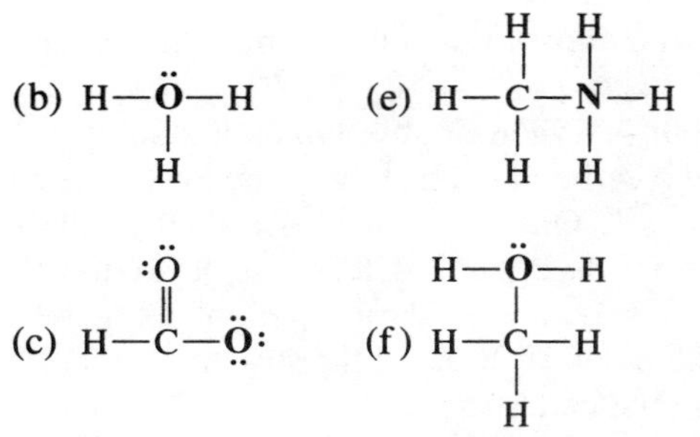

(b) H—Ö—H   (e) H—C—N—H
with H below O; (e) has H H above C and N, and H H below C and N

(c) H—C—Ö: with :Ö above C (double bond)   (f) H—C—H with H—Ö—H above and H below

1.8 RESONANCE

One problem with Lewis structures is that they impose an artificial **location** on the electrons. As a result, more than one *equivalent* Lewis structure can be written for many molecules and ions. Consider, for example, the carbonate ion (CO_3^{2-}). We can write three *different* but *equivalent* structures, **1–3**.

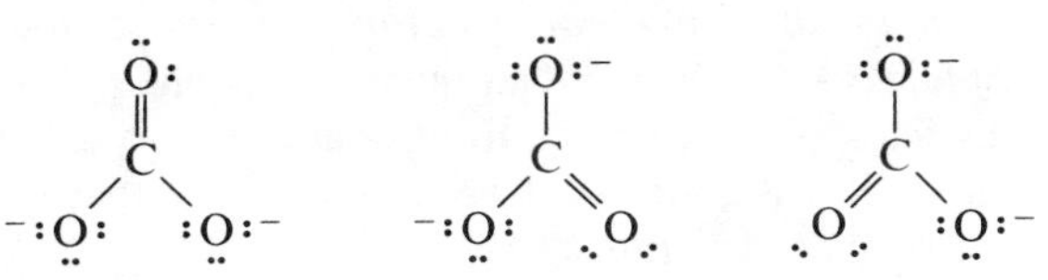

Notice two important features of these structures. First, each atom has the noble gas configuration. Second, *and this is especially important,* we can convert one structure into any other by *changing only the positions of the electrons.* We do not need to change the relative positions of the atomic nuclei. For example, if we move the electron pairs in the manner indicated by the curved arrows* in structure **1**, we change structure **1** into structure **2**:

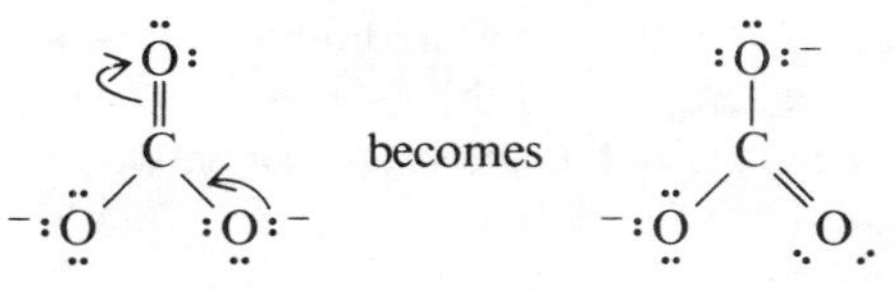

becomes

In a similar way we can change structure **2** into structure **3**:

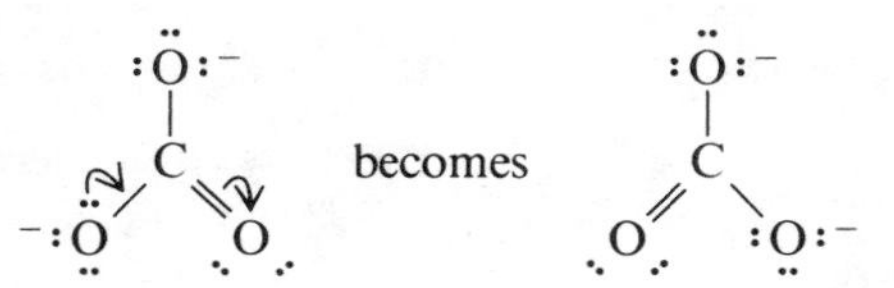

becomes

---

* The use of curved arrows is described in more detail later (Section 3.4). We should point out now that the curved arrows show movement of pairs of electrons, not atoms, and that the tail of the arrow begins at the current position of the electron pair, while the head of the arrow shows the new location of the electron pair.

Structures **1–3**, although not identical, *are equivalent*. None of them, however, fits important data about the carbonate ion.

X-Ray studies have shown that carbon–oxygen double bonds are shorter than single bonds. The same kind of study of the carbonate ion shows, however, that all of its carbon–oxygen bonds *are of equal length*. One is not shorter than the others as would be expected from the representations **1**, **2**, or **3**. Clearly none of the three structures agrees with this evidence. In each structure, **1–3**, one carbon–oxygen bond is a double bond and the other two are single bonds. None of the structures, therefore, is correct. How, then, should we represent the carbonate ion?

One way is through a theory called **resonance theory.** This theory states that whenever a molecule or ion can be represented by two or more Lewis structures *that differ only in the positions of the electrons,* two things will be true:

1.   None of these structures, which we call **resonance structures** or **resonance contributors,** will be a correct representation for the molecule. None will be in complete accord with the physical or chemical properties of the substance.

2.   The actual molecule or ion will be better represented by a *hybrid of these structures.*

   Resonance structures, then, are not structures for the actual molecule or ion; they exist only in theory. As such they can never be isolated. No single contributor adequately represents the molecule or ion. In resonance theory we view the carbonate ion, which is, of course, a real entity, as having a structure that is a **hybrid** of these three **hypothetical** resonance structures.

What would a hybrid of structures **1–3** be like? Look at the structures and look especially at a particular carbon–oxygen bond, say, the one at the top. This carbon–oxygen bond is a double bond in one structure (**1**) and a single bond in the other two (**2** and **3**). The actual carbon–oxygen bond, since it is a hybrid, must be something in between a double bond and a single bond. Because the carbon–oxygen bond is a single bond in two of the structures and a double bond in only one it must be more like a single bond than a double bond. It must be like a one- and one-third bond. We could call it a partial double bond. And, of course, what we have just said about any one carbon–oxygen bond will be equally true of the other two. Thus all of the carbon–oxygen bonds of the carbonate ion are partial double bonds, and *all are equivalent.* All of them *should be* the same length, and this is exactly what experiments tell us. They are all 1.28 Å long, a distance which is intermediate between that of a carbon–oxygen single bond (1.43 Å) and that of a carbon–oxygen double bond (1.20 Å).

One other important point: By convention, when we draw resonance structures, we connect them by double-headed arrows to indicate clearly that they are hypothetical, not real. For the carbonate ion we write them this way:

We should not let these arrows, or the word "resonance," mislead us into thinking that the carbonate ion fluctuates between one structure and another. These structures exist only on paper; therefore, the carbonate ion cannot fluctuate among them. It is also important to distinguish between resonance and **an equilibrium.** In an equilibrium between two, or more, species, it is quite correct to think of different structures and moving (or fluctuating) atoms, *but not in the case of resonance* (as in the carbonate ion). Here the atoms do not move, and the "structures" exist only on paper. An equilibrium is indicated by ⇌ and resonance by ↔.

How can we write the structure of the carbonate ion in a way that will indicate its actual structure? We may do two things: we may write all of the resonance structures as we have just done and let the reader mentally fashion the hybrid or we may write a non-Lewis structure that attempts to represent the hybrid. For the carbonate ion we might do the following:

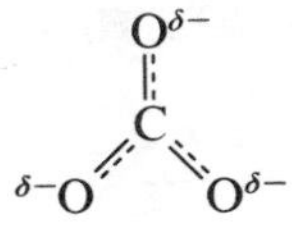

$$O^{\delta-}$$
$$\parallel$$
$$C$$
$$_{\delta-}O \diagup \qquad \diagdown O^{\delta-}$$

The bonds are indicated by a combination of a solid line and a dashed line. This is to indicate that the bonds are something in between a single bond and a double bond. As a rule, we use a solid line whenever a bond appears in all structures, and a dashed line when a bond exists in one or more but not all. We also place a $\delta-$ (read partial minus) beside each oxygen to indicate that something less than a full negative charge resides on each oxygen atom. (In this instance each oxygen atom has two-thirds of a full negative charge.)

SAMPLE PROBLEM

The following is one way of writing the structure of the nitrate ion.

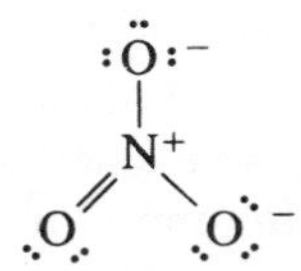

$$:\ddot{O}:^{-}$$
$$\mid$$
$$N^{+}$$
$$\diagup \qquad \diagdown$$
$$:\ddot{O} \qquad \ddot{O}:^{-}$$

However, considerable physical evidence indicates that all three nitrogen–oxygen bonds are equivalent and that they have the same length, a bond distance between that expected for a nitrogen–oxygen single bond and a nitrogen–oxygen double bond. Explain this in terms of resonance theory.

ANSWER:

We recognize that if we move the electron pairs in the following way, we can write three *different* but *equivalent* structures for the nitrate ion:

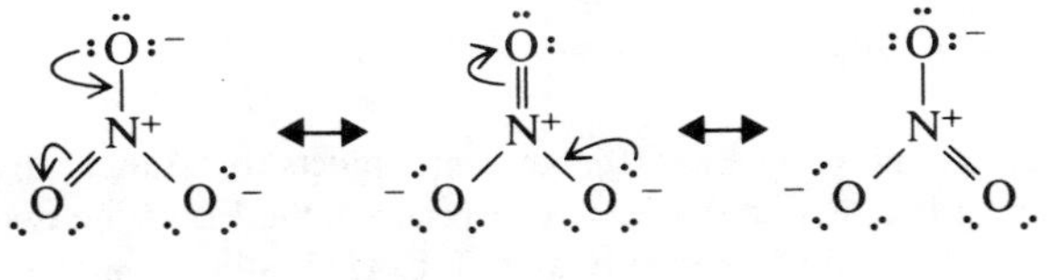

Since these structures differ from one another *only in the positions of their electrons,* they are *resonance structures* or *resonance contributors.* As such, no single structure taken alone will adequately represent the nitrate ion. The actual molecule will be best represented by a *hybrid of these three structures.* We might write this hybrid in the following way to indicate that all of the bonds are equivalent and that they are more than single bonds and less than double bonds. We also indicate that each oxygen atom bears an equal partial negative charge. This charge distribution corresponds to what we find experimentally.

$$
\begin{array}{c}
O^{\delta-} \\
\parallel \\
{}^{\delta-}O^{\diagdown} N^{+} {}_{\diagdown} O^{\delta-}
\end{array}
\qquad
\begin{array}{l}
\textbf{Hybrid structure for the} \\
\textbf{nitrate ion}
\end{array}
$$

PROBLEM 1.4

(a) Write two resonance structures for the formate ion HCO_2^-. (The hydrogen and oxygen atoms are bonded to the carbon.) (b) Explain what these structures predict for the carbon–oxygen bond lengths of the formate ion, and (c) for the electrical charge on the oxygen atoms.

1.9 ENERGY CHANGES

Since we will be talking frequently about the energies of chemical systems, perhaps we should pause here for a brief review. *Energy* is defined as the capacity to do work. The two fundamental types of energy are **kinetic energy** and **potential energy.**

Kinetic energy is the energy an object has because of its motion; it equals one half the object's mass multiplied by the square of its velocity (i.e., $\frac{1}{2} mv^2$).

Potential energy is stored energy. It exists only when an attractive or repulsive force exists between objects. Two balls attached to each other by a spring can have their potential energy increased when the spring is stretched or compressed (Fig. 1.3). If the spring is stretched, an attractive force will exist between the balls. If it is compressed, a repulsive force will exist. In either instance releasing the balls will cause the potential energy (stored energy) of the balls to be converted into kinetic energy (energy of motion).

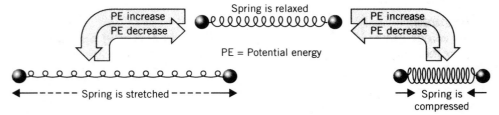

FIGURE 1.3 Potential energy (PE) exists between objects that either attract or repel each other. When the spring is either stretched or compressed, the PE of the two balls increases. (Adapted with permission from J. E. Brady and G. E. Humiston, *General Chemistry: Principles and Structure,* 1st ed., Wiley, New York, p. 18.)

Chemical energy is a form of potential energy. It exists because attractive and repulsive electrical forces exist between different pieces of the molecules. Nuclei attract electrons, nuclei repel each other, and electrons repel each other.

It is usually impractical (and often impossible) to describe the *absolute* amount of potential energy contained by a substance. Thus we usually think in terms of its *relative potential energy*. We say that one system has *more* or *less* potential energy than another.

Another term that chemists frequently use in this context is the term **stability** or **relative stability.** *The relative stability of a system is inversely related to its relative potential energy.* The *more* potential energy an object has, the *less stable* it is. Consider, as an example, the relative potential energy and the relative stability of snow when it lies high on a mountainside and when it lies serenely in the valley below. Because of the attractive force of gravity, the snow high on the mountain *has greater potential energy and is much less stable* than the snow in the valley. This greater potential energy of the snow on the mountainside can become converted to the enormous kinetic energy of an avalanche. By contrast, the snow in the valley, with its lower potential energy and with its greater stability, is incapable of releasing such energy.

1.9A Potential Energy and Covalent Bonds

Atoms and molecules possess potential energy—often called chemical energy—that can be released as heat when they react. Because heat is associated with molecular motion, this release of heat results from a change from potential energy to kinetic energy.

From the standpoint of covalent bonds, the state of greatest potential energy is the state of free atoms, the state in which the atoms are not bonded to each other at all. This is true because the formation of a chemical bond is always accompanied by the lowering of the potential energy of the atoms (cf. Fig. 1.8). Consider as an example the formation of hydrogen molecules from hydrogen atoms:

$$\text{H} \cdot + \text{H} \cdot \longrightarrow \text{H}-\text{H} \quad \Delta H^\circ = -104 \text{ kcal mol}^{-1} \, (-435 \text{ kJ mol}^{-1})^*$$

The potential energy of the atoms decreases by 104 kcal mol^{-1} as the covalent bonds form. This potential energy change is illustrated graphically in Fig. 1.4.

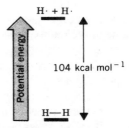

FIGURE 1.4   The relative potential energies of hydrogen atoms and a hydrogen molecule.

*A kilocalorie of energy (1000 cal) is the amount of energy in the form of heat required to raise by 1°C the temperature of 1 kg (1000 g) of water at 15°C. The unit of energy in SI units is the joule, J, and 1 cal = 4.184 J. (Thus 1 kcal = 4.184 kJ.)

A convenient way to represent the relative potential energies of molecules is in terms of their relative **enthalpies** or **heat contents,** *H.* (*Enthalpy* comes from *en* + Gk: *thalpein* to heat.) The difference in relative enthalpies of reactants and products in a chemical change is called the enthalpy change and is symbolized by $\Delta H°$. [The Δ (delta) in front of a quantity usually means the difference, or change, in the quantity. The superscript ° indicates that the measurement is made under standard conditions.]

By convention, the sign of $\Delta H°$ for **exothermic** reactions (those evolving heat) is negative. **Endothermic** reactions (those that absorb heat) have a positive $\Delta H°$. The heat of reaction, $\Delta H°$, measures the change in enthalpy of the atoms of the reactants as they are converted to products. For an exothermic reaction the atoms have a smaller enthalpy as products than they do as reactants. For endothermic reactions, the reverse is true.

1.10 QUANTUM MECHANICS

In 1926 a new theory of atomic and molecular structure was advanced independently and almost simultaneously by three men: Erwin Schrödinger, Werner Heisenberg, and Paul Dirac. This theory, called **wave mechanics** by Schrödinger or **quantum mechanics** by Heisenberg, has become the basis from which we derive our modern understanding of bonding in molecules.

The formulation of quantum mechanics that Schrödinger advanced is the form that is most often used by chemists. In Schrödinger's publication the motion of the electrons is described in terms that take into account the wave nature of the electron.* Schrödinger developed a way to convert the mathematical expression for the total energy of the system consisting of one proton and one electron — the hydrogen atom — into another expression called a **wave equation.** This equation is then solved to yield not one but a series of solutions called **wave functions.**

Wave functions are most often denoted by the Greek letter psi (ψ), and each wave function (ψ function) corresponds to a different state for the electron. Corresponding to each state, and calculable from the wave equation for the state, is a particular energy.

Each state is a sublevel where one or two electrons can reside. *The solutions to the wave equation for a hydrogen atom can also be used* (with appropriate modifications) *to give sublevels for the electrons of higher elements.*

A wave equation is simply a tool for calculating two important properties: These are the energy associated with the state and the relative probability of an electron residing at particular places in the sublevel (Section 1.11). When the value of a wave equation is calculated for a particular point in space relative to the nucleus, the result may be a positive number or a negative number (or zero). These signs are sometimes called **phase signs.** They are characteristic of all equations that describe waves. We do not need to go into the mathematics of waves here, but a simple analogy will help us understand the nature of these phase signs.

Imagine a wave moving across a lake. As it moves along, the wave has crests and troughs; that is, it has regions where the wave rises above the average level of the lake or falls below it (Fig. 1.5). Now, if an equation were to be written for this wave, the wave function (ψ) would be plus (+) in regions where the wave is above the average level of the lake (i.e., in crests) and it would be minus (−) in regions where the wave is

---

*The idea that the electron has the properties of a wave as well as those of a particle was proposed by Louis de Broglie in 1923.

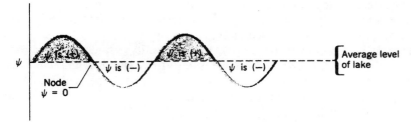

FIGURE 1.5 A wave moving across a lake is viewed along a slice through the lake. For this wave the wave function, ψ, is plus ($+$) in crests and minus ($-$) in troughs. At the average level of the lake it is zero; these places are called nodes.

below the average level (i.e., in troughs). The relative magnitude of ψ (called the amplitude) will be related to the distance the wave rises above or falls below the average level of the lake. At the places where the wave is exactly at the average level of the lake, the wave function will be zero. Such a place is called a **node.**

One other characteristic of waves is their ability to reinforce each other or to interfere with one another. Imagine two waves approaching each other as they move across a lake. If the waves meet so that a crest meets a crest, that is, so that *waves of the same phase sign meet each other,* the waves **reinforce** each other, they add together, and the resulting wave is larger than either individual wave. On the other hand, if a crest meets a trough, that is, if waves of opposite sign meet, the waves **interfere** with each other, they subtract from each other, and the resulting wave is smaller than either individual wave. (If the two waves of opposite sign meet in precisely the right way, complete cancellation can occur.)

The wave functions that describe the motion of an electron in an atom or molecule are, of course, different from the equations that describe waves moving across lakes. And when dealing with the electron we should be careful not to take analogies like this too far. Electron wave functions, however, are like the equations that describe water waves in that they have phase signs and nodes, and *they undergo reinforcement and interference.*

1.11 ATOMIC ORBITALS

For a short time after Schrödinger's proposal in 1926, a precise physical interpretation for the electron wave function eluded early practitioners of quantum mechanics. It remained for Max Born, a few months later, to point out that the square of ψ *could* be given a precise physical meaning. According to Born, ψ^2 for a particular location (x,y,z) expresses the **probability** of finding an electron at that particular location in space. If ψ^2 is large in a unit volume of space, the probability of finding an electron in that volume is great—we say that the **electron probability density** is large. Conversely if ψ^2 for some other unit volume of space is small, the probability of finding an electron there is low.* Plots of ψ^2 in three dimensions generate the shapes of the familiar s, p, and d atomic orbitals, which we use as our models for atomic structure.

The f orbitals are practically never used in organic chemistry, and we shall not concern ourselves with them in this book. The d orbitals will be discussed briefly later

---

*Integration of ψ^2 over all space must equal 1; that is, the probability of finding an electron somewhere in all of space is 100%.

when we discuss compounds in which *d* orbital interactions are important. The *s* and *p* orbitals are, by far, the most important in the formation of organic molecules and, at this point, we shall limit our discussion to them.

An orbital is a region of space where the probability of finding an electron is large. The shapes of *s* and *p* orbitals are shown in Fig. 1.6. There is a finite, but very small, probability of finding an electron at greater distances from the nucleus. The volumes that we typically use to illustrate an orbital are those volumes that would contain the electron 90–95% of the time.

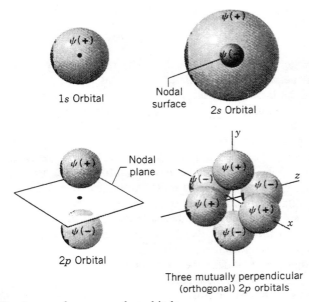

1s Orbital

Nodal surface

2s Orbital

Nodal plane

2p Orbital

Three mutually perpendicular (orthogonal) 2p orbitals

FIGURE 1.6   The shapes of some *s* and *p* orbitals.

Both the 1*s* and 2*s* orbitals are spheres (as are all higher *s* orbitals) (Fig. 1.6). The 2*s* orbital contains a nodal surface, that is, an area where $\psi = 0$. In the inner portion of the 2*s* orbital, ψ_{2s} is negative.

The 2*p* orbitals have the shape of two almost-touching spheres. The phase sign of the 2*p* wave function, ψ_{2p}, is positive in one lobe (or sphere) and negative in the other. A nodal plane separates the two lobes of a *p* orbital, and the three *p* orbitals are arranged in space so that their axes are mutually perpendicular.

You should not associate the sign of the wave function with anything having to do with electrical charge. As we said earlier the $(+)$ and $(-)$ signs associated with ψ are simply the arithmetic signs of the wave function in that region of space. The $(+)$ and $(-)$ signs **do not** imply a greater or lesser probability of finding an electron either. The probability of finding an electron is ψ^2, and ψ^2 is always positive. (Squaring a negative number always makes it positive.) Thus the probability of finding the electron in the $(-)$ lobe of a *p* orbital is the same as that of the $(+)$ lobe. The significance of the $(+)$ and $(-)$ signs will become clear later when we see how atomic orbitals combine to form molecular orbitals and when we see how covalent bonds are formed.

There is a relationship between the number of nodes of an orbital and its energy: ***The greater the number of nodes, the greater the energy.*** We can see an example here; the 2*s* and 2*p* orbitals have one node each and they have greater energy than a 1*s* orbital, which has no nodes.

The relative energies of the lower energy orbitals are as follows. Electrons in 1*s* orbitals have the lowest energy because they are closest to the positive nucleus. Electrons in 2*s* orbitals are next lowest in energy. Electrons of 2*p* orbitals have equal but still higher energy. (Orbitals of equal energy are said to be **degenerate orbitals.**)

We can use these relative energies to arrive at the electronic configuration of any atom in the first two rows of the periodic table. We need only follow a few simple rules.

1. **The aufbau principle:** Orbitals are filled so that those of lowest energy are filled first. (*Aufbau* is German for ''building up.'')

2. **The Pauli exclusion principle:** A maximum of two electrons may be placed in each orbital *but only when the spins of the electrons are paired.* An electron spins about its own axis. For reasons that we cannot develop here, an electron is permitted only one or another of only two possible spin orientations. We usually show these orientations by arrows, either ↑ or ↓. Thus two spin-paired electrons would be designated ↑↓. Unpaired electrons, which are not permitted in the same orbital, are designated ↑ ↑ (or ↓ ↓).

3. **Hund's rule:** When we come to orbitals of equal energy (degenerate orbitals) such as the three *p* orbitals, we add one electron to each *with their spins unpaired* until each of the degenerate orbitals contains one electron. (This allows the electrons, which repel each other, to be farther apart.) Then we begin adding a second electron to each degenerate orbital so that the spins are paired.

If we apply these rules to some of the second-row elements of the periodic table, we get the results shown in Fig. 1.7.

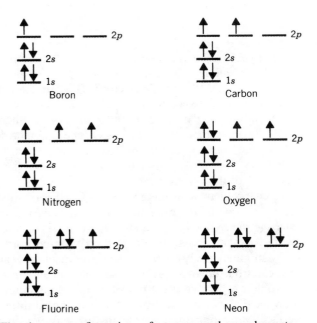

FIGURE 1.7 The electron configurations of some second-row elements.

1.12 MOLECULAR ORBITALS

For the organic chemist the greatest utility of atomic orbitals is in using them as models for understanding how atoms combine to form molecules. We shall have much more to say about this subject in subsequent chapters, for, as we have already said, covalent bonds are central to the study of organic chemistry. First, however, we shall concern ourselves with a very simple case: the covalent bond that is formed when two hydrogen atoms combine to form a hydrogen molecule. We shall see that the description of the formation of the H—H bond is the same as, or at least very similar to, the description of bonds in more complex molecules.

Let us begin by examining what happens to the total energy of two hydrogen atoms with electrons of opposite spins when they are brought closer and closer together. This can best be shown with the curve shown in Fig. 1.8.

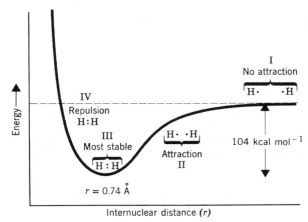

FIGURE 1.8   The potential energy of the hydrogen molecule as a function of internuclear distance.

When the atoms of hydrogen are relatively far apart (**I**) their total energy is simply that of two isolated hydrogen atoms. As the hydrogen atoms move closer together (**II**), each nucleus increasingly attracts the other's electron. This attraction more than compensates for the repulsive force between the two nuclei (or the two electrons), and the result of this attraction *is to lower the energy of the total system.* When the two nuclei are 0.74 Å apart (**III**), the most stable (lowest energy) state is obtained. This distance, 0.74 Å, corresponds to the *bond length* for the hydrogen molecule. If the nuclei are moved closer together (**IV**) the repulsion of the two positively charged nuclei predominates, and the energy of the system rises.

There is one serious problem with this model for bond formation. We have assumed that the electrons are essentially motionless and that as the nuclei come together they will be stationary in the region between the two nuclei. Electrons do not behave that way. Electrons move about, and according to the **Heisenberg uncertainty principle,** we cannot know simultaneously the position and momentum of an electron. That is, we cannot pin the electrons down as precisely as our explanation suggests.

We avoid this problem when we use a model based on quantum mechanics and *orbitals,* because now we describe the electron in terms of probabilities (ψ^2) of finding it at particular places. By treating the electron in this way we do not violate the uncertainty principle, because we do not talk about where the electron is precisely. We talk instead about where the *electron probability density* is large or small.

Thus an orbital explanation for what happens when two hydrogen atoms combine to form a hydrogen molecule is the following: As the hydrogen atoms approach each other, their 1s orbitals (ψ_{1s}) begin to overlap. As the atoms move closer together, orbital overlap increases until the **atomic orbitals** (AOs) combine to become **molecular orbitals (MOs).** The molecular orbitals that are formed encompass both nuclei and, in them, the electrons can move about both nuclei. They are not restricted to the vicinity of one nucleus or the other as they were in the separate atomic orbitals. Molecular orbitals, like atomic orbitals, *may contain a maximum of two spin-paired electrons.*

When atomic orbitals combine to form molecular orbitals, *the number of molecular orbitals that result always equals the number of atomic orbitals that combine.* Thus in the formation of a hydrogen molecule the *two* atomic orbitals combine to produce *two* molecular orbitals. Two orbitals result because the mathematical properties of wave functions permit them to be combined by either *addition* or *subtraction.* That is, they can combine either *in* or *out of* phase. What are the natures of these new molecular orbitals?

One molecular orbital, called the **bonding molecular orbital** (ψ_{molec}) contains both electrons in the lowest energy state, or *ground* state, of a hydrogen molecule. It is formed when the atomic orbitals combine in the way shown in Fig. 1.9. Here atomic orbitals combine by *addition,* and this means that atomic *orbitals of the same phase sign overlap.* Such overlap leads to *reinforcement* of the wave function in the region between the two nuclei. Reinforcement of the wave function not only means that the value of ψ is larger between the two nuclei, it means that ψ^2 is larger as well. Moreover, since ψ^2 expresses the probability of finding an electron in this region of space, we can now understand how orbital overlap of this kind leads to bonding. It does so by increasing the electron probability density in exactly the right place—in the region of space between the nuclei. When the electron density is large here, the attractive force of the nuclei for the electrons more than offsets the repulsive force acting between the two nuclei (and between the two electrons). This extra attractive force is, of course, the ''glue'' that holds the atoms together.

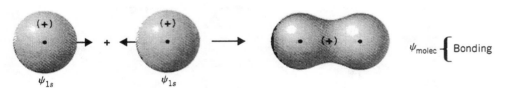

FIGURE 1.9 The overlapping of two hydrogen 1s atomic orbitals to form a bonding molecular orbital.

The second molecular orbital, called the **antibonding molecular orbital** (ψ^*_{molec}) contains no electrons in the ground state of the molecule. It is formed by subtraction in the way shown in Fig. 1.10. [Subtraction means that the phase sign of one orbital has been changed from (+) to (−).] Here, because *orbitals of opposite phase overlap,* the wave functions *interfere* with each other in the region between the two nuclei and a node is produced. At the node $\psi = 0$, and on either side of the node ψ is small. This means that in the region between the nuclei ψ^2 is also small. Thus if electrons were to occupy the antibonding orbital, the electrons would avoid the region between the nuclei. There would be only a small attractive force of the nuclei for the electrons. Repulsive forces (between the two nuclei and between the two electrons) would be greater than the attractive forces. Having electrons in the antibonding orbital would not tend to hold the atoms together; it would tend to make them fly apart.

What we have just described has its counterpart in a mathematical treatment called the LCAO (linear combination of atomic orbitals) method. In the LCAO treatment,

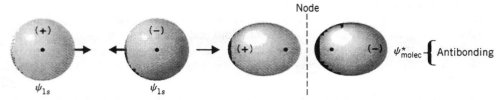

FIGURE 1.10 The overlapping of two hydrogen $1s$ atomic orbitals to form an antibonding molecular orbital.

wave functions for the atomic orbitals are combined in a linear fashion (by addition or subtraction) in order to obtain new wave functions for the molecular orbitals.

Molecular orbitals, like atomic orbitals, correspond to particular energy states for an electron. Calculations show that the relative energy of an electron in the bonding molecular orbital of the hydrogen molecule is substantially less than its energy in a ψ_{1s} atomic orbital. These calculations also show that the energy of an electron in the antibonding molecular orbital is substantially greater than its energy in a ψ_{1s} atomic orbital.

An energy diagram for the molecular orbitals of the hydrogen molecule is shown in Fig. 1.11. Notice that electrons are placed in molecular orbitals in the same way that they were in atomic orbitals. Two electrons (with their spins opposed) occupy the bonding molecular orbital, where their total energy is less than in the separate atomic orbitals. This is, as we have said, the *lowest electronic energy state* or *ground state* of the hydrogen molecule. (An electron may occupy the antibonding orbital in what is called an *excited state* for the molecule. This state forms when the molecule in the ground state absorbs a photon of light of proper energy.)

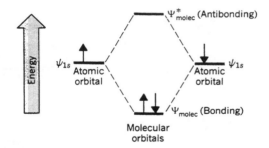

FIGURE 1.11 Energy diagram for the hydrogen molecule. Combination of two atomic orbitals. ψ_{1s} gives two molecular orbitals, ψ_{molec} and ψ_{molec}^*. The energy of ψ_{molec} is lower than that of the separate atomic orbitals, and in the lowest electronic energy state of molecular hydrogen it contains both electrons.

1.13 THE STRUCTURE OF METHANE: sp^3 HYBRIDIZATION

The s and p orbitals used in the quantum mechanical description of the carbon atom, given in Section 1.11, were based on calculations for hydrogen atoms. These simple s and p orbitals do not, when taken alone, provide a satisfactory model for the *tetravalent-tetrahedral* carbon of methane (see Problem 1.5). However, a satisfactory model of methane's structure that is based on quantum mechanics *can* be obtained through an approach called **orbital hybridization.** Orbital hybridization, in its simplest terms, is nothing more than a mathematical approach that involves the combining of individual wave functions for *s* and *p* orbitals to obtain wave functions for new orbitals. The new orbitals have, *in varying proportions,* the properties of the original orbitals taken separately. These new orbitals are called **hybrid atomic orbitals.**

According to quantum mechanics the electronic configuration of a carbon atom in its lowest energy state—called the *ground state*—is that given here.

$$C \quad \uparrow\downarrow \quad \uparrow\downarrow \quad \uparrow \quad \uparrow \quad \underline{\hspace{1em}}$$
$$1s \quad 2s \quad 2p \quad 2p \quad 2p$$

Ground state of a carbon atom

The valence electrons of a carbon atom (those used in bonding) are those of the *outer level,* that is, the 2*s* and 2*p* electrons.

Hybrid atomic orbitals that account for methane's structure can be obtained by combining the wave functions of the 2*s* orbital of carbon with those of the three 2*p* orbitals. The mathematical procedure for hybridization can be approximated by the illustration that is shown in Fig. 1.12.

In this model, four orbitals are mixed—or hybridized—and four new hybrid orbitals are obtained. The hybrid orbitals are called *sp³* orbitals to indicate that they have one part the character of an *s* orbital and three parts the character of a *p* orbital. The mathematical treatment of orbital hybridization also shows that *the four sp³ orbit-*

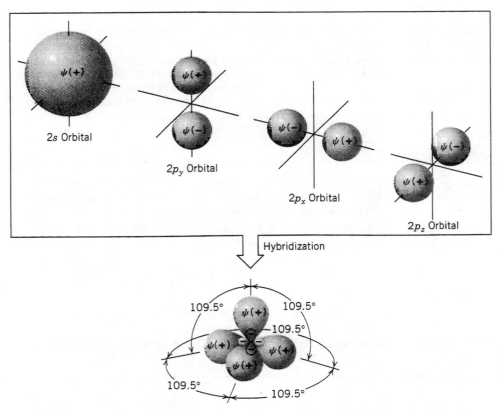

FIGURE 1.12 Hybridization of atomic orbitals of a carbon atom to produce *sp³*-hybrid orbitals.

als should be oriented at angles of 109.5° with respect to each other. This is precisely the spatial orientation of the four hydrogen atoms of methane.

If, in our imagination, we visualize the formation of methane from an sp^3-hybridized carbon atom and four hydrogen atoms, the process might be like that shown in Fig. 1.13. For simplicity we show only the formation of the *bonding molecular orbital* for each carbon–hydrogen bond. We see that an sp^3-hybridized carbon gives a *tetrahedral structure for methane, and one with four equivalent C—H bonds*.

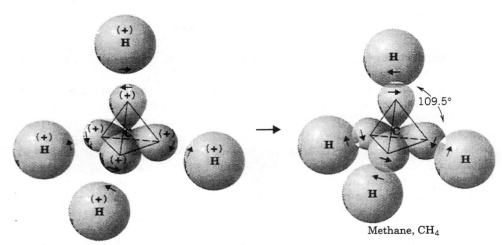

Methane, CH_4

FIGURE 1.13 The formation of methane from an sp^3-hybridized carbon atom. In orbital hybridization we combine orbitals, *not* electrons. The electrons can then be replaced in the hybrid orbitals as necessary for bond formation, but always in accordance with the Pauli principle of no more than two electrons (with opposite spin) in each orbital. In this illustration we have placed one electron in each of the hybrid carbon orbitals. In this illustration, too, we have shown only the bonding molecular orbital of each C—H bond because these are the orbitals that contain the electrons in the lowest energy state of the molecule.

PROBLEM 1.5 _____

(a) Consider a carbon atom in its ground state. Would such an atom offer a satisfactory model for the carbon of methane? If not, why not? (*Hint:* Consider whether or not a ground state carbon atom could be tetravalent, and consider the bond angles that would result if it were to combine with hydrogen atoms.)
(b) What about a carbon atom in the excited state:

$$C \quad \underline{\uparrow\downarrow} \quad \underline{\uparrow} \quad \underline{\uparrow} \quad \underline{\uparrow} \quad \underline{\uparrow}$$
$$ \quad 1s \quad\; 2s \quad 2p_x \quad 2p_y \quad 2p_z$$

Excited state of a carbon atom

Would such an atom offer a satisfactory model for the carbon of methane? If not, why not?

_____

In addition to accounting properly for the shape of methane, the orbital hybridization model also explains the very strong bonds that are formed between carbon and hydrogen. To see how this is so, consider the shape of the individual sp^3 orbital shown in Fig. 1.14. Because the sp^3 orbital has the character of a p orbital, the positive lobe of the sp^3 orbital is large and is extended quite far into space.

FIGURE 1.14 The shape of an sp^3 orbital.

It is the positive lobe of the sp^3 orbital that overlaps with the positive $1s$ orbital of hydrogen to form the bonding molecular orbital of a carbon–hydrogen bond (Fig. 1.15). Because the positive lobe of the sp^3 orbital is large and is extended into space, the overlap between it and the $1s$ orbital of hydrogen is also large, and the resulting carbon–hydrogen bond is quite strong.

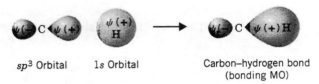

sp^3 Orbital $1s$ Orbital   Carbon–hydrogen bond
(bonding MO)

FIGURE 1.15 Formation of a C—H bond.

The bond formed from the overlap of an sp^3 orbital and a $1s$ orbital is an example of a **sigma bond** (Fig. 1.16). The term *sigma bond* is a general term applied to those bonds in which orbital overlap gives a bond that is *circularly symmetrical in cross section when viewed along the bond axis. **All purely single bonds are sigma bonds.***

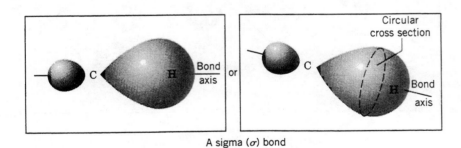

A sigma (σ) bond

FIGURE 1.16 A sigma (σ) bond.

From this point on we shall often show only the bonding molecular orbitals because they are the ones that contain the electrons when the molecule is in its lowest energy state. Consideration of antibonding orbitals is important when a molecule absorbs light and in explaining certain reactions. We shall point out these instances later.

1.14 THE STRUCTURE OF BORANE: *sp²* HYBRIDIZATION

Borane (BH_3), a molecule that can be detected only at low pressures, has a triangular (trigonal planar) shape with three equivalent boron–hydrogen bonds. In its ground state the boron atom has the following electronic configuration. Only one orbital contains a single electron that might be used to overlap with an *s* orbital containing the unpaired electron in a hydrogen atom.

B ⇅ ⇅ ↑ __ __
  1s 2s 2p 2p 2p

Boron atom ground state

H
120° | 120°
B
H 120° H

Triangular structure of BH₃

Clearly, the *s* and *p* orbitals of the ground state will not furnish a satisfactory model for the trivalent and triangularly bonded boron of BH_3.

PROBLEM 1.6

(a) What valence would you expect a boron atom in its ground state to have?

(b) Consider an excited state of boron in which one $2s$ electron is promoted to a vacant $2p$ orbital. Show how this state of boron also fails to account for the structure of BH_3.

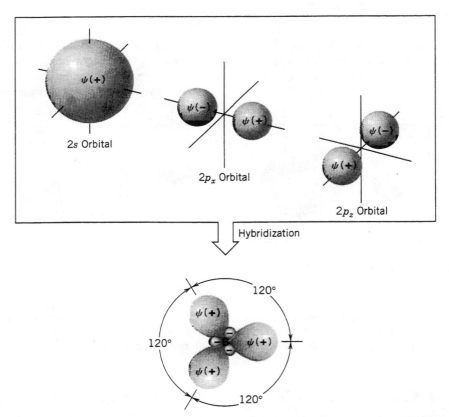

FIGURE 1.17 A representation of the mathematical procedure for the hybridization of one $2s$ orbital and two $2p$ orbitals of boron to produce three sp^2-hybrid orbitals.

Once again we use a model based on the mathematical process of orbital hybridization. Here, however, we combine the $2s$ orbital with only two of the $2p$ orbitals. Mixing three orbitals as shown in Fig. 1.17 gives three equivalent hybrid orbitals and these orbitals are sp^2 orbitals. They have one part the character of an s orbital and two parts the character of a p orbital. Calculations show that these orbitals are pointed toward the corners of an equilateral triangle with angles of 120° between their axes. These orbitals, then, are just what we need to account for the trivalent, trigonal planar boron atom of borane.

By placing one of the valence electrons in each of the three sp^2 orbitals and allowing these orbitals to overlap with an s orbital containing one electron from each of three hydrogen atoms, we obtain the structure shown in Fig. 1.18. Notice that the boron atom still has a vacant p orbital, the one that we did not hybridize.

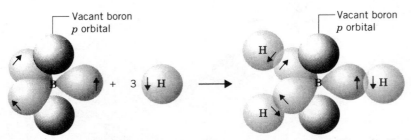

FIGURE 1.18   A representation of the formation of the bonding MOs of borane from an sp^2-hybridized boron atom and three hydrogen atoms.

We shall see in Section 2.4 that sp^2 hybridization offers a satisfactory model for carbon atoms that form double bonds.

1.15   THE STRUCTURE OF BERYLLIUM HYDRIDE: *sp* HYBRIDIZATION

Beryllium hydride (BeH_2) is a linear molecule; the bond angle is 180°.

$$\overset{\overset{\displaystyle\frown}{180°}}{H\text{—}Be\text{—}H}$$

In its ground state the beryllium atom has the following electronic configuration:

Be ↑↓ ↑↓

1s 2s 2p 2p 2p

In order to account for the structure of BeH_2 we again need a model based on orbital hybridization. Here (Fig. 1.19) we hybridize one s orbital with one p orbital and obtain two sp orbitals. Calculations show that these sp orbitals are oriented at an angle of 180°. The two p orbitals that were not mixed are vacant. Beryllium can use these hybrid orbitals to form bonds to two hydrogen atoms in the way shown in Fig. 1.20.

We shall see in Section 2.5 that sp hybridization offers a satisfactory model for carbon atoms that form triple bonds.

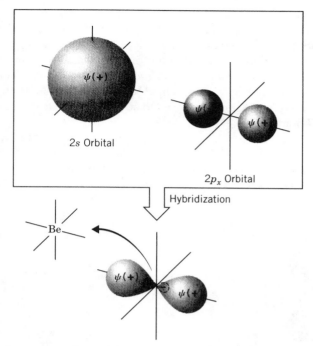

FIGURE 1.19 A representation of the mathematical procedure for the hybridization of one $2s$ orbital and one $2p$ orbital of beryllium to produce two sp-hybrid orbitals.

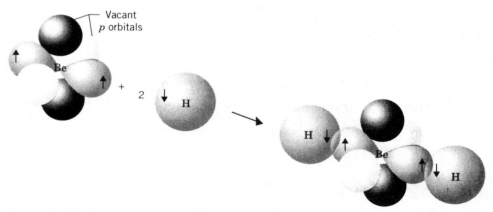

FIGURE 1.20 A representation of the formation of the bonding MOs of BeH_2 from an sp-hybridized beryllium atom and two hydrogen atoms.

1.16 A Summary of Important Concepts that Come From Quantum Mechanics

1. An **atomic orbital (AO)** corresponds to a region of space about the nucleus of a single atom where there is a high probability of finding an electron. Atomic orbitals called s orbitals are spherical; those called p orbitals are like two almost-tangent spheres. Orbitals can hold a maximum of two electrons when their spins

are paired. Orbitals are described by a wave function, ψ, and each orbital has a characteristic energy. The phase signs associated with an orbital may be $(+)$ or $(-)$.

2. When atomic orbitals overlap, they combine to form **molecular orbitals (MOs).** Molecular orbitals correspond to regions of space encompassing two (or more) nuclei where electrons are to be found. Like atomic orbitals, molecular orbitals can hold up to two electrons if their spins are paired.

3. When atomic orbitals with the same phase sign interact they combine to form a **bonding molecular orbital:**

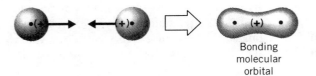

Bonding
molecular
orbital

The electron probability density of a bonding molecular orbital is large in the region of space between the two nuclei where the negative electrons hold the positive nuclei together.

4. An **antibonding molecular orbital** forms when orbitals of opposite phase sign overlap:

Node

An antibonding orbital has higher energy than a bonding orbital. The electron probability density of the region between the nuclei is small and it contains a **node**—a region where $\psi = 0$. Thus, having electrons in an antibonding orbital does not help hold the nuclei together. The internuclear repulsions tend to make them fly apart.

5. The **energy of electrons** in a bonding molecular orbital is less than the energy of the electrons in their separate atomic orbitals. The energy of electrons in an antibonding orbital is greater than that of electrons in their separate atomic orbitals.

6. The **number of molecular orbitals** always equals the number of atomic orbitals from which they are formed. Combining two atomic orbitals will always yield two molecular orbitals—one bonding and one antibonding.

7. **Hybrid atomic orbitals** are obtained by mixing (hybridizing) the wave functions for orbitals of a different type (i.e., s and p orbitals) but from the same atom.

8. Hybridizing three p orbitals with one s orbital yields four sp^3 **orbitals.** Atoms that are sp^3 hybridized direct the axes of their four sp^3 orbitals toward the corners of a tetrahedron. The carbon of methane is sp^3 hybridized and **tetrahedral.**

9. Hybridizing two p orbitals with one s orbital yields three sp^2 **orbitals.** Atoms that are sp^2 hybridized point the axes of three sp^2 orbitals toward the corners of an equilateral triangle. The boron atom in BF_3 is sp^2 hybridized and **trigonal planar.**

10. Hybridizing one p orbital with one s orbital yields two sp **orbitals.** Atoms that are sp hybridized orient the axes of their two sp orbitals in opposite directions (at an

angle of 180°). The beryllium atom of BeH_2 is sp hybridized and BeH_2 is a **linear** molecule.

11. **A sigma bond** (a type of single bond) is one in which the electron density has circular symmetry when viewed along the bond axis. In general, the skeletons of organic molecules are constructed of atoms linked by sigma bonds.

1.17   MOLECULAR GEOMETRY: THE VALENCE SHELL ELECTRON-PAIR REPULSION (VSEPR) MODEL

We have been discussing the geometry of molecules on the basis of theories that arise from quantum mechanics. It is possible, however, to predict the arrangement of atoms in molecules and ions on the basis of a theory called the **valence shell electron-pair repulsion (VSEPR) theory.** Consider the following examples found in Sections 1.17A–F.

We apply VSEPR theory in the following way:

1. We consider molecules (or ions) in which the central atom is covalently bonded to two or more atoms or groups.

2. We consider all of the valence electron pairs of the central atom—both those that are shared in covalent bonds, called **bonding pairs,** and those that are unshared, called **nonbonding pairs** or **unshared pairs.**

3. Because electron pairs repel each other, the electron pairs of the valence shell tend to stay as far apart as possible. The repulsion between nonbonding pairs is generally greater than that between bonding pairs.

4. We arrive at the geometry of the molecule by considering all of the electron pairs, bonding and nonbonding, but we describe the shape of the molecule or ion by referring to the positions of the nuclei (or atoms) and not by the positions of the electron pairs.

Consider the following examples.

1.17A Methane

The valence shell of methane contains four pairs of bonding electrons. Only a tetrahedral orientation will allow four pairs of electrons to have the maximum possible separation (Fig. 1.21). Any other orientation, for example, a square planar arrangement, places the electron pairs closer together.

Thus, in the case of methane, the VSEPR model accommodates what we have known since the proposal of van't Hoff and Le Bel (Section 1.3B): The molecule of methane has a tetrahedral shape.

PROBLEM 1.7 _____

Part of the reasoning that led van't Hoff and Le Bel to propose a tetrahedral shape for molecules of methane was based on the number of isomers possible for substituted methanes. For example, only one compound with the formula CH_2Cl_2 has ever been found (i.e., there is no isomeric form). Consider both a square planar structure and a tetrahedral structure for CH_2Cl_2 and explain how this observation supports a tetrahedral structure.

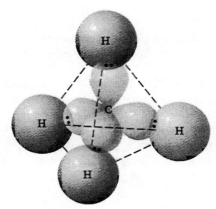

FIGURE 1.21 A tetrahedral shape for methane allows the maximum separation of the four bonding electron pairs.

The bond angles for any atom that has a regular tetrahedral structure are 109.5°. A representation of these angles in methane is shown in Fig. 1.22.

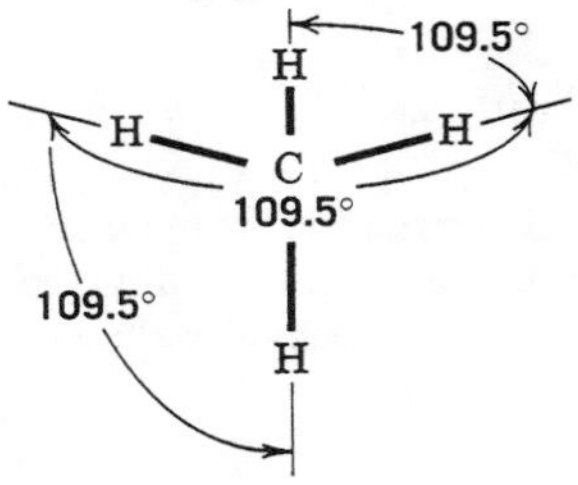

FIGURE 1.22 The bond angles of methane are 109.5°.

1.17B Ammonia

The geometry of a molecule of ammonia is a **trigonal pyramid.** The bond angles in a molecule of ammonia are 107°, a value very close to the tetrahedral angle (109.5°). We can write a general tetrahedral structure for the electron pairs of ammonia by placing the nonbonding pair at one corner (Fig. 1.23). A *tetrahedral arrangement* of the electron pairs explains the *trigonal pyramidal* arrangement of the four atoms. The bond angles are 107° (not 109.5°) because the nonbonding pair occupies more space than the bonding pairs.

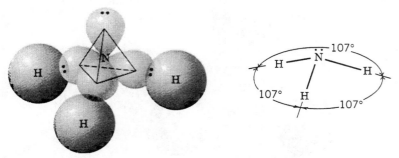

FIGURE 1.23 The tetrahedral arrangement of the electron pairs of an ammonia molecule that results when the nonbonding electron pair is considered to occupy one corner. This arrangement of electron pairs explains the trigonal pyramidal shape of the NH_3 molecule.

1.17C Water

A molecule of water has an **angular** or **bent geometry.** The H—O—H bond angle in a molecule of water is 105°, an angle that is also quite close to the 109.5° bond angles of methane.

We can write a general tetrahedral structure for the electron pairs of a molecule of water *if we place the two nonbonding electron pairs at corners of the tetrahedron.* Such a structure is shown in Fig. 1.24. A *tetrahedral arrangement* of the electron pairs accounts for the *angular arrangement* of the three atoms. The bond angle is less than 109.5° because the nonbonding pairs are effectively "larger" than the bonding pairs and, therefore, the structure is not perfectly tetrahedral.

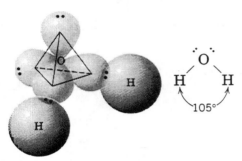

FIGURE 1.24 An approximately tetrahedral arrangement of the electron pairs of a molecule of water that results when the pairs of nonbonding electrons are considered to occupy corners. This arrangement accounts for the angular shape of the H_2O molecule.

1.17D Boron Trifluoride

Boron, a Group **IIIA** element, has only three outer level electrons. In the compound boron trifluoride (BF_3) these three electrons are shared with three fluorine atoms. As a result, the boron atom in BF_3 has only six electrons (three bonding pairs) around it. Maximum separation of three bonding pairs occurs when they occupy the corners of an equilateral triangle. Consequently, in the boron trifluoride molecule the three fluorine atoms lie in a plane at the corners of an equilateral triangle (Fig. 1.25). Boron trifluoride is said to have a *trigonal planar structure.* The bond angles are 120°.

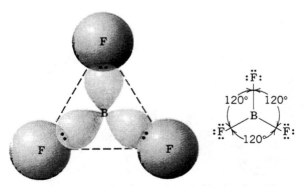

FIGURE 1.25 The triangular (trigonal planar) shape of boron fluoride maximally separates the three bonding pairs.

1.17E Beryllium Hydride

The central beryllium atom of BeH_2 has only two electron pairs around it; both electron pairs are bonding pairs. These two pairs are maximally separated when they are on opposite sides of the central atom as shown in the following structures. This arrangement of the electron pairs accounts for the linear geometry of the BeH_2 molecule and its bond angle of 180°.

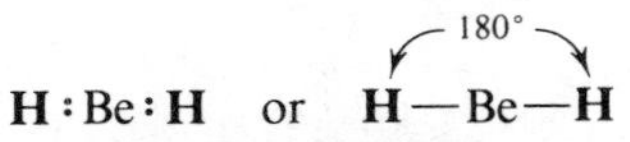

$$H:Be:H \quad \text{or} \quad H\!\!-\!\!Be\!\!-\!\!H$$

Linear geometry of BeH₂

PROBLEM 1.8

Use VSEPR theory and predict the geometry of each of the following molecules and ions:

(a) BH_4^- (c) NH_4^+ (e) BH_3 (g) SiF_4

(b) BeF_2 (d) H_2S (f) CF_4 (h) $:CCl_3^-$

1.17F Carbon Dioxide

The VSEPR method can also be used to predict the shapes of molecules containing multiple bonds if we assume that *all of the electrons of a multiple bond act as though they were a single unit,* and, therefore, are located in the region of space between the two atoms joined by a multiple bond.

This principle can be illustrated with the structure of a molecule of carbon dioxide (CO_2). The central carbon atom of carbon dioxide is bonded to each oxygen atom by a double bond. Carbon dioxide is known to have a linear shape; the bond angle is 180°.

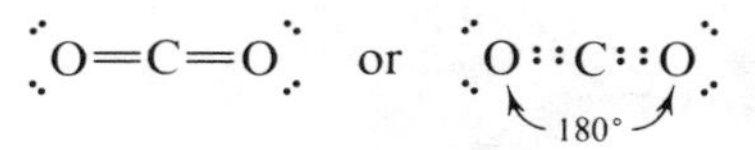

$$\ddot{O}\!\!=\!\!C\!\!=\!\!\ddot{O} \quad \text{or} \quad \ddot{O}::C::\ddot{O}$$

The four electrons of each double bond act as a single unit and are maximally separated from each other

Such a structure is consistent with a maximum separation of the two groups of four bonding electrons. (The nonbonding pairs associated with the oxygen atoms have no effect on the shape.)

PROBLEM 1.9

Predict the bond angles of   (a) $H_2C\!\!=\!\!CH_2$,   (b) $HC\!\!\equiv\!\!CH$,   (c) $HC\!\!\equiv\!\!N$.

The shapes of several simple molecules and ions as predicted by VSEPR theory are shown in Table 1.4. In this table we have also included the hybridization state of the central atom.

TABLE 1.4 Shapes of molecules and ions from VSEPR theory

NUMBER OF ELECTRON PAIRS			HYBRIDIZATION STATE OF CENTRAL ATOM	SHAPE OF MOLECULE OR ION[a]	EXAMPLES
Bonding	Nonbonding	Total			
2	0	2	sp	Linear	BeH_2
3	0	3	sp^2	Trigonal planar	BF_3, CH_3^+
4	0	4	sp^3	Tetrahedral	CH_4, NH_4^+
3	1	4	$\sim sp^3$	Trigonal pyramidal	NH_3, CH_3^-
2	2	4	$\sim sp^3$	Angular	H_2O

[a] Excluding nonbonding pairs.

1.18 POLAR COVALENT BONDS

When two atoms of different electronegativities form a covalent bond, the electrons are not shared equally between them. The atom with greater electronegativity draws the electron pair closer to it, and a **polar covalent bond** results. (One definition of *electronegativity* is *the ability of an element to attract electrons that it is sharing in a covalent bond.*) An example of such a polar covalent bond is the one in hydrogen chloride. The chlorine atom, with its greater electronegativity, pulls the bonding electrons closer to it. This makes the hydrogen atom somewhat electron deficient and gives it a *partial* positive charge ($\delta+$). The chlorine atom becomes somewhat electron rich and bears a *partial* negative charge ($\delta-$).

$$\overset{\delta+}{H} \quad \overset{\delta-}{:\ddot{Cl}:}$$

Because the hydrogen chloride molecule has a partially positive end and a partially negative end, it is a dipole, and it has a **dipole moment.**

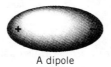

A dipole

The dipole moment is a physical property that can be measured experimentally. It is defined as the product of the magnitude of the charge in electrostatic units (esu) and the distance that separates them in centimeters (cm).

Dipole moment = charge (in esu) × distance (in cm)

$$\mu = e \times d$$

The charges are typically on the order of 10^{-10} esu and the distances are on the order of 10^{-8} cm. Dipole moments, therefore, are typically on the order of 10^{-18} esu cm. For convenience, this unit, 1×10^{-18} esu cm, is defined as one **debye** and is abbreviated D. (The unit is named after Peter J. W. Debye, a chemist born in the Netherlands, who taught at Cornell University from 1936–1966. Debye won the Nobel prize in 1936.)

The direction of polarity of a polar bond can be symbolized by a vector quantity ⊢→. The crossed end of the arrow is the positive end and the arrow head is the negative end.

$$(\text{positive end}) \vdash\!\!\!\rightarrow (\text{negative end})$$

In HCl, for example, we would indicate the direction of the dipole moment in the following way:

$$\begin{array}{c} H\!-\!Cl \\ \vdash\!\!\!\rightarrow \end{array}$$

If necessary, the length of the arrow can be used to indicate the magnitude of the dipole moment. Dipole moments, as we shall see in Section 1.19, are very useful quantities in accounting for physical properties of compounds.

PROBLEM 1.10

Give the direction of the dipole moment (if any) for each of the following molecules:

(a) HF ,   (b) IBr,   (c) Br_2,   (d) F_2

1.19 POLAR AND NONPOLAR MOLECULES

In the discussion of dipole moments in Section 1.18, our attention was restricted to simple diatomic molecules. Any *diatomic* molecule in which the two atoms are *different* (and thus have different electronegativities) will, of necessity, have a dipole moment. If we examine Table 1.5, however, we find that a number of molecules (e.g.,

TABLE 1.5   Dipole moments of some simple molecules

FORMULA	μ (D)	FORMULA	μ (D)
H_2	0	CH_4	0
Cl_2	0	CH_3Cl	1.87
HF	1.91	CH_2Cl_2	1.55
HCl	1.08	$CHCl_3$	1.02
HBr	0.80	CCl_4	0
HI	0.42	NH_3	1.47
BF_3	0	NF_3	0.24
CO_2	0	H_2O	1.85

CCl_4, CO_2) consist of more than two atoms, have *polar* bonds, *but have no dipole moment.* Now that we have an understanding of the shapes of molecules we can understand how this can occur.

Consider a molecule of carbon tetrachloride (CCl_4). Because the electronegativity of chlorine is greater than that of carbon, each of the carbon–chlorine bonds in CCl_4 is polar. Each chlorine atom has a partial negative charge, and the carbon atom is considerably positive. Because a molecule of carbon tetrachloride is tetrahedral (Fig. 1.26), however, *the center of positive charge and the center of negative charge coincide, and the molecule has no net dipole moment.*

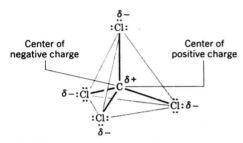

FIGURE 1.26 Charge distribution in carbon tetrachloride.

This result can be illustrated in a slightly different way: If we use arrows (+→) to represent the direction of polarity of each bond, we get the arrangement of bond moments shown in Fig. 1.27. Since the bond moments are vectors of equal magnitude arranged tetrahedrally, their effects cancel. Their vector sum is zero. The molecule has *no net dipole moment.*

Cl

Cl—C—Cl

Cl

$\mu = 0$ D

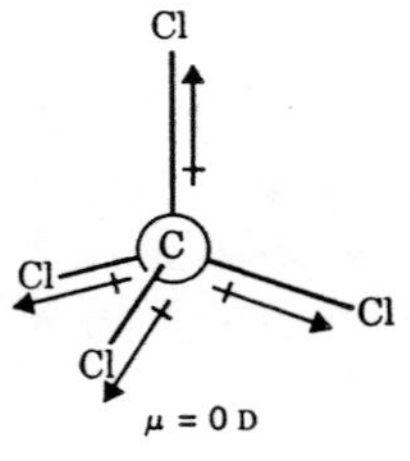

FIGURE 1.27 A tetrahedral orientation of equal bond moments causes their effects to cancel.

The chloromethane molecule (CH_3Cl) has a net dipole moment of 1.87 D. Since carbon and hydrogen have electronegativities (Table 1.2) that are nearly the same, the contribution of three C—H bonds to the net dipole is negligible. The electronegativity difference between carbon and chlorine is large, however, and this highly polar C—Cl bond accounts for most of the dipole moment of CH_3Cl (Fig. 1.28).

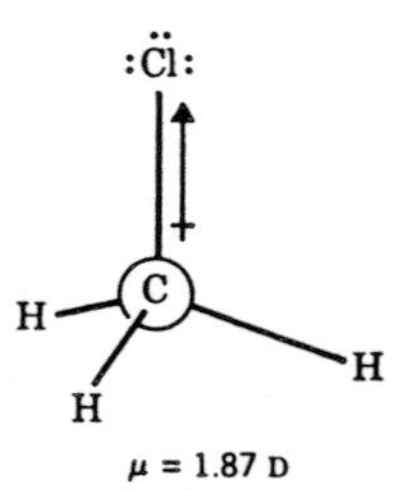

:Cl:

H—C—H

H

$\mu = 1.87$ D

FIGURE 1.28 The dipole moment of chloromethane arises mainly from the highly polar carbon–chlorine bond.

PROBLEM 1.11

Boron trifluoride (BF_3) has no dipole moment ($\mu = 0$). Explain how this observation confirms the geometry of BF_3 predicted by VSEPR theory.

PROBLEM 1.12

Tetrachloroethene ($CCl_2{=}CCl_2$) does not have a dipole moment. Explain this fact on the basis of the shape of $CCl_2{=}CCl_2$.

PROBLEM 1.13

Sulfur dioxide (SO_2) has a dipole moment ($\mu = 1.63$ D); on the other hand, carbon dioxide (CO_2) has no dipole moment ($\mu = 0$). What do these facts indicate about the geometries of the two molecules?

Unshared pairs of electrons make large contributions to the dipole moments of water and ammonia. Because an unshared pair has no atom attached to it to partially neutralize its negative charge, an unshared electron pair contributes a large moment directed away from the central atom (Fig. 1.29). (The O—H and N—H moments are also appreciable.)

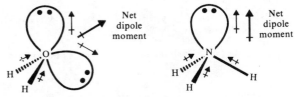

FIGURE 1.29   Bond moments and the resulting dipole moment of water and ammonia.

PROBLEM 1.14

Using a three-dimensional formula, show the direction of the dipole moment of CH_3OH.

PROBLEM 1.15

Trichloromethane ($CHCl_3$, also called *chloroform*) has a larger dipole moment than $CFCl_3$. Use three-dimensional structures and bond moments to explain this fact.

1.20 REPRESENTATION OF STRUCTURAL FORMULAS

Organic chemists use a variety of ways to write structural formulas. The most common types of representations are shown in Fig. 1.30. The **dot structure** shows all of the valence electrons, but writing it is tedious and time consuming. The other representations are more convenient and are, therefore, more often used.

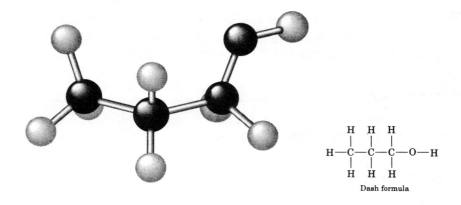

$$CH_3CH_2CH_2OH$$
Condensed formula

FIGURE 1.30 Structural formulas for propyl alcohol.

In fact, we often omit unshared pairs when we write formulas unless there is a reason to include them. For example,

Dot structure = Dash formula = CH_3OCH_3
Condensed formula

1.20A Dash Structural Formulas

If we look at the model for propyl alcohol given in Fig. 1.30 and compare it with the formulas given there, we find that the chain of atoms is straight in all the formulas. In the model, which corresponds more accurately to the actual shape of the molecule, the chain of atoms is not at all straight. Also of importance is this: ***Atoms joined by single bonds can rotate relatively freely with respect to one another.*** (We discuss this point further in Section 2.2B.) This relatively free rotation means that the chain of atoms in propyl alcohol can assume a variety of arrangements like those that follow:

It also means that all of the dash structures that follow are *equivalent* and all represent propyl alcohol. (Notice that in these formulas we represent the bond angles as being 90° not 109.5°. This convention is followed simply for convenience in printing.)

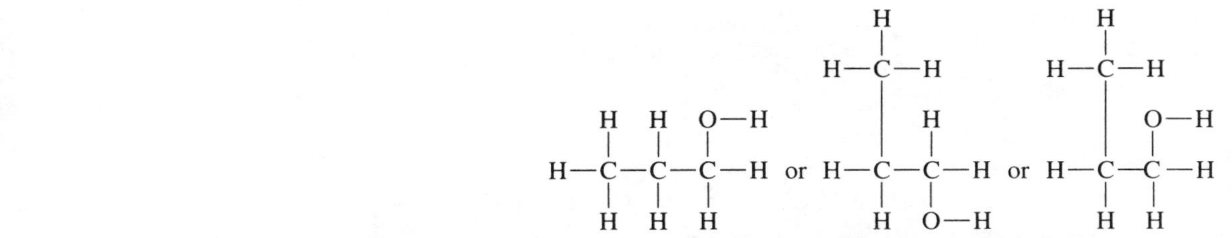

$$
\begin{array}{ccc}
& H & H \\
& | & | \\
& H-C-H & H-C-H \\
H \ \ H \ \ O-H & | & | \\
| \ \ \ | \ \ \ | & H & O-H \\
H-C-C-C-H \quad \text{or} \quad & H-C-C-H \quad \text{or} \quad & H-C-C-H \\
| \ \ \ | \ \ \ | & | \ \ \ | & | \ \ \ | \\
H \ \ H \ \ H & H \ \ O-H & H \ \ H
\end{array}
$$

Equivalent dash formulas for propyl alcohol

Structural formulas such as these indicate the way in which the atoms are attached to each other and *are not* representations of the actual shapes of the molecule. They show what is called the **connectivity** of the atoms. *Constitutional isomers (Section 1.3A) have different connectivity, and, therefore, must have different structural formulas.*

Consider the compound called isopropyl alcohol, whose formula we might write in a variety of ways:

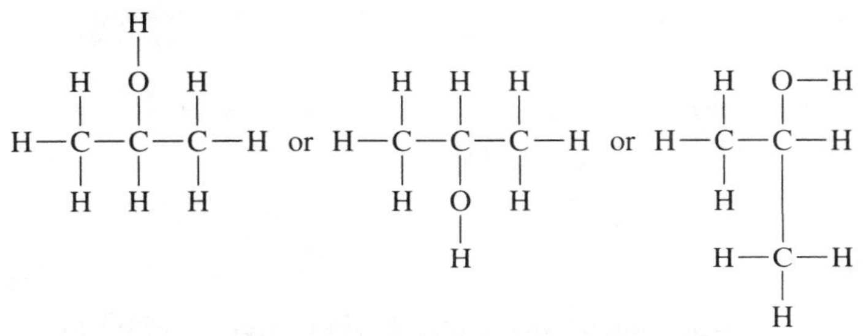

Equivalent dash formulas for isopropyl alcohol

Isopropyl alcohol is a constitutional isomer (Section 1.3A) of propyl alcohol because its atoms are connected in a different order and both compounds have the same molecular formula, C_3H_8O. In isopropyl alcohol the OH group is attached to the central carbon; in propyl alcohol it is attached to an end carbon.

One other point: In problems you will often be asked to write structural formulas for all the isomers with a given molecular formula. Do not make the error of writing several equivalent formulas, like those that we have just shown, mistaking them for different constitutional isomers.

PROBLEM 1.16 _____

There are actually three constitutional isomers with the molecular formula C_3H_8O. We have seen two of them in propyl alcohol and isopropyl alcohol. Write a dash formula for the third isomer.

1.20B Condensed Structural Formulas

Condensed structural formulas are easier to write than dash formulas and, when we become familiar with them, they will impart all the information that is contained in the dash structure. In condensed formulas all of the hydrogen atoms that are attached to a particular carbon are usually written immediately after that carbon. In fully condensed formulas, all of the atoms that are attached to the carbon are usually written immediately after that carbon. For example,

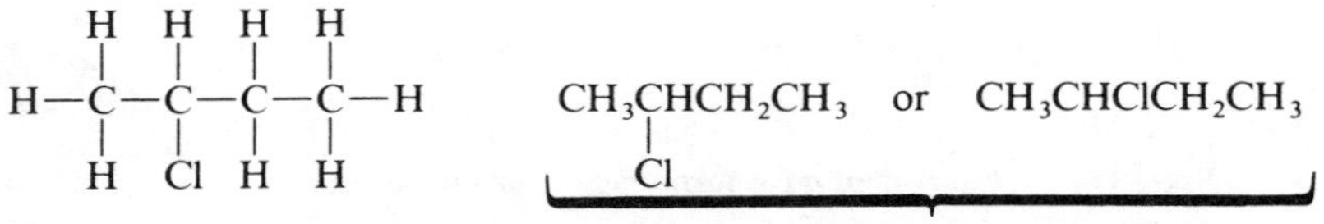

    Dash formula   **Condensed formulas**

$CH_3CHCH_2CH_3$ or $CH_3CHClCH_2CH_3$

The condensed formula for isopropyl alcohol can be written in four different ways:

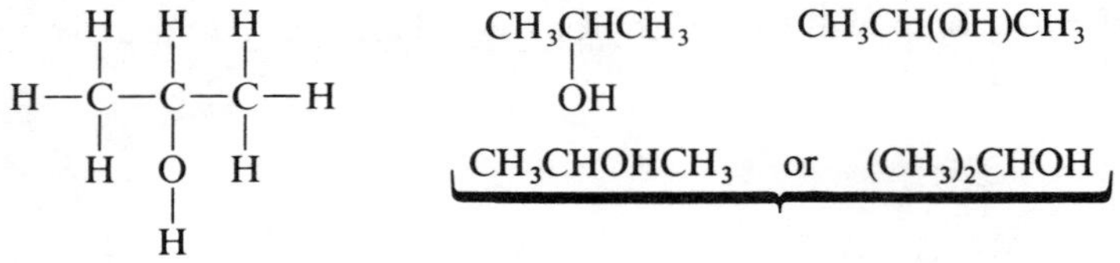

CH_3CHCH_3 $CH_3CH(OH)CH_3$

$CH_3CHOHCH_3$ or $(CH_3)_2CHOH$

    Dash formula   **Condensed formulas**

SAMPLE PROBLEM

Write a condensed structural formula for the compound that follows:

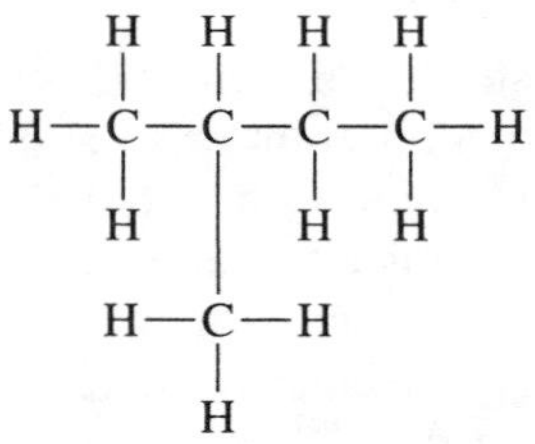

ANSWER:

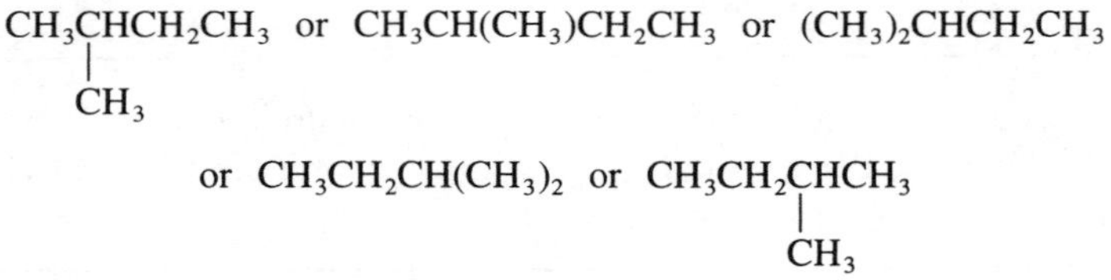

$CH_3CHCH_2CH_3$ or $CH_3CH(CH_3)CH_2CH_3$ or $(CH_3)_2CHCH_2CH_3$

CH_3

or $CH_3CH_2CH(CH_3)_2$ or $CH_3CH_2CHCH_3$

CH_3

1.20C Cyclic Molecules

Organic compounds not only have their carbon atoms arranged in chains, they can also have them arranged in rings. The compound called cyclopropane has its carbon atoms arranged in a three-membered ring.

Formulas for cyclopropane

1.20D Bond-Line Formulas

More and more organic chemists are using a very simplified formula called a **bond-line formula** to represent structural formulas. The bond-line representation is the quickest of all to write because it shows only the carbon skeleton. The number of hydrogen atoms necessary to fulfill the carbon atoms' valences are assumed to be present, but we do not write them in. Other atoms (e.g., O, Cl, N) *are* written in. Each intersection of two or more lines and the end of a line represents a carbon atom unless some other atom is written in

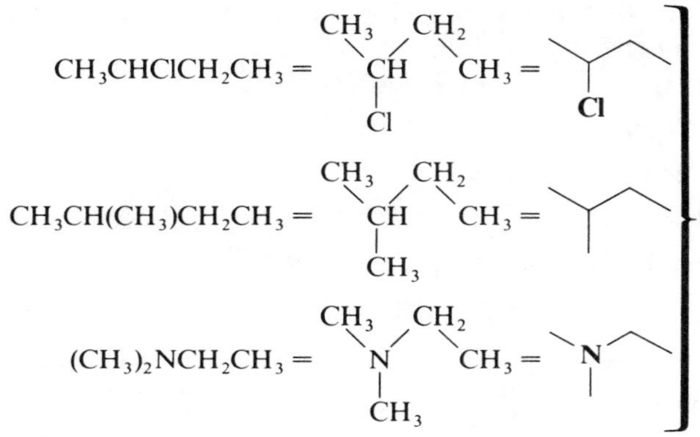

Bond-line formulas

Bond-line formulas are often used for cyclic compounds:

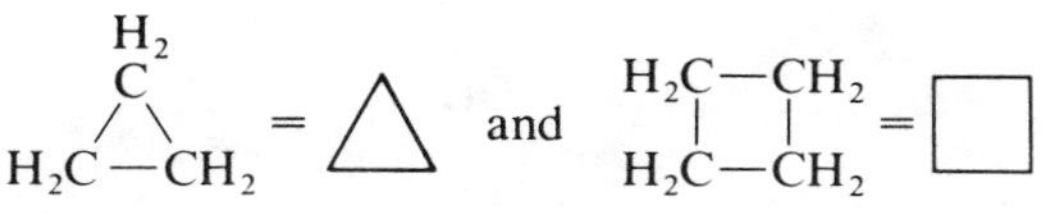

Multiple bonds are also indicated in bond-line formulas. For example,

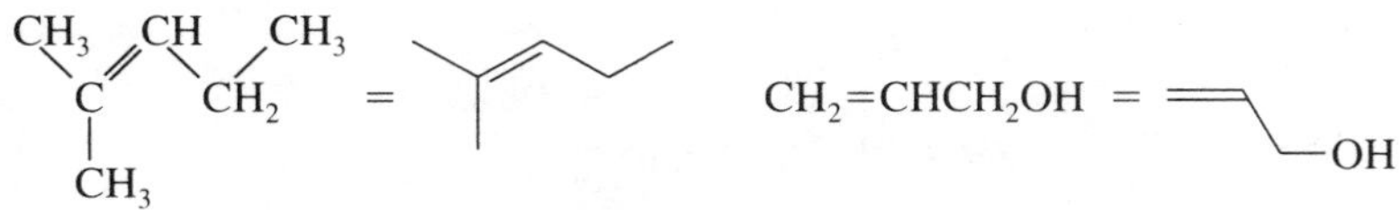

$CH_2=CHCH_2OH$ =

SAMPLE PROBLEM

Write the bond-line formula for $CH_3CHCH_2CH_2CH_2OH$.
$|$
CH_3

ANSWER:

First, we outline the carbon skeleton, including the OH group as follows:

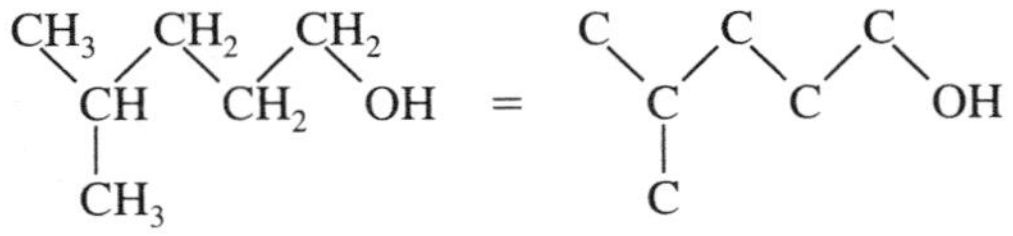

Thus, the bond-line formula is

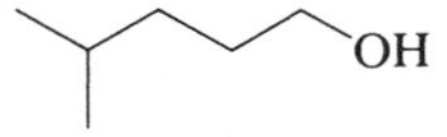

PROBLEM 1.17

Outline the carbon skeleton of the following condensed structural formulas and then write each as a bond-line formula.

(a) $(CH_3)_2CHCH_2CH_3$

(b) $(CH_3)_2CHCH_2CH_2OH$

(c) $(CH_3)_2C{=}CHCH_2CH_3$

(d) $CH_3CH_2CH_2CH_2CH_3$

(e) $CH_3CH_2CH(OH)CH_2CH_3$

(f) $CH_2{=}C(CH_2CH_3)_2$

(g) $CH_3\overset{\displaystyle O}{\overset{\|}{C}}CH_2CH_2CH_2CH_3$

(h) $CH_3CHClCH_2CH(CH_3)_2$

PROBLEM 1.18

Which molecules in Problem 1.17 form sets of constitutional isomers?

PROBLEM 1.19

Write dash formulas for each of the following bond-line formulas:

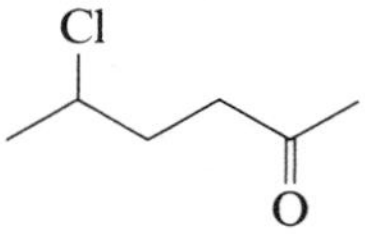

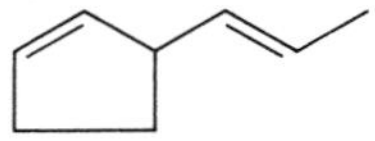

1.20E Three-Dimensional Formulas

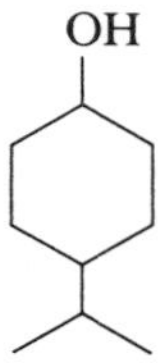

None of the formulas that we have described so far conveys any information about how the atoms of a molecule are arranged in space. There are several types of representations that do this. The type of formula that we shall use is shown in Fig. 1.31. In his representation, bonds that project upward out of the plane of the paper are indicated by a wedge (━◄), those that lie behind the plane are indicated with a dashed wedge (⫽⫽⫽), and those bonds that lie in the plane of the page are indicated by a line (—). Generally we only use three-dimensional formulas when it is necessary to convey information about the shape of the molecule.

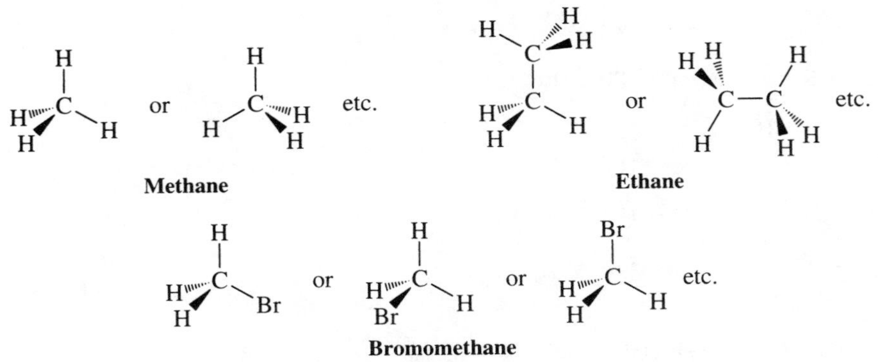

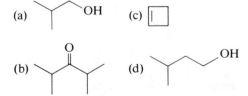

FIGURE 1.31   Three-dimensional formulas using wedge–dashed wedge–line formulas.

PROBLEM 1.20

Write three-dimensional (wedge–dashed wedge–line) representations for each of the following: (a) CH_3Cl, (b) CH_2Cl_2, (c) CH_2BrCl, (d) CH_3CH_2Cl.

ADDITIONAL PROBLEMS

1.21 Which of the following ions possess the electron configuration of a noble gas?

(a) Na^+ (c) F^+ (e) Ca^{2+} (g) O^{2-}

(b) Cl^- (d) H^- (f) S^{2-} (h) Br^+

1.22 Write Lewis structures for each of the following:

(a) $SOCl_2$ (b) $POCl_3$ (c) PCl_5 (d) $HONO_2$ (HNO_3)

1.23 Give the formal charge (if one exists) on each atom of the following:

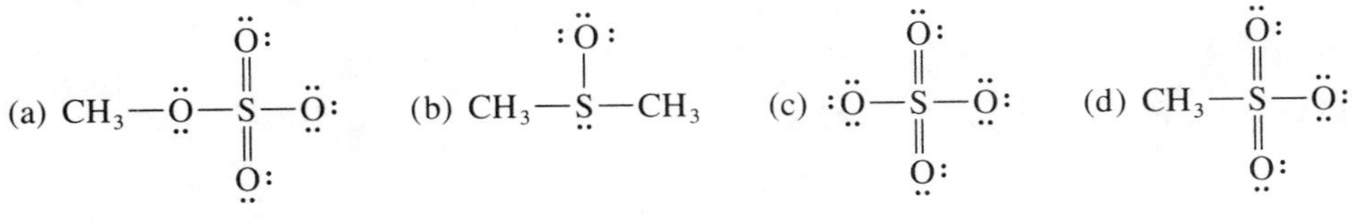

(a) $CH_3\!-\!\ddot{O}\!-\!\overset{\displaystyle \overset{..}{O}:}{\underset{\displaystyle \underset{..}{O}:}{S}}\!-\!\ddot{O}:$ (b) $CH_3\!-\!\overset{\displaystyle :\!\ddot{O}:}{S}\!-\!CH_3$ (c) $:\!\ddot{O}\!-\!\overset{\displaystyle \ddot{O}:}{\underset{\displaystyle \underset{..}{O}:}{S}}\!-\!\ddot{O}:$ (d) $CH_3\!-\!\overset{\displaystyle \overset{..}{O}:}{\underset{\displaystyle \underset{..}{O}:}{S}}\!-\!\ddot{O}:$

1.24 Write a condensed structural formula for each compound given here.

(a) [structure: isopropyl–OH]   (c) [square structure with double bond]

(b) [structure with C=O]   (d) [structure with OH]

1.25 What is the molecular formula for each of the compounds given in Problem 1.24?

1.26 Consider each pair of structural formulas that follow and state whether the two formulas represent the same compound, whether they represent different compounds that are constitutional isomers of each other, or whether they represent different compounds that are not isomeric.

(a) 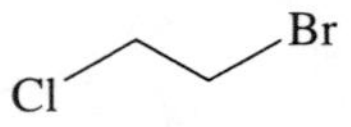 $Cl\diagup\diagdown\diagup Br$ and $Cl\diagdown\diagup\diagdown\diagup Br$

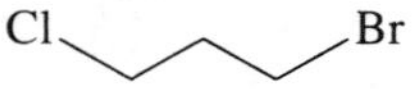

(b) 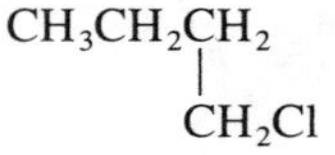 $CH_3CH_2CH_2$ and $ClCH_2CH(CH_3)_2$
    |
    CH_2Cl

(c) 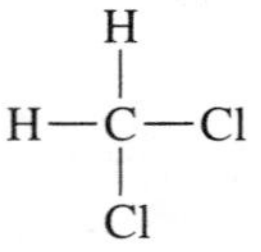
$$\begin{array}{c} H \\ | \\ H-C-Cl \\ | \\ Cl \end{array} \quad and \quad \begin{array}{c} H \\ | \\ Cl-C-Cl \\ | \\ H \end{array}$$

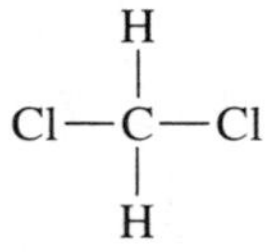

(d) 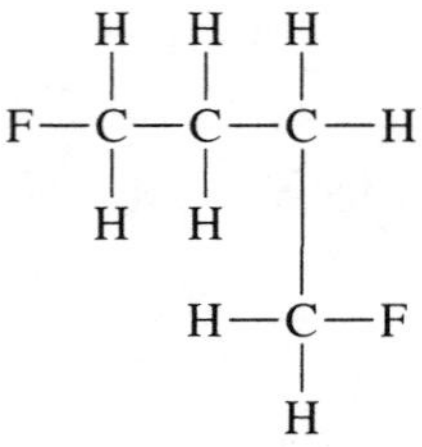
$$\begin{array}{c} H \quad H \quad H \\ | \quad\ | \quad\ | \\ F-C-C-C-H \\ | \quad\ | \\ H \quad H \\ \ \\ H-C-F \\ | \\ H \end{array} \quad and \quad CH_2FCH_2CH_2CH_2F$$

(e) 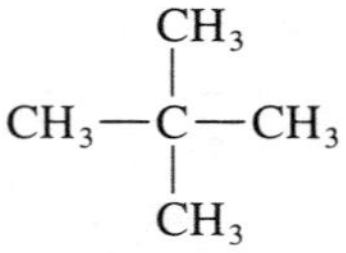
$$\begin{array}{c} CH_3 \\ | \\ CH_3-C-CH_3 \\ | \\ CH_3 \end{array} \quad and \quad (CH_3)_3C-CH_3$$

(f) $CH_2{=}CHCH_2CH_3$ and
$$\begin{array}{c} CH_3 \\ | \\ CH \\ \diagup\ \diagdown \\ H_2C-CH_2 \end{array}$$

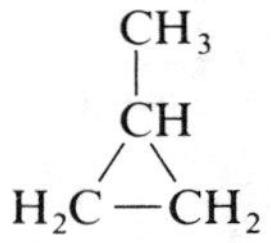

(g) $CH_3OCH_2CH_3$ and
$$\begin{array}{c} O \\ \| \\ CH_3-C-CH_3 \end{array}$$

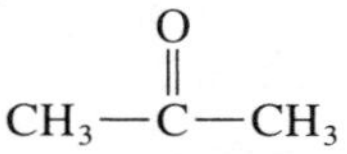

(h) 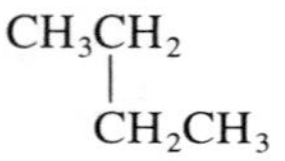 CH_3CH_2 and $CH_3CH_2CH_2CH_3$
    |
    CH_2CH_3

(i) $CH_3OCH_2CH_3$ and
$$\begin{array}{c} O \\ \| \\ C \\ \diagup\ \diagdown \\ H_2C-CH_2 \end{array}$$

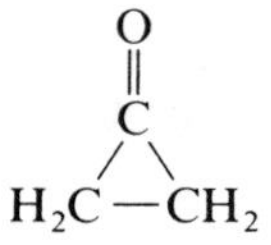

(j) $CH_2ClCHClCH_3$ and $CH_3CHClCH_2Cl$

(k) $CH_3CH_2CHClCH_2Cl$ and CH_3CHCH_2Cl
                                      |
                                  CH_2Cl

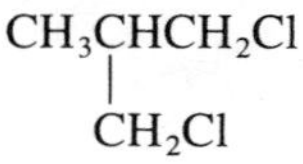

(l) 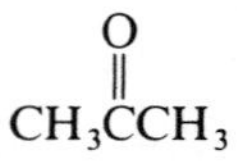
$$\begin{array}{c} O \\ \| \\ CH_3CCH_3 \end{array} \quad and \quad \begin{array}{c} O \\ \| \\ C \\ \diagup\ \diagdown \\ H_2C-CH_2 \end{array}$$

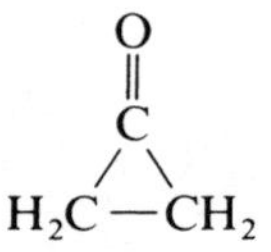

(m) 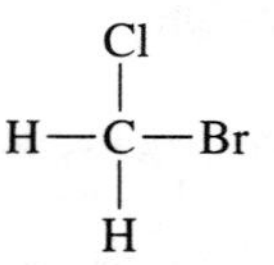
$$\begin{array}{c} Cl \\ | \\ H-C-Br \\ | \\ H \end{array} \quad and \quad \begin{array}{c} H \\ | \\ Cl-C-Br \\ | \\ H \end{array}$$

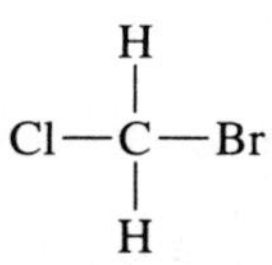

(n) CH_3—$\overset{\displaystyle CH_3}{\underset{\displaystyle H}{\overset{|}{\underset{|}{C}}}}$—H and CH_3—$\overset{\displaystyle H}{\underset{\displaystyle H}{\overset{|}{\underset{|}{C}}}}$—$CH_3$

(o) [three-dimensional structures] and [three-dimensional structures]

(p) [three-dimensional structures] and [three-dimensional structures]

1.27 Write a three-dimensional formula for each of the following molecules. If the molecule has a net dipole moment, indicate its direction with an arrow, ⟶. If the molecule has no net dipole moment, you should so state. (You may ignore the small polarity of C—H bonds in working this and similar problems.)

(a) CH_3F (c) CHF_3 (e) CH_2FCl (g) BeF_2 (i) CH_3OH

(b) CH_2F_2 (d) CF_4 (f) BCl_3 (h) CH_3OCH_3 (j) CH_2O

1.28 Rewrite each of the following using bond-line formulas:

(a) $CH_3CH_2CH_2\overset{\displaystyle O}{\overset{||}{C}}CH_3$

(b) $CH_3\underset{\displaystyle CH_3}{\overset{|}{C}}HCH_2CH_2\underset{\displaystyle CH_3}{\overset{|}{C}}HCH_2CH_3$

(c) $(CH_3)_3CCH_2CH_2CH_2OH$

(d) $CH_3CH_2\underset{\displaystyle CH_3}{\overset{|}{C}}HCH_2\overset{\displaystyle O}{\overset{||}{C}}OH$

(e) CH_2=$CHCH_2CH_2CH$=$CHCH_3$

(f)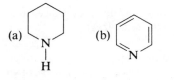

1.29 Write a dash formula for each of the following showing any unshared electron pairs:

(a) [piperidine ring structure]   (b) [pyridine ring structure]   (c) $(CH_3)_2NCH_2CH_3$ (d) [tetrahydrofuran ring structure]

1.30 Write structural formulas of your choice for all of the constitutional isomers with the molecular formula C_4H_8.

1.31 Write structural formulas for at least three constitutional isomers with the molecular formula CH_3NO_2. (In answering this question you should assign a formal charge to any atom that bears one.)

1.32   Chloromethane (CH_3Cl) has a larger dipole moment ($\mu = 1.87$ D) than fluoromethane (CH_3F) ($\mu = 1.81$ D), even though fluorine is more electronegative than chlorine. Explain.

1.33   Cyanic acid ($H\!-\!O\!-\!C\!\equiv\!N$) and isocyanic acid ($H\!-\!N\!=\!C\!=\!O$) differ in the positions of their electrons but their structures do not represent resonance structures.   (a) Explain.   (b) Loss of a proton from cyanic acid yields the same anion as that obtained by loss of a proton from isocyanic acid. Explain.

1.34   Consider a chemical species (either a molecule or an ion) in which a carbon atom forms three single bonds to three hydrogen atoms, and in which the carbon atom possesses no other electrons.   (a) What formal charge would the carbon atom have?   (b) What total charge would the species have?   (c) What shape would you expect this species to have?   (d) What would you expect the hybridization state of the carbon atom to be?

1.35   Consider a chemical species like the one in the previous problem in which a carbon atom forms three single bonds to three hydrogen atoms, but in which the carbon atom possesses an unshared electron pair.   (a) What formal charge would the carbon atom have?   (b) What total charge would the species have?   (c) What shape would you expect this species to have?   (d) What would you expect the hybridization state of the carbon atom to be?

1.36   Consider another chemical species like the ones in the previous problems in which a carbon atom forms three single bonds to three hydrogen atoms, but in which the carbon atom possesses a single unpaired electron.   (a) What formal charge would the carbon atom have?   (b) What total charge would the species have?   (c) Given that the shape of this species is trigonal planar, what would you expect the hybridization state of the carbon atom to be?

1.37   Ozone (O_3) is found in the upper atmosphere where it absorbs highly energetic ultraviolet (UV) radiation and thereby provides the surface of the earth with a protective screen (cf. Section 9.11C). One possible resonance structure for ozone is the following:

$$\ddot{O} \diagup\!\!\!\!\diagdown \;\; :\ddot{O} \qquad \ddot{O}:$$

(a) Assign any necessary formal charges to the atoms in this structure.   (b) Write another equivalent resonance structure for ozone.   (c) What do these resonance structures predict about the relative lengths of the two oxygen-oxygen bonds of ozone?   (d) The structure above, and the one you have written, assumes an angular shape for the ozone molecule. Is this shape consistent with VSEPR theory? Explain your answer.   (e) What experimentally measurable quantity would allow you to prove that the ozone molecule is angular and not linear? Explain.

1.38   Write resonance structures for the azide ion, N_3^-. Explain how these resonance structures account for the fact that both bonds of the azide ion have the same length.

1.39   Write structural formulas of the type indicated: (a) Bond-line formulas for seven constitutional isomers with the formula $C_4H_{10}O$.   (b) Condensed structural formulas for two constitutional isomers with the formula C_2H_7N.   (c) Condensed structural formulas for four constitutional isomers with the formula C_3H_9N.   (d) Bond-line formulas for three constitutional isomers with the formula C_5H_{12}.

1.40   Consider each of the following molecules in turn: (a) dimethyl ether, $(CH_3)_2O$, (b) trimethylamine, $(CH_3)_3N$,   (c) trimethylboron, $(CH_3)_3B$, and   (d) dimethylberyllium, $(CH_3)_2Be$. Describe the hybridization state of the central atom (i.e., O, N, B, or Be) of each molecule, tell what bond angles you would expect at the central atom, and state whether or not the molecule would have a dipole moment.

1.41   Analyze the statement: For a molecule to be polar, the presence of polar bonds is necessary, but it is not a sufficient requirement.

1.42   In Chapter 15 we will learn how the nitronium ion, NO_2^+, forms when concentrated nitric and sulfuric acid are mixed.   (a) Write a Lewis structure for the nitronium ion.   (b) What geometry does VSEPR theory predict for the NO_2^+ ion?   (c) Give a species that has the same number of electrons as NO_2^+.

CHAPTER 2

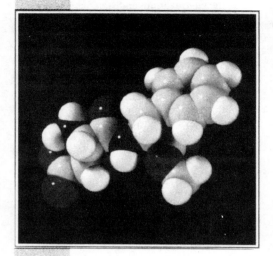

Aspartame
(Problem 2.15)

REPRESENTATIVE CARBON COMPOUNDS

2.1 CARBON–CARBON COVALENT BONDS

Carbon's ability to form strong covalent bonds to other carbon atoms is the single property of the carbon atom that—more than any other—accounts for the very existence of a field of study called organic chemistry. It is this property too that accounts in part for carbon being the element around which most of the molecules of living organisms are constructed. Carbon's ability to form as many as four strong bonds to other carbon atoms and to form strong bonds to hydrogen, oxygen, sulfur, and nitrogen atoms as well, provides the necessary versatility of structure that makes possible the vast number of different molecules required for complex living organisms.

2.2 METHANE AND ETHANE: REPRESENTATIVE ALKANES

Methane (CH_4) and ethane (C_2H_6) are two members of a broad family of organic compounds called **hydrocarbons.** Hydrocarbons, as the name implies, are compounds whose molecules contain only carbon and hydrogen atoms. Methane and ethane also belong to a subgroup of hydrocarbons known as **alkanes** whose members do not have multiple bonds between carbon atoms. *Hydrocarbons whose molecules have a carbon–carbon double bond* are called *alkenes,* and *those with a carbon–carbon* **triple bond** are called *alkynes.* Hydrocarbons that contain a special ring that we shall introduce in Section 2.7 and study in Chapter 14 are called aromatic hydrocarbons.

Generally speaking, compounds such as the alkanes, whose molecules contain only single bonds, are referred to as **saturated compounds** because these compounds contain the maximum number of hydrogen atoms that the carbon compound can possess. Compounds with multiple bonds, such as alkenes, alkynes, and aromatic hydrocarbons are called **unsaturated compounds,** because they possess fewer than the maximum number of hydrogen atoms, and are capable of reacting with hydrogen under the proper conditions. We shall have more to say about this in Chapter 7.

2.2A Sources of Methane

Methane was one major component of the early atmosphere of this planet. Methane is still found in the atmosphere of Earth, but no longer in appreciable amounts. It is, however, a major component of the atmosphere of Jupiter, Saturn, Uranus, and Neptune. Recently, methane has also been detected in interstellar space—far from the Earth (10^{16} km) in a celestial body that emits radio waves in the constellation Orion.

On Earth, methane is the major component of natural gas, along with ethane and other low molecular weight alkanes. The United States is currently using its large reserves of natural gas at a very high rate. Because the components of natural gas are important in industry, efforts are being made to develop coal-gasification processes to provide alternative sources.

Some living organisms produce methane from carbon dioxide and hydrogen.

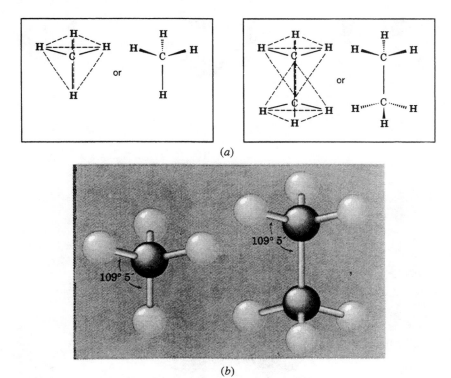

(a)

(b)

FIGURE 2.1 (a) Two ways of representing the structures of methane and ethane that show the tetrahedral arrangements of the atoms around carbon. (b) Ball-and-stick models of methane and ethane.

These very primitive creatures called *methanogens* may be the Earth's oldest organisms, and they may represent a separate form of evolutionary development. Methanogens can survive only in an anaerobic (i.e., oxygen-free) environment. They have
been found in ocean trenches, in mud, in sewage, and in cows' stomachs.

2.2B The Structure of Ethane

The bond angles at the carbon atoms of ethane, and of all alkanes, are also tetrahedral
like those in methane. In the case of ethane (Fig. 2.1), each carbon atom is at one
corner of the other carbon atom's tetrahedron; hydrogen atoms are situated at the other
three corners.

A satisfactory model for ethane (and for other alkanes as well) can be provided by
sp^3-hybridized carbon atoms (Section 1.13). Figure 2.2 shows how we might imagine
the bonding molecular orbitals of an ethane molecule being constructed from two
sp^3-hybridized carbon atoms and six hydrogen atoms.

The carbon–carbon bond of ethane is a *sigma bond* (Section 1.13), formed by two
overlapping sp^3 orbitals. (The carbon–hydrogen bonds are also sigma bonds. They are
formed from overlapping carbon sp^3 orbitals and hydrogen s orbitals.)

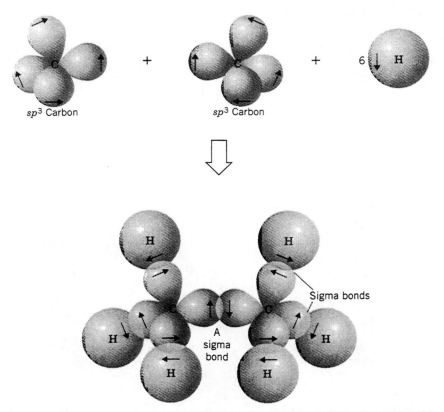

FIGURE 2.2 The formation of the bonding molecular orbitals of ethane from two sp^3-hy-
bridized carbon atoms and six hydrogen atoms. All of the bonds are sigma bonds. (Antibonding sigma molecular orbitals—called σ^* orbitals—are formed in each instance as well, but
for simplicity these are not shown.)

Because a sigma bond (i.e., any nonmultiple bond) has circular symmetry along the bond axis, *rotation of groups joined by a single bond does not usually require a large amount of energy.* Consequently, groups joined by single bonds rotate relatively freely with respect to one another. (We discuss this point further in Section 4.6.)

2.3 ALKENES: COMPOUNDS CONTAINING THE CARBON– CARBON DOUBLE BOND; ETHENE (ETHYLENE) AND PROPENE

The carbon atoms of virtually all of the molecules that we have considered so far have used their four valence electrons to form four single covalent bonds to four other atoms. We find, however, that many important organic compounds exist in which carbon atoms share more than two electrons with another atom. In molecules of these compounds some bonds that are formed are multiple covalent bonds. When two carbon atoms share two pairs of electrons, for example, the result is a carbon–carbon double bond.

$$\ddot{C} \!:\! \ddot{C} \quad \text{or} \quad {\Large {}_{/}^{\backslash}C{=}C_{\backslash}^{/}}$$

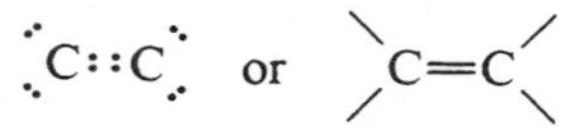

Hydrocarbons whose molecules contain a carbon–carbon double bond are called **alkenes.** Ethene (C_2H_4) and propene (C_3H_6) are both alkenes. (Ethene is also called ethylene, and propene is sometimes called propylene.)

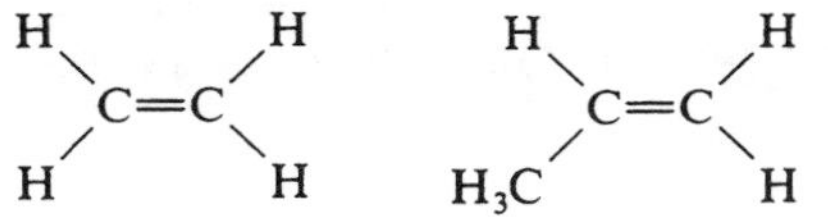

$$\begin{array}{cc} \text{H}\diagdown\diagup\text{H} \\ \text{C}{=}\text{C} \\ \text{H}\diagup\diagdown\text{H} \\ \textbf{Ethene} \end{array} \qquad \begin{array}{cc} \text{H}\diagdown\diagup\text{H} \\ \text{C}{=}\text{C} \\ \text{H}_3\text{C}\diagup\diagdown\text{H} \\ \textbf{Propene} \end{array}$$

In ethene the only carbon–carbon bond is a double bond. Propene has one carbon–carbon single bond and one carbon–carbon double bond.

The spatial arrangement of the atoms of alkenes is different from that of alkanes. The six atoms of ethene are coplanar, and the arrangement of atoms around each carbon atom is triangular (Fig. 2.3). In Section 2.4 we shall see how the structure of ethene can be explained on the basis of the same kind of orbital hybridization, sp^2, that we learned about for BH_3 (Section 1.14).

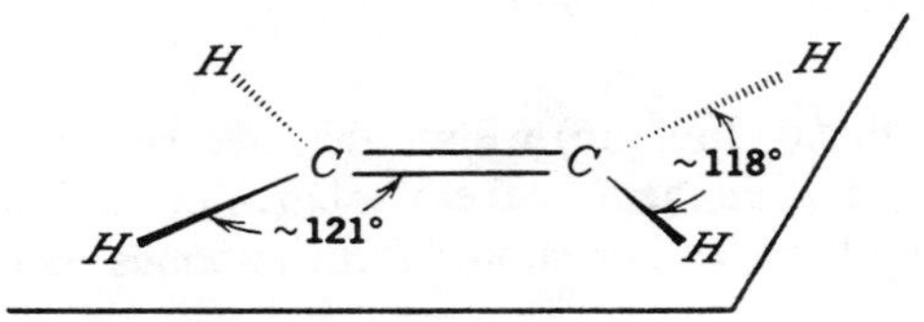

FIGURE 2.3 The structure and bond angles of ethene.

2.4 ORBITAL HYBRIDIZATION AND THE STRUCTURE OF ALKENES

A satisfactory model for the carbon–carbon double bond can be based on sp^2-hybridized carbon atoms.*

The mathematical mixing of orbitals that furnish the sp^2 orbitals for our model can be visualized in the way shown in Fig. 2.4. The $2s$ orbital is mathematically mixed (or hybridized) with two of the $2p$ orbitals. (The hybridization procedure applies only to the orbitals, not to the electrons.) One $2p$ orbital is left unhybridized. One electron is then placed in each of the sp^2-hybrid orbitals and one electron remains in the $2p$ orbital.

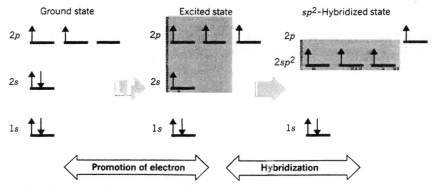

FIGURE 2.4   A process for obtaining sp^2-hybridized carbon atoms.

The three sp^2 orbitals that result from hybridization are directed toward the corners of a regular triangle (with angles of 120° between them). The carbon p orbital that is not hybridized is perpendicular to the plane of the triangle formed by the hybrid sp^2 orbitals (Fig. 2.5).

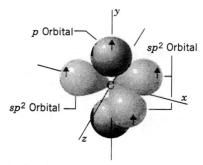

FIGURE 2.5   An sp^2-hybridized carbon atom.

In our model for ethene (Fig. 2.6) we see that two sp^2-hybridized carbon atoms form a sigma (σ) bond between them by the overlap of one sp^2 orbital from each. The remaining sp^2 orbitals of the carbon atoms form σ bonds to four hydrogen atoms

*An alternative model for the carbon–carbon bond is discussed in an article by W. E. Palke, *J. Am. Chem. Soc.*, **1986,** *108,* 6543–6544.

through overlap with the $1s$ orbitals of the hydrogen atoms. These five bonds account for 10 of the 12 bonding electrons of ethene, and they are called the **σ-bond framework.** The bond angles that we would predict on the basis of sp^2-hybridized carbon atoms (120° all around) are quite close to the bond angles that are actually found (Fig. 2.3).

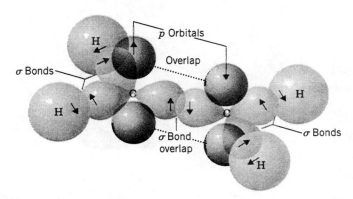

FIGURE 2.6 A model for the bonding molecular orbitals of ethene formed from two sp^2-hybridized carbon atoms and four hydrogen atoms.

The remaining two bonding electrons in our model are located in the p orbitals of each carbon atom. We can better visualize how these p orbitals interact with each other if we replace the σ bonds by lines. This is shown in Fig. 2.7. We see that the parallel p orbitals *overlap above and below the plane of the σ framework.* This sideways overlap of the p orbitals results in a new type of covalent bond, known as a **pi (π) bond.** Note the difference in shape of the bonding molecular orbital of a π bond as contrasted to that of a σ bond. A σ bond has cylindrical symmetry about a line connecting the two bonded nuclei. A π bond has a nodal plane passing through the two bonded nuclei.

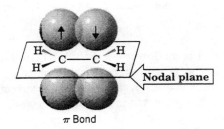

FIGURE 2.7 The overlapping p orbitals of ethene to make a π bond.

According to molecular orbital theory, both bonding and antibonding π molecular orbitals are formed when p orbitals interact in this way to form a π bond. The bonding π orbital (Fig. 2.8) results when p-orbital lobes of like signs overlap; the antibonding π orbital is formed when p-orbital lobes of opposite signs overlap.

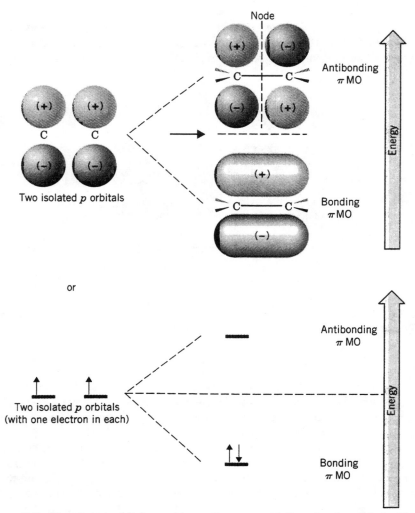

FIGURE 2.8 How two p orbitals combine to form two π (pi) molecular orbitals. The bonding MO is of lower energy. The higher energy antibonding MO contains an additional node. (Both orbitals have a node in the plane containing the C and H atoms.)

The bonding π orbital is the lower energy orbital and contains both π electrons (with opposite spins) in the ground state of the molecule. The region of greatest probability of finding the electrons in the bonding π orbital is a region generally situated above and below the plane of the σ-bond framework between the two carbon atoms. The antibonding π^* orbital is of higher energy, and it is not occupied by electrons when the molecule is in the ground state. It can become occupied, however, if the molecule absorbs light of the right frequency and an electron is promoted from the lower energy level to the higher one. The antibonding π^* orbital has a nodal plane between the two carbon atoms.

To summarize: In our model based on orbital hybridization, the carbon–carbon double bond is viewed as consisting of two different kinds of bonds, *a σ bond and a π bond*. The σ bond results from two overlapping sp^2 orbitals end-to-end and is symmetrical about an axis linking the two carbon atoms. The π bond results from a sideways overlap of two p orbitals; it has a nodal plane like a p orbital. In the ground state the electrons of the π bond are located between the two carbon atoms but generally above and below the plane of the σ-bond framework.

Electrons of the π bond have greater energy than electrons of the σ bond. The relative energies of the σ and π molecular orbitals (with the electrons in the ground state) are shown in the following figure. (The σ^* orbital is the antibonding sigma orbital.)

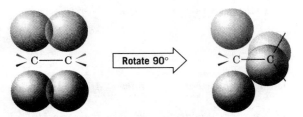

2.4A Restricted Rotation and the Double Bond

The $\sigma-\pi$ model for the carbon–carbon double bond also accounts for an important property of the double bond: *There is a large barrier to free rotation associated with groups joined by a double bond.* Maximum overlap between the p orbitals of a π bond occurs when the axes of the p orbitals are exactly parallel. Rotating one carbon of the double bond 90° (Fig. 2.9) breaks the π bond, for then the axes of the p orbitals are perpendicular and there is no net overlap between them. Estimates based on thermochemical calculations indicate that the strength of the π bond is 63 kcal mol^{-1}. This, then, is the barrier to rotation of the double bond. It is markedly higher than the rotational barrier of groups joined by carbon–carbon single bonds (3–6 kcal mol^{-1}). While groups joined by single bonds rotate relatively freely at room temperature, those joined by double bonds do not.

FIGURE 2.9 Rotation of a carbon atom of a double bond through an angle of 90° results in the breaking of the π bond.

2.4B Cis–Trans Isomerism

Restricted rotation of groups joined by a double bond causes a new type of isomerism that we illustrate with the two dichloroethenes written in the following structures.

cis-1,2-Dichloroethene   *trans*-1,2-Dichloroethene

These two compounds are isomers; they are different compounds that have the same molecular formula. We can tell that they are different compounds by trying to super-pose a model of one on a model of the other. We find that it cannot be done. By superpose we mean that we place one model on the other *so that all parts of each coincide.*

We indicate that they are different isomers by attaching the prefixes cis or trans to their names (cis, Latin: on this side; trans, Latin: across). *cis*-1,2-Dichloroethene and *trans*-1,2-dichloroethene are not constitutional isomers because the connectivity of the atoms is the same in each. The two compounds **differ only in the arrangement of their atoms in space.** Isomers of this kind are classified formally as **stereoisomers,** but often they are called simply cis–trans isomers. (We shall study stereoisomerism in detail in Chapters 4 and 5.)

The structural requirements for cis–trans isomerism will become clear if we consider a few additional examples. 1,1-Dichloroethene and 1,1,2-trichloroethene do not show this type of isomerism.

1,1-Dichloroethene
(no cis–trans isomerism)

1,1,2-Trichloroethene
(no cis–trans isomerism)

1,2-Difluoroethene and 1,2-dichloro-1,2-difluoroethene do exist as cis–trans isomers. Notice that we designate the isomer with two identical groups on the same side as being cis.

cis-**1,2-Difluoroethene**   *trans*-**1,2-Difluoroethene**

cis-**1,2-Dichloro-1,2-difluoroethene**   *trans*-**1,2-Dichloro-1,2-difluoroethene**

Clearly, then, *cis–trans isomerism of this type is not possible if one carbon atom of the double bond bears two identical groups.*

PROBLEM 2.1

Which of the following alkenes can exist as cis–trans isomers? Write their structures.

(a) CH_2=$CHCH_2CH_3$ (c) CH_2=$C(CH_3)_2$

(b) CH_3CH=$CHCH_3$ (d) CH_3CH_2CH=$CHCl$

Cis–trans isomers have different physical properties. They have different melting points and boiling points, and often cis–trans isomers differ markedly in the magni-

TABLE 2.1   Physical properties of cis–trans isomers

COMPOUND	MELTING POINT (°C)	BOILING POINT (°C)	DIPOLE MOMENT (D)
cis-1,2-Dichloroethene	− 80	60	1.90
trans-1,2-Dichloroethene	− 50	48	0
cis-1,2-Dibromoethene	− 53	112.5	1.35
trans-1,2-Dibromoethene	− 6	108	0

tude of their dipole moments. Table 2.1 summarizes some of the physical properties of two pairs of cis–trans isomers.

PROBLEM 2.2

Indicate the direction of the important bond moments in each of the following compounds (neglect C—H bonds). You should also give the direction of the net dipole moment for the molecule. If there is no net dipole moment state that $\mu = 0$.

(a) cis-CHF=CHF   (c) CH_2=CF_2

(b) trans-CHF=CHF   (d) CF_2=CF_2

PROBLEM 2.3

Write structural formulas for all of the alkenes with the formula   (a) $C_2H_2Br_2$, and   (b) with the formula $C_2Br_2Cl_2$. In each instance designate compounds that are cis–trans isomers of each other.

2.5 ALKYNES: COMPOUNDS CONTAINING THE CARBON–CARBON TRIPLE BOND; ETHYNE (ACETYLENE) AND PROPYNE

Hydrocarbons in which two carbon atoms share three pairs of electrons between them, and are thus bonded by a triple bond, are called **alkynes.** The two simplest alkynes are ethyne and propyne.

$$H—C≡C—H \qquad CH_3—C≡C—H$$
Ethyne   **Propyne**
(acetylene)   **(C_3H_4)**
(C_2H_2)

Ethyne, a compound that is also called acetylene, consists of linear molecules. The H—C≡C bond angles of ethyne molecules are 180°.

$$H—C≡C—H$$
180°   180°

2.6 ORBITAL HYBRIDIZATION AND THE STRUCTURE OF ALKYNES

We can account for the structure of ethyne on the basis of orbital hybridization as we did for ethane and ethene. In our model for ethane (Section 2.2B) we saw that the carbon orbitals are sp^3 hybridized, and in our model for ethene (Section 2.4) we saw that they are sp^2 hybridized. In our model for ethyne we shall see that the carbon atoms are *sp hybridized* and resemble the hybrid orbitals of BeH_2 (Section 1.15).

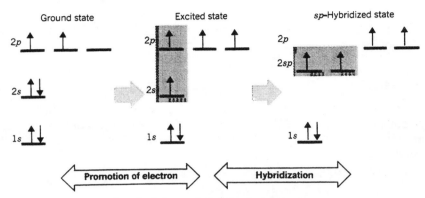

FIGURE 2.10 A process for obtaining *sp*-hybridized carbon atoms.

The mathematical process for obtaining the *sp*-hybrid orbitals of ethyne can be visualized in the following way (Fig. 2.10). The 2s orbital and one 2p orbital of carbon are hybridized to form two *sp* orbitals. The remaining two 2p orbitals are not hybridized. Calculations show that the *sp*-hybrid orbitals have their large positive lobes oriented at an angle of 180° with respect to each other. The 2p orbitals that were not hybridized are perpendicular to the axis that passes through the center of the two *sp* orbitals (Fig. 2.11).

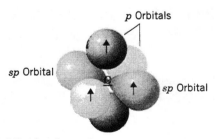

FIGURE 2.11 An *sp*-hybridized carbon atom.

We envision the bonding molecular orbitals of ethyne being formed in the following way (Fig. 2.12). Two carbon atoms overlap *sp* orbitals to form a sigma bond between them (this is one bond of the triple bond). The remaining two *sp* orbitals at each carbon atom overlap with *s* orbitals from hydrogen atoms to produce two sigma C—H bonds. The two *p* orbitals on each carbon atom also overlap side to side to form two π bonds. These are the other two bonds of the triple bond. If we replace the σ bonds of this illustration with lines, it is easier to see how the *p* orbitals overlap. Thus we see that the carbon–carbon triple bond consists of two π bonds and one σ bond.

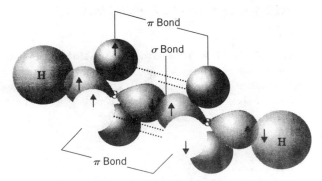

FIGURE 2.12 Formation of the bonding molecular orbitals of ethyne from two *sp*-hybridized carbon atoms and two hydrogen atoms. (Antibonding orbitals are formed as well but these have been omitted for simplicity.)

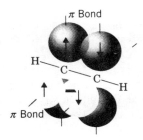

The two π bonds create a cylinder of π electrons around the central sigma bond; as a result there is no restriction of rotation of groups joined by a triple bond.

2.6A Bond Lengths of Ethyne, Ethene, and Ethane

The carbon–carbon triple bond is shorter than the carbon–carbon double bond, and the carbon–carbon double bond is shorter than the carbon–carbon single bond. The carbon–hydrogen bonds of ethyne are also shorter than those of ethene, and the carbon–hydrogen bonds of ethene are shorter than those of ethane. This illustrates a general principle: *The shortest C—H bonds are associated with those carbon orbitals with the greatest s character.* The *sp* orbitals of ethyne—50% *s* (and 50% *p*) in character—form the shortest C—H bonds. The *sp³* orbitals of ethane—25% *s* (and 75% *p*) in character—form the longest C—H bonds. The differences in bond lengths and bond angles of ethyne, ethene, and ethane are summarized in Fig. 2.13.

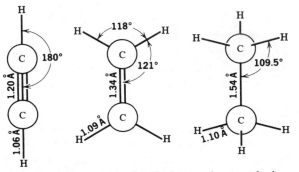

FIGURE 2.13 Bond angles and bond lengths of ethyne, ethene, and ethane.

2.7 BENZENE: A REPRESENTATIVE AROMATIC HYDROCARBON

In Chapter 14 we shall study in detail a group of unsaturated cyclic hydrocarbons known as **aromatic compounds.** The compound known as **benzene** is the prototypical aromatic compound. Benzene can be written as a six-membered ring with alternating single and double bonds, called a Kekulé structure after August Kekulé (Section 1.3), who first conceived of this representation.

**Kekulé structure
for benzene**

or

**Bond line representation
of Kekulé structure**

Even though the Kekulé structure is frequently used for benzene compounds, there is much evidence that this representation is inadequate and incorrect. For example, if benzene had alternating single and double bonds as the Kekulé structure indicates, we would expect the lengths of the carbon–carbon bonds around the ring to be alternately longer and shorter, as we typically find with carbon–carbon single and double bonds (Fig. 2.3). In fact, the carbon–carbon bonds of benzene are all the same length (1.39 Å), a value in between that of a carbon–carbon single bond and a carbon–carbon double bond. There are two ways of dealing with this problem: with resonance theory or with molecular orbital theory.

If we use resonance theory, we visualize benzene as being represented by either of two equivalent Kekulé structures:

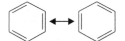

**Two contributing Kekulé structures
for benzene**

**A representation of the
resonance hybrid**

Based on the principles of resonance theory (Section 1.8) we recognize that benzene cannot be represented adequately by either structure, but that, instead, *it should be visualized as a hybrid of the two structures.* We represent this hybrid by a hexagon with a circle in the middle. Resonance theory, therefore, solves the problem we encountered in understanding how all of the carbon–carbon bonds are the same length. According to resonance theory, the bonds are not alternating single and double bonds, they are a resonance hybrid of the two: Any bond that is a single bond in the first contributor is a double bond in the second, and vice versa. Therefore, we should expect *all of the carbon–carbon bonds to be the same,* to be one- and one-half bonds, and to have a bond length in between that of a single bond and a double bond. That is, of course, what we actually find.

In the molecular orbital explanation, which we shall describe in much more depth in Chapter 14, we begin by recognizing that the carbon atoms of the benzene ring are sp^2 hybridized. Therefore, each carbon has a p orbital that has one lobe above the plane of the ring and one lobe below.

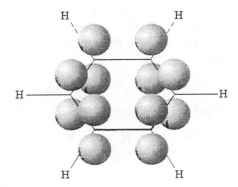

Although the depiction of *p* orbitals in our illustration does not show this, each lobe of each *p* orbital, above and below the ring, overlaps with the lobe of a *p* orbital on each atom on either side of it. This kind of overlap of *p* orbitals leads to a set of bonding molecular orbitals that encompass all of the carbon atoms of the ring. Therefore, the six electrons associated with these *p* orbitals (one from each) are **delocalized** about all six carbon atoms of the ring. This delocalization of electrons explains how all the carbon–carbon bonds are equivalent and have the same length. In Section 14.7B, when we study nuclear magnetic resonance spectroscopy, we shall present convincing physical evidence for this delocalization of the electrons.

When the benzene ring is attached to some other group of atoms in a molecule, it is called a **phenyl group** and it is represented in several ways:

$$\text{◯— or ◯— or } C_6H_5\text{— or Ph— or } \phi\text{—}$$

Ways of representing a phenyl group

The combination of a phenyl group and a $—CH_2—$ group is called a **benzyl group.**

$$\text{◯—CH}_2\text{— or ◯—CH}_2\text{— or } C_6H_5CH_2\text{—}$$

Ways of representing a benzyl group

2.8 FUNCTIONAL GROUPS

One great advantage of the structural theory is that it enables us to classify the vast number of organic compounds into a relatively small number of families based on their structures. (The end papers inside the front cover of this text give the most important of these families.) The molecules of compounds in a particular family are characterized by the presence of a certain arrangement of atoms called a **functional group.**

A functional group is the part of a molecule where most of its chemical reactions occur. It is the part that effectively determines the compound's chemical properties (and many of its physical properties as well). The functional group of an alkene, for example, is its carbon–carbon double bond. When we study the reactions of alkenes in greater detail in Chapter 8, we shall find that most of the chemical reactions of alkenes are the chemical reactions of the carbon–carbon double bond.

The functional group of an alkyne is its carbon–carbon triple bond. Alkanes do not have a functional group. Their molecules have carbon–carbon single bonds and carbon–hydrogen bonds, but these bonds are present in molecules of almost all organic molecules, and C—C and C—H bonds are, in general, much less reactive than common functional groups.

2.8A Alkyl Groups and the Symbol R

Alkyl groups are the groups that we identify for purposes of naming compounds. They are groups that would be obtained by removing a hydrogen atom from an alkane:

Alkane	*Alkyl Group*	*Abbreviation*
CH_4 **Methane**	CH_3- **Methyl group**	Me—
CH_3CH_3 **Ethane**	CH_3CH_2- or C_2H_5- **Ethyl group**	Et—
$CH_3CH_2CH_3$ **Propane**	$CH_3CH_2CH_2-$ **Propyl group**	Pr—
$CH_3CH_2CH_3$ **Propane**	$CH_3\overset{\mid}{C}HCH_3$ or $CH_3\overset{\overset{CH_3}{\mid}}{C}H-$ **Isopropyl group**	*i*-Pr—

While only one alkyl group can be derived from methane and ethane (the **methyl** and **ethyl** groups, respectively), two groups can be derived from propane. Removal of a hydrogen from one of the end carbon atoms gives a group that is called the **propyl** group; removal of a hydrogen from the middle carbon atom gives a group that is called the **isopropyl** group. The names and structures of these groups are used so frequently in organic chemistry that you should learn them now.

We can simplify much of our future discussion if, at this point, we introduce a symbol that is widely used in designating general structures of organic molecules: The symbol R. *R is used as a general symbol to represent any alkyl group.* For example, R might be a methyl group, an ethyl group, a propyl group, or an isopropyl group.

CH_3-	Methyl	
CH_3CH_2-	Ethyl	All of these can be designated by R
$CH_3CH_2CH_2-$	Propyl	
$CH_3\overset{\mid}{C}HCH_3$	Isopropyl	

Thus, the general formula for an alkane is R—H.

2.9 ALKYL HALIDES OR HALOALKANES

Alkyl halides are compounds in which a halogen atom (fluorine, chlorine, bromine, or iodine) replaces a hydrogen atom of an alkane. For example, CH_3Cl and CH_3CH_2Br are alkyl halides. Alkyl halides are also called **haloalkanes.**

Alkyl halides are classified as being primary (1°), secondary (2°), or tertiary (3°).* **This classification is based on the carbon atom to which the halogen is directly attached.** If the carbon *atom* that bears the halogen is attached to only one other carbon, the carbon atom is said to be a **primary carbon atom** and the alkyl halide is classified as a **primary alkyl halide.** If the carbon that bears the halogen is itself attached to two other carbon atoms, then the carbon is a **secondary carbon** and the alkyl halide is a **secondary alkyl halide.** If the carbon that bears the halogen is attached to three other carbon atoms, then the carbon is a **tertiary carbon** and the alkyl halide is a **tertiary alkyl halide.** Examples of primary, secondary, and tertiary alkyl halides are the following:

1° Carbon

$$H-\overset{\overset{\displaystyle H}{|}}{\underset{\underset{\displaystyle H}{|}}{C}}-\overset{\overset{\displaystyle H}{|}}{\underset{\underset{\displaystyle H}{|}}{C}}-Cl$$

1° Alkyl chloride

2° Carbon

$$H-\overset{\overset{\displaystyle H}{|}}{\underset{\underset{\displaystyle H}{|}}{C}}-\overset{\overset{\displaystyle H}{|}}{\underset{\underset{\displaystyle Cl}{|}}{C}}-\overset{\overset{\displaystyle H}{|}}{\underset{\underset{\displaystyle H}{|}}{C}}-H$$

2° Alkyl chloride

3° Carbon

$$CH_3-\overset{\overset{\displaystyle CH_3}{|}}{\underset{\underset{\displaystyle CH_3}{|}}{C}}-Cl$$

3° Alkyl chloride

PROBLEM 2.4

Write structural formulas (a) for two constitutionally isomeric primary alkyl bromides with the formula C_4H_9Br, (b) for a secondary alkyl bromide, and (c) for a tertiary alkyl bromide with the same formula.

PROBLEM 2.5

Although we shall discuss the naming of organic compounds later when we discuss the individual families in detail, one method of naming alkyl halides is so straightforward that it is worth describing here. We simply name the alkyl group attached to the halogen and add the word *fluoride, chloride, bromide, or iodide.* Write formulas for (a) ethyl fluoride and (b) isopropyl chloride. What are names for (c) $CH_3CH_2CH_2Br$, (d) CH_3CHFCH_3, and (e) C_6H_5I ?

2.10 ALCOHOLS

Methyl alcohol (more systematically called methanol) has the structural formula CH_3OH and is the simplest member of a family of organic compounds known as **alcohols.** The characteristic functional group of this family is the hydroxyl (OH) group attached to a sp^3-hybridized carbon atom. Another example of an alcohol is ethyl alcohol, CH_3CH_2OH (also called ethanol).

$$-\overset{|}{\underset{|}{C}}-\overset{..}{\underset{..}{O}}-H$$

This is the functional group of an alcohol

---

*Although we use the symbols 1°, 2°, 3°, we do not *say* first degree, second degree, and third degree; we say *primary, secondary,* and *tertiary.*

Alcohols may be viewed in two ways structurally: (1) as hydroxy derivatives of alkanes, and (2) as alkyl derivatives of water. Ethyl alcohol, for example, can be seen as an ethane molecule in which one hydrogen has been replaced by a hydroxyl group, or as a water molecule in which one hydrogen has been replaced by an ethyl group.

Ethyl group

CH₃CH₃   CH₃CH₂   H

Ethane   Ethyl alcohol   Water
                (ethanol)

As with alkyl halides, alcohols are classified into three groups: primary (1°), secondary (2°), or tertiary (3°) alcohols. ***This classification is also based on the degree of substitution of the carbon to which the hydroxyl group is directly attached.*** If the carbon has only one other carbon attached to it, the carbon is said to be a **primary carbon** and the alcohol is a **primary alcohol.**

Ethyl alcohol   Geraniol   Benzyl alcohol)
(a 1° alcohol)   (a 1° alcohol with (a 1° alcohol)
                       the odor of roses)

If the carbon atom that bears the hydroxyl group also has two other carbon atoms attached to it, this carbon is called a secondary carbon, and the alcohol is a secondary alcohol, and so on.

(a 2° alcohol)   Menthol
                        (a 2° alcohol found
                        in peppermint oil)

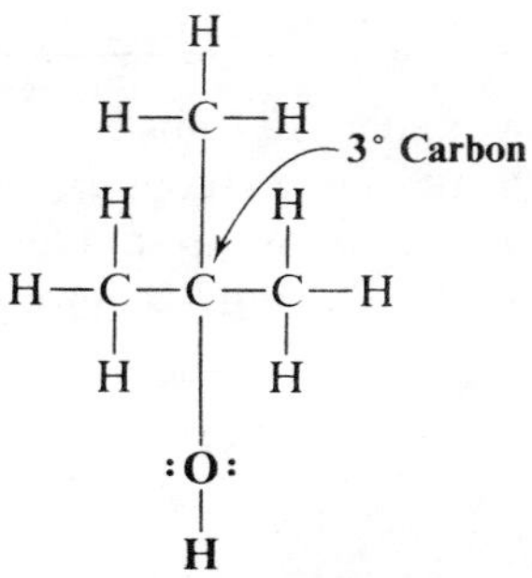

(a 3° alcohol)

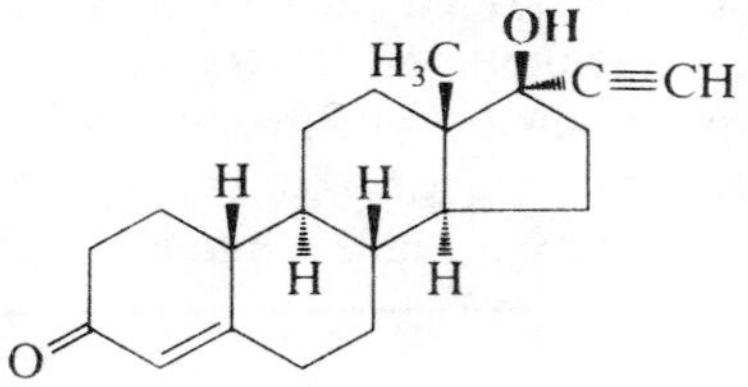

Norethindrone
(an oral contraceptive that contains a 3° alcohol
group, as well as a ketone group and carbon–
carbon double and triple bonds)

PROBLEM 2.6

Write structural formulas for   (a) two primary alcohols,   (b) a secondary alcohol, and   (c) a tertiary alcohol all having the molecular formula $C_4H_{10}O$.

PROBLEM 2.7

One way of naming alcohols is to name the alkyl group that is attached to the —OH and add the word *alcohol*. Write the structures of   (a) propyl alcohol and (b) isopropyl alcohol.

2.11 ETHERS

Ethers have the general formula R—O—R or R—O—R′ where R′ may be an alkyl group different from R. They can be thought of as derivatives of water in which both hydrogen atoms have been replaced by alkyl groups. The bond angle at the oxygen atom of an ether is only slightly larger than that of water.

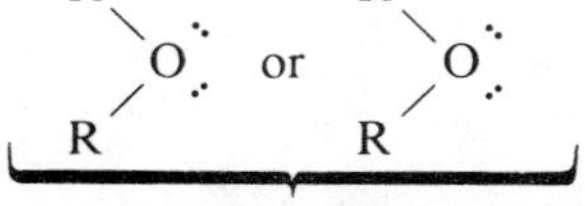

General formula for an ether

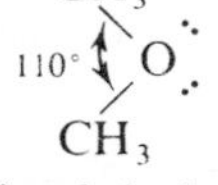

Dimethyl ether
(a typical ether)

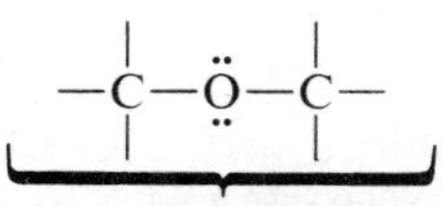

The functional group
of an ether

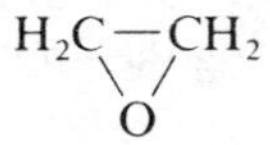

Ethylene
oxide

Tetrahydrofuran
(THF)

Two cyclic ethers

PROBLEM 2.8 _____

One way of naming ethers is to name the two alkyl groups attached to the oxygen atom in alphabetical order and add the word *ether*. If the two alkyl groups are the same, we use the prefix *di-*, for example, as in *dimethyl ether*. Write structural formulas for (a) diethyl ether, (b) ethyl propyl ether, and (c) ethyl isopropyl ether.   (d) What name would you give to $CH_3OCH_2CH_2CH_3$, (e) to $(CH_3)_2CHOCH(CH_3)_2$, and (f) to $CH_3OC_6H_5$?

2.12 AMINES

Just as alcohols and ethers may be considered as organic derivatives of water, amines may be considered as organic derivatives of ammonia.

$$H{-}\overset{\cdot\cdot}{N}{-}H \qquad R{-}\overset{\cdot\cdot}{N}{-}H \qquad C_6H_5CH_2CHCH_3 \qquad H_2NCH_2CH_2CH_2CH_2NH_2$$
$$\underset{\text{Ammonia}}{|} \qquad \underset{\text{(an amine)}}{|} \qquad \underset{\underset{\text{(a dangerous stimulant)}}{\text{Amphetamine}}}{NH_2} \qquad \underset{\underset{\text{(found in decaying meat)}}{\text{Putrescine}}}{}$$

Amines are classified as primary, secondary, or tertiary amines. **This classification is based on** *the number of organic groups that are attached to the nitrogen atom:*

$$R{-}\overset{\cdot\cdot}{N}{-}H \qquad R{-}\overset{\cdot\cdot}{N}{-}H \qquad R{-}\overset{\cdot\cdot}{N}{-}R''$$
$$\underset{\underset{\text{amine}}{\text{A primary (1°)}}}{H} \qquad \underset{\underset{\text{amine}}{\text{A secondary (2°)}}}{R'} \qquad \underset{\underset{\text{amine}}{\text{A tertiary (3°)}}}{R'}$$

Notice that this is quite different from the way alcohols and alkyl halides are classified. Isopropylamine, for example, is a primary amine even though its —NH_2 group is attached to a secondary carbon atom. It is a primary amine because only one organic group is attached to the nitrogen atom.

Isopropylamine
(a 1° amine)   (a cyclic 2° amine)

PROBLEM 2.9 _____

One way of naming amines is to name in alphabetical order the alkyl groups attached to the nitrogen atom, using the prefixes *di-* and *tri-* if the groups are the same. An example is *isopropylamine* for $(CH_3)_2CHNH_2$. Write formulas for (a) propylamine, (b) trimethylamine, and (c) ethylisopropylmethylamine. What are names for (d) $CH_3CH_2CH_2NHCH(CH_3)_2$, (e) $(CH_3CH_2CH_2)_3N$, (f) $C_6H_5NHCH_3$, and (g) $C_6H_5N(CH_3)_2$?

PROBLEM 2.10 _____

Which amines in Problem 2.9 are   (a) primary amines,   (b) secondary amines, and   (c) tertiary amines?

_____

Amines are like ammonia (Section 1.17B) in having a trigonal pyramidal shape. The C—N—C bond angles of trimethylamine are 108.7°, a value very close to the H—C—H bond angles of methane. Thus, for all practical purposes, the nitrogen atom of an amine can be considered to be sp^3 hybridized. This means that the unshared electron pair occupies an sp^3 orbital, and so it is considerably extended into space. This is important because, as we shall see, the unshared electron pair is involved in almost all of the reactions of amines.

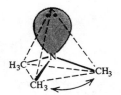

Bond angle = 108.7°

PROBLEM 2.11 _____

Amines are like ammonia in being weak bases. They do this by using their unshared electron pair to accept a proton.   (a) Show the reaction that would take place between trimethylamine and HCl.   (b) What hybridization state would you expect for the nitrogen atom in the product of this reaction?

_____

2.13 ALDEHYDES AND KETONES

Aldehydes and ketones both contain the **carbonyl group**—a group in which a carbon atom has a double bond to oxygen.

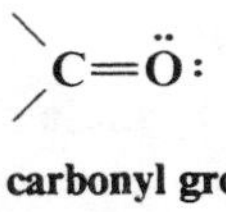

$$\diagdown \atop \diagup C=\ddot{O}:$$

The carbonyl group

The carbonyl group in aldehydes is bonded to at least one *hydrogen atom,* and in ketones it is bonded to *two carbon atoms.* Using R, we can designate the general formula for an aldehyde as

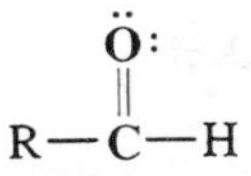

$$\overset{\ddot{O}:}{\underset{}{\overset{\|}{R-C-H}}} \qquad \text{R may also be H}$$

and the general formula for a ketone as

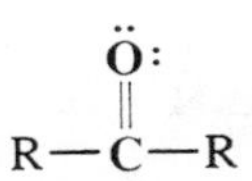

$$\overset{\ddot{O}:}{\overset{\|}{R-C-R}} \quad \text{or} \quad \overset{\ddot{O}:}{\overset{\|}{R-C-R'}}$$

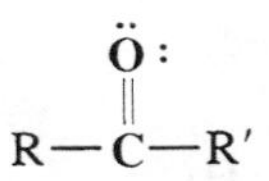

(where R′ is an alkyl group different from R).

Some examples of aldehydes and ketones are

Aldehydes

$$\overset{\ddot{O}:}{\underset{}{\|}}$$
$$H-C-H$$
Formaldehyde

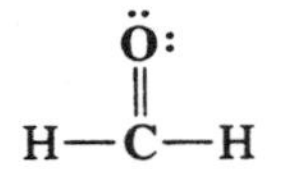

$$\overset{\ddot{O}:}{\underset{}{\|}}$$
$$CH_3-C-H$$
Acetaldehyde

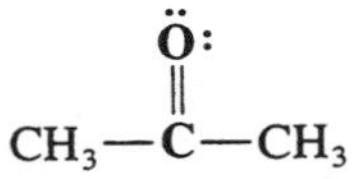

$$\overset{\ddot{O}:}{\underset{}{\|}}$$
$$C_6H_5-C-H$$
Benzaldehyde

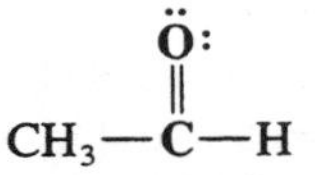

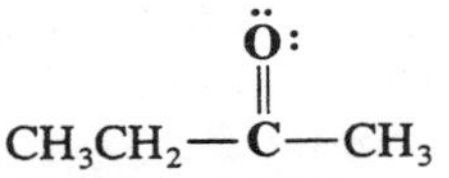

$$\underset{H}{\overset{C_6H_5}{\diagdown}}C=C\underset{\underset{O}{\overset{\|}{C-H}}}{\overset{H}{\diagup}}$$

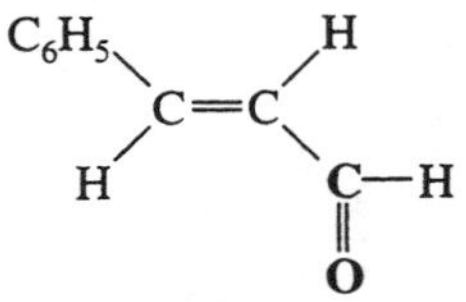

***trans*-Cinnamaldehyde**
(present in cinnamon)

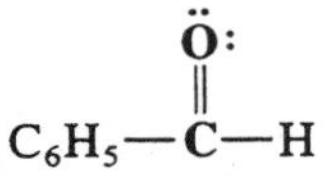

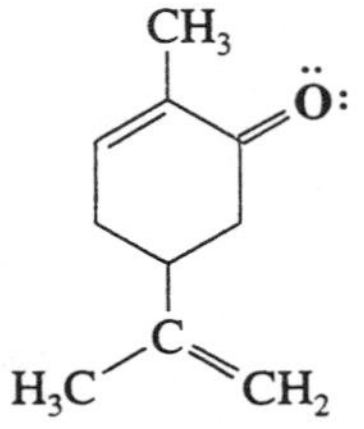

Ketones

$$\overset{\ddot{O}:}{\underset{}{\|}}$$
$$CH_3-C-CH_3$$
Acetone

$$\overset{\ddot{O}:}{\underset{}{\|}}$$
$$CH_3CH_2-C-CH_3$$
Ethyl methyl ketone

Carvone
(from spearmint)

Aldehydes and ketones have a trigonal planar arrangement of groups around the carbonyl carbon atom. The carbon atom is sp^2 hybridized. In formaldehyde, for example, the bond angles are as follows:

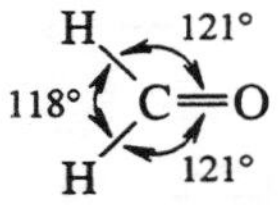

$$\underset{H}{\overset{H}{}}\,118°\left\{\underset{121°}{\overset{121°}{C=O}}\right.$$

2.14 CARBOXYLIC ACIDS, AMIDES, AND ESTERS

2.14A Carboxylic Acids

Carboxylic acids have the general formula $R-\overset{\overset{O}{\|}}{C}-O-H$. The functional group, $-\overset{\overset{O}{\|}}{C}-O-H$, is called the **carboxyl group** (**carbonyl** + **hydroxyl**). (Colloquially, carboxylic acids are often just called "organic acids.")

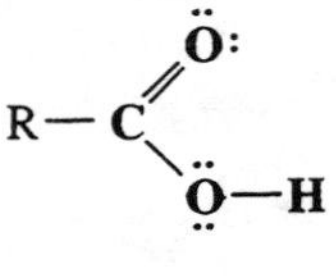

$$R-\overset{\overset{\ddot{O}:}{\diagup}}{\underset{\ddot{O}-H}{C}} \qquad or \qquad R\,CO_2H \qquad or \qquad R\,COOH$$

A carboxylic acid

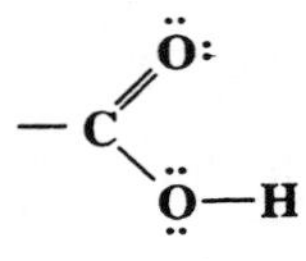

$$-\overset{\overset{\ddot{O}:}{\diagup}}{\underset{\ddot{O}-H}{C}} \qquad or \qquad -CO_2H \qquad or \qquad -COOH$$

The carboxyl group

Examples of carboxylic acids are formic acid, acetic acid, and benzoic acid.

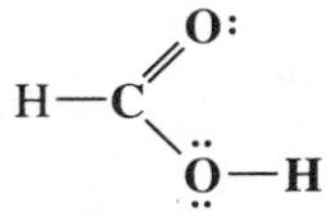

$$H-C\overset{\ddot{O}:}{\underset{\ddot{O}-H}{}}\qquad \text{or}\qquad HCO_2H \qquad \text{or}\qquad HCOOH$$

Formic acid

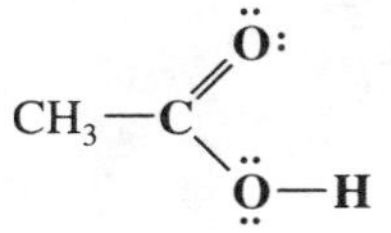

$$CH_3-C\overset{\ddot{O}:}{\underset{\ddot{O}-H}{}}\qquad \text{or}\qquad CH_3CO_2H \qquad \text{or}\qquad CH_3COOH$$

Acetic acid

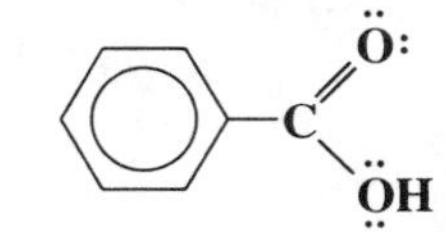

$$C_6H_5-C\overset{\ddot{O}:}{\underset{\ddot{O}H}{}}\qquad \text{or}\qquad C_6H_5CO_2H \qquad \text{or}\qquad C_6H_5COOH$$

Benzoic acid

Formic acid is an irritating liquid produced by ants. (The sting of the ant is caused, in part, by formic acid being injected under the skin.) Acetic acid, the substance responsible for the sour taste of vinegar, is produced when certain bacteria act on the ethyl alcohol of wine and cause the ethyl alcohol to be oxidized by air.

2.14B Amides

Amides have the formulas $RCONH_2$, $RCONHR'$, or $RCONR'R''$. Specific examples are the following:

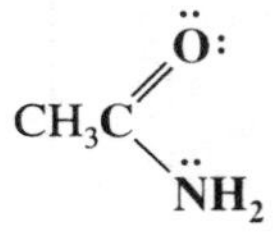

$$CH_3C\overset{\ddot{O}:}{\underset{\ddot{N}H_2}{}}\qquad CH_3C\overset{\ddot{O}:}{\underset{\ddot{N}HCH_3}{}}\qquad CH_3C\overset{\ddot{O}}{\underset{\underset{CH_3}{|}}{N-CH_3}}$$

Acetamide 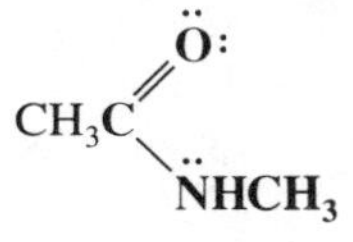   **N-Methylacetamide** 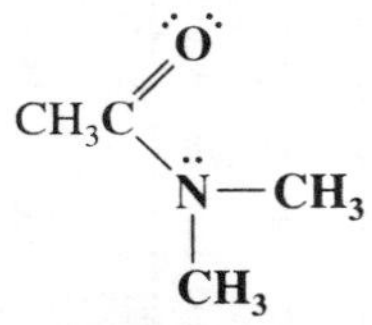   **N,N-Dimethylacetamide**

The *N*- and *N,N*- indicate that the substituents are attached to the nitrogen atom.

2.14C Esters

Esters have the general formula RCO_2R' (or $RCOOR'$).

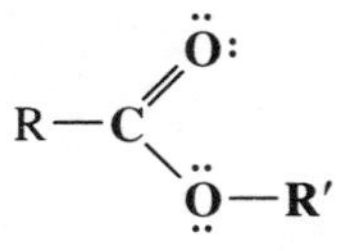

$$R-C\overset{\ddot{O}:}{\underset{\ddot{O}-R'}{}}\qquad \text{or}\qquad RCO_2R' \qquad \text{or}\qquad RCOOR'$$

General formula for an ester

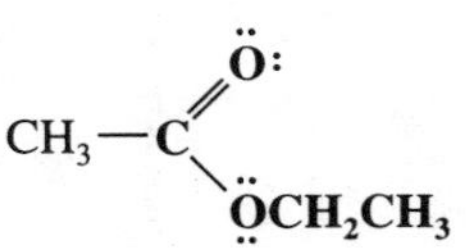

$$CH_3-C\overset{\ddot{O}:}{\underset{\ddot{O}CH_2CH_3}{}}\qquad \text{or}\qquad CH_3CO_2CH_2CH_3 \qquad \text{or}\qquad CH_3COOCH_2CH_3$$

A specific ester called ethyl acetate

TABLE 2.2 Important families of organic compounds

FAMILY

	ALKANE	ALKENE	ALKYNE	ARENE	HALOALKANE	ALCOHOL	ETHER	AMINE	ALDEHYDE	KETONE	CARBOXYLIC ACID	ESTER	AMIDE
Specific example	CH_3CH_3	$CH_2{=}CH_2$	$HC{\equiv}CH$	(benzene ring)	CH_3CH_2Cl	CH_3CH_2OH	CH_3OCH_3	CH_3NH_2	$\overset{O}{\overset{\|\|}{CH_3CH}}$	$\overset{O}{\overset{\|\|}{CH_3CCH_3}}$	$\overset{O}{\overset{\|\|}{CH_3COH}}$	$\overset{O}{\overset{\|\|}{CH_3COCH_3}}$	$\overset{O}{\overset{\|\|}{CH_3CNH_2}}$
IUPAC name	Ethane	Ethene	Ethyne	Benzene	Chloro-ethane	Ethanol	Methoxy-methane	Methan-amine	Ethanal	Propanone	Ethanoic acid	Methyl ethanoate	Ethanamide
Common name[a]	Ethane	Ethylene	Acetylene	Benzene	Ethyl chloride	Ethyl alcohol	Dimethyl ether	Methyl-amine	Acetal-dehyde	Acetone	Acetic acid	Methyl acetate	Acetamide
General formula	RH	$RCH{=}CH_2$ $RCH{=}CHR$ $R_2C{=}CHR$ $R_2C{=}CR_2$	$RC{\equiv}CH$ $RC{\equiv}CR$	ArH	RX	ROH	ROR	RNH_2 R_2NH R_3N	$\overset{O}{\overset{\|\|}{RCH}}$	$\overset{O}{\overset{\|\|}{RCR}}$	$\overset{O}{\overset{\|\|}{RCOH}}$	$\overset{O}{\overset{\|\|}{RCOR}}$	$\overset{O}{\overset{\|\|}{RCNH_2}}$ $\overset{O}{\overset{\|\|}{RCNHR}}$ $\overset{O}{\overset{\|\|}{RCNR_2}}$
Functional group	C—H and C—C bonds	$\diagdown\!\diagup C{=}C\diagdown\!\diagup$	—C≡C—	Aromatic ring	—C—X	—C—OH	—C—O—C—	—C—N—	O=C—H	O=C—C—C—	O=C—OH	O=C—OC—	O=C—N—

[a] These names are also accepted by the IUPAC.

Esters can be made from an acid and an alcohol through the loss of a molecule of water. For example:

$$CH_3-C\overset{O}{\underset{OH}{\diagdown}} \quad + \quad HOCH_2CH_3 \quad \xrightarrow{H^+} \quad CH_3-C\overset{O}{\underset{OCH_2CH_3}{\diagdown}} \quad + \quad H_2O$$

Acetic acid   Ethyl alcohol   Ethyl acetate

2.15 SUMMARY OF IMPORTANT FAMILIES OF ORGANIC COMPOUNDS

A summary of the important families of organic compounds is given in Table 2.2. You should learn to identify these common functional groups as they appear in other more complicated molecules.

2.16 PHYSICAL PROPERTIES AND MOLECULAR STRUCTURE

So far, we have said little about one of the most obvious characteristics of organic compounds, that is, *their physical state or phase.* Whether a particular substance is a solid, or a liquid, or a gas would certainly be one of the first observations that we would note in any experimental work. The temperatures at which transitions occur between phases, that is, melting points (mp) and boiling points (bp), are also among the more easily measured physical properties. Melting points and boiling points are also useful in identifying and isolating organic compounds.

Suppose, for example, we have just carried out the synthesis of an organic compound that is known to be a liquid at room temperature and 1-atm pressure. If we know the boiling point of our desired product, and the boiling points of byproducts and solvents that may be present in the reaction mixture, we can decide whether or not simple distillation will be a feasible method for isolating our product.

In another instance our product might be a solid. In this case, in order to isolate the substance by crystallization, we need to know its melting point and its solubility in different solvents.

The physical constants of known organic substances are easily found in handbooks and other reference books.* Table 2.3 lists the melting and boiling points of some of the compounds that we have discussed in this chapter.

Often in the course of research, however, the product of a synthesis is a new compound—one that has never been described before. In these instances, success in isolating the new compound depends on making reasonably accurate estimates of its melting point, boiling point, and solubilities. Estimations of these macroscopic physical properties are based on the most likely structure of the substance and on the forces that act between molecules and ions. The temperatures at which phase changes occur are an indication of the strength of these intermolecular forces.

2.16A Ion–Ion Forces

The **melting point** of a substance is the temperature at which an equilibrium exists between the well-ordered crystalline state and the more random liquid state. If the

---

*Two useful handbooks are *Handbook of Chemistry,* N. A. Lange, Ed., McGraw-Hill, New York and *CRC Handbook of Chemistry and Physics,* CRC, Boca Raton, FL.

TABLE 2.3   Physical properties of representative compounds

COMPOUND	STRUCTURE	mp (°C)	bp (°C) (1 atm)
Methane	CH_4	-182.6	-162
Ethane	CH_3CH_3	-183	-88.2
Ethene	$CH_2{=}CH_2$	-169	-102
Ethyne	$HC{\equiv}CH$	-82	-84 subl[a]
Chloromethane	CH_3Cl	-97	-23.7
Chloroethane	CH_3CH_2Cl	-138.7	13.1
Ethyl alcohol	CH_3CH_2OH	-115	78.5
Acetaldehyde	CH_3CHO	-121	20
Acetic acid	CH_3CO_2H	16.6	118
Sodium acetate	CH_3CO_2Na	324	dec[a]
Ethylamine	$CH_3CH_2NH_2$	-80	17
Diethyl ether	$(CH_3CH_2)_2O$	-116	34.6
Ethyl acetate	$CH_3CO_2CH_2CH_3$	-84	77

[a] In this table dec = decompose and subl = sublimes.

substance is an ionic compound, such as sodium acetate (Table 2.3), the forces that hold the ions together in the crystalline state are the strong electrostatic lattice forces that act between the positive and negative ions in the orderly crystalline structure. In Fig. 2.14 each sodium ion is surrounded by negatively charged acetate ions, and each acetate ion is surrounded by positive sodium ions. A large amount of thermal energy is required to break up the orderly structure of the crystal into the disorderly open structure of a liquid. As a result, the temperature at which sodium acetate melts is quite high, 324°C. The *boiling points* of ionic compounds are higher still, so high that most ionic organic compounds decompose before they boil. Sodium acetate shows this behavior.

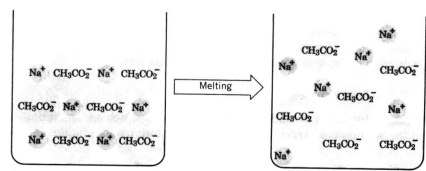

FIGURE 2.14   The melting of sodium acetate.

2.16B Dipole–Dipole Forces

Most organic molecules are not fully ionic but have instead a *permanent dipole moment* resulting from a nonuniform distribution of the bonding electrons (Section 1.19). Acetone and acetaldehyde are examples of molecules with permanent dipoles because the carbonyl group that they contain is highly polarized. In these compounds, the attractive forces between molecules are much easier to visualize. In the liquid or solid state, dipole–dipole attractions cause the molecules to orient themselves so that the positive end of one molecule is directed toward the negative end of another (Fig. 2.15).

FIGURE 2.15 Dipole–dipole interactions between acetone molecules.

2.16C Hydrogen Bonds

Very strong dipole–dipole attractions occur between hydrogen atoms bonded to small, strongly electronegative atoms (O, N, or F) and nonbonding electron pairs on other such electronegative atoms (Fig. 2.16). This type of intermolecular force is called a **hydrogen bond.** The hydrogen bond (bond dissociation energy about 1–9 kcal mol^{-1}) is weaker than an ordinary covalent bond, but is much stronger than the dipole–dipole interactions that occur in acetone.

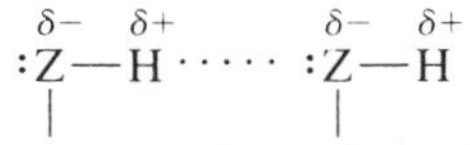

$$\overset{\delta-}{:}\!Z\!\!-\!\!\overset{\delta+}{H} \cdots\cdots \overset{\delta-}{:}\!Z\!\!-\!\!\overset{\delta+}{H}$$

FIGURE 2.16 The hydrogen bond. Z is a strongly electronegative element, usually oxygen, nitrogen, or fluorine.

Hydrogen bonding accounts for the fact that ethyl alcohol has a much higher boiling point ($+78.5°C$) than dimethyl ether ($-24.9°C$) even though the two compounds have the same molecular weight. Molecules of ethyl alcohol, because they have a hydrogen atom covalently bonded to an oxygen atom, can form strong hydrogen bonds to each other.

$$CH_3CH_2 \underset{:O}{\overset{\delta-}{\diagdown}}\!\!-\!\!\overset{\delta+}{H} \cdots \overset{\delta-}{:O:}\!\overset{\overset{\delta+}{H}}{\diagup}_{CH_2CH_3}$$

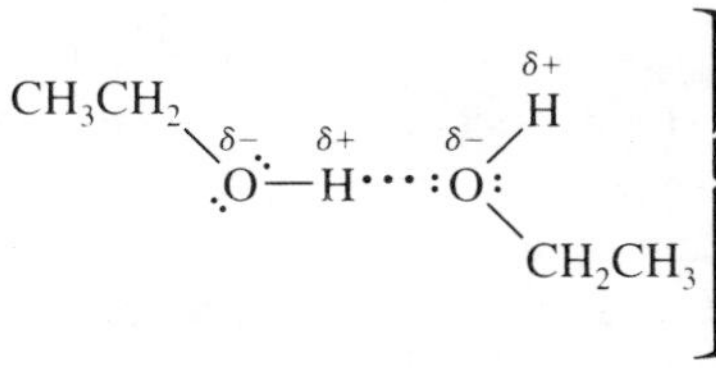

The dotted bond is a hydrogen bond. Strong hydrogen bonding is limited to molecules having a hydrogen atom attached to an O, N, or F atom

Molecules of dimethyl ether, because they lack a hydrogen atom attached to a strongly electronegative atom, cannot form strong hydrogen bonds to each other. In dimethyl ether the intermolecular forces are weaker dipole–dipole interactions.

PROBLEM 2.12 _____

The compounds in each part below have the same (or similar) molecular weights. Which compound in each part would you expect to have the higher boiling point? Explain your answers. (a) $CH_3CH_2CH_2CH_2OH$ or $CH_3CH_2OCH_2CH_3$, (b) $(CH_3)_3N$ or $CH_3CH_2NHCH_3$, (c) $CH_3CH_2CH_2CH_2OH$ or $HOCH_2CH_2CH_2OH$.

A factor (in addition to polarity and hydrogen bonding) that affects the *melting point* of many organic compounds is the compactness and rigidity of their individual molecules. Molecules that are symmetrical generally have abnormally high melting points. *tert*-Butyl alcohol, for example, has a much higher melting point than the other isomeric alcohols shown here.

$$
\begin{array}{cccc}
\overset{\displaystyle CH_3}{\underset{\displaystyle CH_3}{CH_3-C-OH}} & CH_3CH_2CH_2CH_2OH & \overset{\displaystyle CH_3}{CH_3CHCH_2OH} & \overset{\displaystyle CH_3}{CH_3CH_2CHOH} \\
\textbf{\textit{tert}-Butyl alcohol} & \textbf{Butyl alcohol} & \textbf{Isobutyl alcohol} & \textbf{\textit{sec}-Butyl alcohol} \\
\textbf{mp, 25°C} & \textbf{mp, -90°C} & \textbf{mp, -108°C} & \textbf{mp, -114°C}
\end{array}
$$

PROBLEM 2.13 _____

Which compound would you expect to have the higher melting point, propane or cyclopropane? Explain your answer.

2.16D van der Waals Forces

If we consider a substance like methane where the particles are nonpolar molecules, we find that the melting point and boiling point are very low: $-182.6°C$ and $-162°C$, respectively. Instead of asking, "Why does methane melt and boil at low temperatures?" a more appropriate question might be "Why does methane, a nonionic, nonpolar substance, become a liquid or a solid at all?" The answer to this question can be given in terms of attractive intermolecular forces called **van der Waals forces** (or **London forces** or **dispersion forces**).

An accurate account of the nature of van der Waals forces requires the use of quantum mechanics. We can, however, visualize the origin of these forces in the following way. The average distribution of charge in a nonpolar molecule (such as methane) over a period of time is uniform. At any given instant, however, *because electrons move,* the electrons and therefore the charge may not be uniformly distributed. Electrons may, in one instant, be slightly accumulated on one part of the molecule and, as a consequence, *a small temporary dipole will occur* (Fig. 2.17). This temporary dipole in one molecule can induce opposite (attractive) dipoles in surrounding molecules. It does this because the negative (or positive) charge in a portion of one molecule will distort the electron cloud of an adjacent portion of another molecule causing an opposite charge to develop there. These temporary dipoles change constantly, but the net result of their existence is to produce attractive forces between nonpolar molecules, and thus make possible the existence of their liquid and solid states.

FIGURE 2.17 Temporary dipoles and induced dipoles in nonpolar molecules resulting from a nonuniform distribution of electrons at a given instant.

One important factor that determines the magnitude of van der Waals forces is the relative **polarizability** of the electrons of the atoms involved. By polarizability we mean *the ability of the electrons to respond to a changing electric field.* Relative polarizability depends on how loosely or tightly the electrons are held. In the halogen family, for example, polarizability increases in the order F < Cl < Br < I. Fluorine atoms show a very low polarizability because their electrons are very tightly held; they are close to the nucleus. Iodine atoms are large and hence are more easily polarized. Their valence electrons are far from the nucleus. Atoms with unshared pairs are generally more polarizable than those with only bonding pairs. Thus a halogen substituent is more polarizable than an alkyl group of comparable size. Table 2.4 gives the relative magnitude of van der Waals forces and dipole–dipole interactions for several simple compounds. Notice that except for the molecules where strong hydrogen bonds are possible, van der Waals are far more important than dipole–dipole interactions.

The *boiling point* of a liquid is the temperature at which the vapor pressure of the liquid equals the pressure of the atmosphere above it. For this reason, the boiling points of liquids are *pressure dependent,* and boiling points are always reported as occurring at a particular pressure, as 1 atm (or at 760 torr), for example. A substance that boils at 150°C at 1-atm pressure will boil at a substantially lower temperature if the pressure is reduced to, for example, 0.01 torr (a pressure easily obtained with a vacuum pump). The normal boiling point given for a liquid is its boiling point at 1 atm.

In passing from a liquid to a gaseous state the individual molecules (or ions) of the substance must separate considerably. Because of this, we can understand why ionic organic compounds often decompose before they boil. The thermal energy required to completely separate (volatilize) the ions is so great that chemical reactions (decompositions) occur first.

Nonpolar compounds, where the intermolecular forces are very weak, usually boil at low temperatures even at 1-atm pressure. This is not always true, however, because of other factors that we have not yet mentioned: the effects of molecular weight and

TABLE 2.4 Attractive energies in simple molecular solids

| MOLECULE | DIPOLE MOMENT (D) | ATTRACTIVE ENERGIES (kcal mol⁻¹) | | MELTING POINT (°C) | BOILING POINT (°C) |
		DIPOLE–DIPOLE	VAN DER WAALS		
H_2O	1.85	8.7[a]	2.1	0	100
NH_3	1.47	3.3[a]	3.5	− 78	− 33
HCl	1.08	0.8[a]	4.0	− 115	− 85
HBr	0.80	0.2	5.2	− 88	− 67
HI	0.42	0.006	6.7	− 51	− 35

[a] These dipole–dipole attractions are called hydrogen bonds.

molecular size. Heavier molecules require greater thermal energy in order to acquire velocities sufficiently great to escape the liquid surface, and because their surface areas are usually much greater, intermolecular van der Waals attractions are also much larger. These factors explain why nonpolar ethane (bp, $-88.2°C$) boils higher than methane (bp, $-162°C$) at a pressure of 1 atm. It also explains why, at 1 atm, the even heavier and larger nonpolar molecule decane ($C_{10}H_{22}$) boils at $+174°C$.

Fluorocarbons (compounds containing only carbon and fluorine) have extraordinarily low boiling points when compared to hydrocarbons of the same molecular weight. The fluorocarbon C_5F_{12}, for example, has a slightly lower boiling point than pentane (C_5H_{12}) even though it has a far higher molecular weight. The important factor in explaining this behavior is the very low polarizability of fluorine atoms that we mentioned earlier, resulting in very small van der Waals forces. The fluorocarbon polymer called *Teflon* [$-(CF_2CF_2)_n$, see Section 9.10] has self-lubricating properties, which are exploited in making "nonstick" frying pans and lightweight bearings.

2.16E Solubilities

Intermolecular forces are of primary importance in explaining the **solubilities** of substances. Dissolution of a solid in a liquid is, in many respects, like the melting of a solid. The orderly crystal structure of the solid is destroyed, and the result is the formation of the more disorderly arrangement of the molecules (or ions) in solution. In the process of dissolving, too, the molecules or ions must be separated from each other, and energy must be supplied for both changes. The energy required to overcome lattice energies and intermolecular or interionic attractions comes from the formation of new attractive forces between solute and solvent.

Consider the dissolution of an ionic substance as an example. Here both the lattice energy and interionic attractions are large. We find that water and only a few other very polar solvents are capable of dissolving ionic compounds. These solvents dissolve ionic compounds by **hydrating** or **solvating** the ions (Fig. 2.18).

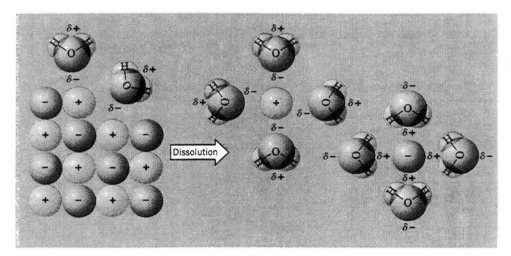

FIGURE 2.18 The dissolution of an ionic solid in water, showing the hydration of positive and negative ions by the very polar water molecules. The ions become surrounded by water molecules in all three dimensions, not just the two shown here.

Water molecules, by virtue of their great polarity, as well as their very small compact shape, can very effectively surround the individual ions as they are freed from the crystal surface. Positive ions are surrounded by water molecules with the negative end of the water dipole pointed toward the positive ion; negative ions are solvated in exactly the opposite way. Because water is highly polar, and because water is capable of forming strong hydrogen bonds, the *dipole–ion* attractive forces are also large. The energy supplied by the formation of these forces is great enough to overcome both the lattice energy and interionic attractions of the crystal.

A rule of thumb for predicting solubilities is that "like dissolves like." Polar and ionic compounds tend to dissolve in polar solvents. Polar liquids are generally miscible with each other. Nonpolar solids are usually soluble in nonpolar solvents. On the other hand, nonpolar solids are insoluble in polar solvents. Nonpolar liquids are usually mutually miscible, but nonpolar liquids and polar liquids "like oil and water" do not mix.

Methanol and water are miscible in all proportions; so too are mixtures of ethanol and water, and mixtures of both propyl alcohols and water. In these cases the alkyl groups of the alcohols are relatively small, and the molecules therefore resemble water more than they do an alkane. Another factor in understanding their solubility is that the molecules are capable of forming strong hydrogen bonds to each other.

If the carbon chain of an alcohol is long, however, we find that the alcohol is much less soluble in water. Decyl alcohol (see following structure) with a chain of 10 carbon atoms is only very slightly soluble in water. Decyl alcohol resembles an alkane more than it does water. The long carbon chain of decyl alcohol is said to be **hydrophobic** (*hydro,* water; *phobic,* fearing or avoiding — "water avoiding"). Only the OH group, a rather small part of the molecule, is **hydrophilic** (*philic,* loving or seeking — "water seeking"). (On the other hand, decyl alcohol is quite soluble in nonpolar solvents.)

Decyl alcohol

An explanation for why nonpolar groups such as long alkane chains avoid an aqueous environment, for the so-called **hydrophobic effect**, is complex. The most important factor seems to involve an **unfavorable entropy change** in the water. Entropy changes (Section 3.8) have to do with changes from a relatively ordered state to a more disordered one, or the reverse. Changes from order to disorder are favorable, whereas changes from disorder to order are unfavorable. For a nonpolar hydrocarbon chain to be accommodated by water, the water molecules have to form a more ordered structure around the chain, and for this, the entropy change is unfavorable.

2.16F Guidelines for Water Solubility

Organic chemists usually define a compound as water soluble if at least 3 g of the organic compound dissolves in 100 mL of water. We find that for compounds containing one hydrophilic group—and thus capable of forming strong hydrogen bonds—the following approximate guidelines hold: Compounds with one to three carbon atoms are water soluble, compounds with four or five carbon atoms are borderline, and compounds with six carbon atoms or more are insoluble.

When a compound contains more than one hydrophilic group these guidelines do not apply. Polysaccharides (Chapter 22), proteins (Chapter 24), and nucleic acids (Chapter 25) all contain thousands of carbon atoms *and all are water soluble.* They dissolve in water because they also contain thousands of hydrophilic groups.

2.16G Intermolecular Forces in Biochemistry

Later, after we have had a chance to examine in detail the properties of the molecules that make up living organisms, we shall see how intermolecular forces are extremely important in the functioning of cells. Hydrogen bond formation, the hydration of polar groups, and the tendency of nonpolar groups to avoid a polar environment all cause complex protein molecules to fold in precise ways—ways that allow them to function as biological catalysts of incredible efficiency. The same factors allow molecules of

TABLE 2.5 Attractive electric forces

ELECTRIC FORCE	RELATIVE STRENGTH	TYPE	EXAMPLE
Cation–anion (in a crystal)	Very strong	$\oplus$ $\ominus$	Lithium fluoride crystal lattice
Covalent bonds	Strong ($36-125$ kcal mol^{-1})	Shared electron pairs	H—H (104 kcal mol^{-1}) CH$_3$—CH$_3$ (88 kcal mol^{-1}) I—I (36 kcal mol^{-1})
Ion–dipole	Moderate		Na$^+$ in water (see Fig. 2.18)
Dipole–dipole (including hydrogen bonds)	Moderate to weak ($1-9$ kcal mol^{-1})		
van der Waals	Variable	Transient dipole	Interactions between methane molecules

hemoglobin to assume the shape needed to transport oxygen. They allow proteins and molecules called glycosphingolipids to function as cell membranes. Hydrogen bonding alone gives molecules of certain carbohydrates a globular shape that makes them highly efficient food reserves in animals. It gives molecules of other carbohydrates a rigid linear shape that makes them perfectly suited to be structural components in plants.

2.17 SUMMARY OF ATTRACTIVE ELECTRIC FORCES

The attractive forces occurring between molecules and ions that we have studied so far are summarized in Table 2.5.

ADDITIONAL PROBLEMS

2.14 Classify each of the following compounds as an alkane, alkene, alkyne, alcohol, aldehyde, amine, and so forth.

(a)

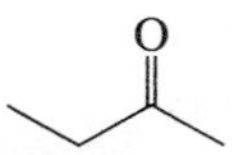

(b) 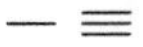 — ≡

(c) 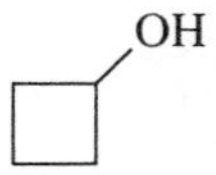 (obtained from oil of cloves)

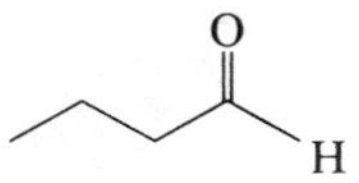

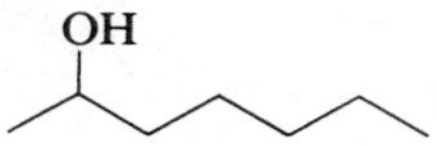

(d)

(e)

(f) 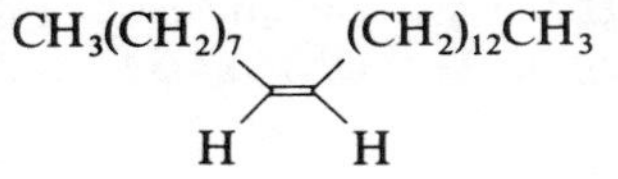 (sex attractant of common house fly)

2.15 Identify all of the functional groups in each of the following compounds:

(a) 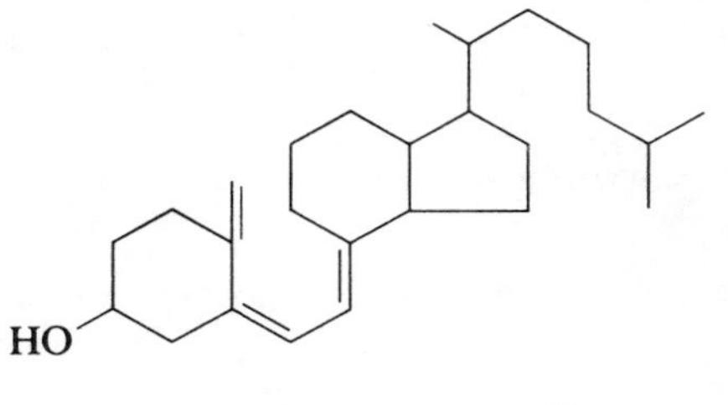 Vitamin D$_3$

(b) 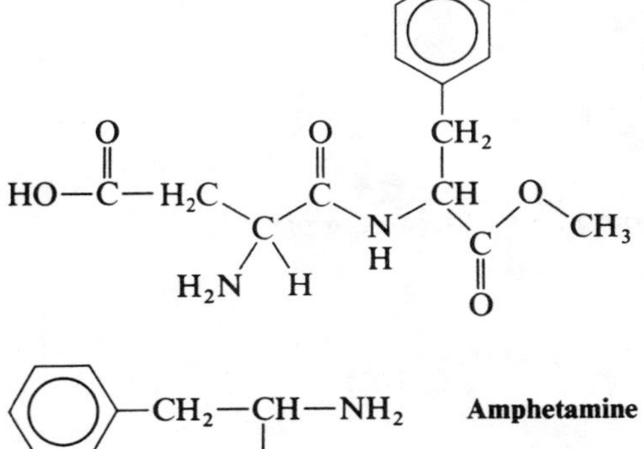 Aspartame

(c) 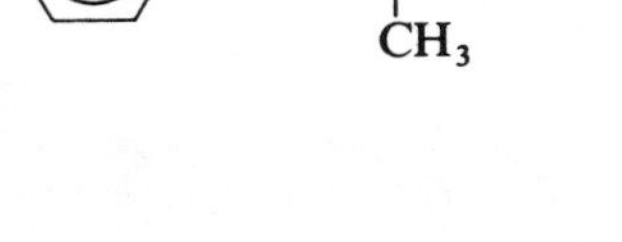 Amphetamine

(d) 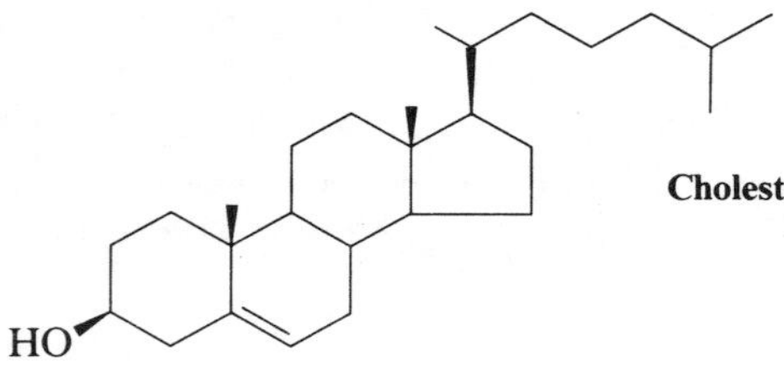 **Cholesterol**

HO

(e) 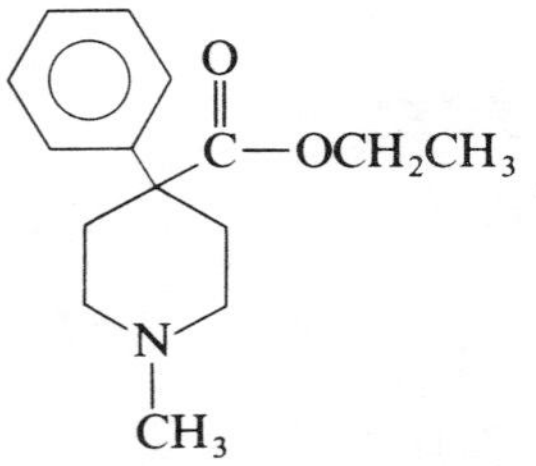 **Demerol**

O
‖
C—OCH$_2$CH$_3$

N
|
CH$_3$

(f)

O
‖
H

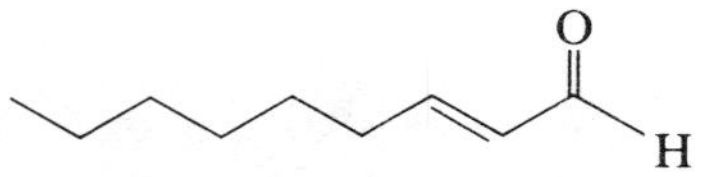

**A cockroach repellent found
in cucumbers**

(g)

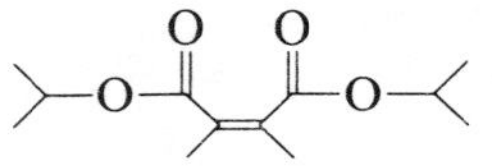

O   O
‖   ‖
>—O—C   C—O—<

A synthetic cockroach repellent

2.16 There are four alkyl bromides with the formula C$_4$H$_9$Br. Write their structural formulas and classify each as to whether it is a primary, secondary, or tertiary alkyl bromide.

2.17 There are seven isomeric compounds with the formula C$_4$H$_{10}$O. Write their structures and classify each compound according to its functional group.

2.18 Write structural formulas for four compounds with the formula C$_3$H$_6$O and classify each according to its functional group.

2.19 Classify the following alcohols as primary, secondary, or tertiary:

(a) (CH$_3$)$_3$CCH$_2$OH

(d) OH

(b) CH$_3$CH(OH)CH(CH$_3$)$_2$

(c) (CH$_3$)$_2$C(OH)CH$_2$CH$_3$

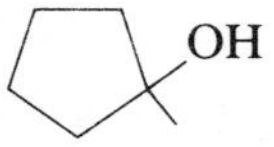

(e) 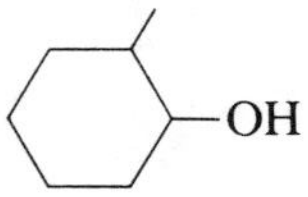 —OH

2.20 Classify the following amines as primary, secondary, or tertiary:

(a) CH$_3$NHCH(CH$_3$)$_2$

(e) HN

(b) CH$_3$CH$_2$CH(CH$_3$)CH$_2$NH$_2$

(c) (CH$_3$CH$_2$)$_3$N

(d) (C$_6$H$_5$)$_2$CHCH$_2$NHCH$_3$

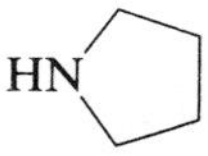

(f) 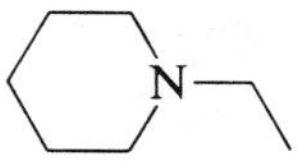 N—

2.21 Write structural formulas for each of the following:

(a) Three ethers with the formula $C_4H_{10}O$.

(b) Three primary alcohols with the formula C_4H_8O.

(c) A secondary alcohol with the formula C_3H_6O.

(d) A tertiary alcohol with the formula C_4H_8O.

(e) Two esters with the formula $C_3H_6O_2$.

(f) Four primary alkyl halides with the formula $C_5H_{11}Br$.

(g) Three secondary alkyl halides with the formula $C_5H_{11}Br$.

(h) A tertiary alkyl halide with the formula $C_5H_{11}Br$.

(i) Three aldehydes with the formula $C_5H_{10}O$.

(j) Three ketones with the formula $C_5H_{10}O$.

(k) Two primary amines with the formula C_3H_9N.

(l) A secondary amine with the formula $C_3H_{11}N$.

(m) A tertiary amine with the formula $C_3H_{11}N$.

(n) Two amides with the formula C_2H_5NO.

2.22 Which compound in each of the following pairs would have the higher boiling point? Explain your answers.

(a) $CH_3CH_2CH_2OH$ or $CH_3CH_2OCH_3$

(b) $CH_3CH_2CH_2OH$ or $HOCH_2CH_2OH$

(c) 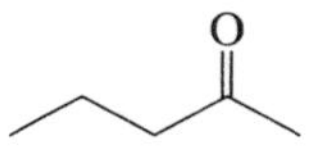 [structure] or [structure] OH

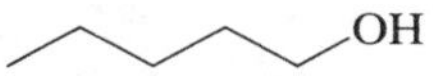

(d) 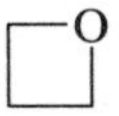 [structure] or [structure]—OH

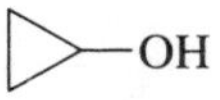

(e) 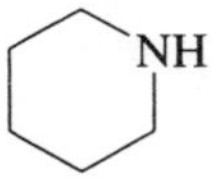 [structure] NH or [structure] N—CH$_3$

(f) [structure with F] or [structure with F, F]

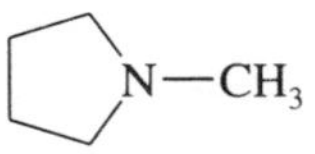

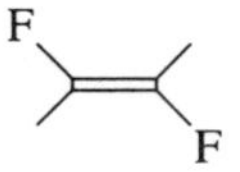

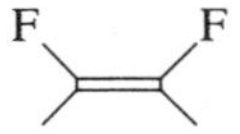

(g) 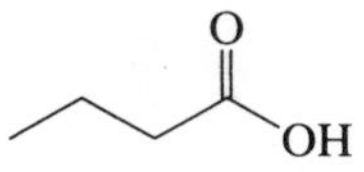 [structure] OH or [structure]

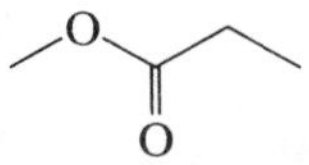

(h) Hexane $CH_3(CH_2)_4CH_3$ or nonane $CH_3(CH_2)_6CH_3$

(i) 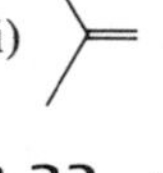 [structure] or [structure] O

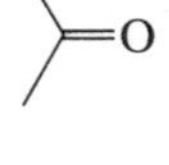

2.23 There are four amides with the formula C_3H_7NO. (a) Write their structures. (b) One of these amides has a melting and boiling point that is substantially lower than that of the other three. Which amide is this? Explain your answer.

2.24 Cyclic compounds of the general type shown here are called lactones. What functional group does a lactone contain?

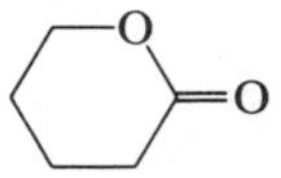

2.25   Hydrogen fluoride has a dipole moment of 1.82 D; its boiling point is 19.34°C. Ethyl fluoride (CH_3CH_2F) has an almost identical dipole moment and has a larger molecular weight, yet its boiling point is -37.7°C. Explain.

2.26   Which of the following solvents should be capable of dissolving ionic compounds? (a) liquid SO_2;   (b) liquid NH_3;   (c) benzene;   (d) CCl_4

ANSWERS TO SELECTED PROBLEMS

CHAPTER 1

1.8 (a), (c), (f), (g) are tetrahedral; (e) is trigonal planar; (b) is linear; (d) is angular; (h) is trigonal pyramidal.

1.11 VSEPR theory predicts a trigonal structure for BF_3; this causes the bond moments to cancel.

1.13 The fact that SO_2 has a dipole moment indicates that the molecule is angular, not linear.

1.18 (a) and (d); (b) and (e); and (c) and (f).

1.26 (a), (g), (i), (l), represent different compounds that are not isomeric; (c–e), (h), (j), (m), (n), (o) represent the same compound; (b), (f), (k), (p) represent constitutional isomers.

1.33 (a) The structures differ in the positions of the nuclei.

1.35 (a) A negative charge; (b) a negative charge; (c) trigonal pyramidal.

CHAPTER 2

2.1 cis–trans Isomers are not possible for (a) and (c).

2.5 (c) Propyl bromide; (d) isopropyl fluoride; (e) phenyl iodide.

2.8 (a) $CH_3CH_2OCH_2CH_3$; (b) $CH_3CH_2OCH_2CH_2CH_3$; (e) diisopropyl ether.

2.12 (a) $CH_3CH_2CH_2CH_2OH$ would boil higher because its molecules can form hydrogen bonds to each other; (c) $HOCH_2CH_2CH_2OH$ would boil higher because it can form more hydrogen bonds.

2.14 (a) Ketone; (c) alcohol; (e) alcohol.

2.15 (a) 3 Alkene, and a 2° alcohol; (c) phenyl and 1° amine; (e) phenyl, ester and 3° amine; (g) alkene and 2 ester groups.

2.21 (f) $CH_3CH_2CH_2CH_2CH_2Br$; $(CH_3)_2CHCH_2CH_2Br$; $CH_3CH_2CH(CH_3)CH_2Br$; $(CH_3)_3CCH_2Br$.

2.24 Ester

INDEX